I B	II B	III B	IV B	V B	VI B	VII B	O
						1 H 1.00797	2 He 4.0026
		5 B 10.811	6 C 12.01115	7 N 14.0067	8 O 15.9994	9 F 18.9984	10 Ne 20.183
		13 Al 26.9815	14 Si 28.086	15 P 30.9738	16 S 32.064	17 Cl 35.453	18 Ar 39.948
28 Ni 58.71	29 Cu 63.54	30 Zn 65.37	31 Ga 69.72	32 Ge 72.59	33 As 74.9216	34 Se 78.96	35 Br 79.909	36 Kr 83.80
46 Pd 106.4	47 Ag 107.870	48 Cd 112.40	49 In 114.82	50 Sn 118.69	51 Sb 121.75	52 Te 127.60	53 I 126.9044	54 Xe 131.30
78 Pt 195.09	79 Au 196.967	80 Hg 200.59	81 Tl 204.37	82 Pb 207.19	83 Bi 208.980	84 Po	85 At	86 Rn

64 Gd 157.25	65 Tb 158.924	66 Dy 162.50	67 Ho 164.930	68 Er 167.26	69 Tm 168.934	70 Yb 173.04	71 Lu 174.97
96 Cm	97 Bk	98 Cf	99 Es	100 Fm	101 Md	102 No	103 Lw

Concepts and Models of
Inorganic Chemistry

Concepts and Models
of Inorganic Chemistry

BODIE E. DOUGLAS
University of Pittsburgh

DARL H. MC DANIEL
University of Cincinnati

BLAISDELL PUBLISHING COMPANY
A Division of Ginn and Company
WALTHAM, MASSACHUSETTS · TORONTO · LONDON

TO
Gladys and Marty

Preface

This book is intended for use as a text in advanced undergraduate courses in inorganic chemistry, with physical chemistry as a prerequisite or at least a corequisite. It is also suitable for a beginning graduate course for students who have not had an advanced undergraduate course. The level of the treatment will stimulate the student to use his preparation in chemistry and physics. An inorganic chemistry course should present the challenge of modern inorganic chemistry and at the same time unify many of the principles and facts presented in earlier courses.

A textbook should serve a number of functions. The first and foremost of these is to acquaint the reader with the theory which undergirds the subject. This is particularly important in chemistry where observations in the laboratory are used to make inferences about the unseen behavior of molecular species. The chemist creates mental models to rationalize the behavior he seeks to describe, and he spends much of his time dealing with these models. A fruitful model serves not only to organize a number of observations, but also as a basis for prediction and to stimulate testing of the model by critical experiments. In this text we present some of the models and concepts of inorganic chemistry in current use. Some are models in the literal sense that they may be visualized and drawings or physical models made, as with shapes of orbitals, while some may not readily be pictured in physical space, as in the case of energy levels.

As well as providing a theoretical base for the subject, a new book in any area should keep the reader up to date. This can be done only if the new ideas appearing in the literature are selectively introduced into the text. Recent topics introduced in this text include crystal field theory, molecular orbitals, boron hydrides, and compounds of the rare gases.

A text should also organize and present effectively ideas which have proven of value for some time. The bases for concepts such as electronegativity and ionic radii are explored here.

The first four chapters present the models and concepts fundamental to inorganic chemistry. Although this book was written with a one-semester course in view, it is not expected that all chapters will necessarily be covered in one semester. Chapters V through XII may be treated as virtually independent topics with material to be selected at the discretion of the instructor. Frequent cross-references are given to facilitate such usage. Many instructors will prefer to refer students to Chapter XII (structural tools), introducing lecture material as needed for other chapters.

Some of the topics within individual chapters are included primarily to serve as a springboard for more advanced courses. For example, the treatment of spectroscopic terms given here provides the left-hand side of an Orgel diagram. The development of the right-hand side may then be carried out in a course in coordination compounds. The brief review of symmetry (Appendix C) and the discussion of the application of symmetry to molecular orbitals (Appendix D) represent extensions, which are becoming increasingly important, of the material in the text. It seemed most appropriate to separate this material from the main body of the text to provide better continuity for those instructors who do not cover this material.

Tables and figures have been used liberally throughout this book. These contain information essential to the portions of the text where they appear and are appropriately indexed. The Appendices and references included in each chapter are intended to extend the usefulness of the book beyond the classroom. It is hoped that the student will find it a useful reference source, which will continue to be of value after he has finished with it as a text.

The authors would like to thank Dr. Elmer Amma for the preparation of a treatment on molecular orbitals, Appendix D, and Dr. Alan Searcy for the example problem on the use of approximation methods in establishing half-cell emf values. We are indebted to our many friends and colleagues who read parts of the manuscript during its preparation and made numerous helpful suggestions. Among these we would like especially to thank Drs. C. H. Brubaker, Jr., T. B. Cameron, J. C. Carter, Joyce Corey, H. S. Frank, H. H. Jaffé, W. L. Jolly, L. N. Mulay, and D. K. Straub. For critically reading the entire manuscript we would like to express our gratitude to Dr. Gordon Atkinson. Finally, we would like to acknowledge the less specific, but no less important, contributions of our teachers and colleagues, who will be aware of their influence in the development of the ideas in this text.

Contents

Chapter XII. EXPERIMENTAL METHODS FOR THE ELUCIDATION OF STRUCTURE AND BONDING OF CHEMICAL COMPOUNDS

Concepts and Models
of Inorganic Chemistry

CHAPTER I

Atomic Structure
and the Periodic Table

Historical Background

A systematic approach to inorganic chemistry is today almost synonymous with a study of the periodic relationships of the elements and their compounds. Such an organization has an empirical foundation built during the last century and a theoretical justification of half a century.

Within a decade following the presentation of a consistent set of atomic weights by Stanislav Cannizzaro at the Karlsruhe conference in 1860, various forms of the periodic table appeared in France, England, Germany, and Russia. The role played by Cannizzaro's list of atomic weights in the development of the periodic table can be/better appreciated when one considers that an attempt in 1852 by Gladstone to find a relationship between the atomic weights and other properties of the elements failed, due to the lack of a consistent set of atomic weights. The greatest share of credit for the periodic table is usually given to Dimitri Mendeleyev and properly so, for it was the realization of his bold prophecy of new elements and their properties that led to the almost immediate acceptance of the periodic law. The following predictions were made by Mendeleyev in 1871 about an element that was discovered by Boisbaudran in 1875.*

> The properties of ekaaluminum, according to the periodic law, should be the following:
> Its atomic weight will be 68. Its oxide will have the formula El_2O_3; its salts will present the formula ElX_3. Thus, for example, the chloride of ekaaluminum will be $ElCl_3$; it will give for analysis 39% metal and 61% chlorine and will be more volatile than $ZnCl_2$. The sulfide El_2S_3, or oxysulfide $El_2(S,O)_3$, will be precipitated by H_2S and will be insoluble in ammonium sulfide. The metal will be easily obtained by reduction; its density will be 5.9, accordingly its atomic volume will be 11.5; it will be soft, and fusible at a very low temperature. It will not be oxidized on contact with air; it will decompose water when heated to redness. The pure liquid metal will not be attacked by acids and only slowly by alkali. The oxide El_2O_3 will have a specific gravity of approximately 5.5; it should be soluble in strong acids, forming an amorphous hydrate insoluble in water, dissolving in acids and alkali. The oxide of ekaaluminum will form the neutral salts and basic $El_2(OH,X)_6$, but no acid salts; the alum $KEl(SO_4)_2 \cdot 12H_2O$ will be more soluble than the corresponding salt of aluminum and less

---

* D. Mendeleyev, *Compt. Rend.*, **81**, 969 (1875) [citing *J. Russian Chem. Soc.*, **3**, 47 (1871)].

crystallizable. The basic properties of El_2O_3 being more pronounced than those of Al_2O_3 and less than that of ZnO . . . it will be precipitated by barium carbonate. The volatility as well as the other properties of the salts of ekaaluminum will be a mean between those of Al and In. It is probable that the metal in question will be discovered by spectral analysis as have been In and Tl.

An examination of the above predicted properties for gallium indicates some of the properties that vary systematically with the position of the element in the periodic table—physical properties of the element and its compounds (specific gravity, hardness, melting point, boiling point, etc.), spectrographic properties, and chemical properties (formulas of possible compounds, acidic and basic properties of compounds, etc.). In fact, properties of the elements or their compounds that cannot be correlated by means of the periodic table are somewhat exceptional.*

Much of this book will be devoted to attempting to understand the underlying principles which bring about these periodic relationships, i.e., properties that show greater than average similarity for elements, which lie in the periodic table (*a*) in a vertical column (called a group), (*b*) in a horizontal row (called a period), (*c*) within a given area (bounded by elements of two or more groups and two or more periods), and (*d*) on diagonals. The following are illustrative of these types of relationships. Elements in a group have similar arc and spark spectra, often similar valences, similar crystal structures both for the element and for particular series of compounds, etc. Elements in a given period have similar maximum coordination numbers in their compounds. The compounds of the second period elements Li, Be, and B show many similarities to the compounds of the third period elements Mg, Al, and Si to which they are diagonally related. Finally, there are numerous properties, such as classification of the elements as metals, metalloids, and nonmetals, that have an area relationship to the periodic table. The area relationships are often the most difficult to explain because of the wider possible variation of the factors that may be involved. Thus it may be difficult to explain in an *a priori* fashion why the carbides of a given area are explosive, but it is certainly worthwhile to know if one contemplates making carbides or acetylides of elements lying in or near such a known area.

Before proceeding to the theoretical basis of the periodic table, the following steps in its evolution may be noted.

By 1829, Döbereiner had pointed out that there were a number of cases in which three elements, or triads, have similar chemical properties. Further, there is one member of a triad for which the properties are very close to the mean value of the other two —this is particularly true of the atomic weights.

Between 1860 and 1870, periodic tables were prepared by Newland, Meyer, and Mendeleyev by listing the elements in the order of increasing atomic weights and then grouping them according to chemical properties. In the table of Mendeleyev the triads of Döbereiner always fell within the same group. It may, at first, appear odd that for the group VIII elements more than one element is listed in a period, but the elements iron, cobalt, and nickel form a triad of Döbereiner and hence have to appear in the same group. Mendeleyev reassigned atomic weights to a number of elements in order to

* One of the major classes of "exceptional" properties is nuclear properties, i.e., nuclear magnetic moments, isotopic abundance, etc. These properties, however, may be rationalized on the basis of a "shell theory of the nucleus," which is analogous to the theoretical justification of the chemical periodic table. See B. H. Flowers, *J. Chem. Educ.*, **37**, 610 (1960).

obtain a fit with the chemical properties of the other elements in the group. Later evaluations confirmed the need for reordering the atomic weights of some of the elements, but firmly established a reversal in atomic weights, as compared to the position in the periodic table, for several pairs of elements (Te and I, Co and Ni are the early known cases.)

As the rare earth elements were discovered, difficulty was encountered in fitting these elements into the table. This led Basset and later Thomsen to propose the extended form of the table generally accepted today. (See Figure 1.1.) Further, from a consideration of the change of group valence from −1 for the halogens to +1 for the alkali metals, Thomsen reasoned that one should expect a group of elements lying between groups VII and I and having either infinite or zero valence. Since a valence of infinity is unacceptable from a chemical viewpoint, he proposed that a group of elements of zero valence separated the highly electronegative halogens from the highly electropositive alkali metals. He proceeded to predict the atomic weights of these elements as 4, 20, 36, 84, 132, and 212. He felt that these elements should terminate each period. Unfortunately, Thomsen did not publish these remarkable predictions until after argon had been discovered.*

The last stage in the empirical development of the periodic table came in 1913 when Moseley found the x-ray emission from different elements had characteristic frequencies (ν), which varied in a regular fashion with the ordinal number of the elements as they appear in the table. The empirical relationship, which he found, was

$$\nu = k(Z - \sigma)^2$$

where Z is the ordinal or atomic number, ν is the characteristic x-ray frequency, and k and σ are constants for a given series. No reversals in atomic number occur in the periodic table, hence, it is a more fundamental property of an element than the atomic weight.

The empirical evolution of the periodic table had reached its peak. It was now possible to make a strictly ordered list of the elements with definite indication of missing elements. Each period terminated with a rare gas and it was possible to tell how many elements belonged to each period.

Atomic Structure and the Theoretical Basis of the Periodic Table

The theoretical basis of the periodic table had to await the development of a clearer picture of the atom. The concept of atoms as fundamental or indivisible particles had to be abandoned at the beginning of this century. Studies of cathode rays and canal rays led to the recognition of the existence of negative and positive charges within the atom. Further complexity of the atom could be inferred from emission spectra of gaseous substances in magnetic fields (the Zeeman effect) and the discovery of radioactivity. Not only did radioactivity indicate the atom was not a fundamental unit, but it provided a probe with which to examine the atom. From the scattering of alpha particles by thin metal foils, Rutherford arrived at a nuclear model of the atom, with a nucleus carrying a number of unit charges equal to approximately one half the atomic weight of the element. Van den Broek pointed out that the use of the ordinal number of the ele-

* J. Thomsen, *Z. Anorg. Chem.*, **9**, 283 (1895).

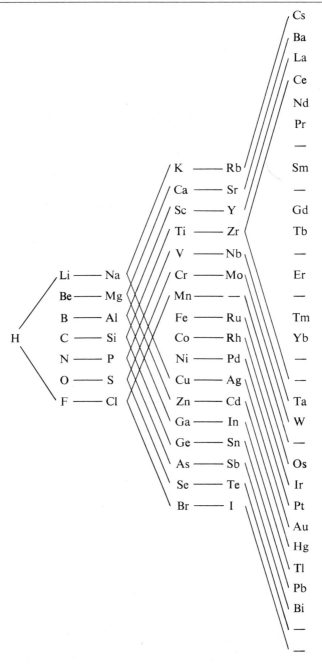

FIGURE 1.1. *Long form of periodic table.* [*Proposed by J. Thomsen,*
Z. Anorg. Chem., *9, 190 (1895).*]

ment in the periodic table, i.e., the atomic number, for the number of unit charges on the nucleus improved the fit of the alpha scattering data. Moseley also associated the atomic number with the nuclear charge.

Bohr Model of the Atom

A major advance in the understanding of the atom was the development by Niels Bohr of a model of the atom that could account for the spectra of hydrogen-like atoms (i.e., one electron, one nucleus—H, He[+], Li[2+], etc.). To develop his model Bohr accepted some past notions, rejected some, and assumed some new ones:

(1) The Rutherford nuclear model of the atom was accepted.

(2) The theories of Planck and of Einstein that radiant energy is quantized in units of $h\nu$, where h is Planck's constant and ν is the frequency of the radiant energy, were accepted.

(3) The classical electrodynamic theory that a charged particle undergoing acceleration must emit electromagnetic radiation was rejected for electrons within atoms.

(4) The electron was assumed to travel in circular orbits.

(5) Not all possible orbits were permitted. Only those for which the electron had a specified angular momentum were acceptable (i.e., the angular momentum was quantized).

(6) It was postulated that radiation was emitted or absorbed only when the electron jumped from one orbit to another, the energy emitted or absorbed corresponding to the difference in the energies for the initial and final states of the system.

(7) Except as noted above, classical physics was assumed to be applicable to the atom.

Before going further, it is well to note here that the Bohr assumption of circular orbits has been shown to be much too restrictive. Assumptions *(1)*, *(2)*, *(3)*, and *(6)* are retained in wave mechanics, whereas *(5)* comes as a result of the one arbitrary assumption of wave mechanics. Accordingly, we will not pay too much attention to the geometry of the Bohr model, but rather shall be more concerned with the energy states of the atom based on Bohr's model.

From *(1)* and *(4)* above, the Bohr model for hydrogen-like atoms may be pictured as having a heavy nucleus bearing a charge of Ze (where Z is the atomic number and e is the magnitude of the charge on the electron) with an electron of charge e and mass m traveling with a velocity v in an orbit of radius r from the nucleus. (See Figure 1.2.)

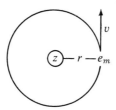

FIGURE 1.2. *Bohr model of hydrogen-like atoms.*

The following relationships result from the assumptions listed above:

(a) From classical physics *(7)* one may equate the centripetal force with the

coulombic attraction

$$\frac{mv^2}{r} = \frac{Ze^2}{r^2}$$

or

(a¹)
$$mv^2r = Ze^2$$

(b)   The total energy, E, is the sum of the kinetic and potential energy

$$E = \frac{1}{2}mv^2 - \frac{Ze^2}{r}$$

(b¹)
$$E = -\frac{1}{2}\frac{Ze^2}{r} \quad \text{[substituting from (a) for } \frac{1}{2}mv^2\text{]}$$

(c)   Quantizing the angular momentum

$$mvr = n\left(\frac{h}{2\pi}\right)$$

where n (called the quantum number) must be an integer and h is Planck's constant.

(d)   From $a \div c$

$$v = Ze^2\frac{2\pi}{nh}$$

(e)   From (a¹) and (d)

$$r = \frac{Ze^2}{mv^2} = \frac{n^2h^2}{4\pi^2mZe^2}$$

(f)   From (b¹) and (e)

$$E = -\frac{2\pi^2mZ^2e^4}{n^2h^2} = \frac{E_{(n=1)}}{n^2}$$

This equation gives the energy of hydrogen-like atoms in various quantum states. For the hydrogen atom itself the lowest energy state, i.e., the quantum state for $n = 1$, has the value of -13.6 eV or -313.6 kcal/mole. The lowest energy state for an atom (or ion or molecule) is called the *ground state*. The first higher energy state above the ground state is called the *first excited state*; the next higher state is called the *second excited state*, etc. The first excited state of the hydrogen atom would be that state having a quantum number of two. The amount of energy needed to promote an atom from the ground state to a given excited state is called the *excitation potential*. The amount of energy needed to remove an electron from an atom in its ground state is called the *ionization potential*. The *separation energy* is the amount of energy necessary to remove an electron from an atom in a particular excited state. These relationships are illustrated in Figure 1.3, which gives an energy level diagram for the hydrogen atom on which examples of some of the above are illustrated. In such a diagram only the ordinate has meaning.

Some conclusions about hydrogen-like atoms that may be made on the basis of the

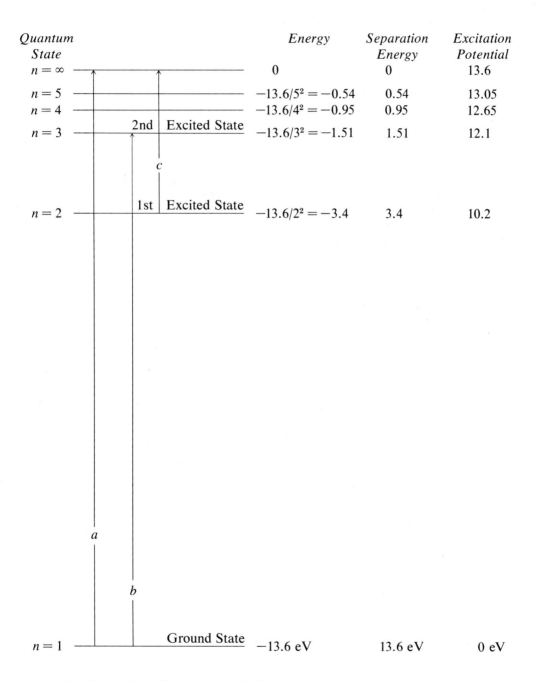

FIGURE 1.3. *Energy level diagram for the hydrogen atom. Line a corresponds to the ionization potential, 13.6 eV. Line b corresponds to the excitation potential necessary to produce the 2nd excited state, i.e., 12.1 eV. Line c corresponds to the separation energy of the 1st excited state, 3.4 eV.*

Bohr model are: *(1)* The ionization potential for the removal of the single electron is proportional to Z^2. *(2)* The radius of the hydrogen atom in the ground state is 0.529 Å and for hydrogen-like atoms it is inversely proportional to Z. The radius of the atom in excited states is proportional to n^2. *(3)* In the ground state the electron is traveling with a velocity of 2.2×10^8 cm/sec and accordingly creates a magnetic field of 1.25×10^5 gauss at the nucleus.

As has been mentioned, one of the major achievements of the Bohr model of the atom was its ability to account for the spectra of hydrogen-like atoms. By the time Bohr proposed his model of the atom, spectroscopists had formulated many empirical rules dealing with line spectra of atoms. Among these rules, the one having the greatest influence on Bohr was that frequency, ν, or wave number, $\omega \equiv 1/\lambda$, of the numerous individual lines observed in a given spectrum can be reduced to the difference between a smaller number of terms. For atomic H the terms take the form R/n^2 where R is a constant, called the Rydberg constant (having a value of $109, 677.581$ cm^{-1}) and n is an integer. Thus, empirically, all of the lines of the spectrum of atomic hydrogen have wave numbers given by the equation

$$\omega = \frac{R}{n_1{}^2} - \frac{R}{n_2{}^2} = T_1 - T_2$$

According to Bohr's theory

$$h\nu = E_2 - E_1 = hc\omega$$

The term values of the spectroscopist are thus virtually identical to energy levels within the atom, differing only in sign (due to defining the potential energy of the ionized atom as zero) and a constant factor of hc (which essentially takes care of the difference in units). From Bohr's theory the Rydberg constant is given by $2\pi^2me^4/h^3c$. The excellent agreement between the value calculated from these fundamental constants and the spectroscopically derived value gave strong support to Bohr's theory.

The Bohr theory, with some modification, was found to be capable of explaining the Moseley relationship between characteristic x-ray spectra and atomic number. The excited state for emission of x rays was postulated as one in which a low energy electron had been knocked out of a polyelectronic atom. An electron from a higher energy state could then drop down to the lower empty orbit. In a polyelectronic atom a given electron will be partially shielded from the positive charge of the nucleus by the electrons between it and the nucleus. The effective nuclear charge may be taken as $Z - \sigma$, where σ represents the shielding effect of underlying electrons. For an electron dropping from an $n = 2$ state to an $n = 1$ state in a polyelectron ion, the Bohr theory would thus predict

$$\nu = \frac{2\pi^2m(Z - \sigma)^2e^4}{h^3} \left(\frac{1}{n_2{}^2} - \frac{1}{n_1{}^2} \right)$$

or

$$\nu = \frac{3}{4} Rc(Z - \sigma)^2$$

The values of the shielding constants for the K and L series support the conclusion of 2 and 8 electrons, respectively, in these "shells."

Bohr–Sommerfeld Model of the Atom

Sommerfeld modified the Bohr treatment by specifying that the electron travel in elliptical orbits, with the nucleus at one of the foci, circular orbits being simply a special case of elliptical orbits. The electron traveling in an elliptical orbit would have, in addition to its angular momentum, a component of momentum along the radial direction. Both momenta were quantized, i.e., taken as units of $h/2\pi$. The two resulting quantum numbers were called the azimuthal quantum number, designated as k, and the radial quantum number, n_r. The sum of these quantum numbers, $k + n_r$, corresponded to the principal quantum number n of the Bohr theory. Except for relativity effects, which will not be discussed here, the total energy still depended on n in the same fashion as in the Bohr theory. Just as n determined the size of the Bohr orbits, the elliptical orbits in the Sommerfeld treatment have a major axis equal in length to the diameter calculated for a Bohr orbit of a given n state. The ratio of the major to the minor axis is equal to n/k. The possible orbits for $n = 3$ are shown in Figure 1.4.

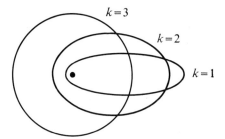

FIGURE 1.4. *Bohr–Sommerfeld orbits for $n = 3$.*

Although these levels, in the absence of relativity effects, would be of equal energy in a one electron system, when lower orbits are filled, the most elliptical orbit (i.e., 3_1) will have the lowest energy for a given n value due to the penetration of the underlying filled orbits.

The quantum numbers n and k are sufficient to describe elliptical orbits in a plane, but another quantum number is necessary to describe the orientation of the plane of the ellipse in space. Not all orientations are possible—only those in which the component of momentum along the z axis is quantized. The energies of the states corresponding to different orientations differ in a directional magnetic field and hence the quantum number associated with these states is called the magnetic quantum number.

Finally, Uhlenbeck and Goudsmit postulated that the electron itself has a spin and a corresponding spin angular momentum, which is quantized, only a spin angular momentum of $\frac{1}{2}(h/2\pi)$ being allowed. In a directional magnetic field the momentum associated with the spin can only be parallel or antiparallel to a magnetic field, thus giving rise to a magnetic spin quantum number, m_s.

Thus, in the dozen years following Bohr's postulate of the quantization of orbital angular momentum of the electron in circular orbits, the postulate of quantization was extended to *all* momenta associated with a particle or system. For the electron in the atom it is necessary to specify at least four such quantized momenta to determine the system uniquely. Three of these momenta may be associated with the three coordinates defining 3-dimensional space and the fourth with the spin of the electron. Other momenta, which are derivable from these four, or from which these four may be derived, serve equally well. The interaction of these momenta suggested a vector model of the atom, but discussion of this will be deferred until after a brief discussion of the wave mechanics.

Wave Mechanics

WAVE PROPERTIES OF MATTER

The Einstein equation for the energy of a photon, $E = h\nu$, may be combined with the Einstein equation relating mass and energy, $E = mc^2$, to give an expression for the momentum of a photon, $mc = h\nu/c$. Compton applied the laws of conservation of energy and conservation of momentum to the collision of a photon with a free electron and predicted the change in momentum or frequency of the photon for various angles of the scattered radiation relative to the incident radiation. Measurements of the scattering of x rays by the "free" electron of graphite verified the predictions, thus proving that photons have momenta.

De Broglie* suggested that the particle-wave dualism phenomenon is not restricted to light, but that all particles must have an associated wave. For particles in general the wavelength of the associated waves is given by

$$\lambda = \frac{h}{mv} \tag{1.1}$$

where m is the mass of a particle traveling with a velocity v. The wave properties predicted for matter have been verified for free particles by experiments in which diffraction patterns have been observed for beams of electrons, neutrons, and atoms, respectively.

In a classical wave picture, the intensity of a light wave is proportional to the square of the amplitude of the wave. In a photon picture, the intensity of a light beam is proportional to the number of photons striking a given area. If both representations are to be valid, then the number of photons striking a given area in a given time period must be proportional to the square of the amplitude of the light wave striking that area. Since a given area may be subdivided into an infinite number of smaller areas while a light beam would have a finite number of photons, the above statement may be modified to read that the *probability of finding a photon* in a given area is proportional to the square of the amplitude of the light wave falling on that area. Or, *for any particle*, the probability of finding a particle in a given volume is proportional to the square of the amplitude of the wave associated with the particle in the given volume. In terms of de Broglie's matter waves, the Bohr quantization condition specifies that the circumference of the orbit must be a whole multiple of the wavelength associated with the electron in the orbit, i.e., $n\lambda = 2\pi r$, which would give rise to a standing wave. Replacing λ by h/mv gives equation (c) (p. 6).

* L. de Broglie, *Ann. Phys.*, **3**, 22–128 (1925).

A reciprocal relationship between wave properties and properties of matter may be seen by rearranging the equations $E = h\nu$ and $\lambda = h/p$ (where p stands for momentum and replaces the mv of Equation 1.1) to give

$$h = ET = p\lambda \qquad (1.2)$$

(where T is the period of vibration, $T = 1/\nu$).

Energy and momentum are usually associated with particle properties, whereas period and wavelength are associated with wave properties. When one of these (E or p) is large the other (T or λ) will be small. Thus at long wavelengths, such as radiowaves, it is difficult to show particle behavior, while at very short wavelengths, such as γ rays, it is difficult to show wave behavior.

An equation having a form very similar to Equation 1.2 was proposed by Heisenberg and has become known as Heisenberg's uncertainty principle. This equation, $(\Delta P_x)(\Delta X) \geq h$, states that the product of the uncertainty of the momentum of a particle with respect to a given coordinate and the uncertainty in position with respect to the same coordinate must be equal to, or greater than, Planck's constant. This uncertainty is not due to experimental errors but rather to the inherent indeterminacy in describing both position and momentum simultaneously. A corollary, due to Bohr, states that we cannot in a single experiment show simultaneously particle and wave properties of radiation.

In the Bohr–Sommerfeld model of the atom both the momentum and position of the electron with respect to each coordinate were specified. It is not possible to have such precise knowledge of both momenta and position according to the uncertainty principle. On other grounds the quantum number k appeared to give an incorrect orbital angular momentum and had empirically been replaced by $k - 1$.

The Schrödinger Equation

In 1927, Schrödinger proposed an equation that specified no discrete orbits, but instead was an equation describing the wave associated with the electron. This equation, given below, has become the basis for wave mechanics.

$$\frac{\partial^2\psi}{\partial x^2} + \frac{\partial^2\psi}{\partial y^2} + \frac{\partial^2\psi}{\partial z^2} + \frac{8\pi^2 m}{h^2}(E - V)\psi = 0$$

In this equation ψ is the amplitude of the wave function associated with the electron, E is the total energy of the system, V is the potential energy of the system (equal to $-e^2/r$ for hydrogen), m is the mass of the electron, h is Planck's constant, and x, y, and z are the usual Cartesian coordinates. The frequency of the wave describing the electron is related to its energy by $E = h\nu$. Compared to Bohr's postulates given on p. 5 the last statement replaces No. *(5)* and the wave form of the equation replaces No. *(4)*, the other postulates being retained.

Since the probability of finding the electron in a given volume element is proportional to ψ^2, ψ itself must be a single valued function with respect to the spatial coordinates, it must be a continuous function, and it must become zero at infinity. These conditions are imposed as boundary conditions on the wave equation.

The transformation of the wave equation for the hydrogen atom into polar coordinates facilitates the separation of variables and solution of the equation. The position variables in polar coordinates are r, θ, and ϕ, where r is the radial distance of a point from the origin, θ is the inclination of the radial line to the z axis, and ϕ is the angle made with the x axis by the projection of the radial line in the xy plane. (See Figure 1.5.)

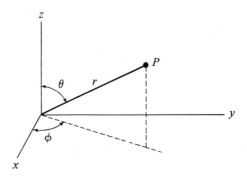

FIGURE 1.5. *Variables of polar coordinates.*

The solutions for ψ are called wave functions and may be expressed as the product of three functions each of which depends on only one of the coordinates.

$$\psi(r, \theta, \phi) = R(r)\Theta(\theta)\Phi(\phi)$$

The boundary conditions require that certain constants that enter into the solution of the wave equation take on only integral values. These constants are called quantum numbers and are designated by n, l, and m_l. n is called the principal quantum number and may take on the values 1, 2, 3, . . . , etc.; l may have the values of 0, 1, . . . , up to $n-1$; m_l can have values ranging from $-l$ through 0 to $+l$. The wave functions, ψ, which are solutions of the Schrödinger equation, are commonly called orbitals. Orbitals for which $l = 0, 1, 2, 3$, and 4, respectively, are called s, p, d, f, and g orbitals.

SOLUTIONS OF THE SCHRÖDINGER EQUATION FOR ONE ELECTRON IN A FREE ATOM

The radial part of the wave function depends only on the n and l values and has an exponential term e^{-r/na_0}, where a_0 is 0.529 Å, and a pre-exponential term involving a polynomial of the $n-1$ degree. The radial functions* for $n = 1, l = 0$; $n = 2, l = 0$; and $n = 2, l = 1$ are

$$R_{1,0} = \frac{1}{\sqrt{\pi}} \left(\frac{1}{a_0}\right)^{3/2} e^{-r/a_0}$$

$$R_{2,0} = \frac{1}{4\sqrt{2\pi}} \left(\frac{1}{a_0}\right)^{3/2} \left(2 - \frac{r}{a}\right) e^{-r/2a_0}$$

$$R_{2,1} = \frac{1}{4\sqrt{6\pi}} \left(\frac{1}{a_0}\right)^{3/2} \left(\frac{r}{a}\right) e^{-r/2a_0}$$

* From L. Pauling, *The Nature of the Chemical Bond*, Third Edition, © 1960 by Cornell University. Used by permission of Cornell University Press.

Plots of the radial part of the ψ function, R, versus the distance from the nucleus are given in Figure 1.6 for $n = 1$, $n = 2$, and $n = 3$ with appropriate l values.

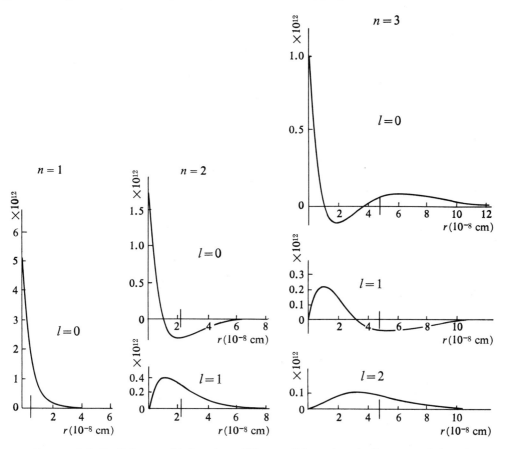

FIGURE 1.6. *Radial part of ψ function of H-atom [from* Atomic Spectra and Atomic Structure, *G. Herzberg (New York: Dover Publications, 1944) p. 40].*

The probability of finding the electron in a volume element of fixed size located (essentially) at some given point at a distance r from the nucleus is given by $R^2 d\tau$ (where $d\tau$ is the elemental volume unit). The probability that the electron is to be found at a distance r from the nucleus is given by $(4\pi r^2)R^2 dr$. This is the probability that the electron will be found in a spherical shell of thickness dr at a distance from the nucleus ranging from r to $r + dr$. Curves showing $R^2 d\tau$ and $(4\pi r^2)R^2 dr$ versus r are given in Figure 1.7. $R^2 d\tau$ (or more generally $\psi^2 d\tau$) is sometimes referred to as the electron probability distribution density, or more simply as the electron density. The shape of the surfaces for which ψ (and consequently ψ^2) is constant is referred to as the shape of the orbital.* Representations of cross-sectional slices of the atom show the surfaces

* Some wave functions may involve imaginary numbers. In such cases $\psi\psi^*$ replaces ψ^2 where ψ^* is the complex conjugate of ψ. In such cases the shape of the electron probability distribution function, $\psi\psi^*$, has physical meaning, but that of the orbital does not. This is the case for the orbitals beyond the s orbitals in the case of the isolated atom.

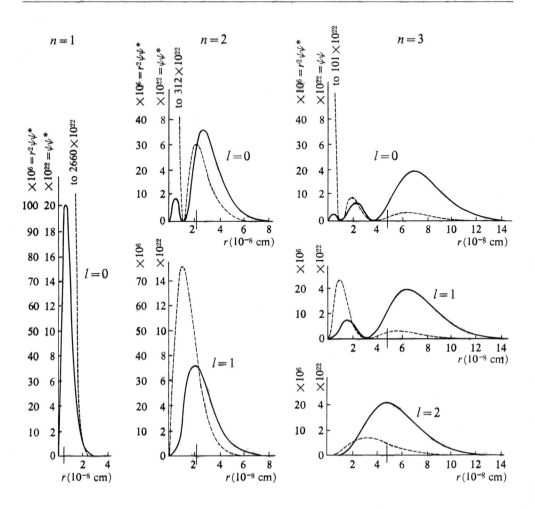

FIGURE 1.7. *Radial probability distribution functions of the hydrogen atom. Dashed curves represent R^2; solid curves represent r^2R^2* [*from* Atomic Spectra and Atomic Structure, G. Herzberg (New York: Dover Publications, 1944) p. 43].

of constant electron density as contour lines. For free atoms these contour lines would simply be concentric circles.

SOLUTIONS OF THE SCHRÖDINGER EQUATION WITH A SINGLE DESIGNATED CARTESIAN COORDINATE AXIS

The electron distribution curves in Figure 1.7 are those for an atom in free space, that is, where there is no basis for assigning one or more cartesian reference axes and consequently Θ^2 and Φ^2 are constant. When one coordinate axis can be assigned, as when the atom is in an external unidirectional magnetic field (or in linear molecules, as discussed in Chapter II) then Θ and Θ^2 are not constant. The probability of finding an electron is now given by $R^2\Theta^2 d\tau$. Θ is dependent on the quantum numbers l and m. The functions Θ (given in Table 1.1) and Θ^2 are shown plotted in polar coordinates in Figure 1.8.

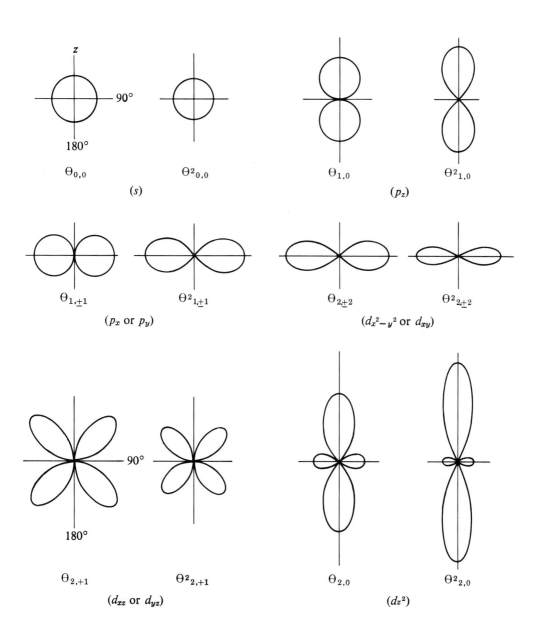

FIGURE 1.8. $\Theta_{l,m}$ *and* Θ^2 *for the hydrogen atom.*

TABLE 1.1
Θ Functions for the Hydrogen Atom[a]

$l = 0$, s orbitals:

$$\Theta_{00}(\theta) = \frac{\sqrt{2}}{2}$$

$l = 1$, p orbitals:

$$\Theta_{10}(\theta) = \frac{\sqrt{6}}{2} \cos\theta$$

$$\Theta_{1\pm1}(\theta) = \frac{\sqrt{3}}{2} \sin\theta$$

$l = 2$, d orbitals:

$$\Theta_{20}(\theta) = \frac{\sqrt{10}}{4} (3\cos^2\theta - 1)$$

$$\Theta_{2\pm1}(\theta) = \frac{\sqrt{15}}{2} \sin\theta\cos\theta$$

$$\Theta_{2\pm2}(\theta) = \frac{\sqrt{15}}{4} \sin^2\theta$$

$l = 3$, f orbitals:

$$\Theta_{30}(\theta) = \frac{3\sqrt{14}}{4}\left(\frac{5}{3}\cos^3\theta - \cos\theta\right)$$

$$\Theta_{3\pm1}(\theta) = \frac{\sqrt{42}}{8} \sin\theta(5\cos^2\theta - 1)$$

$$\Theta_{3\pm2}(\theta) = \frac{\sqrt{105}}{4} \sin^2\theta\cos\theta$$

$$\Theta_{3\pm3}(\theta) = \frac{\sqrt{70}}{8} \sin^2\theta$$

[a] From L. Pauling, *The Nature of the Chemical Bond*, Third Edition, © 1960 by Cornell University. Used by permission of Cornell University Press.

Since $\psi\psi^*$ is independent of ϕ where only one axis can be designated, rotation of the Θ^2 curves about the z axis produces surfaces giving angular dependence of the electron distribution function. These are shown here in Figure 1.9. It should be noted that, except for the s electron distribution, the angular dependence of $\psi\psi^*$ only gives an approximation of the shape of the total $\psi\psi^*$ function. Contours of the p_z and d_{z^2} electrons obtained from $\psi\psi^* = R^2\Theta^2$ are given in Figure 1.10.

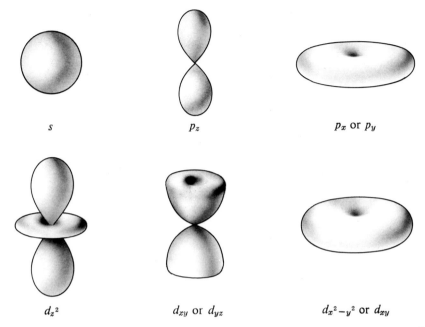

FIGURE 1.9. *Angular dependence of $\psi\psi^*$ with a single designated Cartesian axis (z).*

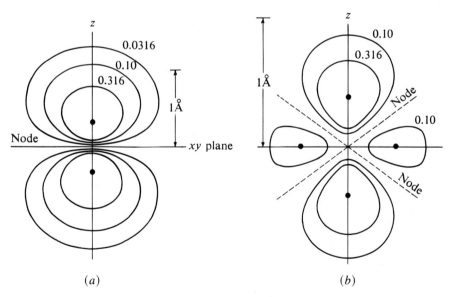

FIGURE 1.10. (a) *Contours of constant ψ^2 at 0.0316, 0.10, and 0.316 of maximum for a C 2_{p_z} orbital. The xy plane is a nodal surface. (b) Contours of constant ψ^2 at 0.10 and 0.316 of maximum for a Ti(III) $3d_{z^2}$ orbital. [from E. A. Ogryzlo and G. Porter, J. Chem. Educ., 40, 258 (1963)].*

SOLUTIONS OF THE SCHRÖDINGER EQUATION WITH
ALL CARTESIAN AXES DESIGNATED

In cases where all Cartesian reference coordinate axes may be assigned to an atom (as in nonlincar molecules) the Φ^2 functions dependent on ϕ are the appropriate ones to use. Table 1.2 gives these solutions of Φ, which are different for different values of the magnetic quantum number m_l. Plots of Φ and Φ^2 for different values of m are given in Figure 1.11.

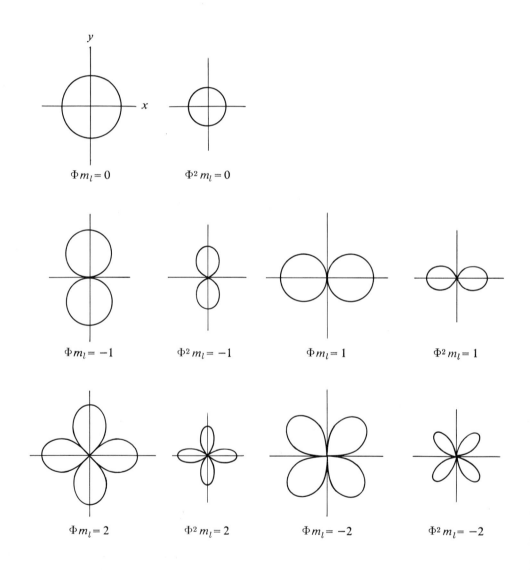

FIGURE 1.11. Φ and Φ^2 for the hydrogen atom.

The total angular dependence of the wave function, $\psi(\theta, \phi)$, is simply the product of Θ and Φ, both taken for the same value of m_l. For a given l and m, $\psi(\theta, \phi)$ has a fixed value for every direction in space. A three-dimensional plot of $\psi(\theta, \phi)$ results in a surface for each value of l and m_l. These are sketched in Figure 1.12 for l values through $l = 2$.

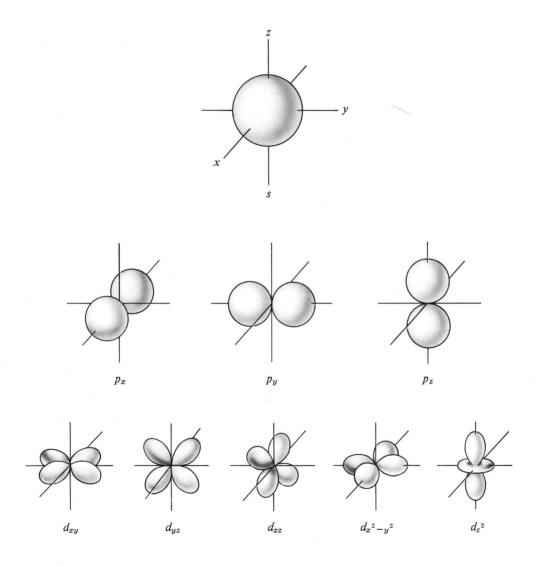

FIGURE 1.12. *Total angular dependence of the wave function, $\psi(\theta, \phi)$ with all Cartesian coordinates fixed [d-functions after R. G. Pearson, Chem. Eng. News, 37, 72 (1959)].*

TABLE 1.2
Φ_{m_l} *Functions for the Hydrogen Atom*[a]

$$\Phi_0(\phi) = \frac{1}{\sqrt{2\pi}} \qquad \text{or} \qquad \Phi_0(\phi) = \frac{1}{\sqrt{2\pi}}$$

$$\Phi_1(\phi) = \frac{1}{\sqrt{2\pi}} e^{i\phi} \qquad \text{or} \qquad \Phi_{1\cos}(\phi) = \frac{1}{\sqrt{\pi}} \cos\phi$$

$$\Phi_{-1}(\phi) = \frac{1}{\sqrt{2\pi}} e^{-i\phi} \qquad \text{or} \qquad \Phi_{1\sin}(\phi) = \frac{1}{\sqrt{\pi}} \sin\phi$$

$$\Phi_2(\phi) = \frac{1}{\sqrt{2\pi}} e^{i2\phi} \qquad \text{or} \qquad \Phi_{2\cos}(\phi) = \frac{1}{\sqrt{\pi}} \cos 2\phi$$

$$\Phi_{-2}(\phi) = \frac{1}{\sqrt{2\pi}} e^{-i2\phi} \qquad \text{or} \qquad \Phi_{2\sin}(\phi) = \frac{1}{\sqrt{\pi}} \sin 2\phi$$

[a] From L. Pauling, *The Nature of the Chemical Bond*, Third Edition, © 1960 by Cornell University. Used by permission of Cornell University Press.

These $\psi(\theta, \phi)$ surfaces are often referred to as orbitals and, indeed, serve very satisfactorily for most arguments concerned with chemical bonding. It should be realized, however, that the variation of ψ in space is the product of $\psi(R)$ and $\psi(\theta, \phi)$ at every point in space. A slice of the ψ function yields contours such as were shown in Figure 1.10. A major conceptual difference is that the angular contribution to $\psi\psi^* (\theta, \phi)$ for the three p orbitals may be represented as shown in Figure 1.13 whereas for the total $\psi\psi^*(r, \theta, \phi)$ the corresponding figure would have a spherical distribution.

Some consequences of the spatial orientation of the orbitals will be discussed in Chapter II under the heading of shapes of molecules and also in Chapter X under ligand field theory.

INTERPRETATIONS OF THE SCHRÖDINGER EQUATION

Some further interpretations of the Schrödinger equation and comparisons with the Bohr–Sommerfeld treatment may be in order. As explained earlier, if an experiment were performed to detect the electron as a particle, the probability of finding the electron in a given volume element would be given by $\psi\psi^* d\tau$. The polemical question may

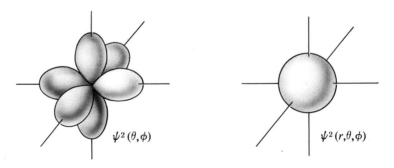

FIGURE 1.13. $\psi^2(\theta,\phi)$ *surfaces and a single contour surface* $\psi^2(r,\theta,\phi)$
for a complete set of p-orbitals.

be raised as to the nature of the electron in the unperturbed atom. One view, commonly held, is that the electron exists as a particle, which spends an amount of time in each volume unit proportional to $\psi\psi^*$ for that volume unit. Due to the very rapid motion of the electron, over a period of time as long as, say, a microsecond the electron appears to be smeared out and one may speak of the electron as forming a cloud whose charge density in any given volume element would be $\psi\psi^*d\tau$. The path traveled by the electron would be unpredictable according to the uncertainty principle. This view ignores the problem of classical electrodynamics predicting that an electron traveling around the nucleus would radiate energy and collapse. It also ignores the question of how the electron passes through the surfaces of zero electron density corresponding to $\psi = 0$. On the other hand, the view may be taken that the electron in the atom *is* a wave. The electron distribution would be static and there would be no emission of radiation. Just as the total energy of a vibrating string may be withdrawn by a probe at any point except a node, so an interaction with the electron wave at any point other than a node would affect the entire electron wave.

We may say that the electron distributions with nodal surfaces resulting from the Schrödinger equation are a direct consequence of the *assumption* of wave character of the electron, just as the elliptical orbits were assumed in the Bohr-Sommerfeld treatment. Since the wave equation assumes less about the position of the electron than the assumption of elliptical orbits (just as the elliptical orbits are less restrictive than circular orbits) it has a greater chance of being universally applicable. For the one electron case many of the conclusions from the Bohr-Sommerfeld treatment are in quantitative or qualitative agreement with the results from the Schrödinger equation, especially regarding energies, average distance of the electron from the nucleus, and penetration.

Electronic Configurations and the Periodic Table

We have just seen that an orbital is uniquely determined by the three quantum numbers n, l, and m_l. Since l can have the values of zero up to $n - 1$ and m_l can have the values of $-l$ through zero to $+l$, for a given value of n there will be n^2 orbitals. Table 1.3 shows the quantum numbers, orbital designation, and shell description corresponding to the orbitals through $n = 3$.

TABLE 1.3
Orbital and Shell Designations for Different Quantum States

Value of n	1	2	2	2	2	3	3	3	3	3	3	3	3	3
Value of l	0	0	1	1	1	0	1	1	1	2	2	2	2	2
Value of m_l	0	0	−1	0	1	0	−1	0	1	−2	−1	0	1	2
Orbital designation	1s	2s	2p	2p	2p	3s	3p	3p	3p	3d	3d	3d	3d	3d
Shell designation	K		L								M			

The shell designation stands for the orbitals of a given principal quantum number n; $K, L, M, N \ldots$, corresponding to values of n of $1, 2, 3, 4 \ldots$, respectively. The letters s, p, d, f, g of the orbital designation indicate l values of $0, 1, 2, 3, 4 \ldots$, respectively, while the number preceeding the letter gives the principal quantum number. Thus a 3p electron is one having $l = 1$ and $n = 3$. When Cartesian axes are meaningful the different p and d orbitals may be designated as p_x, p_y, p_z and d_{z^2}, $d_{x^2-y^2}$, d_{xy}, d_{xz}, and d_{yz}.

The formation of polyelectronic atoms may be considered to take place by adding electrons successively to hydrogen-like orbitals. The number of electrons that may occupy each orbital is limited to two and these must have the magnetic moment associated with their spins opposed.* The electrons enter the lowest available empty orbital, the energy of the orbitals being approximately in the order

$$1s < 2s < 2p < 3s < 3p < 4s \lesssim 3d < 4p < 5s \lesssim 4d < 6s \sim 5d \sim 4f < 6p$$

Where the approximate inequality is indicated, the order given is that for the lighter elements. At high atomic numbers the order of increasing energy is that of increasing n, and within a given shell, with increasing l. Where there is more than one orbital having the same n and l value (such as the p orbitals), each individual orbital will be filled with a single electron before any of the equivalent orbitals are occupied by pairs of electrons. The occupancy of the orbitals, usually called the *electronic configuration*, is given in Table 1.4 for the known elements. The superscripts indicate the number of electrons in a given set of orbitals, i.e., for nitrogen the $1s^2 2s^2 2p^3$ indicates that there are two electrons in the $1s$ orbital, two in the $2s$ orbital, and one electron in each of the three p orbitals. Alternatively the electronic configurations are sometimes shown more graphically by drawing a circle or square to designate each individual orbital or "cell" and using a dot or arrow to indicate the occupancy of an orbital by an electron. The configuration for nitrogen can be represented as

$1s$	$2s$	$2p$	or	$1s$	$2s$	$2p$
⇅	⇅	↑ ↑ ↑		⦂	⦂	⦁ ⦁ ⦁

* This is known as the Pauli exclusion principle. The nonelectrostatic repulsive force between two electrons of the same spin is known as the Pauli force and comes into play very sharply at short range. The nonpenetrability of matter and the shapes of molecules are determined largely by Pauli forces. See p. 61 and p. 92, Chapter II.

TABLE 1.4
Electron Configurations of the Elements

Element	K	L		M			N				O				P		Q
	$1s$	$2s$	$2p$	$3s$	$3p$	$3d$	$4s$	$4p$	$4d$	$4f$	$5s$	$5p$	$5d$	$5f$	$6s$	$6p$	$6d$	$7s$
1. H	1																
2. He	2																
3. Li	2	1															
4. Be	2	2															
5. B	2	2	1														
6. C	2	2	2														
7. N	2	2	3														
8. O	2	2	4														
9. F	2	2	5														
10. Ne	2	2	6														
11. Na	2	2	6	1													
12. Mg	2	2	6	2													
13. Al	2	2	6	2	1												
14. Si	2	2	6	2	2												
15. P	2	2	6	2	3												

TABLE 1.4 – *Continued*
Electron Configurations of the Elements

Element	K	L		M			N				O				P			Q
	1s	2s	2p	3s	3p	3d	4s	4p	4d	4f	5s	5p	5d	5f	6s	6p	6d	7s
16. S	2	2	6	2	4													
17. Cl	2	2	6	2	5													
18. Ar	2	2	6	2	6													
19. K	2	2	6	2	6		1											
20. Ca	2	2	6	2	6		2											
21. Sc	2	2	6	2	6	1	2											
22. Ti	2	2	6	2	6	2	2											
23. V	2	2	6	2	6	3	2											
24. Cr	2	2	6	2	6	5	1											
25. Mn	2	2	6	2	6	5	2											
26. Fe	2	2	6	2	6	6	2											
27. Co	2	2	6	2	6	7	2											
28. Ni	2	2	6	2	6	8	2											
29. Cu	2	2	6	2	6	10	1											
30. Zn	2	2	6	2	6	10	2											
31. Ga	2	2	6	2	6	10	2	1										
32. Ge	2	2	6	2	6	10	2	2										
33. As	2	2	6	2	6	10	2	3										
34. Se	2	2	6	2	6	10	2	4										
35. Br	2	2	6	2	6	10	2	5										
36. Kr	2	2	6	2	6	10	2	6										
37. Rb	2	2	6	2	6	10	2	6			1							
38. Sr	2	2	6	2	6	10	2	6			2							
39. Y	2	2	6	2	6	10	2	6	1		2							
40. Zr	2	2	6	2	6	10	2	6	2		2							
41. Nb	2	2	6	2	6	10	2	6	4		1							
42. Mo	2	2	6	2	6	10	2	6	5		1							
43. Tc	2	2	6	2	6	10	2	6	5		2							
44. Ru	2	2	6	2	6	10	2	6	7		1							
45. Rh	2	2	6	2	6	10	2	6	8		1							
46. Pd	2	2	6	2	6	10	2	6	10									
47. Ag	2	2	6	2	6	10	2	6	10		1							
48. Cd	2	2	6	2	6	10	2	6	10		2							
49. In	2	2	6	2	6	10	2	6	10		2	1						
50. Sn	2	2	6	2	6	10	2	6	10		2	2						
51. Sb	2	2	6	2	6	10	2	6	10		2	3						
52. Te	2	2	6	2	6	10	2	6	10		2	4						
53. I	2	2	6	2	6	10	2	6	10		2	5						
54. Xe	2	2	6	2	6	10	2	6	10		2	6						
55. Cs	2	2	6	2	6	10	2	6	10		2	6			1			
56. Ba	2	2	6	2	6	10	2	6	10		2	6			2			

TABLE 1.4—*Continued*
Electron Configurations of the Elements

Element	K	L		M			N				O				P			Q
	1s	2s	2p	3s	3p	3d	4s	4p	4d	4f	5s	5p	5d	5f	6s	6p	6d	7s
57. La	2	2	6	2	6	10	2	6	10		2	6	1		2			
58. Ce	2	2	6	2	6	10	2	6	10	2	2	6			2			
59. Pr	2	2	6	2	6	10	2	6	10	3	2	6			2			
60. Nd	2	2	6	2	6	10	2	6	10	4	2	6			2			
61. Pm	2	2	6	2	6	10	2	6	10	5	2	6			2			
62. Sm	2	2	6	2	6	10	2	6	10	6	2	6			2			
63. Eu	2	2	6	2	6	10	2	6	10	7	2	6			2			
64. Gd	2	2	6	2	6	10	2	6	10	7	2	6	1		2			
65. Tb	2	2	6	2	6	10	2	6	10	9	2	6			2			
66. Dy	2	2	6	2	6	10	2	6	10	10	2	6			2			
67. Ho	2	2	6	2	6	10	2	6	10	11	2	6			2			
68. Er	2	2	6	2	6	10	2	6	10	12	2	6			2			
69. Tm	2	2	6	2	6	10	2	6	10	13	2	6			2			
70. Yb	2	2	6	2	6	10	2	6	10	14	2	6			2			
71. Lu	2	2	6	2	6	10	2	6	10	14	2	6	1		2			
72. Hf	2	2	6	2	6	10	2	6	10	14	2	6	2		2			
73. Ta	2	2	6	2	6	10	2	6	10	14	2	6	3		2			
74. W	2	2	6	2	6	10	2	6	10	14	2	6	4		2			
75. Re	2	2	6	2	6	10	2	6	10	14	2	6	5		2			
76. Os	2	2	6	2	6	10	2	6	10	14	2	6	6		2			
77. Ir	2	2	6	2	6	10	2	6	10	14	2	6	7		2			
78. Pt	2	2	6	2	6	10	2	6	10	14	2	6	9		1			
79. Au	2	2	6	2	6	10	2	6	10	14	2	6	10		1			
80. Hg	2	2	6	2	6	10	2	6	10	14	2	6	10		2			
81. Tl	2	2	6	2	6	10	2	6	10	14	2	6	10		2	1		
82. Pb	2	2	6	2	6	10	2	6	10	14	2	6	10		2	2		
83. Bi	2	2	6	2	6	10	2	6	10	14	2	6	10		2	3		
84. Po	2	2	6	2	6	10	2	6	10	14	2	6	10		2	4		
85. At	2	2	6	2	6	10	2	6	10	14	2	6	10		2	5		
86. Rn	2	2	6	2	6	10	2	6	10	14	2	6	10		2	6		
87. Fr	2	2	6	2	6	10	2	6	10	14	2	6	10		2	6		1
88. Ra	2	2	6	2	6	10	2	6	10	14	2	6	10		2	6		2
89. Ac	2	2	6	2	6	10	2	6	10	14	2	6	10		2	6	1	2
90. Th	2	2	6	2	6	10	2	6	10	14	2	6	10		2	6	2	2
91. Pa	2	2	6	2	6	10	2	6	10	14	2	6	10	2	2	6	1	2
92. U	2	2	6	2	6	10	2	6	10	14	2	6	10	3	2	6	1	2
93. Np	2	2	6	2	6	10	2	6	10	14	2	6	10	4	2	6	1	2
94. Pu	2	2	6	2	6	10	2	6	10	14	2	6	10	5	2	6	1	2
95. Am	2	2	6	2	6	10	2	6	10	14	2	6	10	7	2	6		2
96. Cm	2	2	6	2	6	10	2	6	10	14	2	6	10	7	2	6	1	2
97. Bk	2	2	6	2	6	10	2	6	10	14	2	6	10	8	2	6	1	2

TABLE 1.4—*Continued*
Electron Configurations of the Elements

Element	K	L		M			N				O				P			Q
	1s	2s	2p	3s	3p	3d	4s	4p	4d	4f	5s	5p	5d	5f	6s	6p	6d	7s
98. Cf	2	2	6	2	6	10	2	6	10	14	2	6	10	9	2	6	1	2
99. Es	2	2	6	2	6	10	2	6	10	14	2	6	10	10	2	6	1	2
100. Fm	2	2	6	2	6	10	2	6	10	14	2	6	10	11	2	6	1	2
101. Mv	2	2	6	2	6	10	2	6	10	14	2	6	10	12	2	6	1	2
102. No	2	2	6	2	6	10	2	6	10	14	2	6	10	13	2	6	1	2
103. Lw	2	2	6	2	6	10	2	6	10	14	2	6	10	14	2	6	1	2

The periodic chemical and physical behavior of the elements is a consequence of the periodic recurrence of the same outermost electronic configuration. Each period of the table begins with an element having an s^1 configuration (hydrogen or the alkali metals) and ends with an element having an inert gas configuration ($1s^2$ or s^2p^6). The makeup of the periodic table in terms of the orbitals being filled is illustrated in Figure 1.14. Taking into account the number of elements involved, the periods are sometimes designated as the very short period (1st), the short periods (2nd and 3rd), the long periods (4th and 5th), and the very long periods (6th and 7th). The elements having an incompletely filled set of s and p orbitals (with their other sets of orbitals either completely filled or completely empty) are called representative elements. Within a given group of the periodic table the representative elements have the same outermost electronic configuration, with the principal quantum numbers corresponding to the period number. The ionic states and covalent states formed by the representative elements are directly related to the electronic configuration of the elements and are reasonably predictable (p. 41, Chapter II).

The elements having an incompletely filled set of d orbitals are called transition elements. This definition is not exact, since within the nickel group elements the defini-

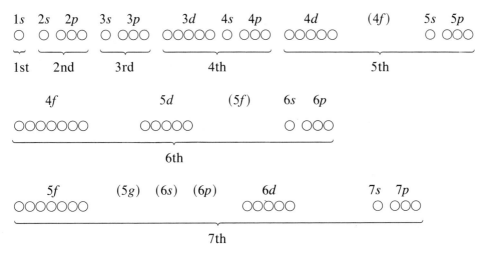

FIGURE 1.14. *Makeup of the conventional long form of the periodic table.*

tion would exclude Pd, which has a d^{10} configuration. Despite this unique configuration, the chemistry of palladium belongs with that of nickel and platinum and it is properly termed a transition metal. Copper, silver, and gold, although unambiguously classified as representative elements by the definition given here, are often considered as transition metals due to the electronic configurations of their 2^+ or 3^+ ions. Although the ground state configurations within a transition element group are not always the same (see V, Nb, Ta; Cr, Mo, W; Fe, Ru, Os; Co, Rh, Ir; Ni, Pd, Pt), the differences in energy between the ground state configuration and the "group configuration" are small.

Filling the f orbitals gives rise to a series of fourteen elements called the inner transition series. There are two known series of inner transition elements, the lanthanides and actinides.

Vector Model of the Atom and Spectroscopic Terms

From the Bohr–Sommerfeld model for hydrogen-like atoms, a very slight dependence of the energy state of the atom on the angular momentum of the electron was predicted due to relativity effects, i.e., the $2s^1$ and $2p^1$ configurations were predicted to be slightly different.* Search for these differences in hydrogen-like atoms by high resolution spectroscopy revealed more energy levels than expected. These data led to the conclusion that the $2p^1$ configuration (and higher states beyond the s) could have two energy states, which differ in the interaction of the orbit angular momentum and the spin angular momentum of the electron. These are pictured in Figure 1.15.

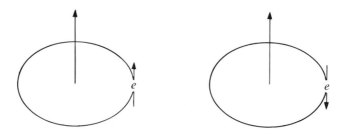

Figure 1.15. *Possible alignments of orbit and spin angular momenta for a one electron atom. An "adjusted" angular momentum of $(k-1)(h/2\pi)$ must be used.*

Although the wave equation abandons the picture of specific orbits for the electron, the property of angular momentum for an electron in an orbital is retained; angular momentum is associated with rotation of the electron cloud. The new angular momentum quantum number l is more satisfactory than k. The interaction of the quantized orbital angular momentum with the quantized spin angular momentum produces a resultant total angular momentum, which is also quantized. Thus for a $2p$ electron the vector sum of the orbital angular momentum, $l(h/2\pi)$, and the spin angular momentum, $s(h/2\pi)$, may be either $(l+\frac{1}{2})(h/2\pi)$ or $(l-\frac{1}{2})(h/2\pi)$. The resultant total angular momentum is $j(h/2\pi)$; the new quantum j sometimes is referred to as the "inner quantum

---

* Present data indicate that for hydrogen-like atoms, terms of the same j value are identical in energy except for the $^2S_{1/2}$ term which lies 0.0354 cm^{-1} *above* the $^2P_{1/2}$ term. C. E. Moore, "Atomic Energy Levels," Vol. I, *Natl. Bur. Std. (U.S.) Circ.,* **467** (1949).

number." For the hydrogen atom in the $2p^1$ configuration the two possible j states have a difference in energy of 0.3651 cm^{-1}. (For hydrogen-like atoms the difference increases with Z^4.) These two states would be designated in spectroscopic notation as $2^2P_{1/2}$ and $2^2P_{3/2}$, the superprefix 2 indicating the term is one of a doublet, the subscript $\frac{1}{2}$ or $\frac{3}{2}$ indicating the j quantum number, the capital P indicating a term (or energy state) rather than an electron configuration, and finally the preceeding 2 indicating the principal quantum number. Spectroscopic term notation will be discussed further in the section dealing with polyelectronic atoms. The doublet terms of the hydrogen-like atoms (and the difference in s, p, and d orbitals of the same quantum number) give rise to fine structure in the spectrum. A further interaction of the total angular momentum of the electron with the spin angular momentum *of the nucleus* gives rise to a further very slight splitting of the energy levels, which results in a hyperfine structure of the spectrum.*

In a weak unidirectional magnetic field the two P terms are each split into $2j+1$ terms differing in energy by an amount which is proportional to the applied field strength. These states are characterized by a quantum number m_j which may have a value of $j, j-1, \ldots, -j$. The component of total angular momentum in the direction of the field is $m_j(h/2\pi)$. With a magnetic field present the $^2P_{1/2}$ term thus yields two terms and the $^2P_{3/2}$ term yields four terms. The splitting into six terms for the ^2P state in a magnetic field is related to the fact that there are six ways of placing an electron in p orbitals which differ in the values of m_l and/or m_s. The number of different ways m electrons can be placed in a given set of orbitals in accordance with the Pauli exclusion principle is given by

$$\text{No. of Configurations} = \prod_{N=1}^{N=m} \frac{2(2l+1)-N+1}{N} \tag{1.3}$$

where l is the l quantum number of the set of orbitals and Π stands for the product of the terms evaluated successively from $N=1$ up to $N=m$. Thus there are 252 different configurations for a d^5 state $\left(10 \times \frac{9}{2} \times \frac{8}{3} \times \frac{7}{4} \times \frac{6}{5}\right)$. This is equivalent to saying there are 10 different ways of placing the 1st electron in the set of orbitals, 9 different ways of placing the 2nd electron in the set of orbitals, 8 for the 3rd, etc., but since these choices are not independent one must divide by the number of electrons added at each stage, i.e., $10 \times \frac{9}{2} \times \frac{8}{3} \cdots$. A few of these would be as follows:

m_l	2	1	0	−1	−2
	↑	↑	↑	↑	↑
	↓	↓	↓	↓	↓
etc.	↑	↓	↑	↑	↑

In a strong magnetic field each of these would have a different energy, and even in the absence of a magnetic field there would be 30 different energy states. If there are

---

* See Chapter V in G. Herzberg, *Atomic Spectra and Atomic Structure* (New York: Dover Publications, 1944) for details of this effect.

several types of orbitals which are partially occupied the total number of electronic configurations will be the product of those possible for each set of orbitals, i.e., for d^5s the total would be 252×2 or 504.

In a polyelectronic atom the individual l values combine vectorially to give a resultant L, and the individual s values combine to give a resultant S. Filled shells or subshells have a resultant $L = 0$ and $S = 0$. In general L may have integer values ranging from the smallest difference of l values to the sum of the l values, while S may take on the values, differing by whole numbers, from $\frac{1}{2}$ to $\frac{n}{2}$ (for odd n), or from 0 to $\frac{n}{2}$ (for even n), where n is the number of unpaired electrons. The M_L and M_S values are the sum of the respective m_l or m_s values for the system. For a given L value there can exist M_L values of $-L, (-L+1), \ldots, 0, \ldots, L-1, L$; there are $2L + 1$ possible M_L states and similarly for a given S value there are $2S + 1$ possible M_S states. The L and S values, which represent the quantum mechanically allowed orbital angular momentum states and the spin angular momentum states, respectively, combine vectorially to produce J values, representing the total angular momentum states. J may have values running from $(L - S)$ to $(L + S)$ in integer steps. Thus the number of J states for given L and S values is $2S + 1$, if $L \geq S$.

The different energy states of an atom or ion are usually given spectroscopic term designations of the form

$$n^a T_j$$

where n may be the principal quantum number or simply a running number or even the electronic configuration (as, for example $3d^4 \; {}^5D_2$ in which $n = 3d^4$); a is a number equal to $2S + 1$ and is called the multiplicity of the term, T is a capital letter S, P, D, F, G, H, I, $\ldots$, corresponding to the value of L; and j is the numerical J value.

Derivation of Spectroscopic Terms from Electronic Configurations

Spectroscopic terms may be derived for nonequivalent electrons (electrons differing in values of the quantum numbers n or l) by obtaining all of the possible values of L as the vector sums of the individual l values, and obtaining all of the possible values of S as the vector sums of the individual s values. The terms for a $2p^1 3p^1$ electronic configuration would have L values of 0, 1, and 2 and S values of 0 and 1, giving ${}^1S$, ${}^1P$, ${}^1D$ and ${}^3S$, ${}^3P$, and ${}^3D$ terms.

Fewer terms arise from equivalent electrons (electrons having the same values of n and l) due to the Pauli exclusion principle. Thus for a $2p^2$ configuration a value of $L = 2$ results only for the cases in which l_1 and l_2 are similarly oriented and hence m_{l_1} and m_{l_2} are identical. Accordingly, for $L = 2$ the values of m_{s_1} and m_{s_2} must differ and $S = 0$. Hence only the singlet term is permitted for $L = 2$, i.e., ${}^1D$. The Pauli exclusion principle may be applied to aid in determining spectral terms for equivalent electrons by noting that the M_L and M_S values obtained from the L and S values must also correspond to those obtained from the sum of the individual m_l and m_s values, respectively. To obtain all of the M_L and M_S values it is necessary to write all possible individual electronic configurations and obtain M_L and M_S for each configuration. The complexity of the problem of determining all possible configurations is reduced somewhat by grouping configurations having the same number of singly occupied orbitals. The

M_S values need be determined only once for such a group—there will be 2^n M_S values where n is the number of singly occupied orbitals. The possible M_S values for n electrons occupying individual orbitals may be obtained by adding 1/2, and by subtracting 1/2, from the possible M_S values for the case of $(n-1)$ individual electrons.

A given spectroscopic term having definite L and S values will have $2L+1$ possible M_L values ranging from $-L$ to $+L$ and for each of these M_L values there will be $2S+1$ possible M_S values ranging from $-S$ to $+S$ in unit steps.

TABLE 1.5
Orbital Configurations for a p^2 Case

m_l			$M_L = \Sigma m_l$	$M_S = \Sigma m_s$
1	0	−1		
×			2	0
	×		0	0
		×	−2	0
∘	∘		1	−1, 0, 0, +1
∘		∘	0	−1, 0, 0, +1
	∘	∘	−1	−1, 0, 0, +1

The orbital configurations for a $2p^2$ configuration are given in Table 1.5 with the values of M_L and M_S. × represents a doubly occupied orbital and ∘ represents a singly occupied orbital. These M_L and M_S data are tabulated in the array given in Figure 1.16.

↑ M_L	M_S → −1	0	+1
2		1	
1	1	2	1
0	1	3	1
−1	1	2	1
−2		1	

FIGURE 1.16. *An array for a p^2 configuration showing the number of individual configurations of a given M_L and M_S.*

Inspection shows the array of M_L and M_S values in Figure 1.16 consists of the sum of the following arrays which may be identified with their spectroscopic states through their maximum M_L and M_S values.

↑ M_L	M_S: 0
2	1
1	1
0	1
−1	1
−2	1

$L = 2$, $S = 0$ Term: ^1D

$$
\begin{array}{c|ccc}
\uparrow & 1 & 1 & 1 & 1 \\
M_L & 0 & 1 & 1 & 1 \\
 & -1 & 1 & 1 & 1 \\
\hline
 & & -1 & 0 & +1
\end{array}
\qquad
\begin{array}{l}
L=1 \\
S=1
\end{array}
\text{Term: } {}^3P
$$

$$M_S \rightarrow$$

$$
M_L \qquad 0 \;\; \boxed{1} \atop 0
\qquad
\begin{array}{l}
L=0 \\
S=0
\end{array}
\text{Term: } {}^1S
$$

$$M_S$$

Thus a $2p^2$ configuration would give rise to the terms ${}^1D$, ${}^3P$, and ${}^1S$.

Let us now consider a d^5 case. The possible electronic configurations involve $\times\times°$, $\times°°°$, and $°°°°°$ where $\times$ represents a doubly occupied orbital and $°$ represents a singly occupied orbital. The possible M_S values for $\times\times°$ are $+1/2$ and $-1/2$; for $\times°°°$ the possible M_S values are $3/2$, $1/2$, $1/2$, $1/2$, $-1/2$, $-1/2$, $-1/2$, and $-3/2$; for $°°°°°$ the possible M_S values are $5/2$, $3/2(5)$, $1/2(10)$, $-1/2(10)$, $-3/2(5)$, and $-5/2$—the numbers in parentheses give the number of each type of M_S value.

The different possible M_L values may now be sought for the d^5 case. For the $\times\times°$ case there are five different ways to place the first pair in the orbitals, and four for the second, but since the two pairs are indistinguishable this is divided by two (for the two pairs present) and for each of these configurations for the pairs there are three ways of placing the single electron in the remaining orbitals (not counting spin orientation). This gives $5 \times \frac{4}{2} \times 3$ or 30 orbital configurations for $\times\times°$, each of which has two spin con-

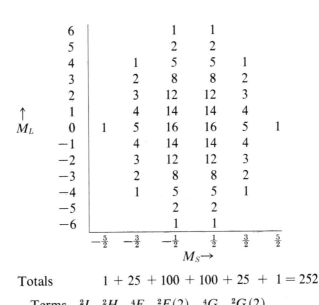

Totals $1 + 25 + 100 + 100 + 25 + 1 = 252$

Terms ${}^2I$ ${}^2H$ ${}^4F$ ${}^2F(2)$ ${}^4G$ ${}^2G(2)$
       ${}^4D$ ${}^2D(3)$ ${}^4P$ ${}^2P$ ${}^6S$ ${}^2S$

FIGURE 1.17. *An array for a d^5 configuration showing the number of individual configurations of a given M_L and M_S.*

figurations. By similar reasoning the $\times^{\circ\circ\circ}$ case has $5 \times 4 \times \frac{3}{2} \times \frac{2}{3}$ or 20 orbital configurations, each of which has eight spin configurations, and finally the one possible $^{\circ\circ\circ\circ\circ}$ orbital configuration has 32 spin configurations. The orbital configurations are shown in Table 1.6 along with the M_L values and M_S values. The number of configurations of a given M_L and M_S are tabulated in the array shown in Figure 1.17. In this array the number of configurations of a given M_L and M_S is the same as the number of configurations for $-M_L$ and $-M_S$ or $-M_L, +M_S$ or $M_L, -M_S$.

TABLE 1.6
Orbital Configurations for a d^5 Case

m_l							m_l						
2	1	0	−1	−2	$M_L=\Sigma m_l$	$M_S=\Sigma m_s$	2	1	0	−1	−2	M_L	M_S
×	×	°			6	$\frac{1}{2}, -\frac{1}{2}$	×		°	°	°	1	$\frac{3}{2}, \frac{1}{2}(3), -\frac{1}{2}(3), -\frac{3}{2}$
×	×		°		5		×	°		°	°	2	
×	×			°	4		×	°	°		°	3	
×	°	×			5		×	°	°	°		4	
×		×	°		3		°	×	°	°		3	
×		×		°	2			×	°	°	°	−1	
×	°		×		3		°	×		°	°	1	
×		°	×		2		°	×	°		°	2	
×			×	°	0		°	°	×	°		2	
×	°			×	1			°	×	°	°	−2	
×		°		×	0		°		×	°	°	−1	
×			°	×	−1		°	°	×		°	1	
°	×	×			4		°	°	°	×		1	
	×	×	°		1			°	°	×	°	−3	
	×	×		°	0		°		°	×	°	−2	
°	×		×		2		°	°		×	°	−1	
	×	°	×		0		°	°	°		×	−1	
	×		×	°	−2			°	°	°	×	−4	
°	×			×	0		°		°	°	×	−3	
	×	°		×	−2		°	°		°	×	−2	
	×		°	×	−3								
°		×	×		0		°	°	°	°	°	0	$\frac{5}{2}(1), \frac{3}{2}(5), \frac{1}{2}(10)$
	°	×	×		−1								$-\frac{5}{2}(1), -\frac{3}{2}(5), -\frac{1}{2}(10)$
		×	×	°	−4								
°		×		×	−2								
	°	×		×	−3								
		×	°	×	−5								
°			×	×	−4								
	°		×	×	−5								
		°	×	×	−6								

The spectroscopic terms may be obtained by noting the highest M_L and within this restriction the highest M_S values, in this case $M_L = 6$, $M_S = 1/2$, i.e., a ^2I term. Subtracting the array for this term gives the new array shown in Figure 1.18, and repeating

M_L	$-\frac{5}{2}$	$-\frac{3}{2}$	$-\frac{1}{2}$	$\frac{1}{2}$	$\frac{3}{2}$	$\frac{5}{2}$
5			1	1		
4		1	4	4	1	
3		2	7	7	2	
2		3	11	11	3	
1		4	13	13	4	
0	1	5	15	15	5	1
−1		4	13	13	4	
−2		3	11	11	3	
−3		2	7	7	2	
−4		1	4	4	1	
−5			1	1		

$M_S \rightarrow$

FIGURE 1.18. *Array of M_L and M_S values for a d^5 configuration after subtracting the array for a ^2I term.*

this process we find successively the terms ^2H, ^4F, $^2F(2)$, ^4G, $^2G(2)$, ^4D, $^2D(3)$, ^4P, ^2P, ^6S, and ^2S.

There is an equivalence in the possible configurations for electrons and for vacancies in a subshell, identical spectroscopic terms arising for a given number of electrons *or* vacancies in a given subshell. The same spectroscopic terms arise from a p^1 or p^5 configuration or from a d^2 or d^8 configuration.

The spectroscopic terms arising from configurations containing more than one partially filled subshell may be derived in the general manner given or may be derived from the combination of each term for each subshell, i.e., $L = \overrightarrow{L_1} + \overrightarrow{L_2}$ and $S = \overrightarrow{S_1} + \overrightarrow{S_2}$. The L values from the combination of L_1 and L_2 would run in unit steps from $L_2 - L_1$ to $L_2 + L_1$.

Energy Levels in Polyelectronic Atoms

Penetration Effects

Since filled shells have $L = 0$ and $S = 0$ the alkali metals should exhibit hydrogen-like spectroscopic terms. They do, but the energy differences between n^2S, n^2P, n^2D, etc., terms are much greater. As mentioned earlier, this may be accounted for in terms of the greater penetration of the underlying filled shells by an ns electron than an np electron; the np electron, in turn, shows greater penetration than the nd, etc.

An alternative way of discussing penetration effects is to speak of the effective nuclear charge acting on a particular electron. This effective nuclear charge is the actual nuclear charge less the screening effect due to other electrons in the atom. Slater has developed a set of empirical rules for calculating the screening effect of other electrons on a particular electron.* These rules are as follows:

(1) The electrons are grouped in the order $1s$; $2s$ and $2p$; $3s$ and $3p$; $3d$; $4s$ and $4p$; $4d$; $4f$; etc., ns and np being considered as a single group.

(2) Electrons in groups lying above that of a particular electron do not shield it at all.

* Summarized by C. A. Coulson in *Valence* (Oxford: Clarendon Press, 1952) p. 141.

(3) A shielding of 0.35 is contributed by each other electron in the same group (except for a $1s$ electron which contributes 0.30 to the shielding of the other $1s$ electron).

(4) For d and f electrons the shielding from underlying groups is 1.00 for each electron in the underlying group. For s, p electrons the shielding from the immediately underlying shell (i.e., $n - 1$) is 0.85 for each electron; the shielding from groups further in is 1.00 for each electron.

Ideally, Slater's rules should permit the calculation of the energy level of any electron in any atom or ion by the formula

$$E = \frac{-(Z - S)^2}{n^2} \ 13.6 \text{ eV}$$

where Z is the nuclear charge, S is the shielding constant, and n is the principal quantum number of the electron. Unfortunately, values calculated in this fashion may differ from those obtained from spectroscopic studies by as much as a factor of five. Nevertheless, the effective nuclear charges $(Z - S)$ calculated from Slater's rules have been used for such purposes as calculating ionic radii (see p. 108, Chapter III) and electronegativities of the elements (see problem 25, Chapter II).

Another approach to penetration has been to use $(n - \delta)$ in place of the principal quantum number. The value of δ is called the quantum defect. It decreases rapidly with increasing l.

Spin–Orbit Interactions

The separation of the doublet terms, due to the spin orientation of the one outermost electron, is intermediate between that expected for a hydrogen-like atom of atomic number Z and a hydrogen-like atom with an effective atomic number of one. The doublet separation is greatest for P terms and decreases with increasing L of the term, as expected on the basis of penetration of underlying filled shells. Except for cases of high atomic numbers (i.e., Rb, Cs) the splitting of doublet terms is relatively small (i.e., for the $4p^1 \ ^2P$ term of K the splitting is 57.72 cm^{-1}).

Spin–Spin Interactions

In a partially filled subshell with more than one electron the effect of spin interactions of the electrons may be fairly large. Thus the energy difference between the $3d^4 \ ^5D_2$ term and the $3d^4 \ ^1D_2$ term of V^+ ion is 20944.87 cm^{-1}. The low energy term arises from a configuration involving *four unpaired* electrons, while the high energy term has two *pairs* of electrons. The primary reason for the difference in energy of these terms is the difference in exchange energy between pairs of electrons having the same m_s quantum number, i.e., the same spin. Four unpaired electrons, ↑ ↑ ↑ ↑ , have six distinct pairs which may have similar spin orientation, while two pairs, ↑↓ ↑↓ , have only two distinct pairs which may have similar spin orientations.

Hund's Rules and Ground State Terms

The lowest energy term arising from a given configuration may be selected from the possible terms by means of Hund's rules. It will be the one with maximum S (and accordingly maximum multiplicity) and, within this restriction, maximum L; the J value will be the minimum one for subshells less than half-filled and the maximum one for shells more than half-filled. The ground state term for a given configuration may easily be found in the following manner without deriving all the possible terms. An electronic configuration is written with the orbitals filled in the order of decreasing m_l; each orbital is singly occupied before any orbital is doubly occupied. The sum of the m_l values for this configuration will give the L value of the term, the S value will be one half the number of singly occupied orbitals. For a d^2 case this would give

$$m_l = \quad +2 \qquad +1 \qquad 0 \qquad -1 \qquad -2$$

$$\odot \qquad \odot \qquad \bigcirc \qquad \bigcirc \qquad \bigcirc$$

$$L = 2 + 1 = 3 \qquad\qquad S = 1/2 \times 2 = 1$$

The L of 3 gives an F term; the S of 1 gives a multiplicity of 3. Combination of L and S gives J values of 2, 3, and 4; the lowest is selected in this case since the d orbitals are less than half-filled. The ground state term for a d^2 configuration is accordingly a $^3F_2$ term.

Ionization Potentials

The ionization potential of an atom has been defined (p. 6) as the energy needed to remove an electron from an atom in its ground state. The second ionization potential is the additional energy needed to remove the second electron, etc. Table 1.7 gives the ionization potentials as derived from the analysis of atomic spectra.

TABLE 1.7
Ionization Potentials of the Elements[a] (in eV)

Z	Element	I	II	III	IV	V	VI	VII	VIII
1	H	13.595							
2	He	24.581	54.403						
3	Li	5.390	75.619	122.419					
4	Be	9.320	18.206	153.850	217.657				
5	B	8.296	25.149	37.920	259.298	340.127			
6	C	11.256	24.376	47.871	64.476	391.986	489.84		
7	N	14.53	29.593	47.426	77.450	97.863	551.925	666.83	
8	O	13.614	35.108	54.886	77.394	113.873	138.080	739.114	871.12
9	F	17.418	34.98	62.646	87.14	114.214	157.117	185.139	953.60
10	Ne	21.559	41.07	63.5	97.02	126.3	157.91		
11	Na	5.138	47.29	71.65	98.88	138.37	172.09	208.444	264.155
12	Mg	7.644	15.031	80.12	109.29	141.23	186.49	224.90	265.957
13	Al	5.984	18.823	28.44	119.96	153.77	190.42	241.38	284.53
14	Si	8.149	16.34	33.46	45.13	166.73	205.11	246.41	303.07
15	P	10.484	19.72	30.156	51.354	65.007	220.414	263.31	309.26
16	S	10.357	23.4	35.0	47.29	72.5	88.029	280.99	328.80
17	Cl	13.01	23.80	39.90	53.5	67.80	96.7	114.27	348.3
18	Ar	15.755	27.62	40.90	59.79	75.0	91.3	124.0	143.46

TABLE 1.7—*Continued*
Ionization Potentials of the Elements[a] *(in eV)*

Z	Element	I	II	III	IV	V	VI	VII	VIII
19	K	4.339	31.81	46	60.90	82.6	99.7	118	155
20	Ca	6.111	11.868	51.21	67	84.39	109	128	143.3
21	Sc	6.54	12.80	24.75	73.9	92	111	139	159
22	Ti	6.82	13.57	27.47	43.24	99.8	120	141	172
23	V	6.74	14.65	29.31	48	65	129	151	174
24	Cr	6.764	16.49	30.95	50	73	91	161	185
25	Mn	7.432	15.636	33.69	52	76	*100*	119	196
26	Fe	7.87	16.18	30.643	56.8		*103*	*130*	151
27	Co	7.86	17.05	33.49			83.1	*133*	*163*
28	Ni	7.633	18.15	35.16					*168*
29	Cu	7.724	20.29	36.83					
30	Zn	9.391	17.96	39.70					
31	Ga	6.00	20.51	30.70	64.2				
32	Ge	7.88	15.93	34.21	45.7	93.4			
33	As	9.81	18.63	28.34	50.1	62.6	127.5		
34	Se	9.75	21.5	32	43	68	82	155	
35	Br	11.84	21.6	35.9	47.3	59.7	88.6	103	193
36	Kr	13.996	24.56	36.9	*52.5*	*64.7*	*78.5*	*111.0*	*126*
37	Rb	4.176	27.5	40	*52.6*	*71.0*	*84.4*	*99.2*	*136*
38	Sr	5.692	11.027	*43.6*	57	*71.6*	*90.8*	*106*	*122.3*
39	Y	6.38	12.23	20.5	*61.8*	77	*93.0*	*116*	*129*
40	Zr	6.84	13.13	22.98	34.33	*82.3*	99	*116*	*139*
41	Nb	6.88	14.32	25.04	38.3	50	103	125	*141*
42	Mo	7.10	16.15	27.13	46.4	61.2	68	126	153
43	Tc	7.28	15.26	29.54					
44	Ru	7.364	16.76	28.46					
45	Rh	7.46	18.07	31.05					
46	Pd	8.33	19.42	32.92					
47	Ag	7.574	21.48	34.82					
48	Cd	8.991	16.904	37.47					
49	In	5.785	18.86	28.03	54.4				
50	Sn	7.342	14.628	30.49	40.72	72.3			
51	Sb	8.639	16.5	25.3	44.1	56	108	*119*	
52	Te	9.01	18.6	31	38	60	72	137	
53	I	10.454	19.09	*33*		*71*	*83*	*104*	170
54	Xe	12.127	21.2	32.1	44	60	83	*102*	*126*
55	Cs	3.893	25.1	35				*108*	*122*
56	Ba	5.210	10.001	35.5					*127*
57	La	5.61	11.43	19.17					
58	Ce	6.5	12.3	20	33.3				
59	Pr	5.7		23.2					

TABLE 1.7—*Continued*
Ionization Potentials of the Elements[a] *(in eV)*

Z	Element	I	II	III	IV	V	VI	VII	VIII
60	Nd	5.7							
61	Pm								
62	Sm	5.64	11.2						
63	Eu	5.67	11.24						
64	Gd	6.16	12						
65	Tb	6.7							
66	Dy	6.8							
67	Ho								
68	Er								
69	Tm								
70	Yb	6.23	12.10						
71	Lu	6.15	14.7						
72	Hf	7	14.9						
73	Ta	7.88	16.2						
74	W	7.98	17.7						
75	Re	7.87	16.6						
76	Os	8.7	17						
77	Ir	9	*17*						
78	Pt	9.0	18.56						
79	Au	9.22	20.5						
80	Hg	10.43	18.751	34.2	72	82			
81	Tl	6.106	20.42	29.8	50.7				
82	Pb	7.415	15.028	31.93	42.31	68.8			
83	Bi	7.287	16.68	25.56	45.3	56.0	88.3		
84	Po	8.43	*19.4*	*27.3*					
85	At	9.5	*20.1*	*29.3*					
86	Rn	10.746	*21.4*	*29.4*					
87	Fr	3.83	*22.5*	*33.5*					
88	Ra	5.277	10.144						
89	Ac	6.9	12.1	20					
90	Th		*11.5*	*20.0*	29.38				
91	Pa								
92	U	4							
93	Np								
94	Pu	5.1							
95	Am	6.0							
96	Cm								
97	Bk								

[a] Italicized values from W. Finkelnburg and W. Humbach, *Naturwiss.*, **42**, 35 (1955), other values from C. E. Moore, Circular of the National Bureau of Standards 467, Atomic Energy Levels, Vol. III, 1958 or R. W. Kiser, Tables of Ionization Potentials, U. S. Atomic Energy Commission TID 6142 (1960).

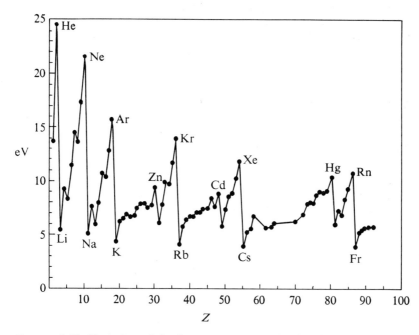

FIGURE 1.19. *Variation of the first ionization potential with atomic number.*

The first ionization potentials have been plotted against the atomic numbers of the elements in Figure 1.19. *In general, the ionization potential increases on crossing a period (i.e., Li through Ne) and decreases on descending in a group (He through Rn).* These trends and many of the variations within these may be rationalized in terms of the electronic configurations of elements involved. On crossing a period the principal quantum number for the electron being removed remains constant, but the *effective nuclear charge* increases due to incomplete nuclear shielding by electrons of the same quantum number. On descending in a given group, the principal quantum number increases regularly and relatively more rapidly than the effective nuclear charge. Variations from or within these trends are due primarily to changes in the type of orbital from which the electron is taken, or in changes of the multiplicity of the ground state term. Elements with a ground state $^1S_0$ term have higher ionization potentials than their neighboring elements (see exceptions below). This will be the ground state term for any element that has an outermost completely filled shell or subshell. The exceptions to this rule are the alkaline earth metals having a transition metal as a neighbor. In this case the orbit of the *s* electron of the transition metal may be thought of in terms of the Bohr–Sommerfeld model as penetrating the *d* orbits, and hence, as the *d* electrons are filled in to build up the transition metals the effective nuclear charge increases. Accordingly, the ionization potential increases in a fairly regular fashion from the alkali metal through zinc or its congeners. In the case of mercury, not only the *d* orbitals, but also the *f* orbitals have been filled in, and the penetration effect is much larger. The ionization potential of mercury is almost as great as that of radon. Following the zinc family elements the ionization potential drops sharply for Ga, In, and Tl since the electron involved is a *p* electron which occupies a less penetrating orbit. A similar, but smaller, drop in ionization potential following Be and Mg may also be accounted for in terms of the change in the ionizing electron from an s to a p electron. The higher ionization potential of nitrogen and its congeners, as compared to those of their neighbors, may be attributed to the stabilizing influence of the spin–spin interactions which are highest in filled and half-filled subshells.

Successive ionization potentials increase in magnitude due to the smaller number of electrons left to shield the ionizing electron from the nuclear charge. The variation in the second ionization potential with atomic number is very similar to that for the first ionization potential except that it is displaced by one atomic number. Some similarity persists for the third and higher ionization potentials, again with the provision that isoelectronic ions (those having the same number of electrons) be compared. Thus, the highest ionization potentials always occur for ions of the noble gas configurations.

Ahrens* has pointed out that the oxidation states (see p. 42, Chapter II) of the elements in their compounds may be correlated by the difference in ionization potential for successive states, Δ_I. If Δ_I is around 10 or 11 eV or less, the lower state is not stable. Consider the values for Al:

$$\Delta_{1,2} = 12.8 \text{ eV}$$
$$\Delta_{2,3} = 9.6$$
$$\Delta_{3,4} = 91.5$$

Although compounds of Al(I) are stable as gaseous species [AlCl(g)], they are unknown as solids. No compounds of Al(II) are known. Al(III) is the only stable state for Al compounds under usual conditions. Δ_I values of around 16 or above usually lead to stable states. Since Δ is always high at the noble gas configuration, these configurations are frequently found for the elements in their compounds. The $s^2p^6d^{10}$ configuration is also one where Δ is high and it too is a common configuration for positive ions.

GENERAL REFERENCES

Herzberg, G., *Atomic Spectra and Atomic Structure* (New York: Dover Publications, 1944).
Pauling, L., *The Nature of the Chemical Bond* (Ithaca: Cornell University Press, 1960).
Sanderson, R. T., *Chemical Periodicity* (New York: Reinhold Publishing Corp., 1960).

Problems

1.   Bohr postulated that lines in the emission spectrum from hydrogen in highly excited states, such as $n = 20$ would not be observed under ordinary laboratory conditions, due to the large size of such atoms and the much greater probability of atom collision deactivation as compared to radiation deactivation. Using the Bohr model, calculate the

* Ahrens, L. H., *J. Inorg. Nucl. Chem.*, **2**, 290 (1956).

ratio of the cross-sectional area of a hydrogen atom in the $n = 20$ state to that of one in the $n = 1$ state.

2. According to the Bohr model of the atom what would be the size of a Ne^{9+} ion? What would the ionization potential be for this ion? What would the excitation potential be for the first excited state?

3. Calculate the energy (eV) released in the transition of a hydrogen atom from the state $n = 3$ to $n = 1$. The wavelength of the radiation emitted in this transition may be found from the relation λ (in Å) $= 12398/E(eV)$ (often remembered as the approximate $\lambda = 12345/eV$). Calculate the wavelengths of all spectral lines that could be observed from a collection of hydrogen atoms excited by a potential of 12 V.

4. Assuming a screening of 1/2 for an s electron, calculate the wavelength expected for the K_α x-ray line of Tc.

5. The Balmer series in the hydrogen spectrum originates from transitions between $n = 2$ states and higher states. Compare the wavelengths for the first three lines in the Balmer series with those expected for similar transitions in Li^{2+}.

6. Bohr's original assumption for the selection of the stationary states of a system was that "the ratio between total energy, emitted during the formation of the configuration, and the frequency of revolution of the electron is an entire multiple of $h/2$." Show that for circular orbits this assumption is the equivalent of Equation (c), p. 6.

7. Draw the Bohr–Sommerfeld orbits corresponding to $n = 5$, $k = 5$ and $n = 5$, $k = 1$. To what *orbitals* would these correspond?

8. Explain briefly the observation that the energy difference between the $1s^2 2s^1\ ^2S_{1/2}$ state and the $1s^2 2p^1\ ^2P_{1/2}$ state for Li is 14904 cm^{-1}, whereas for Li^{2+} the $2s^1\ ^2S_{1/2}$ and the $2p^1\ ^2P_{1/2}$ states differ by only 2.4 cm^{-1}.

9. Without consulting Table 1.4 give the electronic configurations of isolated gaseous atoms of N, P, Cr, and Zr.

10. Give the electronic configuration for the following (indicate and label individual orbitals): (a) V^{3+}, (b) Ga, (c) Fe^{2+}.

11. Using the p orbitals for an example, distinguish between the angular part of the probability function, the radial part of the probability function, and a probability contour. Draw simple sketches to illustrate. How would each of these be affected by a change in the principal quantum number, n?

12. What spectral terms (only 1 for each array) are indicated by the following arrays of M_L and M_S values?

M_L			
2	1	1	1	1
1	1	1	1	1
0	1	1	1	1
−1	1	1	1	1
−2	1	1	1	1
	$-\frac{3}{2}$	$-\frac{1}{2}$	$+\frac{1}{2}$	$+\frac{3}{2}$

$M_S \rightarrow$

M_L			
0	1	1	1
	−1	0	+1

$M_S \rightarrow$

13. An array for an f^{12} configuration summarizing the number of individual configurations of a given M_L and M_S value is given below. What spectral terms may be obtained from an f^{12} configuration?

M_L	$M_S = -1$	$M_S = 0$	$M_S = 1$
6		1	
5	1	2	1
4	1	3	1
3	2	4	2
2	2	5	2
1	3	6	3
0	3	7	3
−1	3	6	3
−2	2	5	2
−3	2	4	2
−4	1	3	1
−5	1	2	1
−6		1	

$M_S \rightarrow$

14. How many different configurations are possible for three electrons in the $2p$ orbitals (i.e., N)? Draw the orbital configurations (7 possible) and construct the array of M_L and M_S values. From these determine the spectral terms arising from a p^3 configuration. Which of these is the ground state term?

15. Using Slater's rules to obtain a shielding constant calculate the 1st, 2nd, and 3rd ionization potentials of carbon. Compare your calculated values with those in Table 1.7.

16. Use the 1st ionization potential of Ne and the 8th ionization potential of Cl from Table 1.7 to calculate the values of S and δ in the empirical equation (for isoelectronic atoms or ions)

$$IP = \frac{(Z - S)^2}{(n - \delta)^2} \, 13.6 \, .$$

Use these values of S and δ to calculate the ionization potential for ions of the neon configuration, i.e., 2nd ionization potential for Na, 3rd for Mg, 4th for Al. Also estimate the electron affinity for fluorine (i.e., the 1st ionization potential of F^-). Use the deviations of the calculated ionization potentials from the spectroscopically observed values for Na, Mg, etc., to give a "correction" for the value calculated for the electron affinity of fluorine.

17. Plot the square of the Θ function for a p_z orbital (Θ_{10}) on polar coordinate paper. Plot the square of the radial function for a $2p$ orbital ($R_{2,0}$). A contour for a $2p$ orbital may be plotted (on polar coordinate paper) from these two curves as follows: The maximum probability will fall at a point with r taken from the maximum in the R^2 plot and θ taken from the maximum in the Θ^2 plot. For a "50%" contour find the values of r where R^2 is 50% of R^2 maximum. Plot these points along the θ of maximum Θ^2. Now let θ vary by 10° and find a new value of Θ^2. Calculate the value of R^2 necessary for $R^2\Theta^2$ to be 50% of $R^2\Theta^2$ maximum. Find the values of r corresponding to the value of R^2 needed. Plot the points for r and θ. Vary θ by 10°, etc., or less until sufficient points have been plotted to define the contour. A set of contours may be constructed in about a day. (Note: p and d orbital contours have been published, but nobody has yet published contours on f orbitals!)

CHAPTER II

Covalent Substances

Simple Interpretation of Covalent Bonding

The beginning student of chemistry is able to write the formulas for many chemical compounds by the application of simple valence theory. We build on this assumed background in order to arrive at descriptions in terms of more useful modern valence theory. It seems profitable first to show how the valence theory presented in elementary courses can be applied and extended.

Those metals that have 1, 2, or 3 electrons in the outer shell and an inert gas configuration in the next to the outermost shell commonly combine with nonmetals by losing the outermost electron(s) to form simple cations. This leaves an ion with an s^2p^6 configuration, such as K^+, Mg^{2+}, or Al^{3+}. Other common electronic configurations for metal ions are $s^2p^6d^{10}$, the pseudo-inert gas configuration, found in such ions as Ag^+, Zn^{2+}, Cd^{2+}, Ga^{3+}, and the configuration $(n-1)s^2p^6d^{10}ns^2$ as in Sn^{2+}, Tl^+, and Sb^{3+} (n is the principal quantum number of the outermost shell). Most of the lanthanide metals form tripositive ions leaving partially filled $4f$ orbitals, while many transition elements form ions having partially filled d orbitals (Au^{3+}, Fe^{2+}, Fe^{3+}, etc.). The nonmetals that require 1 or 2 electrons to complete an inert gas configuration commonly accept the required number of electrons from metals to form simple anions. In these cases valence refers to an ionic state and has a sign associated with it (i.e., oxygen most commonly has an ionic valence of -2). For a monatomic ion the *oxidation number* of the element is the same as the ionic valence, i.e., the charge on the ion. Ionic compounds have structures and compositions which are determined almost entirely by the coulombic interaction among the ions. These substances are treated in the next chapter.

Just as ionic valence states may be predicted from the electronic configuration of the atom, the number of electrons that an atom may share is related to the atomic configuration. The Pauli exclusion principle allows only two electrons with opposed spins to occupy an atomic orbital and when a pair of electrons is shared by two atoms the electron pair is assumed to occupy an atomic orbital on both atoms. The number of shared pairs is termed the covalency.

As a first approximation the covalency will be the same as the number of unpaired s or p electrons initially present in the isolated atom.* Thus the halogen atoms have an

---

* This approximation seems to be particularly valid for diatomic molecules of elements, although pairing of electrons does not always result, even though electrons may be shared. Thus in H_2 two electrons are shared, He is monatomic, in $Li_2(g)$ two electrons are shared, Be(g) is apparently monatomic, in $B_2(g)$ two electrons

electronic configuration of s^2p^5. The covalency expected here is one, since each atom has only one unpaired electron to share. An electron dot picture would represent the X_2 molecule as

$$:\ddot{X}:\ddot{X}:$$

The convention followed in writing electron dot formulas is to place the dots representing the shared pair between the symbols for the two atoms that are bonded. Other electrons in the outer shell are placed elsewhere around the atom, each pair representing a completely filled orbital on that atom. Where orbitals are occupied singly this is indicated by the electron dot picture, as in the carbon atom, $:\dot{C}\cdot$. The valence bond representation replaces the pair of dots by a bar and, in cases where the occupancy of nonbonding atomic orbitals appears obvious, may show only the bonding pairs. Thus the fluorine molecule may be shown either as $|\overline{F}\!-\!\overline{F}|$ or more simply F—F.

For oxygen the electronic configuration of the atom may be represented by

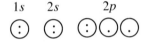

It is expected that oxygen normally will share two electrons. It does this in almost all of its covalent compounds; the valence bond structures below are typical.

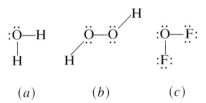

$$(a) \qquad\qquad (b) \qquad\qquad (c)$$

It may be noted that although the covalency of oxygen is two in the three compounds given, the oxidation state of oxygen is -2 in water, -1 in hydrogen peroxide, and $+2$ in oxygen difluoride. The *oxidation state for atoms in covalent compounds* is obtained by assigning the pair of electrons in the valence bonds to the more electronegative atom and then counting the charge on the quasi ion (see Figure 2.1 for some additional examples).

Sulfur has the same outermost electronic configuration as oxygen, except for the presence of empty d orbitals of the same principal quantum number as the valence electrons, i.e.,

$$3s \qquad\qquad 3p \qquad\qquad\qquad 3d$$

It is expected that sulfur will be chemically similar to oxygen and indeed it forms H_2S, H_2S_2, and SF_2 with structures similar to (a), (b), and (c). However, a small promo-

---

are shared, in $C_2(g)$ four electrons are shared, in N_2 six electrons are shared, in O_2 four electrons are shared, in F_2 two electrons are shared, and Ne is monatomic. Some exceptions to this simple rule are $Zn_2(g)$, $Cd_2(g)$, and $Hg_2(g)$, which would be expected to be monatomic; the dissociation energy of these molecules is very low. The atomic orbital, or valence bond, approach gives an incorrect description for O_2 where a diamagnetic molecule is predicted. Accordingly, we should be cautious in regard to making predictions based solely on this bonding picture.

tional energy will produce states having a greater number of unpaired electrons, i.e.,

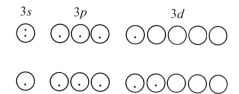

and

If the formation of electron pair bonds with another element by sulfur in one of these excited states is sufficiently energetic to pay for the promotion of electrons, then the covalency of sulfur may be four, or even six. In general, such promotion will only be brought about when sulfur combines with the more electronegative elements, F, O, Cl, or Br. Some valence bond structures for the expected covalent states of 2, 4, and 6 for *S* are given in Figure 2.1.

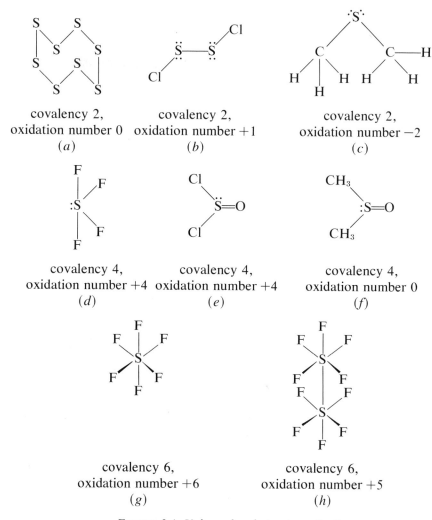

FIGURE 2.1. *Valence bond structures for S.*

The assignment of the oxidation number of -2 to S in (c) follows the convention of naming CS_2 as a sulfide even though the electronegativities of C and S are the same (see p. 86). The covalencies of (e) and (f) are given on the basis of the number of shared electron pairs shown. Other structures might be written involving different numbers of unshared pairs (see below under resonance).

Selenium, tellurium, and polonium have empty low lying d orbitals and, like sulfur, are expected to show covalent states of 2, 4, and 6. Indeed selenium analogs of (a) through (h) and tellurium analogs of (c), (d), (g), and (h) are known.

The availability of empty low lying d orbitals constitutes one of the major differences between the second period elements and the elements of higher periods. The difference in the covalent states for oxygen and the sulfur family has been cited. Similar differences may be pointed out in the halogen family and the nitrogen group of elements. Chlorine, bromine, iodine, and astatine have outermost electronic configurations, which may be represented by

and small promotional energies accordingly could give the states represented by

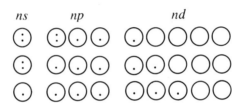

Sharing of the unpaired electrons would lead to covalent states of 1, 3, 5, and 7. These states are exhibited, respectively, in the elements, Cl_2, etc., and in the highest fluorides of chlorine, ClF_3, bromine, BrF_5, and iodine, IF_7. The effect of the increasing difference in electronegativity in this series in bringing about a higher covalent state is apparent. Valence bond structures of these are given in Figure 2.2.

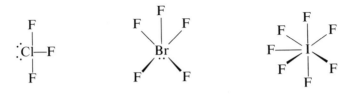

FIGURE 2.2. *Valence bond structures.*

In the group V elements, nitrogen, $1s^2 2s^2 2p^3$, shows the expected covalency of three, while phosphorus, arsenic, and antimony have common covalent states of three and five (Figure 2.3).

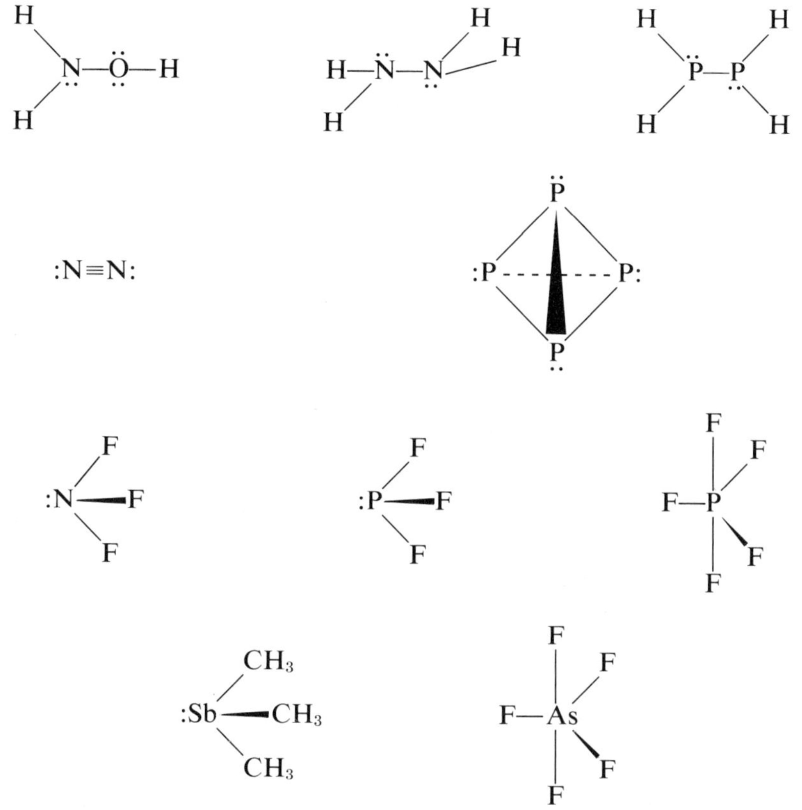

FIGURE 2.3. *Valence bond structures.*

In the carbon family the outermost configuration of the isolated atom is

The promotional energy necessary to produce the ns^1np^3 state is, however, more than compensated for by the formation of the two additional bonds. Hence, the usual covalent state for this family of elements is four.

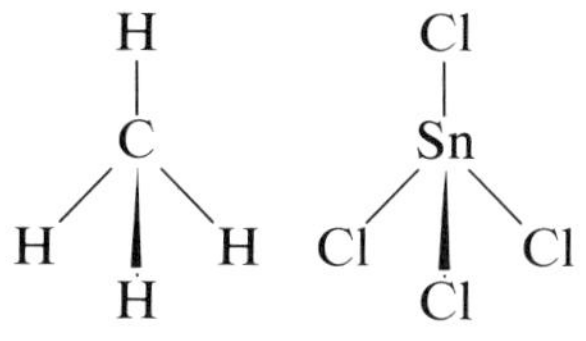

etc.

Coordinate Covalence or Dative Bonding

The most common case of molecule formation in which an *s* electron of carbon is *not* promoted occurs with carbon monoxide. Here one would expect carbon to have achieved the configuration

$$2s \qquad 2p$$

and oxygen to have an s^2p^6 configuration. However, the dissociation energy of CO and the very short C—O bond distance suggest that the valence bond structure is better represented by

$$\overset{(-)}{:}C \equiv \overset{(+)}{O}: \qquad \text{or simply} \qquad :C \equiv O:$$

The arrow in the above formula is a convention used to indicate that oxygen donates *both* of the electrons in the bond. Such a bond, sometimes termed a *coordinate covalent bond* or a *dative bond*, cannot be distinguished from an ordinary covalent bond once it is formed. The charges shown are called *formal charges* and always arise in dative bonding. Formal charges may be calculated by assigning half of the electrons in a covalent bond to each atom and calculating the resulting charge on the quasi ion. The sum of the formal charges in a molecule will be zero; the sum of the formal charges in an ion will be the same as the charge on the ion. Formal charges are useful in evaluating possible alternative valence bond structures, but they should not be interpreted too literally as representing the actual charge distribution within molecules.

By making use of low lying empty orbitals and/or unshared pairs to form dative bonds, higher covalent states may sometimes be achieved than would have been possible otherwise. The covalency of oxygen in the case of CO may be taken as three. The covalency of nitrogen may be increased to four in this manner as in the ammonium ion, tetraalkylammonium ion, and amine oxides.

Phosphorus in a covalent state of three may increase its covalency to four either by donating its unshared pair in dative bonding as in

$$\overset{(+)}{Cl_3P} \rightarrow \overset{(-)}{BBr_3}$$

or by accepting a pair of electrons into a *d* orbital as in

$$\overset{(-)}{Cl_3\ddot{P}} \leftarrow \overset{(+)}{N(CH_3)_3}.$$

An increase in the covalency from five to six may be achieved by phosphorus by accepting a pair of electrons into one of its empty *d* orbitals, i.e.,

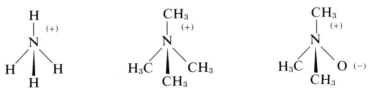

electron configuration of PF_5

electron configuration of PF_6^-

Thus we find that dative bonding in phosphorus compounds allows the covalent states of 4 and 6 as well as the usual states of 3 and 5. This series may be illustrated by the following species:

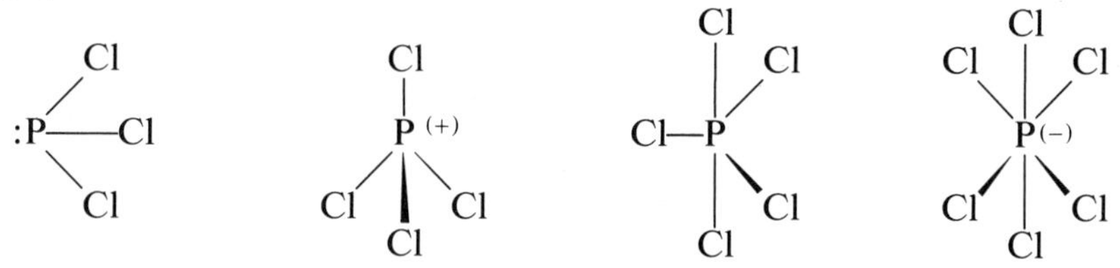

In addition to the covalent states of 1, 3, 5, and 7 mentioned earlier for the heavier halogens, accepting dative bonds allows states of 2, 4, and 6 to be found as in the cases of ICl_2^-, ICl_4^-, and IF_6^-. Donation of electron pairs in dative bonds allows all the halogens, including fluorine, to show covalent states of two, as illustrated in Figure 2.4.

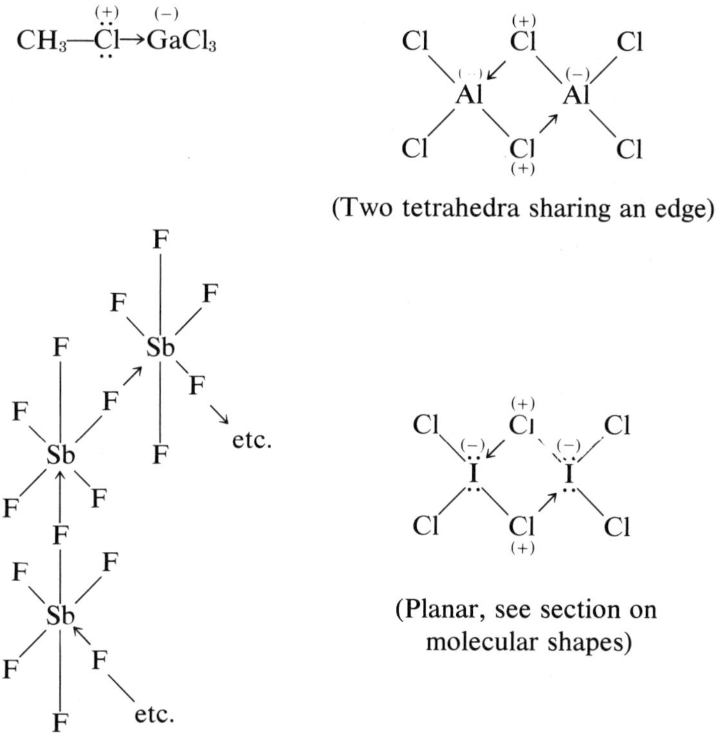

(Two tetrahedra sharing an edge)

(Planar, see section on
molecular shapes)

FIGURE 2.4. *Dative bonds.*

In the case of boron and other group III elements, accepting electrons *via* dative bonds is the rule rather than the exception. Thus the following series of ions or compounds is known for boron.

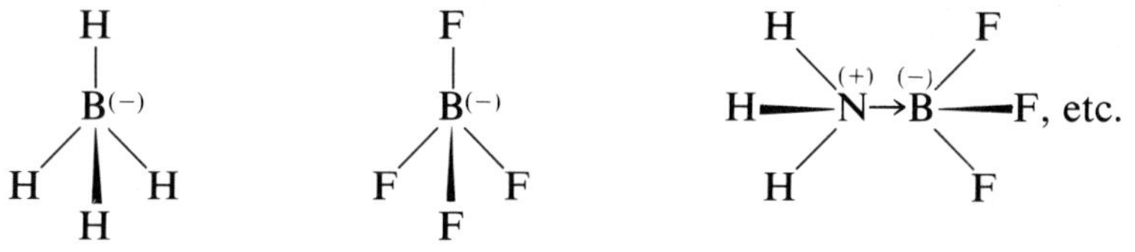

BF$_3$ is isoelectronic and isosteric (i.e., has the same number of electrons and the same shape) with the carbonate and nitrate ions, which are discussed further below. Trimethylboron and the boron hydrides are discussed in a later section.

Resonance

Some molecules or ions cannot be represented adequately by a single valence bond formula. The rules of combination lead to the representation $_{(-)}$ $\overset{\text{O}}{\underset{\text{O—C—O}}{\|}}$ $_{(-)}$ for the carbonate ion, but the oxygen atoms are known to be equivalent and the bond angles are all 120° in the planar ion. The difficulty arises simply because electrons cannot be represented as dots or lines restricted to particular positions. The "fourth" electron pair, which forms a double bond wherever it is written, is not localized in any one of the three bonds, but is somewhat "smeared out" over all three bonds. There are three equivalent bonds, each of which is something between a single and a double bond. In this case the "fourth" bond can be written in any one of the three positions, so that each bond is described as having a bond order of about 1⅓. The bond order of a single bond is 1, a double bond 2, and a triple bond 3.

Pauling introduced the concept of *resonance* to adapt the simple valence bond notation to situations in which electrons are delocalized. Three structures are written for the carbonate ion:

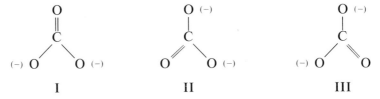

$\qquad\qquad$ I $\qquad\qquad\qquad\qquad\qquad$ II $\qquad\qquad\qquad\qquad\qquad$ III

The three *contributing structures* are not interpreted as having any independent existence. The carbonate ion does *not* consist of a mixture of the three structures, nor is there an equilibrium among the three structures. The simple valence bond notation is inadequate to represent the structure of the carbonate ion, which is not one or all of the above structures but something in between, a *resonance hybrid*. The fact that several structures are written instead of one does not in any way increase the physical reality of any of the structures. The three bonds and the three oxygen atoms are equivalent. The contributing structures are sometimes separated by double headed arrows (↔). This notation should not be confused with the reversible arrows (⇌) used in chemical equilibrium.

The assignment of a bond order of 1⅓ to the C—O bond in carbonates is straightforward since the three most reasonable contributing structures are equivalent. The problem is more complex in the oxyanions of the halogens, the sulfur family, and the phosphorus family. Consider the sulfate ion. Here one may consider the ion as arising completely from dative bonding between a sulfide ion and four oxygen atoms (I) or completely from the sharing of electrons (including the two extra ones) between oxygen, in a covalent state of two, and sulfur in a covalent state of eight (II). In addition to these extremes one may write the intermediate structures III, IV, and V.

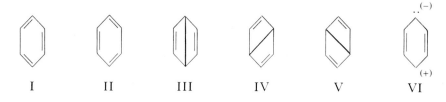

4 equivalent structures   6 equivalent structures   4 equivalent structures

I   II   III   IV   V

The actual structure of the sulfate ion would be an average of all the structures shown (and even, perhaps, some additional ones) weighted according to the number of equivalent structures and their relative energies. The theoretical problem is currently too formidable to arrive at an unambiguous answer, but by applying other criteria (particularly that of bond length) it has been estimated that the bond order in sulfates is approximately 1.8.

The familiar application of resonance to benzene includes the usual Kekulé structures (I and II), the less important Dewar structures (III–V), and unimportant structures such as VI, in which there is charge separation and one carbon has only six electrons.

I   II   III   IV   V   VI

There are rules which permit the elimination of unlikely structures and the selection of the more important contributing structures, i.e., those which are closer to the true resonance hybrid. The following six rules apply:

(1) The contributing structures should have the same or nearly the same atomic positions. The most important contributing structures normally differ only in the positions of electrons. The closer the bond angles and lengths of a contributing structure are to those of the actual molecule, the greater the "contribution" of that structure to the hybrid. The Dewar structures are less important than the Kekulé structures because of the very long bond across the ring. The shape of a molecule corresponding to the Dewar structures would be considerably different from that of benzene.

(2) All contributing structures of a particular molecule must have the same number of unpaired electrons. In structure VI for benzene the charge separation could be avoided by placing one unpaired electron on the top carbon atom and one on the bottom carbon atom, but this possibility is ruled out.

(3) Contributing structures should not differ too widely in the positions of electrons. This can be restated that the contributing structures should not differ greatly in energy. Structure VI for benzene would be expected to be a high energy (or

less stable) structure compared to I and II and would be expected to be much less important, i.e., the resonance hybrid is much closer to the representations of I and II than it is to VI. This rule also eliminates structures in which there are more than 8 electrons around an atom with no additional low energy orbitals.

(4) Like charges should not reside on atoms close together in a contributing structure, but unlike charges should not be greatly separated. This can be interpreted as a special case of rule 3, since the positions of electrons in the unlikely structures will be much different from those in other structures. In HN_3 structure III is probably relatively unimportant because of the (+) charges on adjacent N atoms and also because of the double negative charge on the remaining N atom.

$$HN_3$$

$$\overset{(+)\ (-)}{H-\ddot{N}=N=N:} \qquad (I)$$

$$\overset{(-)\ (+)}{H-\ddot{N}-N\equiv N:} \qquad (II)$$

$$\overset{(+)\ (+)\ (2-)}{H-N\equiv N-\ddot{N}:} \qquad (III)$$

$$N_3^-$$

$$\overset{(-)\ (+)\ (-)}{:N=N=N:}$$

$$\overset{(2-)\ (+)}{:\ddot{N}-N\equiv N:}$$

$$\overset{(+)\ (2-)}{:N\equiv N-\ddot{N}:}$$

The similar structure for the N_3^- ion does not give (+) charges on adjacent N atoms so it should be more important than for the molecular acid. The change in the relative importance of the last contributing structure should result in the same bond order (about 2) for each bond in N_3^-, but a bond order less than 2 for the N—N bond nearer the H atom and a bond order greater than 2 for the terminal N—N bond in HN_3. The fact that there is an additional important contributing structure for the N_3^- ion as compared to HN_3 results in resonance stabilization of the anion. This might be related to the rather great strength of HN_3 as an acid and possibly to the instability of covalent azides generally.

(5) Contributing structures in which negative charge resides on an electronegative element and positive charge resides on an electropositive element are more important than those where the reverse is true. The ionic structure $H^{(+)}F^{(-)}$ is an important one; the ionic structure $H^{(-)}F^{(+)}$ is not. When acetone loses a proton

$$\overset{:O:}{\underset{CH_3C-CH_2^{(-)}}{\parallel}}$$

the anion $CH_3C-CH_2^{(-)}$ is obtained. The contributing structure in which the

$$\overset{:\ddot{O}:^{(-)}}{\underset{CH_3C=CH_2}{\mid}}$$

negative charge is on the oxygen, $CH_3C=CH_2$, is perhaps the more important of the two.

(6) The greater the number of covalent bonds, the greater the importance of a contributing structure. The doubly bonded structures of BF_3, $\overset{F}{\underset{F}{\diagdown}}\overset{(-)\ (+)}{B=F}$, are important because of the formation of an additional covalent bond, even though a fluorine atom acquires a positive formal charge (see p. 58). Here the tendency

to remove the electron deficiency of boron, or to utilize all of the low energy orbitals in the molecule is more important than the charge distribution. In the case of pyridine-*N*-oxide, structures III–V have a favorable distribution of charges from the standpoint of the electronegativity of the atoms involved, but the fact that these structures contain one less bond than the other structures diminishes their importance. Rule 5 indicates that structures VI–VIII should be less important than I and II because the (+) charge is on the more electro-negative nitrogen and the (−) charge is on a carbon atom. The same number of covalent bonds is present in each of these five structures.

The experimental heats of formation of molecules such as CH_4 agree with values obtained by summing the C—H bond energies. A molecule for which resonance is important is more stable than one would predict from any one of the contributing structures. The discrepancy between the calculated and observed heats of formation is called the *resonance energy*. The greater the number of significant contributing structures, the greater the resonance energy. Typical resonance energies (kcal/mole) are: benzene, 37; naphthalene, 75; C=O, 105; and O=C=O, 36. Resonance energies are evaluated with respect to a particular valence bond structure. The increased stability of molecules stabilized by resonance is reflected in the shortening of bond lengths. The bond order corresponding to the observed bond length is usually greater than the average expected from the contributing structures, such as $1\frac{1}{3}$ for CO_3^{2-}.

Planarity is common for molecules of second period elements in which resonance stabilization is important. Contributing structures frequently differ in the positions of double bonds. In order to permit a double bond to be written in any one of several positions with good *p-p* overlap (see p. 57), the molecule must be planar with sp^2 or sp hybridization.

The greater the number of contributing structures, the greater the delocalization of the electronic charge and hence the more stable the molecule. The localization of charge on an atom is usually an unstable situation and occurs only under special circumstances. Ions can be very greatly stabilized if the charge can be delocalized. Hence,

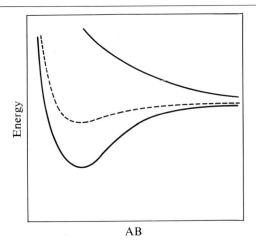

FIGURE 2.5. *Potential energy curves for* H_2.

resonance, in general, will be more important in charged species than in neutral ones. The increasing acidity in the series $HClO$, $HClO_2$, $HClO_3$, and $HClO_4$ is probably determined to a great extent by the greater stability of the anions containing several oxygen atoms because of the greater delocalization of the negative charge. The negative charge in ClO^- must reside for the most part on the oxygen atom. In ClO_4^- the negative charge can be spread over four equivalent oxygen atoms.

Theoretical Treatment of the Covalent Bond

Heitler–London Theory

The first theoretical development of the covalent bond was by Heitler and London.[*] Their treatment of the hydrogen molecule is a good introduction to the discussion of the covalent bond to follow. If we consider two hydrogen atoms brought together without exchange of electrons (structure I) there is a weak attraction at large distances, which becomes a strong repulsion at short distances (dashed curve Figure 2.5). If we consider that at short distances the alternative structure in which the electrons exchange positions (structure II) is just as likely, we see that there is a minimum in the potential energy curve (lower solid curve) which corresponds to the normal H—H distance. (The hydrogen nuclei are represented as H_a and H_b and the electrons as $\cdot 1$ and $\cdot 2$.) The molecule is stabilized at the appropriate H—H distance by the exchange between two

$$I \quad H_a^{\cdot 1 \, 2 \cdot} H_b$$
$$II \quad H_a^{\cdot 2 \, 1 \cdot} H_b$$

equivalent structures, as in resonance stabilization. The wave functions for the individual structures can be written:

$$\psi_I = \psi_a(1)\psi_b(2) \tag{2.1}$$
$$\psi_{II} = \psi_a(2)\psi_b(1) \tag{2.2}$$

* Heitler, W., and F. London, *Z. Physik*, **44**, 455 (1927).

Since the structures are equivalent, their wave functions represent the same energy so Equation 2.3, which can be written as Equation 2.4, will also be a solution to the wave equation (c_1 and c_2 are mixing coefficients).

$$\psi_+ = c_1\psi_I + c_2\psi_{II} \tag{2.3}$$
$$\psi_+ = c_1\psi_a(1)\psi_b(2) + c_2\psi_a(2)\psi_b(1) \tag{2.4}$$

The actual molecule is more stable than either of the structures would indicate, resulting in a minimum in the potential energy curve. The wave equation $\psi_- = c_1\psi_I - c_2\psi_{II}$ represents the situation where no attraction is observed at any distance because the two electrons have parallel spins. (See upper solid curve in Figure 2.5.) Electrons must have opposed spins for favorable interaction.

Pauling has shown that the calculations may be improved by a consideration of ionic structures for the hydrogen molecule. This results in the addition of two more terms to the wave equation 2.3,

$$\text{III} \quad H_a{}^{(+)} \quad :H_b{}^{(-)}$$
$$\text{IV} \quad H_a:{}^{(-)} \quad H_b{}^{(+)}$$

The Heitler–London treatment can be extended to other molecules with the covalent bond resulting from the interaction of electrons with opposed spins on two atoms. The valence electrons of a combining atom must be unpaired. If they are not unpaired in the ground state of the atom, there must be vacant orbitals of low energy available to accommodate the previously spin-paired electrons in separate orbitals. The atomic orbitals involved on each atom must be of the same major quantum number, n, because the orbitals must not differ greatly in energy. An atom can then form a covalent bond for each of its stable valence orbitals. Thus nitrogen with the outer configuration $2s^2 2p_x{}^1 2p_y{}^1 2p_z{}^1$ can form three bonds as in NF_3, but it cannot form NF_5 because the second shell is filled. Phosphorus with the configuration $3s^2 3p_x{}^1 3p_y{}^1 3p_z{}^1$ can form PF_3, and by promoting one $3s$ electron to a vacant $3d$ orbital to give the configuration $3s^1 3p_x{}^1 3p_y{}^1 3p_z{}^1 3d^1$ it can form 5 bonds in PF_5 as discussed earlier (p. 44).

The Heitler–London treatment features the formation of a chemical bond as the result of the pairing of two electrons, one from each bonded atom. The electron density of the shared pair is a maximum between the two bonded atoms. Atoms tend to combine to form closed shells, but the octet is exceeded in PF_5 and SF_6 and is probably not attained in BI_3. As presented, the Heitler–London treatment does not consider the formation of odd electron molecules such as $H_2{}^+$ where no pairing occurs. It does not include the formation of the coordinate covalent bond where one of the bonded atoms furnishes both of the electron pairs, but extensions could include these bonding situations.

Pauling–Slater or Valence Bond Theory

Pauling* and Slater† have extended the Heitler–London theory to make it more general and to account for the directional character of covalent bonds. The main consideration is that stable compounds result from the tendency to fill all stable orbitals with electron pairs, shared or unshared.

* Pauling, L., *J. Am. Chem. Soc.,* **53**, 1367 (1931); *Phys. Rev.* **40**, 891 (1932).
† Slater, J. C., *Phys. Rev.,* **37**, 481 (1931); **38**, 1109 (1931).

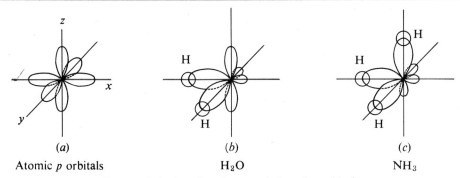

(*a*)	(*b*)	(*c*)
Atomic *p* orbitals	H_2O	NH_3

FIGURE 2.6. *Angular characteristics of p orbitals.*

The shape of a molecule will be determined primarily by the directional character-istics of the orbitals involved. A covalent bond may be described as the result of the overlap of atomic orbitals on two atoms so that the two orbitals can be occupied by an electron pair. In HF the spherically symmetrical *s* orbital of H overlaps with the singly occupied 2*p* orbital of F.

The H_2O molecule results from the overlap of the two singly occupied *p* orbitals of oxygen with the *s* orbital of each of two hydrogen atoms to give an angular molecule [see Figure 2.6*b*]. The *p* orbitals are mutually perpendicular, but the bond angle in water is 104° 27′. The fact that the angle is greater than 90° can be explained as the result of repulsion between the hydrogen atoms. A better approach to the correlation of bond angles will be presented later (p. 61). The ammonia molecule is pyramidal with a bond angle of 106° 47′ as a result of bonding using the three *p* orbitals. One might expect the bond angle to be larger than the angle in the water molecule because of the greater repulsion among the three hydrogen atoms.

Carbon has the outer configuration $2s^2 2p_x^1 2p_y^1$, but by unpairing the 2*s* electrons and promoting one to the completely vacant $2p_z$ orbital, it becomes $2s^1 2p_x^1 2p_y^1 2p_z^1$ as re-quired for the formation of four bonds as in CH_4. The molecular shape is not immedi-ately apparent from the characteristics of the atomic orbitals. The *s* orbital is spherically symmetrical and the three *p* orbitals are mutually perpendicular. Nevertheless, physical and chemical evidence show that the methane molecule is tetrahedral with four equiva-lent bonds. If one considers an atom surrounded by four electron pairs, the mutual repulsion among the electron pairs will result in their orientation toward the apices of a tetrahedron. The wave function, ψ, for the tetrahedrally oriented orbitals, is the linear combination of the atomic wave functions:

$$\psi = a\psi_s + b\psi_{p_x} + c\psi_{p_y} + d\psi_{p_z} \qquad (2.5)$$

One solution yields equivalent orbitals which are more stable (lower energy) than either the *s* or *p* atomic orbitals.

This kind of combination of atomic orbitals to give mixed orbitals is known as *hybridization*. The combination of the *s* and three *p* orbitals gives the *tetrahedral hybrid sp³ orbitals*. One of the hybrid *sp³* orbitals is represented in Figure 2.7.

The *p* lobe with the same sign of the ψ function as that of the *s* orbital is enlarged and the one of opposite sign is diminished. The enlarged lobe of the resulting orbital can give more favorable overlap with the orbital of another atom to form a stronger bond

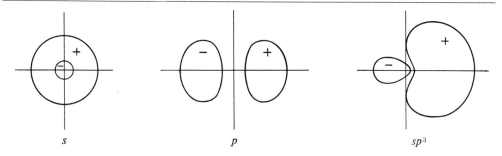

s *p* *sp³*

FIGURE 2.7. *Combination of orbitals to given an sp³ hybrid. The representation of the sp³ orbital is adapted from C. A. Coulson,* Valence *(2nd ed.; Oxford: Clarendon Press, 1961) p. 199 with permission.*

than can either the *p* or *s* orbital alone. The orbital represented is one of the four equivalent *sp³* orbitals.

Other hybrid orbitals are formed as the result of combination of *s*, *p*, and *d* atomic orbitals. Some of the resulting configurations are shown in Figure 2.8 and some are compared to atomic orbitals in Table 2.1. The relative bond strengths for *s-p* hybrid bonds given by Pauling based on combinations of $\psi(2s)$ and $\psi(2p)$ are 1.93 for *sp*, 1.99 for *sp²*, and 2.00 for *sp³*. However, the overlap integral increases in the order *sp³* < *sp²* < *sp*, indicating the greatest orbital overlap for *sp* bonds. The relative bond strengths would be expected to be in the same order. The increasing C—H bond energies in the series CH_4, C_2H_4, and C_2H_2 seem to support increasing bond strength with increasing *s* character for *s-p* hybrids.*

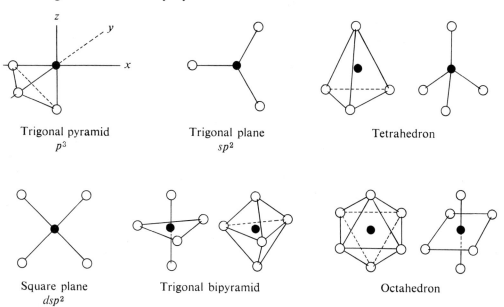

Trigonal pyramid
p^3

Trigonal plane
sp^2

Tetrahedron

Square plane
dsp^2

Trigonal bipyramid

Octahedron

FIGURE 2.8. *Some bonding configurations.*

* Coulson, C. A., *Valence* (2nd ed., London: Oxford University Press, 1961) p. 210.

TABLE 2.1

Atomic or hybrid orbitals	Orientation	Relative bond strength
s	Nondirectional	1.00
p	3 Mutually perpendicular	1.73
sp	Linear	See text
sp²	Planar (120° bond angles)	See text
sp³	Tetrahedral	See text
dsp²	Square Planar	2.694
dsp³	Trigonal bipyramidal	—
d²sp³	Octahedral	2.923

Multiple Bonds

The bonding requirements of each carbon in ethylene, C_2H_4, are satisfied by single bonds to two hydrogen atoms and a double bond between the carbon atoms. The double bond can be represented by the sharing of an edge of two tetrahedra to form two "banana" bonds. Two electrons can be accommodated in each of the orbitals, one above and one below the plane of the molecule as shown in Figure 2.9a.

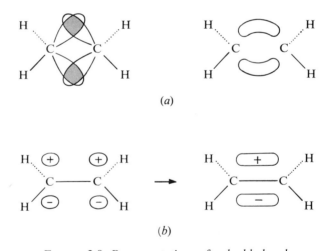

(a)

(b)

FIGURE 2.9. *Representations of a double bond.*

Multiple bonded structures are generally best described in molecular orbital terminology. Although the molecular orbital treatment is to be discussed more fully later (p. 71), a brief discussion is given here for comparison with the valence bond description. In the ethylene molecule, the carbon orbitals can be considered to be hybridized to give three equivalent $sp²$ orbitals (at 120° to each other). Each carbon uses two of the $sp²$ hybrid orbitals for overlap with the $1s$ orbitals of two hydrogens and the remaining

sp^2 orbital for the formation of the carbon–carbon bond. These five bonds are known as *sigma*(σ) *bonds*. A σ bond is a covalent bond in which the electron density is a maximum along the line joining the bonded atoms. The remaining two electrons from the unmixed *p* atomic orbitals of the carbon atoms become paired to form a *pi*(π) *bond*. The electron pair of the π bond occupies the π orbital, which is obtained by the overlap of the two atomic *p* orbitals. The combination of two atomic *p* wave functions to give the molecular π wave function is shown in Figure 2.9*b*. The π orbital picture shows two regions of high electron density, one above and one below the plane of the molecule, but only one electron pair occupies the set of lobes. In contrast, the banana bond picture shows two distinct bonds, each of which may accommodate an electron pair for a total of four electrons.

These two representations are the result of different approaches to chemical bonding, but the final descriptions have been shown to be equivalent.

The ethylene molecule is planar with restricted rotation about the double bond. The HCH bond angle of about 120° is obtained directly from the σ bond hybridization in the molecular orbital representation. The bond angle in the banana bond structure must be explained on the basis of mutual repulsion between the C—H bonding electrons and between them and the 2 banana bonds as compared with the repulsions among 4 equivalent C—H bonds in methane. For conjugated systems where there are alternating single and double bonds, the interactions can be explained readily on the basis of the π bond representation.

Cyclopropane gives a number of reactions characteristic of unsaturated compounds such as ethylene. The similarity between ethylene and cyclopropane is readily seen from the banana bond representation. The ring strain tends to give C—C bonds very similar to the bent or banana bonds in ethylene (Figure 2.10).

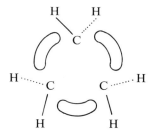

FIGURE 2.10. *Bent bonds in cyclopropane.*

Acetylene, C_2H_2, is a linear molecule, which can be represented by two tetrahedra sharing a face to produce three badly bent banana bonds joining the carbon atoms. However, the π bond representation seems much more satisfactory. The σ bonds are the result of overlap of *sp* hybrids leaving each carbon with two singly occupied *p* orbitals. The unhybridized *p* orbitals of each carbon atom will have the shape of a doughnut since only one direction is defined (Figure 2.11*a*). These orbitals overlap to to give a π orbital, which has cylindrical symmetry and extends over both carbon atoms (Figure 2.11*b*). This can also be considered as the result of the combination of two π orbitals, each having two lobes with their nodal planes intersecting at right angles along

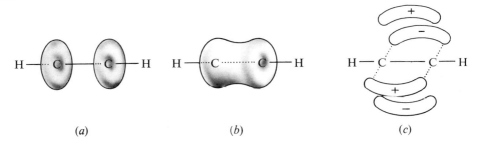

(a)   (b)   (c)

FIGURE 2.11. *Representation of the orbitals in* C_2H_2. *Contours of maximum electron density are sketched.*

the internuclear line (Figure 2.11c). There are four π electrons. The concentration of more electronic charge between the nuclei results in shortening of the bond distance and an increase in bond strength from single to double to triple bonds (Table 2.2).

TABLE 2.2
Bond Lengths and Bond Strengths for Carbon and Nitrogen

	C—C	C=C	C≡C
Bond length Å	1.54	1.35	1.21
Bond energy, kcal/mole	83	146	199
	N—N	N=N	N≡N
Bond length, Å	1.47	1.24	1.10
Bond energy, kcal/mole	39	100	225

MULTIPLE BONDING FOR ELEMENTS BEYOND THE SECOND PERIOD

The double bonding encountered for second period elements is different in extent and in type from that encountered for other elements. Double bonding resulting from the formation of p-p-π bonds (overlap of p orbitals on bonded atoms) is common for the second period elements and diminishes in importance down through a given family. Fluorine and oxygen often form double bonds even at the expense of acquiring a formal positive charge. This serves to delocalize the electrons, diminishing the very high charge density of these small atoms and decreasing the repulsion among the unshared electrons on F or O. The need for such delocalization or for decreasing the repulsion among lone pairs is not so great for larger atoms. The p-p-π orbital overlap is less favorable for larger atoms because the p orbitals are larger and more diffuse. The increase in atomic radius also favors an increase in coordination number, thereby allowing electrons that might have formed π bonds to form σ bonds. The differences in structure between the formally similar compounds of the second and third periods may be noted as follows: BCl_3, $(AlCl_3)_2(g)$; CO_2, $(SiO_2)_x$; HNO_3, $(HPO_3)_x$; N_2O_3, $(P_2O_3)_2$; $N_2O_5(g)$, $(P_2O_5)_2(g)$; CS_2, $(SiS_2)_x$. For each of the compounds of a second period element, discrete molecules are formed because of the tendency to form p-p-π bonds. The compounds of the third period elements are polymeric because of the reduced tendency to form p-p-π bonds and preference for increasing the number of σ bonds through

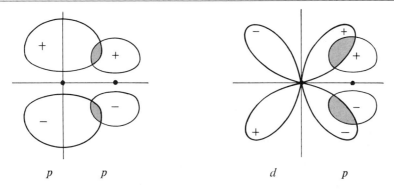

FIGURE 2.12. *p-p-π and d-p-π bonding.*

sharing of the negative partners (Cl, O, and S in examples given). At room temperature the multiple bonded molecules for Si and P analogous to C_2H_4, C_2H_2, and N_2 do not exist in appreciable amounts.

Although *p-p-π* bonding is of little importance in the third and higher period elements, multiple bonding may occur in other ways. For a coordination number of four there are no empty *p* orbitals on the central atom for the formation of *p-p-π* bonds, but the bond length in an ion such as SO_4^{2-} is shorter than would be expected for single bonds. The sulfur atom, unlike the second period elements, has available vacant *d* orbitals of low energy for the formation of *d-p-π* bonds, which result from the overlap of a filled *p* orbital on the oxygen with an empty *d* orbital on sulfur (see Figure 2.12). The *d-p* overlap may be more favorable than *p-p* overlap for large atoms, because the *d* orbitals project out in the general direction of the bond.

Pauling has proposed an *electroneutrality principle* that states that electrons are distributed in a molecule in such a way as to make the residual charge on each atom zero or very nearly zero except that hydrogen and the most electropositive metals can acquire partial positive charge and the most electronegative atoms can acquire partial negative charge. The charge on an atom can be decreased by a change in the polarity, or amount of ionic character, of a bond (see p. 88) or by a change in the amount of multiple bond character of a bond. The formal charge of +3 on Cl in the hypothetical

structure
$$
\begin{bmatrix} O & O \\ & Cl \\ O & O \end{bmatrix}^{-}
$$
is reduced to +2 in
$$
\begin{bmatrix} O & O \\ & Cl \\ O & O \end{bmatrix}^{-}
$$
and zero in
$$
\begin{bmatrix} O & O \\ & Cl \\ O & O \end{bmatrix}^{-}
$$

Bond length data indicate a bond order of about 1.6 in perchlorate ion.* The extent of double bond character (*d-p-π*) might be expected to increase in the series PO_4^{3-}, SO_4^{2-}, ClO_4^{-} as the formal charge on the central atom increases for the single bonded structures. Oxyanions of fluorine are not stable, partly because the high electronegativity of fluorine prohibits a formal positive charge and the positive charge cannot be eliminated by double bond formation because the fluorine does not have vacant low energy orbitals available.

---

* Nightingale, E. R., *J. Phys. Chem.,* **64**, 162 (1960).

Shapes of Simple Molecules from Hybridization

The shape of a molecule, to a first approximation, is determined by its σ bond structure. Unshared electron pairs often occupy hybridized orbitals and hence can be treated as bonded groups in determining the hybridization. Thus the hybridization in NH_3 and H_2O can be considered to be sp^3. The importance of unshared electron pairs in determining molecular shapes is illustrated in Table 2.3.

TABLE 2.3
Shapes of Some Simple Molecules

General formula	Number of unshared electrons on A	σ bonding orbital hybridization	Shape	Examples
AX_2	None	sp	Linear	$O{=}C{=}O$, $S{=}C{=}S$, $H{-}C{\equiv}N$ $\overset{(+)}{O{=}N{=}O}$, $[Cl{-}\overset{(-)}{Ag}{-}Cl]$, $H{-}C{\equiv}C{-}H^a$
	One or more	sp^2 or sp^3	Angular	$H{-}\ddot{O}{:}$, NH_2^-, $:\overset{(+)}{S}$, O_3, $:N$ ...
AX_3	None	sp^2	Planar	BF_3, $[NO_3]^-$, $[CO_3]^{2-}$, $C_2H_4^a$
	One or two	sp^3	Pyramidal	$\ddot{N}H_3$, H_3O^+, PF_3, $[ClO_3]^-$
AX_4	None	sp^3	Tetrahedral	CH_4, NH_4^+, BF_4^-, $SiCl_4$

^{a} Each carbon in C_2H_2 and C_2H_4 corresponds to A in AX_2 and AX_3, respectively.

It is difficult to assess *a priori* the relative importance of various contributing structures or the contribution of a particular type of hybridization in many molecules. Atoms with more low lying orbitals than valence electrons will have reasonably unambiguous σ bond configurations and hence predictable structures (at least for simple molecules). Atoms with more valence electrons than low lying orbitals may contribute these electrons in varying degrees in diverse situations (i.e., in different molecules) and accordingly have several distinct and not easily predictable σ bond structures. In the trimethoxyboron, $B(OCH_3)_3$, molecule the boron hybridization must be sp^2 with bond angles of 120°, but the orbital hybridization of the oxygen atoms is apparently intermediate between sp^3 and sp^2 (Figure 2.13). Any contribution of resonance structures involving double bonding between boron and oxygen would require a lone pair in an atomic p orbital on oxygen for the formation of a π bond. Hence double bonding would favor sp^2 hybridization here. Similarly the P—N bond in H_2N—PH_2 might be p^3, sp^3, or some intermediate combination of N orbitals. The hybridization of the σ bonding orbitals of each nitrogen in N_2O_5 must be sp^2, but the bridging oxygen might be sp^3, sp^2, or even sp.

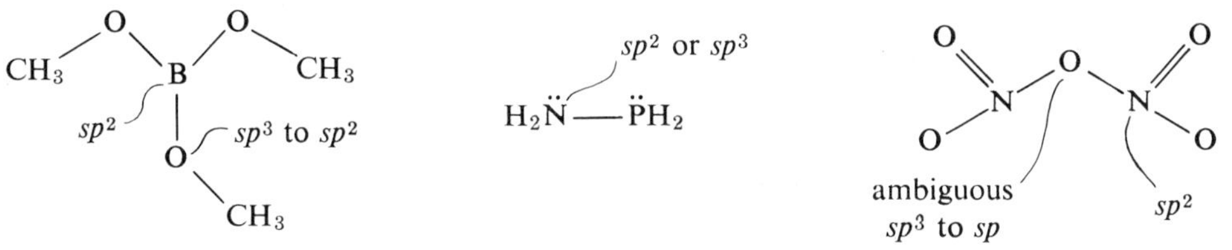

FIGURE 2.13. *Possible assignments of hybridization.*

The Pauli Exclusion Principle and the Prediction of the Shapes of Molecules

The variation of the bond angles of simple molecules can be explained fairly satisfactorily from the consideration of the repulsion among the electron pairs, including bonding and unshared pairs, in the valence shell of the central atom.* The repulsion among the electrons can be considered to arise from the operation of the Pauli Exclusion Principle. Although this principle is usually stated in terms of the energy or the quantum numbers of the electrons, it can be considered to rule out the possibility that two electrons might be at the same point at the same time. Two electrons can be confined to the same orbital only if they have opposed spins. Since the repulsion is greater for electrons of the same spin, the total repulsion is minimized by arranging the electrons of a complete octet in four localized pairs of electrons of opposed spin, each pair directed toward the apex of a tetrahedron. (See p. 67 for further discussion of electron correlation effects.) This is the configuration expected for Ar, F^-, and O^{2-}.

If one of the electron pairs is used for bonding, as in HF, the four pairs are no longer equivalent. The bonding pair now becomes more localized since its electrons are restricted in their motion by two positive nuclei. The repulsion among the electrons in the nonbonding pairs will cause them to spread out to occupy the space made available by the localization of the bonding pair. If two of the electron pairs are used for bonding, as in H_2O, the bond angle will be determined by the repulsions among the four electron pairs. Instead of the normal tetrahedral angle (109° 28') for four equivalent pairs as found in CH_4 and as expected for O^{2-}, the bond angle in H_2O is 104° 27'. Because of the differences in localization the repulsion between electron pairs decreases in the

---

* Gillespie, R. J., and R. S. Nyholm, *Quart. Rev.*, **11**, 339 (1957); R. J. Gillespie, *J. Am. Chem. Soc.*, **82**, 5978 (1960); *J. Chem. Educ.*, **40**, 295 (1963).

(a)   *(b)*

FIGURE 2.14. *(a) Most probable spatial distribution and corresponding trigonal orbitals for three electron pairs confined to a plane. (b) Orbitals for two bonding electron pairs and one lone pair; ● nuclei of bonded atoms [from R. J. Gillespie, J. Am. Chem. Soc., 82, 5978 (1960)].*

order: lone pair–lone pair > lone pair–bonding pair > bonding pair–bonding pair. (See Figure 2.14 for a representation of the distribution of electron pairs confined to a plane.) The localization of the bonding pairs permits the bond angle to close, relative to the tetrahedral angle, in order to decrease repulsion between the lone pairs. In NH_3 the HNH bond angles are 106°47′. The angle is greater than that in H_2O because there are no lone pair–lone pair repulsions. In addition to the restriction of two nuclei, each bonding pair is localized by the repulsion of two other bonding pairs and one lone pair, whereas in water each bonding pair is localized by the repulsion of one other bonding pair and two lone pairs. The variation in bond angles can be approached starting with the tetrahedral CH_4 molecule as a reference. The bond angles in NH_3 are decreased by the presence of the lone pair. In H_2O the bond angle is decreased further by the presence of two lone pairs.

The fact that a single unshared electron causes less repulsion than an unshared electron pair can be seen from a comparison of the bond angles in NO_2 (132°) and in NO_2^- (115°). The lone pair in the nitrite ion causes the bond angle to decrease in comparison with NO_2, which has a single unshared electron. The nitryl ion, NO_2^+, with no unshared electrons on nitrogen, is linear (see Figure 2.15).

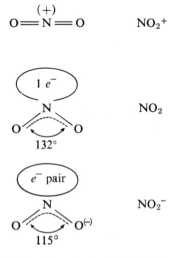

FIGURE 2.15. *Bond angles in NO_2^+, NO_2, and NO_2^-.*

The bond angles decrease in the series NH_3, PH_3, AsH_3, and SbH_3 and in the series H_2O, H_2S, H_2Se, and H_2Te (see Table 2.3). Presumably the increasing size and lower electronegativity of the central atom permits the bonding electrons to be drawn out further, thus decreasing the repulsion between bonding pairs.* The variation in the bond angles in a series such as NH_3, PH_3, AsH_3, and SbH_3 is in the direction to be expected for an increase in p character of the bonds. That is, the bond angles approach the values expected for p^3 bonds rather than for sp^3 hybrid bonds. This is just the opposite of what might be expected since the energy difference between the s and p orbitals is greatest for nitrogen.

The bond angles decrease by large amounts from NH_3 to PH_3 or H_2O to H_2S and by very small amounts for the following members of each series. Gillespie† suggests that the difference arises because N and O are members of the second period for which the octet represents a closed shell. Strong repulsions between the electron pairs result from the fact that the space around the central atom is completely filled. The bond angles for compounds of elements of the second period are rarely less than the tetrahedral angle by more than a few degrees. The members of the later periods can accommodate more than four electron pairs in the valence shell; the maximum is usually six pairs. Six electron pairs in the valence shell of an atom would be expected to give an octahedral arrangement with angles of 90° between electron pairs. The bond angles of the hydrides of the heavier elements of group V and VI seem to approach 90° (See Table 2.4).‡ Thus the repulsion caused by the lone pair in a molecule such as PH_3 would tend to force the bonding pairs closer together until the repulsion among them became great at an angle close to 90°. The difference between the bond angles for the hydrides of each successive member of a family are small because the maximum number of electrons (6) in the valence shell remains constant after the first member of each family, even though the radius continues to increase.

The most striking argument for the great importance of repulsion among electron pairs, in contrast to steric repulsion between atoms, is seen in a comparison of bond angles between hydrogen and fluorine compounds of nitrogen and oxygen. The decrease in the bond angles for NF_3 and F_2O compared to NH_3 and H_2O may be explained on the basis of a decrease in repulsion between bonding pairs as the result of the electrons being drawn out further by the fluorine. The FCF bond angle in the C—F compounds shown in Table 2.4 are also smaller than the HCH bond angles in the corresponding C—H compounds.

The bond angles of the fluorine compounds are smaller than those of the corresponding hydrogen compounds only for the second period elements. Multiple bonding is not possible in NH_3, NF_3, or PH_3, but it is expected to occur in PF_3 using a filled p orbital on F and an empty d orbital on P. The tendency to form multiple bonds is expected to be very great for small atoms (O, N, F) with completed octets because this offers a means of delocalizing the charge for these atoms which have very high charge densities. The formation of partial double bonds would increase the electron density in the bonds

---

* In line with the approach presented earlier (assuming p^3 bonding, see p. 54), one might consider that the angles approach 90° for the larger central atoms because of an increase in the effectiveness of the screening of the protons as the size of the central atom increases.

† Gillespie, R. J., see footnote p. 61.

‡ The angle reported for H_2Te (89° 30′) is less than 90° by such a small amount (and perhaps the difference is not significant) that it cannot be taken to signify a trend.

and cause the bond angles to increase. The bond angle is smaller for PCl_3 than for PF_3 in accordance with an expected decrease in the importance of double bonding involving the larger Cl atom. The need for delocalization of charge is not so great for the larger atom and the larger, more diffuse *p* orbitals of chlorine might give less favorable overlap with the orbitals of phosphorus.

TABLE 2.4[a]

Group IV			Group V		Group VI	
CH_4		109° 28′	NH_3	106° 47′	H_2O	104° 27′
CH_3F	<HCH	110° 0′	NF_3	102° 9′	F_2O	101° 30′
CH_3Cl	<HCH	110° 20′	NH_3	106° 47′	H_2O	104° 27′
CHF_3	<FCF	108° 48′	PH_3	93° 30′	H_2S	92° 16′
$CHCl_3$	<ClCCl	110° 24′	AsH_3	92° 0′	H_2Se	91°
			SbH_3	91° 30′	H_2Te[b]	89° 30′
			NF_3	102° 9′		
H₂C=CH₂		119° 55′	PF_3	104°		
			AsF_3	102°		
			PCl_3	100° 6′		
F₂C=CF₂		114°	$AsCl_3$	98° 25′		
			$SbCl_3$	99° 30′		
			PBr_3[b]	101° 30′		
Cl₂C=CCl₂		113° 30′	PI_3[b]	102°		
H₂C=O		118°				
Cl₂C=O		112° 30′				

[a] Walsh, A. D., *Progress in Stereochemistry,* (London: Butterworths Scientific Publications, 1954) Vol. I, pp. 11–19.
[b] Gillespie, R. J., *J. Am. Chem. Soc.,* **82,** 5978 (1960).

The shapes of molecules can be predicted for configurations other than the tetrahedron in a similar way. Table 2.5 gives the configurations usually encountered. The total of the number of σ (bonding) pairs plus lone pairs gives the configuration to be considered.

TABLE 2.5

Number of σ pairs plus lone pairs	Configuration (considering lone pairs directed as any other group)	Hybridization
2	Linear	sp
3	Trigonal planar	sp^2
4	Tetrahedral	sp^3
5	Trigonal bipyramidal	$d_{z^2}sp^3$
5	Square pyramidal	$d_{x^2-y^2}sp^3$
6	Octahedral	d^2sp^3
7	Pentagonal bypyramidal	d^3sp^3

Gillespie and Nyholm* considered the repulsion among electron pairs as the basis for selecting the most stable isomer of ions or molecules such as those shown in Figure

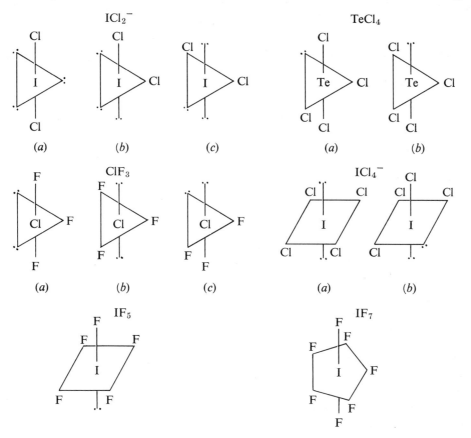

FIGURE 2.16. *Possible structures for some interhalogen compounds.*

* Gillespie, R. J., and R. S. Nyholm, *Quart. Rev.*, **11**, 339 (1957); R. J. Gillespie, *Can. J. Chem.*, **39**, 318 (1961).

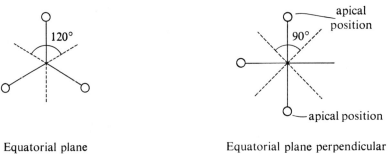

Equatorial plane   Equatorial plane perpendicular
in plane of paper   to plane of paper

FIGURE 2.17. *Angles subtended in a trigonal bipyramid.*

2.16. Searcy* found that the electrostatic interactions are too small to account for differences in stability of the isomers. Nevertheless, lone pairs are still of very great importance in determining the geometry of stable molecules. The two electrons of a lone pair are restricted in space by the requirement that they occupy the same orbital about the central atom. But, within that limitation, the two electrons will remain as widely separated from each other as possible. A bonding pair is restrained to a relatively small solid angle about the central atom by the requirement that the electrons remain close to the nuclei of two atoms. Because of the repulsion between the two electrons, a lone pair acts like an exceptionally large atom and occupies the position providing it the largest solid angle.

Since there are 5 pairs about I in ICl_2^-, the figure with which we begin is the trigonal bipyramid. The positions which allow the largest solid angle are the equatorial positions. Structure (*a*) in Figure 2.16 is the correct one for ICl_2^-. For five equivalent groups, the solid angles can be described by the cross sections as shown in Figure 2.17. The solid angle subtended at an equatorial position is 120° in cross section in the equatorial plane and 90° in cross section perpendicular to the equatorial plane. The solid angle subtended at an apical position is 90° in cross section in any plane perpendicular to the equatorial plane.

Structure (*a*) in Figure 2.16 is the correct one in each case for $TeCl_4$ and ClF_3 since it provides the largest solid angle for the lone pairs. Structures, such as those for $TeCl_4$ and ClF_3, are described in terms of the actual atomic positions and not as trigonal bipyramids. The actual atomic positions would not be quite the same as those implied by a regular trigonal bipyramid with one or more positions occupied by groups (such as lone pairs) not located by common structural methods. Since the five groups are not equivalent, some distortion of the regular figure is to be expected. The structure of $TeCl_4$ can be described as a distorted tetrahedron. ClF_3 has an unsymmetrical planar structure. Searcy obtained reasonable agreement between predicted and reported bond angles for similar molecules and ions whose central atoms are surrounded by five valence electron pairs.

The iodine atom in ICl_4^- is surrounded by six electron pairs, of which two are lone pairs. The basis of the structure should be an octahedron with six equivalent positions.

* Searcy, A. W., *J. Chem. Phys.*, **28**, 1237 (1958); **31**, 1 (1959).

In such a situation where all solid angles are equal, the lone pairs will occupy positions where they are as far removed from one another as possible. The planar structure (*a*) is the correct one for ICl_4^-. For IF_5 only one geometrical isomer is possible because all six positions are equivalent. The structure is described as a tetragonal pyramid. There are no lone pairs in IF_7 and the structure is that of a pentagonal bipyramid.

Linnett's Double Quartet Approach

The previous discussion has emphasized the role of the *electron pair* in bonding, and to a somewhat lesser extent the octet rule of Lewis and Langmuir. As has been seen, more than one valence bond structure is often needed for the description of a molecule and the concept of resonance must be applied if the valence bond approach is used. The octet rule is still more restrictive and cannot handle paramagnetic molecules. A modification of the octet rule by Linnett* permits a satisfactory treatment of many paramagnetic molecules and often allows a single acceptable structure to be written instead of a number of contributing structures.

Linnett considers the distribution of electrons to be determined primarily by two factors: spin correlation effects and charge correlation effects. The spin correlation effects arise from the application of the Pauli Principle, which leads to the conclusion that electrons with the same spin tend to keep apart, while those with opposed spin tend to come together. The charge correlation effects arise because of the repulsion between particles with the same charge. The charge correlation operates in the same direction as the spin correlation to keep electrons of the same spin apart. The spin correlation effect, however, is opposed to the charge correlation for paired electrons. *Linnett proposes that instead of considering the octet as a group of four localized pairs of electrons, it should be considered as two quartets of opposed spin.* (H_2 would have a pair of shared electrons of opposed spin.) The most important interaction is the repulsion among a quartet of electrons of the same spin. This quartet would be expected to have a disposition around the nucleus which is approximately tetrahedral. The correlation between the two quartets would be slight in the absence of other restrictions, e.g., bonding or some preferred orientation, because of the opposition of spin and charge correlation effects. The result would be spherical symmetry for a free atom or ion with a complete octet, e.g., Na^+, Ar, F^-, and O^{2-}. The most probable positions for the electrons of a double quartet are represented in Figure 2.18*a* by the interpenetrating tetrahedra.

The two tetrahedra become strongly correlated by the localization of electrons in bonding pairs. A single covalent bond, as in HF, localizes one electron pair, but permits delocalization of the other electrons as shown in Figure 2.18*b*. The presence of two electron pairs, as in H_2O, causes strong correlation for all four electron pairs as seen in Figure 2.18*c*. Here the lone pairs are seen to be highly directional. In molecules such as H_2O, NH_3, or CH_4 where the two tetrahedra are strongly correlated, the representation of the octet as a double quartet is essentially the same as that for four pairs of electrons. The bent bond representation is used for multiple bonds. Thus a double bond is represented by two tetrahedra sharing an edge and a triple bond by two tetrahedra sharing a face.

* Linnett, J. W., *J. Am. Chem. Soc.*, **83**, 2643 (1961).

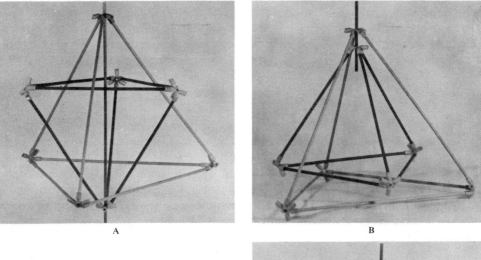

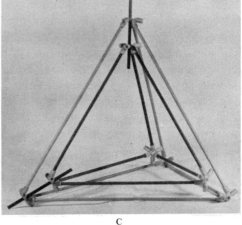

FIGURE 2.18. *Correlation of two quartets.*

Where the two representations (double quartet, D-Q, and four pairs) are equivalent, the usual approach (four pairs) will be used. The D-Q representation usually offers no advantage for diamagnetic molecules, which can be described by a single valence bond structure (no resonance). Nevertheless, there are a number of molecules for which the D-Q representation extends the usefulness of the valence bond picture considerably, reducing the necessity for apparently contrived structures or for the use of many contributing structures.

THE DOUBLE QUARTET REPRESENTATION OF SOME PARAMAGNETIC MOLECULES

The valence bond approach leads one to expect the oxygen molecule to be diamagnetic. One D-Q representation for a diatomic molecule with 12 electrons would group the electrons in two sets of 6 each. The two sets of electrons must coincide in space for this structure (I). If we consider the 12 electrons as being made up of sets of 5 and 7 electrons, the set of 5 electrons of one spin would be expected to be arranged as shown by the ×'s in structure II (two tetrahedra sharing a face). The set of 7 electrons would be expected to be arranged to give two tetrahedra sharing one apex. Structure II provides for interlocking tetrahedra with the apexes of one projecting through the faces

°×O×°O×°   ×°O×°O°×

I   II

of the other. This structure provides for the minimum electron–electron repulsion, both within each group and between groups. It is interesting to note that structure II contains two one electron bonds. However, unlike the extended valence bond representation of O_2 containing two three electron bonds (see p. 76), structure II does not place more than 8 electrons around each oxygen atom.

The usual valence bond representation of NO also violates the octet rule for atoms which should not have more than 8 electrons in the valence shell. The D-Q representation treats the 11 electrons of NO as a set of 5 electrons of one spin and a set of 6 electrons of the opposite spin. Each set is arranged so as to maintain a tetrahedral orientation around each atom, as in the structures for O_2, to give structure III.* This

°N°O° + ×N×O×   °×N×°O×° or |N̈=Ö|

III

representation agrees with the presence of a single unpaired electron. The bond length observed is between that expected for a double and a triple bond. The bond order in III is $2\frac{1}{2}$ because of the presence of a double bond and a one electron bond (see p. 73).

The failure of NO to dimerize (as is common for odd electron molecules) can be explained in several ways. There would be no gain in the number of covalent bonds on forming the dimer, O=N—N=O, and single bonds between very electronegative atoms on which there are unshared electron pairs are surprisingly weak (F_2, H_2O_2, and N_2H_4) while π bonds are very strong (N_2 and O_2). Perhaps this new σ bond, which is formed in the dimer, might be weaker than the bond broken in its formation. The D-Q representation, which is the same as that of the valence bond structure given, points out the strong electron–electron repulsion existing because the two sets of electrons (of opposed spins) are required to adopt the same spatial arrangement in the dimer, whereas this is not true in the monomer.

The cyanogen monomer, CN, has 9 valence electrons. The set of 5 electrons can be arranged as shown for NO. The only reasonable symmetrical arrangement for the group of 4 electrons is that in structure IV where the quartets of the electrons represented by dots are not complete around either atom. A more favorable distribution of formal charges can be achieved in structure V. This structure leads one to expect CN to dimerize to give $(CN)_2$, as it does since an additional bond can be formed in the dimer without any further localization of the electrons.

---

* Note that none of the electrons of the 5 or 6 electron sets are paired, since they have the same spin. A line is used in III to represent two electrons of opposed spin shared between two atoms or on a single atom, even if they are not localized in the same region of space.

$$\times_\circ^\times C \times_\times^\circ \circ N_\circ^\times \quad \text{or} \quad |C \overset{\times}{=} N| \qquad\qquad \times C \times_\circ^\times_\circ N_\circ^\times \quad \text{or} \quad \times C \equiv N|$$

IV   V

ADEQUATE SINGLE STRUCTURE REPRESENTATIONS

The CO_2 molecule (3 atoms and 16 electrons as in OCN^- and CN_2^{2-} also) is usually represented by 3 contributing structures. These same structures and several others can be written using the D-Q approach. However, one of these structures (VI) describes the molecule very well.

$$\times_\circ^\times O \times_\times^\circ \circ C \circ_\circ^\times \times O \circ_\times^\circ \times \quad \text{or} \quad |O \overset{\times}{\underset{\times}{=}} C \overset{\circ}{\underset{\circ}{=}} O|$$

VI

It shows the delocalization of electrons through the molecule, gives a reasonable bond order, gives each atom a formal charge of zero, and minimizes electron–electron repulsion. Single structures can also be written for O_3 (3 atoms and 18 electrons as in SO_2 and NO_2^-) (VII) and benzene (VIII), which make it unnecessary to write several contributing structures.

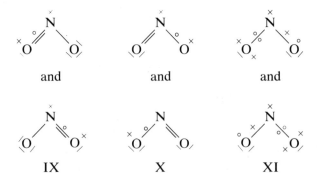

VII   VIII

OTHER APPLICATIONS

The D-Q representations of some paramagnetic molecules (or ions) emphasize the delocalization of electrons, but resonance is still required for an adequate description. NO_2 (3 atoms and 17 electrons) can be represented by three pairs of contributing structures (IX–XI).

and   and   and

IX   X   XI

Of these structures, XI gives the greatest separation of the electrons. A molecule such as ClO_2 or O_3^- (3 atoms and 19 electrons) also requires several contributing structures in the Linnett treatment. (See Problem 14.)

Molecular Orbital Theory (Hund–Mulliken Theory)

The most serious limitation of the Valence Bond Theory is that electrons in molecules are treated as though they are localized and behave almost as they did in the isolated atom. Resonance Theory permits one to get around this difficulty, but with the loss of a simple molecular model provided by the valence bond formulas. Hund* and Mulliken† and others have developed another treatment, which is more satisfactory in cases that cannot be handled adequately by the valence bond approach.

The molecular orbital picture considers that the treatment of the atom can be applied to a single molecule (a diatomic molecule is considered here for simplicity) by taking into account the mutual repulsion among the electrons and the attraction between the electrons and the two nuclei. Each electron in the molecule is described by a wave function ψ. Each ψ is defined by certain quantum numbers, which govern the orbital energy and shape. The Pauli exclusion principle applies to molecular orbitals, so that not more than two electrons (of opposite spin) can occupy the same orbital.

The complete solution of the wave equation for an atom with many electrons is difficult and it is much more difficult for a molecule with 2 or more nuclei. Some simplification is needed. The approach commonly used is the LCAO (Linear Combination of Atomic Orbitals) approximation. In the immediate vicinity of a nucleus the electron is primarily under the influence of that nucleus so that ψ could be approximated by ψ for the atomic orbital (AO). Near nucleus A the molecular orbital (MO) resembles AOψ_A and near nucleus B the MO resembles AO ψ_B, so that

$$\psi = c_A \psi_A + c_B \psi_B$$

or $\hspace{8cm}$ (2.6)

$$\psi = \psi_A + \lambda \psi_B$$

where c_A and c_B are mixing coefficients, replaced by the single coefficient λ. Effective combination of two AO to give a stable MO requires

   (*a*)   that the energies of ψ_A and ψ_B be comparable.

   (*b*)   that the charge clouds of ψ_A and ψ_B of the same sign overlap as much as possible.

   (*c*)   that ψ_A and ψ_B have the same symmetry relative to the molecular axis AB.

Sigma molecular orbitals can be formed by s-s, s-p_x, or p_x-p_x atomic orbitals where the x axis is along the line joining the atomic nuclei as shown in Figure 2.19. A bonding molecular orbital cannot be formed by overlap of an s and one of the p orbitals perpendicular to the molecular axis, because the s orbital must overlap both $+$ and $-$ lobes of the p orbital in this case. *Pi* bonds can be formed by overlap of two p_y or two p_z orbitals perpendicular to the axis. Favorable overlap cannot be obtained between a p_x and a p_y or p_z orbital (see Figure 2.19).

Two orbitals of the same energy, E_A and E_B, can combine to give a sum, $\psi_A + \psi_B$, and a difference, $\psi_A - \psi_B$. The wave function $\psi_A + \psi_B$ increases the probability of finding the electrons between the nuclei (see Figure 2.21), but because the electrons are not re-

---

* Hund, F., *Z. Physik.,* **51**, 788, 793 (1928).

† Mulliken, R. S., *Chem. Rev.,* **9**, 347 (1931); *Rev. Mod. Phys.,* **4**, 1 (1932).

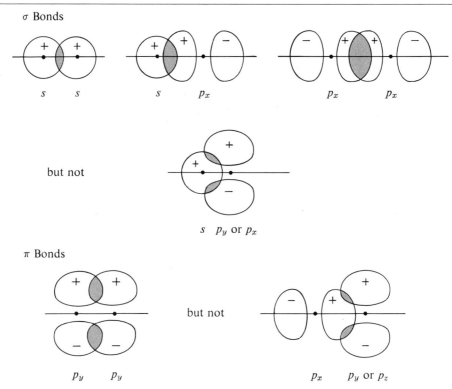

FIGURE 2.19. σ *and* π *bonding.*

stricted to a particular atom, they are delocalized to a greater extent than in the separate atomic orbitals. This molecular orbital is more stable than either of the atomic orbitals. It is called a bonding orbital. The electrons are even more localized in the $\psi_A - \psi_B$ orbital than in the separate atomic orbitals since the probability of finding the electrons in the region between the nuclei is decreased (see Figure 2.21). This molecular orbital is less stable (it has a higher energy) than either of the atomic orbitals (Figure 2.20). It is called an antibonding orbital because it increases the repulsion between the atoms if it is occupied.

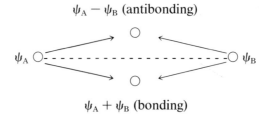

FIGURE 2.20. *Energies of molecular orbitals obtained from the combination of atomic orbitals.*

Electrons in inner closed shells are not affected greatly by neighboring nuclei so they are nonbonding. Orbitals not of the correct symmetry for combination (e.g., s and p_y) are called nonbonding if they are not combined with other orbitals.

The hydrogen molecule results from the combination of two hydrogen atoms, each of which has one electron in the $1s$ orbital. The two atomic orbitals combine as described above to give a bonding molecular orbital and an antibonding molecular orbital. The two electrons can be put into the lower bonding level without using the antibonding level to give a molecule more stable than the separate atoms. The H_2^+ ion is stable in gaseous discharge tubes, but there is only one bonding electron. The single electron bond is about half as strong as an electron pair bond. The H_2^- ion requires that the third electron be put into the antibonding level. A bonding electron pair plus a single electron in the next higher antibonding level is commonly referred to as a three electron bond. The three electron bond also has about half the strength of the electron pair bond because of the antibonding electron. In this case, however, the low nuclear charge does not favor the retention of the antibonding electron. The three electron bond is somewhat more stable in HeH and He_2^+. Each of these species has two bonding electrons and one antibonding electron.

The electrons in molecular orbital energy levels are designated by a new set of quantum numbers given in Table 2.6. The λ quantum number corresponds to the atomic l quantum number. It designates the angular momentum of the electrons in a molecular orbital. The s orbital (2 electrons) can form only σ bonds. The p_x orbital can overlap along the molecular axis to form a σ bond (2 electrons) and the p_y and p_z orbitals can only interact to form 2 π bonds (4 electrons). The d orbitals can overlap along the molecular axis (σ), at 90° to it (δ), or at 45° to it (π). The common molecular orbitals involving s and p orbitals are represented in Figure 2.21.

TABLE 2.6

Atomic orbitals	Values of l (AO)	Values of λ (MO)	Electron groups in molecule
s^2	0	0	σ^2
p^6	1	0, 1	$\sigma^2\pi^4$
d^{10}	2	0, 1, 2	$\sigma^2\pi^4\delta^4$

An approximate energy level diagram for a simple homonuclear diatomic molecule is given in Figure 2.22. The molecular orbital levels are connected to the atomic levels from which they are obtained by dashed lines. The designations for the molecular orbitals are given at the right; the antibonding orbitals are designated by *. The occupancy of the energy levels are shown for the O_2 molecule. The increase in energy among the $x\sigma$, $w\pi$, $v\pi^*$, and $u\sigma^*$ orbitals as shown is the result of the extent of overlap or repulsion. Thus, the overlap is greater for the orbitals directed along the x axis than at 90° to it, resulting in lower energy for the $x\sigma$ orbital than for the $w\pi$ orbitals. The repulsion along the x axis is also greater than at 90° to it. Consequently the $u\sigma^*$ is a higher energy orbital than the $v\pi^*$ orbitals. Some variation in the relative positions is encountered for different molecules and the $w\pi$ level may be below the $x\sigma$ level.† There are two (degenerate) $w\pi$ molecular orbitals resulting from the combination of two p or-

† The ground state for B_2 is paramagnetic with the configuration $KK\ z\sigma^2y\sigma^{*2}w\pi^2$, indicating that the energy of $w\pi$ is lower than that of $x\sigma$. [Herzberg, G., *Molecular Spectra and Molecular Structure. I. Diatomic Molecules* (2nd ed.; Princeton: D. Van Nostrand Co., 1950) pp. 343-344.]

$z\sigma$ — overlap of s orbitals, $\psi_A + \psi_B$

$y\sigma^*$ — antibonding — repulsion of s orbitals, $\psi_A - \psi_B$

$x\sigma$ — overlap of p_x orbitals, $\psi_A + \psi_B$

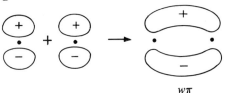

$w\pi$ — overlap of p orbitals perpendicular to the molecular axis
    (p_y and p_z), $\psi_A + \psi_B$

$v\pi^*$ — antibonding — repulsion between p_y or p_z orbitals, $\psi_A - \psi_B$

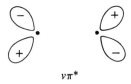

$u\sigma^*$ — antibonding — repulsion between p_z orbitals, $\psi_A - \psi_B$

FIGURE 2.21. *Molecular orbitals: Contours of maximum electron density are sketched.*

bitals of each atom ($p_y + p_y$ and $p_z + p_z$) and there are two $v\pi^*$ molecular orbitals ($p_y - p_y$ and $p_z - p_z$). The orbitals are designated as g (gerade) if they are symmetrical with respect to a center of symmetry or u (ungerade) if there is a change of sign on reflection through a center of symmetry.

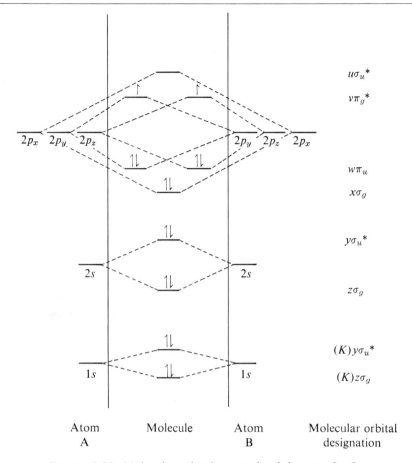

FIGURE 2.22. *Molecular orbital energy level diagram for* O_2.

The configurations for some simple diatomic molecules and ions are obtained by filling the orbitals in the order of increasing energy as shown in Table 2.7.

TABLE 2.7

Molecule or ion	Atomic configuration	Molecular configuration	Bond order	Dissociation energy (eV)
N_2	$1s^2 2s^2 2p^3$	$KK z\sigma^2 y\sigma^{*2} x\sigma^2 w\pi^4$	3	7.373
F_2	$1s^2 2s^2 2p^5$	$KK z\sigma^2 y\sigma^{*2} x\sigma^2 w\pi^4 v\pi^{*4}$	1	1.65
Ne_2	$1s^2 2s^2 2p^6$	$KK z\sigma^2 y\sigma^{*2} x\sigma^2 w\pi^4 v\pi^{*4} u\sigma^{*2}$	0	0
O_2	$1s^2 2s^2 2p^4$	$KK z\sigma^2 y\sigma^{*2} x\sigma^2 w\pi^4 v\pi^{*2}$	2	5.080
O_2^-	—	$KK z\sigma^2 y\sigma^{*2} x\sigma^2 w\pi^4 v\pi^{*3}$	$1\frac{1}{2}$	—

The K shell electrons are designated by the symbol K to indicate that they are essentially unchanged (nonbonding) in molecule formation. The bond order is obtained by subtracting the number of antibonding electrons from the number of bonding electrons and dividing by 2. Ne_2 is seen to be unstable because of a bond order of zero. The observed paramagnetism of O_2 is predicted directly from the molecular orbital description because the two antibonding electrons in the two $v\pi^*$ orbitals will be unpaired in accord with Hund's rule (two degenerate orbitals are available). The molecular orbital energy level diagram is shown for O_2 in Figure 2.22. The valence bond picture, which one would write for O_2 without a knowledge of its paramagnetism, would be $\ddot{O}{=}\ddot{O}$. The fact that the molecule has two unpaired electrons requires that the valence bond structure be changed accordingly. It is commonly written as

$$:\dot{\ddot{O}}{:}\dot{\ddot{O}}{:} \quad \text{or} \quad :\ddot{O}\overset{\cdots}{\cdots}O:$$

The first structure does not agree with the observed bond length, which indicates a bond order of about two, while the second structure with a single bond and two "three electron bonds" agrees with the observed properties of O_2. The "three electron bond" is really a molecular orbital representation since three electrons cannot be accommodated in a single atomic orbital.* The molecular orbital description as given previously has the advantage of predicting the properties of O_2 and it is not a description contrived to agree with the observed properties. The superoxide ion, O_2^-, has a single unpaired electron and a bond order of $1\frac{1}{2}$. The peroxide ion, O_2^{2-}, is diamagnetic with the same configuration as F_2.

Heteroatomic molecules in which both atoms are from the same period can be described similarly. The NO molecule has one unpaired electron ($v\pi^*$) and a bond order of $2\frac{1}{2}$. When the atoms come from different periods, the description can be simplified by designating all electrons below the valence shell and those in the valence shell not interacting with the other atom (or atoms) as nonbonding electrons. For HCl the K and L shells of Cl are nonbonding. The important interaction will be between the s orbital of H and the singly occupied $3p_x$ orbital of the Cl. The $3s$, $3p_y$, and $3p_z$ orbitals are nonbonding because there are no low energy H orbitals to interact with them.

LINEAR MOLECULES

For many polyatomic molecules the LCAO molecular orbital description is not greatly different from the valence bond description except in terminology. The same hybridized orbitals are combined in each case. The MO description is likely to be significantly different from the valence bond description where delocalization is important.

Not all conceivable combinations of atomic orbitals are permissible in forming molecular orbitals in a polyatomic molecule, but only those which give rise to a "correct" wave form. These resemble standing waves in a string for linear molecules. Let us begin with a linear arrangement involving two σ bonds for CO_2, O—C—O. One might assume sp hybridization of the C orbitals. (See Appendix C for the use of sp^3 hybrids in the MO treatment of B_2H_6.) Such "mixing" of the s and p orbitals would result here if the nonbonding σ_p interaction with the σ_s and σ_s^* were also considered and *vice versa*. The σ bonding can be represented by the combinations of orbitals given in Figure 2.23. The wave patterns corresponding to the sign patterns for the MO are shown to the right. Two electron pairs fill the bonding orbitals and the two pairs in the nonbonded orbitals would be localized on the oxygen atoms.

---

* Linnett points out that this is more correctly described as a *one* electron bond. One electron is shared and the two with the same spin are localized on the bonded atoms. The DQ description of O_2 is consistent with its properties (p. 69).

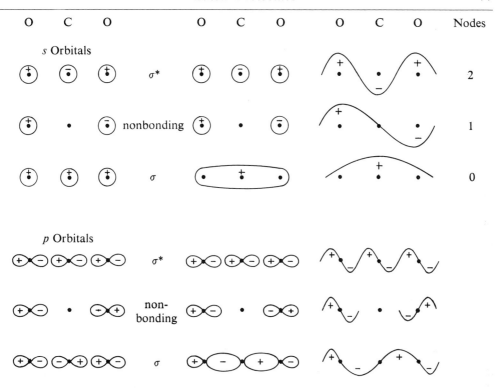

FIGURE 2.23. *Sigma molecular orbitals for* CO_2.

The π bonding can be described by considering one set of p orbitals perpendicular to the molecular axis as shown in Figure 2.24. Note that the number of molecular orbitals is the same as the number of atomic orbitals combined, in this case three. For each bonding MO there must be an antibonding MO. Since only one more combination (of the three) is possible, it must be nonbonding. The most stable (bonding) combination orbital can be written easily with overlapping lobes of the same sign, giving a standing

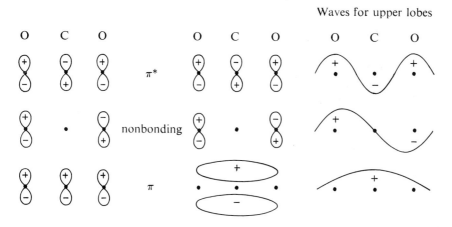

FIGURE 2.24. *Pi molecular orbitals for* CO_2.

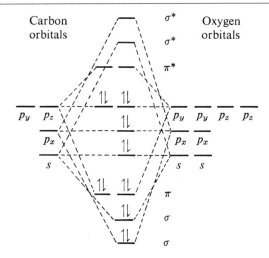

FIGURE 2.25. *Qualitative molecular orbital correlation diagram for* CO_2.

wave with no nodes. The most unstable (antibonding) combination orbital will have adjacent lobes of opposite sign, giving a standing wave with two nodes. The nonbonding orbital will have one node and since the unsymmetrical combinations, e.g., $++-$ for the top lobes, are not permissible,* the coefficient of the carbon orbital must be zero. If the example in Figure 2.24 is taken to apply to the p_z orbitals, the same combinations exist for the p_y orbitals, giving two sets of mutually perpendicular πMO. A qualitative correlation diagram is given in Figure 2.25 for CO_2. All of the bonding and nonbonding orbitals are filled by the 16 electrons in the valence shells. The same terminology is used for linear molecules as for diatomic molecules (σ, π, and δ).

The p_z and p_y orbitals were treated separately, but in a linear molecule these orbitals are combined to give a "doughnut" about the symmetry axis. The resulting πMO, which accommodates 4 electrons, would have cylindrical symmetry as in the acetylene molecule (Figure 2.11).

Ordinary covalent bonds are two-center bonds. Molecular orbitals which extend over three atoms are three-center bonds. Diborane has three-center, two-electron bridge bonds (p. 259) and one of the bonds in B_5H_9 can be described as a five-center bond. Carpenter (see References) has discussed n-center bonds.

The bonding in the newly discovered xenon fluorides, XeF_2 and XeF_4, might be considered to be the same as that usually given for the electronic analogs ICl_2^- and ICl_4^-. The XeF_2 and ICl_2^- are linear and the XeF_4 and ICl_4^- are planar. Bonding in the polyhalide ions has generally been considered to occur through the use of d orbitals of the central atom (p. 47). Rundle† suggested that the use of d orbitals is unlikely because of the especially high promotional energy of the inert gases. He preferred to use 3-center bonds as represented for the p orbitals of CO_2 in Figure 2.23. The XeF_2 could be pictured as having three lone pairs about Xe in sp^2 orbitals with the remaining p orbital of Xe used for the 3-center bond. The bonding MO would contain a single elec-

* The combination of symmetry orbital species must belong to the point group of the molecule. See Appendixes C and D.
† Rundle, R. E., *J. Am. Chem. Soc.*, **85**, 112 (1963).

tron pair spread over the 3 atoms, giving long Xe—F bonds as shown in Figure 2.26. If the dashed line is considered to represent the bonding MO, containing one electron pair, the pair in the nonbonding orbital (not shown) would be localized on the more electronegative F atoms.

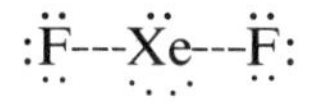

$$:\ddot{F}\text{---}\ddot{X}e\text{---}\ddot{F}:$$

FIGURE 2.26. *Bonding in XeF₂ using a 3-center bond.*

The hydrogen bonded FHF^- ion can be represented by a similar 3-center, 4-electron bond. The 3-center bond can be formed from the hydrogen s orbital and a p or an sp^3 hybrid orbital from each F. The bonding and nonbonding MO would be occupied. The charge is expected to be symmetrically distributed between the F atoms (p. 175) since the electron pair in the nonbonding MO is localized on the F atoms.

The π bonding in butadiene involves a 4-center, 4-electron system. The standing waves can be shown for the combinations of the p orbitals with the signs of the lobes above the plane of molecule as in Figure 2.27. The four π electrons would occupy the two lowest energy orbitals.

In the series of linear molecules of the type C_nO_2, only the compounds with odd values of n (1, 3, and 5) are known.* The first member of the series (CO_2) was discussed. The unknown compound C_2O_2 would have 4-center π orbitals corresponding to those of butadiene. Each of the orbitals shown in Figure 2.27 would represent a degenerate pair for C_2O_2 corresponding to the combinations of the p_y and p_z orbitals (assuming x to be the molecular axis). In the O=C=C=O molecule there are six π electrons. Four electrons could occupy the pair of lowest energy orbitals. The next two electrons should enter the next higher degenerate orbitals singly to give a diradical which might be expected to be unstable.

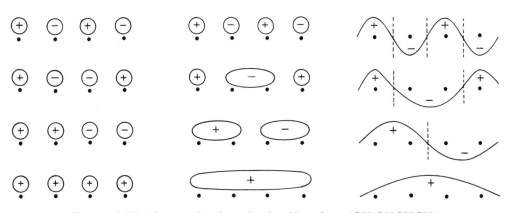

FIGURE 2.27. *The π molecular orbitals of butadiene* ($CH_2CHCHCH_2$).

* The authors are indebted to Professor W. N. Lipscomb of Harvard University for the use of a number of ideas which he presented in a lecture entitled "Some Applications of Molecular Orbitals," which he gave at the University of Pittsburgh as the Phillips Lecturer in 1960. His lecture included discussions of the C_nO_2 compounds and the cyclic C_nH_n compounds.

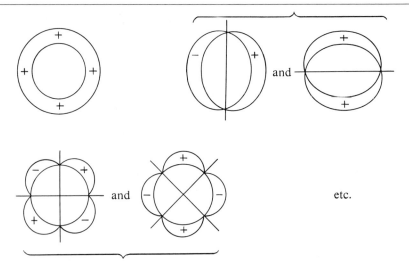

FIGURE 2.28. *Molecular orbital wave patterns for cyclic π systems.*

The C_3O_2 molecule ($O{=}C{=}C{=}C{=}O$) would have five pairs of 5-center MO's analogous to those pictured. The eight electrons could be accommodated in the two pairs of lowest energy orbitals to give a stable spin-paired molecule. A similar situation obtains for other odd values of n (giving even numbers of electron pairs). All molecules with even values of n would exist as diradicals.

PLANAR MOLECULES

For planar molecules the permissible combinations of atomic orbitals can be compared to standing waves on a planar surface. The πMO's for planar ring compounds can be represented as a continuous circle, one wavelength, two wavelengths, etc., around the circle as illustrated in Figure 2.28. The signs refer to those of the lobes of the MO on one side of the plane of the molecule. Beyond the first level the orbitals occur in degenerate pairs except for the highest energy orbital in the case of an even number of atoms in the ring. In this latter case the signs of the orbitals of the individual atoms alternate around the ring. Except for this situation and the lowest energy orbital, the individual atomic orbitals do not necessarily contribute equally to the MO. The wave patterns are the same as those in Figure 2.28 even for molecules with 3-fold or 5-fold axes of symmetry.

The cyclobutadiene molecule, C_4H_4, has four π electrons, but two of these should be unpaired because they occupy doubly degenerate orbitals as shown in Figure 2.29. The resonance contributing structures, which one would draw for cyclobutadiene, do not predict a diradical. It has been suggested that electron correlation effects (neglected in the simple MO treatment) might prevent the degeneracy of the orbitals and permit spin pairing. Attempts to prepare cyclobutadiene have not been successful although derivatives are known. The molecule C_5H_5 would be a free radical and this could be stabilized by the addition of another electron to give $C_5H_5^-$ which is commonly encountered in metal derivatives. The $C_5H_5^-$ ion would have the same configuration as benzene. The

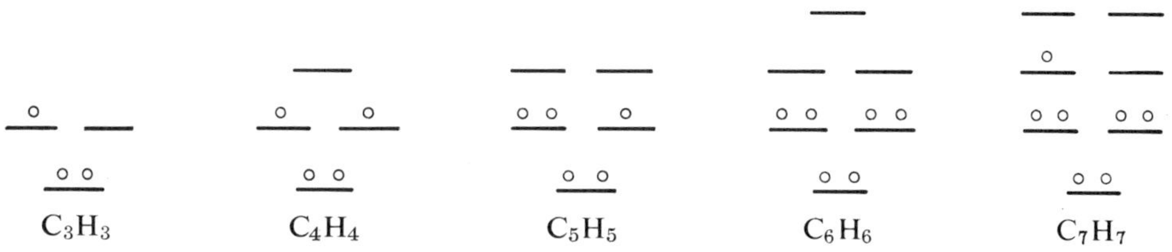

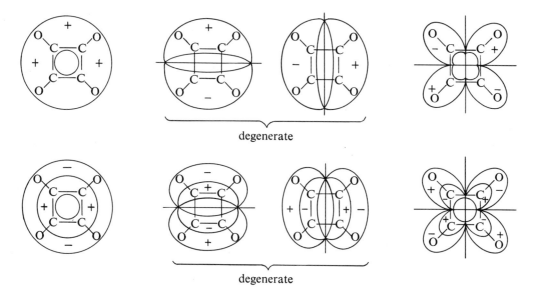

FIGURE 2.29. *Pi molecular orbitals of some planar* C_nH_n *molecules (after Lipscomb).*

molecule C_7H_7 would be a free radical, but this molecule readily loses an electron to give $C_7H_7^+$ which has the benzene configuration. The MO levels make clear the basis for the organic chemist's $(4n + 2)$ rule (the number of π electrons in an aromatic system).

An interesting series of cyclic anions of the type $C_nO_n^{2-}$ has been reported by West and co-workers.* These cyclic π anions have been found to form complexes with several metals. It is interesting to speculate about the extension of the concepts just presented to the compounds $C_3O_3^{2-}$ (unknown), $C_4O_4^{2-}$, $C_5O_5^{2-}$, $C_6O_6^{2-}$, and $C_6O_6^{4-}$. If one treats the CO group as a unit the same description as for the cyclic C_nH_n results. However, since the oxygen atoms, unlike the hydrogen atoms, participate in the π bonding, there should be $2n\pi$ molecular orbitals. Using the concept of the standing wave, one could obtain in each case another set of MO's, analogous to the first, but with different signs for the C and O orbitals to give concentric rings. These orbitals are illustrated in Figure 2.30 for $C_4O_4^{2-}$. The energy level diagrams for the series of anions are shown in Figure 2.31. The number of π electrons is the total number of electrons $(4n + 6n + 2)$ (for the -2 ions) minus the number of electrons used for σ bonds $(2 \times 2n)$

degenerate

degenerate

FIGURE 2.30. *Representations of the* π *molecular orbitals of* $C_4O_4^{2-}$.

* West, R., and H. Y. Niu, *J. Am. Chem. Soc.*, **84**, 1324 (1962); *Chem. Eng. News*, April 23, 1962, p. 40.

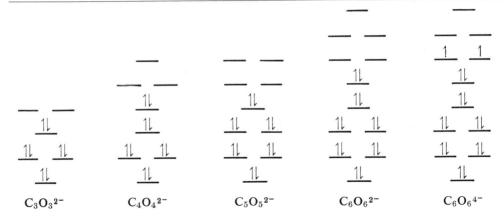

FIGURE 2.31. *Energy level diagrams for the π molecular orbitals of the anions $C_nO_n^{2-}$ and $C_6O_6^{4-}$.*

minus the number of lone pairs on the oxygen atoms $(2 \times 2n)$. The anion $C_6O_6^{4-}$ is represented as a diradical. West and Niu stated that their MO treatment also predicted that this anion would be a diradical, but, in fact, its salts are diamagnetic. They mentioned that possibly electron correlation effects, as suggested for C_4H_4, might remove the degeneracy of the highest level.

The molecular orbital description of the carbonate ion can be approached similarly even though it is not a cyclic system. The ion is planar with 120° bond angles, indicating sp^2 hybridization of the carbon orbitals. The oxygen orbitals used for the formation of σ bonds might be considered to be atomic p orbitals, sp hybrids, or sp^2 hybrids. The sp^2 orbitals should provide favorable overlap and also account for the bonding to be expected in the H_2CO_3 molecule. The assignment of the hybridization of the oxygen orbitals is not critical in obtaining a qualitative MO description of the carbonate ion.

There are three bonding and three antibonding σ orbitals involving the combination of the sp^2 hybrid orbitals of carbon and one orbital of each oxygen. Each oxygen has two nonbonding orbitals (represented as sp^2 orbitals), which can accommodate the lone pairs. The unhybridized carbon p_z orbital can combine with the three unhybridized p_z orbitals of the oxygen atoms to give four molecular orbitals: a bonding π orbital $(+p_C, +p_O+p_O+p_O)$, an antibonding π^* orbital $(+p_C-p_O-p_O-p_O)$, and two more orbitals which are nonbonding. The π bonding orbital consists of two lobes, one above and one below the plane of the ion. Each lobe extends over all four atoms. The antibonding orbital would consist of two concentric waves of opposite sign. Each of the two degenerate nonbonding orbitals would have a second nodal plane as shown in Figure 2.32. The 24 valence shell electrons are accommodated in the bonding and nonbonding orbitals as shown in the qualitative energy level diagram in Figure 2.33.

The application of molecular orbital theory to more complex molecules is aided greatly by the use of symmetry. A treatment of B_2H_6 by E. L. Amma of the University of Pittsburgh using symmetry and character tables is given in Appendix D. The molecular orbitals for some approximately spherical complex molecules can be considered as spherical waves. The treatment of octahedral complexes can be thought of in this way.

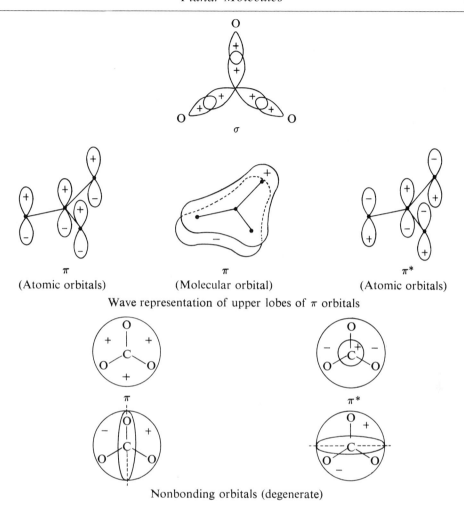

Wave representation of upper lobes of π orbitals

Nonbonding orbitals (degenerate)

FIGURE 2.32. *Representation of the π orbitals of* CO_3^{2-}.

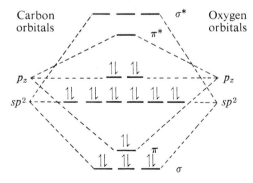

FIGURE 2.33. *Qualitative molecular orbital correlation diagram for* CO_3^{2-}.

Electronegativity

The concept of electronegativity is introduced in modern elementary chemistry courses and we have already used it in the discussion of oxidation states and formal charges in resonance structures. Electronegativity can be defined as the attraction of an atom in a molecule for electrons. A student soon acquires a feeling for the relative electropositive character of metals and electronegative character of nonmetals. Within a periodic family the electronegative character generally decreases with increasing atomic radius although there are some exceptions. A more detailed consideration of the basis for an electronegativity scale is now in order.

Pauling* established a scale of electronegativities based on "excess" bond energies. The energy of the bond, $D(A—B)$, can be considered to be the sum of a nonpolar contribution, $D_{np}(A—B)$, and a polar contribution, $D_p(A—B)$. The nonpolar contribution is the energy expected from the mean of the nonpolar bond energies $D(A—A)$ and $D(B—B)$. The polar contribution, also designated Δ, is a measure of the expected polarity of the bond, the polarity resulting from a displacement of the electronic charge toward one atom. The polarity of the bond is expected to increase with increasing differences in electronegativities (x) of A and B.

$$D(A—B) = D_{np}(A—B) + D_p(A—B) \tag{2.7}$$

$$D_{np}(A—B) = \frac{D_{np}(A—A) + D_{np}(B—B)}{2} \tag{2.8}$$

$$D_p(A—B) = \Delta = D(A—B) - \frac{D_{np}(A—A) + D_{np}(B—B)}{2} \tag{2.9}$$

The Δ values are negative for some of the active metal hydrides, but the negative values can be avoided by using the geometric mean of the bond energies $(\sqrt{D(A—A) \times D(B—B)})$ to give Δ' values. Data are given in Table 2.8 for a few important elements. It can be seen that the sum of the Δ' values for Si—O and O—F does not give the Δ' value for Si—F as might be expected were Δ' the actual difference in electronegativities of the respective elements. The $\sqrt{\Delta'}$ values are more nearly additive so they are used instead. If one compiles an extensive table of $\sqrt{\Delta'}$ values, he has a table of differences in electronegativities. An arbitrary assignment must be made to one element in order to convert the $\sqrt{\Delta'}$ values to electronegativity values for the individual elements.

* Pauling, L., *J. Am. Chem. Soc.*, **54**, 3570 (1932).

TABLE 2.8

Atom A	Atom B	$\sqrt{D(A—A) \times D(B—B)}$	$D(A—B)$ (observed)	Difference Δ'	$\sqrt{\Delta'}$
Si	O	41 kcal	89 kcal	48	6.9
O	F	35	44	9	3.0
Si	F	43	128	85	9.2
H	Cl	79	103	24	4.9
Cl	O	43	49	6	2.5
H	O	59	108	49	7.0

The postulate of the geometric mean is more difficult to apply than the postulate of additivity, since values of Δ can be obtained directly from heats of reaction. Individual bond energies are needed for the calculation of Δ'. Because of the paucity of single bond energies, the Δ values are usually used; for most bonds there is not much difference between the two mean values. Pauling used the relationship:

$$\Delta = 23.06 \ (\chi_A - \chi_B)^2 \tag{2.10}$$

or

$$\chi_A - \chi_B = 0.208 \ \sqrt{\Delta'} \tag{2.11}$$

He was able to assign electronegativity values based on single bond energies to only 14 elements.

Combination of Equations 2.7–2.10 gives the relationship

$$D(A\!-\!B) = \tfrac{1}{2}\{D(A\!-\!A) + D(B\!-\!B)\} + 23.06(\chi_A - \chi_B)^2 \tag{2.12}$$

which implies that the contribution of the new bond to the heat of formation of the substance is equal to Δ or $23.06(\chi_A - \chi_B)^2$. Consequently if the substance consists of diatomic molecules, AB, its heat of formation (ΔH_f) is equal to Δ. In the more general case for the compound AB_n, its heat of formation would be obtained by summing the expression over all of the bonds in the molecule.

$$-\Delta H_f = n \times 23.06(\chi_A - \chi_B)^2 \tag{2.13}$$

or

$$(\chi_A - \chi_B) = 0.208 \ \sqrt{\frac{-\Delta H_f}{n}} \tag{2.14}$$

These relationships assume that the reactants and products have the same number of covalent bonds.

It is necessary to apply a correction for compounds containing N and O because of the extra stability of N_2 and O_2 in their standard states. The triply bonded N_2 molecule is more stable than a hypothetical molecule for which the bond energy is taken as three times the N—N single bond energy (39 kcal/mole). This extra stability is $225 - 3 \times 39 = 108$ kcal/mole N_2 or 54 kcal/N atom. The quantity 54 kcal/N atom serves as a correction for the calculation of the heats of formation of nitrogen compounds. The extra stability of the O_2 molecule is 118.3 kcal/mole $O_2 - 2 \times 33$ kcal/mole O—O = 52 kcal/mole O_2 or 26.0 kcal/O atom. The corrections applied to the Equation 2.13 give

$$-\Delta H_f = n \times 23.06(\chi_A - \chi_B)^2 - 54n_N - 26.0n_O \tag{2.15}$$

where n_N and n_O are the numbers of N and O atoms, respectively, in the compound. In this way Pauling was able to extend the table of electronegativities to include most of the elements.

Allred used the most recent thermochemical data for the calculation of electronegativities of 69 elements. Electronegativities were calculated from single bond energies as described by Pauling where the necessary data were available. Since the M—M bond energies are not known for many metals, the electronegativities were obtained in those cases from the heats of formation of the compounds using Equation 2.15. Electronegativities were calculated for several compounds of M in most cases and averaged to give the values in Table 2.9. Very good agreement was found between electronegativities calculated using Equations 2.10 and 2.15.

TABLE 2.9
The Electronegativity Scale of the Elements[a]

I	II	III	II	II	II	II	II	II	II	I	II	III	IV	III	II	I
H																
2.1																
2.2																
Li	Be											B	C	N	O	F
1.0	1.5											2.0	2.5	3.0	3.5	4.0
1.0	*1.6*											*2.0*	*2.6*	*3.0*	*3.4*	*4.0*
Na	Mg											Al	Si	P	S	Cl
0.9	1.2											1.5	1.8	2.1	2.5	3.0
0.9	*1.3*											*1.6*	*1.9*	*2.2*	*2.6*	*3.2*
K	Ca	Sc	Ti	V	Cr	Mn	Fe	Co	Ni	Cu	Zn	Ga	Ge	As	Se	Br
0.8	1.0	1.3	1.5	1.6	1.6	1.5	1.8	1.8	1.8	1.9	1.6	1.6	1.8	2.0	2.4	2.8
0.8	*1.0*	*1.4*	*1.5*	*1.6*	*1.7*	*1.6*	*1.8*	*1.9*	*1.9*	*1.9*	*1.7*	*1.8*	*2.0*	*2.2*	*2.6*	*3.0*
Rb	Sr	Y	Zr	Nb	Mo	Tc	Ru	Rh	Pd	Ag	Cd	In	Sn	Sb	Te	I
0.8	1.0	1.2	1.4	1.6	1.8	1.9	2.2	2.2	2.2	1.9	1.7	1.7	1.8	1.9	2.1	2.5
0.8	*1.0*	*1.2*	*1.3*		*2.2*		*2.3*	*2.2*	*1.9*	*1.7*	*1.8*	*2.0*	*2.1*			*2.7*
Cs	Ba	La–Lu	Hf	Ta	W	Re	Os	Ir	Pt	Au	Hg	Tl	Pb	Bi	Po	At
0.7	0.9	1.1–1.2	1.3	1.5	1.7	1.9	2.2	2.2	2.2	2.4	1.9	1.8	1.8	1.9	2.0	2.2
0.8	*0.9*	*1.1–1.3*			*2.4*		*2.2*	*2.3*	*2.5*	*2.0*	*2.0*	*2.3*	*2.0*			
		Ac	Th	Pa	U	Np–No	Pu									
		1.1	1.3	1.5	1.7	1.3										
					1.4		*1.3*									

[a] The first value given for each element is Pauling's. The second (italics) is Allred's. The oxidation state for Allred's values is specified at the top of each group. From L. Pauling, *The Nature of the Chemical Bond*, Third Edition, © 1960 by Cornell University, p. 93 and A. L. Allred, *J. Inorg. Nucl. Chem.*, **17**, 215 (1961). Used with permission of Cornell University Press and Pergamon Press, Ltd.

Most of Allred's electronegativity values are essentially the same as those of Pauling. However, in several respects Allred's values are in better agreement with the chemical behavior of the elements than those of Pauling. The alternation in electronegativities of the IIIA and IVA elements is to be expected from the chemistry of these elements and it finds a good explanation in the transition metal contraction and the lanthanide contraction. These effects are discussed more fully elsewhere.*

As the oxidation number or formal charge on an atom increases, the attraction for electrons increases, and hence the electronegativity must increase. The electronegativity values in Table 2.9 are for the oxidation states indicated. Allred's values for a few elements in different oxidation states are given in Table 2.10. The variation is not large, so that a single value to the nearest 0.1 unit is useful for many purposes.

* Sanderson, R. T., *J. Am. Chem. Soc.*, **74**, 4792 (1952); *Chemical Periodicity* (New York: Reinhold Publishing Corporation, 1960); A. L. Allred and E. G. Rochow, *J. Inorg. Nucl. Chem.*, **5**, 264, 269 (1958).

TABLE 2.10
Electronegativities of Some Elements in Different Oxidation States

Mo(II)	2.18	Fe(II)	1.83	Sn(II)	1.80
Mo(III)	2.19	Fe(III)	1.96	Sn(IV)	1.96
Mo(IV)	2.24	Tl(I)	1.62	Pb(II)	1.87
Mo(V)	2.27	Tl(III)	2.04	Pb(IV)	2.33
Mo(VI)	2.35				

Soon after Pauling's scale of electronegativities was proposed, a new basis for an electronegativity scale was proposed by Mulliken.* He sought a more exact relationship between properties of an atom and its electronegativity. He used the *ionization potential* (IP), the energy required for the removal of an electron from a gaseous atom, and the *electron affinity* (EA), the energy involved in the addition of an electron to the gaseous atom. The electronegativity of an element is taken as the average of the ionization potential and the electron affinity (both in electron volts, 1 eV/molecule = 23.06 kcal/mole).

$$\text{Electronegativity} = \frac{\text{IP} + \text{EA}}{2} \tag{2.16}$$

Mulliken's values are about 2.8 times as large as Pauling's values. Mulliken's electronegativity scale has the advantage that different values can be obtained for elements taking into account different ionic states and changes in hybridization. The electronegativity of carbon involved in *sp* hybridization is 0.6 unit higher than for *sp³* hybridization. Extensive sets of orbital electronegativities are now available for atoms in different valence states based on the Mulliken definition of electronegativity.†

Sanderson‡ has proposed a scale of electronegativities or stability ratios based on the compactness of atoms. The stability ratio (SR) of an atom is defined as

$$\text{SR} = \frac{D}{D_i} \tag{2.17}$$

where D is the electron density of the atom and D_i is its "ideal" electron density. D_i is determined for an active element by linear interpolation between the D values for the next higher and lower inert elements.

The stability ratios are very similar to the electronegativity values given by Pauling and Allred. The major difference is that the alternation in stability ratios occurs for periodic groups IIIA, IVA, VA, and VIA. Alternation does not occur in Pauling's table of electronegativities and it occurs only in groups IIIA and IVA in Allred's table. It is interesting that electronegativities have been evaluated from ionization potentials and electron affinities, electron densities, electrostatic calculations, and nuclear magnetic resonance data. The results are as consistent as could be expected with those based on thermochemical data.

* Mulliken, R. S., *J. Chem. Phys.*, **2**, 782 (1934); **3**, 573 (1935).
† Hinze, J., and H. H. Jaffé, *J. Am. Chem. Soc.*, **84**, 540 (1962); J. Hinze, A. Whitehead, and H. H. Jaffé, *ibid.*, **85**, 148 (1963); J. Hinze and H. H. Jaffé, *Can. J. Chem.*, **41**, 1315 (1963); *J. Phys. Chem.*, **67**, 1501 (1963).
‡ Sanderson, R. T., *Chemical Periodicity* (New York: Reinhold Publishing Corporation, 1960) pp. 25–34.

Partial Ionic Character in Covalent Compounds

It has been pointed out that the electron distribution in covalent bonds joining dissimilar atoms is expected to be unsymmetrical with the electron density greater near the more electronegative atom. Polar covalent bonds can be described in terms of shared electrons distributed unsymmetrically or as the resonance hybrid of a covalent structure (electrons shared equally) and an ionic structure (electrons transferred).

Some confusion exists in the use of the terms *polar* and *nonpolar*. The terms have been used synonymously with ionic and covalent, respectively. We shall describe substances as ionic if they give ionic lattices, conducting melts and solutions, etc. We shall reserve the terms polar and nonpolar for different types of covalent bonds. A *nonpolar covalent bond* involves equal or nearly equal sharing of the bonding electrons; the difference in the electronegativities should be less than 0.5. A *polar covalent bond* is one with an appreciable amount of ionic character.

The greater the difference in the electronegativities of bonded atoms, the greater the polarity or ionic character of the bond. This should permit one to determine the ionic character of a bond from an empirical relationship between ionic character and electronegativity differences. The difficulty has been the lack of a method which gives reliable ionic characters for a wide range of compounds in order to establish the empirical relationship. Pauling has used the *dipole moment* as a measure of the polarity and hence of the ionic character of a bond. A diatomic molecule, such as HF, in which the electrons are not shared equally will have a positive and a negative end. Such a molecule acts as a dipole and would tend to become aligned in an electrical field. The force that acts on a dipole to align it in an electrical field is a measure of the dipole moment (p. 434). The greater the ionic character of a bond the greater the charge separation, and the larger the dipole moment.

The electric dipole moment, μ, is the product of the charge at one pole, q, and the distance between poles, d as in

$$\mu = qd \qquad (2.18)$$

Dipole moments are commonly expressed in *Debye units*. One Debye unit is 10^{-10} Å-esu (10^{-18} cm-esu). Two charges equal in magnitude to the charge on an electron (4.8×10^{-10} esu) and separated by a distance of 0.917 Å (the interatomic distance for the HF molecule) would give a dipole moment of 4.4 Debye units. The value of 4.4 Debye units represents the expected dipole moment for HF if it were 100% ionic. The percentage of ionic character is obtained from the ratio of the observed dipole moment to the dipole moment for complete electron transfer. The observed dipole moment for HF is 1.98 Debye units, corresponding to 1.98/4.4 or 45% ionic character. This treatment assumes that the total dipole moment is due to the unsymmetrical distribution of charge in the bond. The unshared electron pairs may contribute significantly to the total moment in some cases.

Pauling derived the relationship

$$\text{Amount of ionic character} = 1 - e^{-(1/4)(\chi_A - \chi_B)^2} \qquad (2.19)$$

from a plot of electronegativity difference *vs.* percentage of ionic character. The percentages of ionic character were originally obtained from the measured dipole moments of HCl, HBr, and HI, which gave 19, 11, and 4% ionic character, respectively, and an estimated 60% ionic character for HF. The relationship has been revised by others to take into account the corrected value for the percentage of ionic character of HF from dipole moment measurements. However, Pauling* indicates that there is justification for the deviation of HF from the equation and that his relationship is probably as useful as the revised ones. These relationships can be used as qualitative guides only. Rough values, which are easy to remember, for electronegativity differences and percentage of ionic character are: 1.0, 20%; 1.5, 40%; 2.0, 60%; and 2.5, 80%.

In the discussion of the use of dipole moments as a guide to ionic character of bonds it must be emphasized that it is the bond moment, not the total dipole moment of a molecule, which must be considered in all cases. The C—F bond is distinctly polar, but the tetrahedral arrangement of the four bonds results in a molecule with zero dipole moment. The hybridization of a bonding orbital also affects the nonbonding orbitals causing the lone pairs of electrons to be distributed asymmetrically. Coulson† reported that the bond moments of the water molecule contribute only about one quarter of the total dipole moment. The lone pair moment provides the major contribution.

Fajans' Rules for the Prediction of Relative Nonpolar Character

Melting points, boiling points, and electrical conductivities serve as rough guides to the degree of nonpolar character of similar compounds. Covalent substances generally have low boiling points, low melting points, and are poor conductors of electricity in the liquid state. Solutions must be considered with caution because of the complete dissociation of some covalent molecules such as HCl in a solvent like water. The melting points, etc., of substances which differ greatly in structure, such as CO_2 and SiO_2, must not be used as an indication of ionic bond character. Carbon dioxide, which consists of discrete molecules with very weak attractive forces (van der Waals' forces) between the molecules, is a gas at ordinary temperatures and pressures. Silicon dioxide is a solid in which the atoms are linked in a three-dimensional network.‡ The larger silicon needs more than 2 oxygen atoms for shielding from other positive silicons and it also forms much less stable double bonds than does carbon. The difference in the melting points of AlF_3 (m.p. 1040°C) and SiF_4 (sublimes at −77°C) does not indicate a great difference in the ionic character of the bonds. The silicon in the SiF_4 molecule is effectively shielded from the fluorides of other SiF_4 molecules and the attractive forces are weak. The aluminum is not shielded on all sides so that there will be very strong interaction between Al and neighboring fluorides to give a three-dimensional network.

Pauling was concerned primarily with the degree of ionic character in covalent bonds. Fajans° discussed the variation in the degree of nonpolar character in ionic compounds in terms of polarization effects. It should be noted that neither treatment needs to be limited to a particular class of compounds. Fajans' rules are concerned with size and charge relationships and with the electronic configuration of the cation. They may be summarized as follows:

---

* Pauling, L., *Nature of the Chemical Bond* (3rd ed., Ithaca: Cornell University Press, 1960) p. 98.
† Coulson, C. A., *Proc. Roy. Soc. (London),* **A207,** 63 (1951).
‡ Such substances are called *giant molecules* or *atomic crystals.* Other examples are diamond, which consists of an interlocking network of tetrahedra, and SiC, which has a similar structure with alternating C and Si atoms.
° Fajans, K., *Naturwissenschaften,* **11,** 165 (1923).

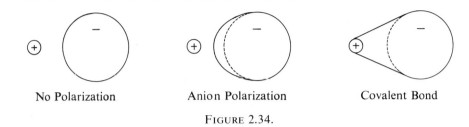

No Polarization   Anion Polarization   Covalent Bond

FIGURE 2.34.

(*1*) Nonpolar character increases with a decrease in cation size or an increase
in cation charge. Very small cations or cations with high charge have high
charge density and consequently tend to distort or polarize the electron cloud
around the anion. The greater the polarization of the anion, the more nonpolar
the bond between the atoms will be (see Figure 2.34). In Table 2.11 one may
compare NaCl and $CaCl_2$, $MgCl_2$ and $AlCl_3$ or $ScCl_3$ for charge effects. $AlCl_3$
and $ScCl_3$, $BeCl_2$, $MgCl_2$, and $CaCl_2$ may be compared for size effects. The
result of large changes in size and charge can be seen by comparing $SnCl_2$ and
$SnCl_4$.

TABLE 2.11

Effect of Cation Charge and Size upon Nonpolar Character of Anhydrous Chlorides

Cation	Radius (Å)	Melting point (°C)	Boiling point (°C)	Equivalent conductance at m.p.
Na^+	0.95	800	1470	133
Ca^{2+}	0.99	772	>1600	51.9
Mg^{2+}	0.65	712	1412	28.8
Al^{3+}	0.50	Subl.	Subl. 178	1.5×10^{-5}
Sc^{3+}	0.81	Subl.	Subl. ~800	15
Be^{2+}	0.31	405	~550	0.066
Mg^{2+}	0.65	712	1412	28.8
Ca^{2+}	0.99	772	>1600	51.9
Sn^{2+}	1.10		606	21.9
Sn^{4+}	0.71		114	0

(*2*) Nonpolar character increases with an increase in anion size or anion charge.
The larger the anion or the higher its negative charge, the more easily it is
polarized by cations because the electrons are held more loosely.

(*3*) Nonpolar character is greater for cations with a noninert gas configuration than
for inert gas type cations. Cations with 8 electron structures cause less distortion, and undergo less distortion themselves, than those with 18 electron structures (pseudo-inert gas structures). If we compare cations of about the same
size (Na^+, Cu^+) the pseudo-inert gas cation has a much higher nuclear charge
and the *d* electrons in the 18 electron outer shell do not effectively shield the
nuclear charge. An anion near a Cu^+ ion, compared to a Na^+ ion, behaves as
though it were under the influence of a greater ionic charge and it is distorted

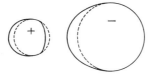

FIGURE 2.35. *Cation and anion polarization.*

to a greater extent. The spherical d electron cloud is also more easily polarized by anions than is an 8 electron shell. This results in some polarization of a pseudo-inert gas cation by the anion. Such polarization of the cation results in even greater "exposure" of the cationic nuclear charge, because the electron cloud of the cation is "squeezed" back toward the far side of the cation. The increased effective nuclear charge further enhances the polarization of the anion (See Figure 2.35 and Table 2.12).

TABLE 2.12

Effect of Electronic Structure of the Cation upon Nonpolar Character of Anhydrous Chlorides

Cation	Cation radius	Melting point (°C)
Na^+	0.95	800
Cu^+	0.96	422
K^+	1.33	776
Ag^+	1.26	455
Ca^{2+}	0.99	772
Cd^{2+}	0.97	568

One of the manifestations of an increase in nonpolar character of inorganic salts is the appearance or enhancement of color. Although oxides of colorless cations are usually white, the corresponding sulfides are likely to be deeply colored if the cation is one which has a tendency to polarize anions. With few exceptions the only white metal sulfides are those of the alkali and alkaline earth metals. In a series of halides of ions such as Ag^+, Hg^{2+}, and Pb^{2+} the fluorides and chlorides are colorless and the bromides are colorless ($PbBr_2$) or faintly colored. The appearance of color in an inorganic salt containing only normally colorless ions is usually an indication of an appreciable amount of nonpolar character or some other unusual structural feature. An appreciable amount of polarization leads to intense absorption bands known as charge transfer bands. The absorption corresponds to the transfer of an electron from one atom to another in the excited state* (see p. 458). Compounds in which the same metal is present in two oxidation states (e.g., Fe_3O_4, Mn_3O_4, Pb_3O_4, $KFe[Fe(CN)_6]$) are usually very intensely colored whenever the metal ions are bridged in such a way as to permit electronic interaction. Defect structures such as encountered in the tungsten bronzes, Na_xWO_3 ($x < 1$), are also likely to produce colored substances. In tungsten bronze some of the Na^+ sites are vacant. A W^{5+} ion is oxidized to W^{6+} for each omission of Na^+ to maintain charge balance.

* Mulliken, R. S., *J. Am. Chem. Soc.*, **74**, 811 (1952).

Weak Interactions in Covalent Substances

The atoms within a covalent molecule are firmly bound together by the covalent bonds, but the molecules are usually very weakly attracted to other molecules by *van der Waals* forces. The weak attraction is responsible for the low boiling points and melting points of molecular substances. The van der Waals forces can be pictured as the attraction which a positive nucleus has for electrons beyond its own radius. There is a finite probability of finding the electrons of an atom at any point out to infinity. The electron density does not fall abruptly to zero at the distance used as the radius of the atom. Since a nucleus must hold its own electrons at distances even greater than the atomic radius, it will attract electrons of other atoms which approach closely. The attractive force increases with the nuclear charge and the number of electrons the two atoms possess.

Instantaneous Dipole–Induced Dipole Interaction

London* presented a quantum mechanical treatment of the attractive forces between neutral molecules in terms of dispersion effects. The attraction between the spherical atoms of the inert gas elements is greater than one might expect for rigidly spherical atoms. Although the distribution of electronic charge is spherically symmetrical on a time average, momentary dipoles can exist. The dipoles which exist for a brief span of time polarize adjacent atoms causing induced dipoles and increasing the force of attraction. These forces are sometimes called *London forces* or *dispersion forces*.† The dispersion forces increase with increasing size and polarizability of the atoms or molecules.

For substances such as nitrogen and hexane, the interaction between molecules is due primarily to the dispersion forces and usually increases with increasing molecular weight. It may be noted, however, that increasing the molecular weight *per se* without a corresponding increase in the dispersion forces has little or no effect on the boiling point. Thus CD_4 has a slightly lower boiling point than CH_4. Similarly, for many fluorocarbons the electrons are held so tightly by the highly electronegative fluorine atoms that the fluorocarbons boil at temperatures close to, or even less than, the corresponding hydrocarbons. A high degree of symmetry or compactness also favors a low boiling point by shielding the electrons deep within the molecule and lessening their interaction with neighboring molecules. Thus branching generally lowers the boiling points of isomeric organic compounds.

Ion–Induced Dipole or Dipole–Induced Dipole Interactions

The attraction between a symmetrical neutral molecule and an ion or a molecule with a permanent dipole moment can be greatly enhanced because of an induced dipole

---

* London, F., *Trans. Faraday Soc.,* **33**, 8 (1937).

† More precisely, the attractive force, which varies inversely with the sixth power of the distance between molecules is termed the London force. A repulsive term, due in the last analysis to the Pauli exclusion principle, drops off more rapidly with distance. The twelfth and ninth powers of intermolecular distance have been used.

in the symmetrical molecule. The inert gases form hydrates that could be the result of dipole–induced dipole interactions, since the more stable hydrates are formed by the larger and more polarizable inert gas atoms. These hydrates are probably more properly regarded as clathrate compounds.

There are few clear-cut cases of ion–induced dipole interactions because in situations where such attractions might occur there are other more important forces present. Thus, the interactions between ions and a nonpolar molecule in an ionic medium would be much less important than the ionic interactions. The greater stability of ammonia complexes of some metals as compared to the aquo (water) complexes can be explained as the result of the greater polarizability of ammonia. Thus the total dipole moment, permanent plus induced, of ammonia in such complexes is greater than that of water in similar complexes (see p. 347).

Ion–Dipole and Dipole–Dipole Interactions

Ions attract the polar water molecules very strongly to form hydrated ions. The hydration energy released provides the energy required for the separation of the ions from the ionic crystal. The effect of the attraction between dipoles can be observed in the boiling points of NF_3 ($-129°C$) and OF_2 ($-144.8°C$) compared to CF_4 ($-161°C$), which has zero dipole moment.

Clathrate Compounds

There are a number of compounds for which the composition appears very strange and unaccountable in terms of the usual bonding forces. The compound $Ni(CN)_2(NH_3)C_6H_6$ was originally thought to be a coordination compound in which there were four groups bonded to the nickel, including the benzene molecule. It has been shown that the compound has a very interesting structure in which half of the nickel ions have a coordination number of six because ammonia molecules are coor-

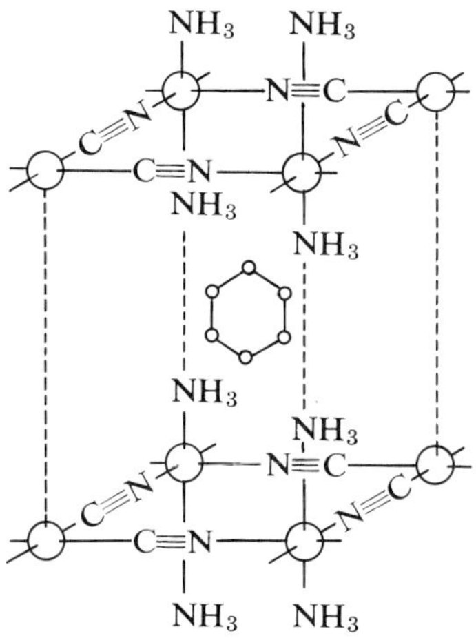

FIGURE 2.36. *The* $Ni(CN)_2(NH_3)C_6H_6$ *clathrate compound (from J. H. Rayner and H. M. Powell,* J. Chem. Soc., *1952, 319).*

dinated above and below the plane. The six-coordinate nickel ions are bonded to the nitrogen of the CN^-. The benzene molecule is trapped in the "holes" in the lattice because it just fits in (Figure 2.36). Compounds in which a molecule is trapped in the "cage" of the crystal lattice are called *clathrate compounds*. Hydroquinone forms a series of compounds, which approach the composition $(C_6H_6O_2)_3 \cdot Y$, where Y can be HCl, HBr, H_2S, SO_2, etc.

Clathrate compounds have become important in the separation of isomeric hydrocarbons. Urea and thiourea have been widely used as the solid phase and recently inorganic complexes have been used for separations such as the recovery of *p*-xylene from either gasolines or from aromatic hydrocarbons of comparable molecular weights by single step operations.*

The tendency for water molecules to form hydrogen bonds produces open structures in the solid state. The holes permit the formation of clathrate compounds of the type $Y \cdot xH_2O$ (where Y may be Xe, Cl_2, Br_2, SO_2, $CHCl_3$, etc., and x varies from about 6 to 17). Several tetraalkyl ammonium salts have been found to give hydrates in which the ions occupy cavities in some type of hydrogen bonded ice structure.† The compounds are of the type $[(n\text{-}C_4H_9)_4N^+]_mX^{m-} \cdot myH_2O$ (where X is F^-, Cl^-, Br^-, CrO_4^{2-}, etc., and y is approximately 32) and $[(i\text{-}C_5H_{11})_4N^+]_mX^{m-} \cdot my'H_2O$ (where X is F^-, Cl^-, CrO_4^{2-}, or WO_4^{2-} and y' is approximately 40). Each type of compound shown represents an isomorphous series. It is unusual to find an isomorphous series of compounds in which the same cation is combined with anions of different charge.

Radii of Atoms in Covalent Compounds

The bond length, the distance between two bonded atoms, in a covalent molecule such as Cl_2 is taken as the sum of the covalent radii of the atoms. Thus the covalent radius of the chlorine atom is one half of the chlorine–chlorine distance (1.998 Å). The covalent radius for nonmetals is often called the atomic radius. The carbon–carbon bond distance in diamond (1.541 Å) is essentially the same as that in ethane (1.543 Å) and other saturated hydrocarbons. Carbon has a single-bond covalent radius of 0.77 Å. The covalent radii of carbon and chlorine can be combined to give 1.76 Å as the expected C—Cl bond distance, the same as that observed for CCl_4.

The single-bond radii of nitrogen and oxygen are not obtained from the bond lengths in N_2 (1.10 Å) and O_2 (1.208 Å) since these molecules contain multiple bonds. Instead the single-bond radii are obtained from the bond lengths in compounds such as hydrazine, H_2NNH_2, and hydrogen peroxide, HOOH. The radius of nitrogen obtained from N_2 (0.55 Å) is the triple-bonded radius. A triple-bonded radius for carbon can be obtained from the carbon–carbon bond length in acetylene (1.21 Å). The triple-bonded radii of carbon and nitrogen can be combined to give the expected bond length (0.55 + 0.60 = 1.15 Å) for a C≡N bond as compared to the observed bond length 1.16 Å for CH_3CN. A double-bonded radius of carbon can be obtained from the carbon–carbon bond length (1.35 Å) in ethylene (see Table 2.2).

* Schaeffer, W. D., W. S. Dorsey, D. A. Skinner, and C. G. Christian, *J. Am. Chem. Soc.,* **79**, 5870 (1957) and F. V. Williams, *ibid.,* **79**, 5876 (1957).
† McMullan, R., and G. A. Jeffrey, *J. Chem. Phys.,* **31**, 1231 (1959).

Covalent radii usually can be assumed to be additive to give bond lengths provided that the bond for which the length is calculated is similar to the bonds used for the evaluation of the covalent radii with respect to bond order, bond hybridization, and bond strength. Schomaker and Stevenson* have attributed the discrepancy between the calculated and observed bond lengths to variations in the bond polarity for most cases where multiple bonding is not believed to be important. Thus the bond length, r_{AB}, can be calculated from the nonpolar radii of A and B and the difference in electronegativities of A and B:

$$r_{AB} = r_A + r_B - 0.09 \, |\chi_A - \chi_B| \tag{2.20}$$

Huggins compiled an extensive table of single-bond lengths and computed "constant energy" radii (r'), which could be combined to give bond lengths allowing for variations in bond energy, using the equation

$$r_{AB} = r_A' + r_B' - 1/2 \log D_{AB} \tag{2.21}$$

where the radii are in Å and D_{AB} is in kcal/mole. The apparent radius of hydrogen shows a particularly large variation in its compounds. Huggins was able to assign each nonmetal a characteristic constant-energy radius, but slightly different radii were assigned to hydrogen in H_2, and in compounds with elements of the second, third, fourth, and fifth periods. Huggins' nonpolar radii and constant-energy radii are given in Table 2.13. Some important bond lengths and bond energies are given in Table 2.14.

* Schomaker, V., and D. P. Stevenson, *J. Am. Chem. Soc.*, **63**, 37 (1941).

TABLE 2.13

Nonpolar (r) and Constant-Energy (r') Atomic Radii (Å)[a]

	r	r'
H (H_2)	0.38	0.88
H (with 2nd period elements)	0.36	0.86
H (with 3rd period elements)	0.34	0.84
H (with 4th period elements)	0.33	0.83
H (with 5th period elements)	0.32	0.82

r		r'	r		r'	r		r'	r		r'
	C			N			O			F	
0.77		1.22	0.75		1.12	0.74		1.12	0.72		1.11
	Si			P			S			Cl	
1.15		1.57	1.11		1.53	1.04		1.46	1.00		1.44
	Ge			As			Se			Br	
1.21		1.61	1.24		1.63	1.17		1.58	1.14		1.56
	Sn			Sb			Te			I	
1.42		1.80	1.45		1.83	1.41		1.79	1.35		1.73

[a] Huggins, M. L., *J. Am. Chem. Soc.*, **75**, 4126 (1953).

TABLE 2.14[a]

Bond	Molecule or crystal	Bond energy (kcal/mole)	Bond distance (Å)	Bond	Molecule or crystal	Bond energy (kcal/mole)	Bond distance (Å)
H—H	H_2	104.2	0.751	Si—Si	Si	53	2.352
H—C	CH_4	99.3	1.093	Si—S	SiS_2	(70)	2.14
H—N	NH_3	93.4	1.014	Si—Cl	$SiCl_4$	91	2.02
H—O	H_2O	110.6	0.957	Si—Br	$SiBr_4$	74	2.15
H—F	HF	135	0.926	Si—I	SiI_4	56	2.43
H—Si	SiH_4	76	1.480				
H—P	PH_3	77	1.42	P—P	P_4(black)	48	2.21
H—S	H_2S	83	1.334	P—Cl	PCl_3	78	2.043
H—Cl	HCl	103.1	1.284	P—Br	PBr_3	63	2.20
H—Ge	GeH_4	(74)	1.53	P—I	PI_3	44	2.47
H—As	AsH_3	(59)	1.523				
H—Se	H_2Se	66	1.47	S—S	S_8	54	2.08
H—Br	HBr	87.4	1.423	S—Cl	S_2Cl_2	61	1.99
H—Sn	CH_3SnH_3	(71)	1.700	S—Br	S_2Br_2	(52)	(2.16)
H—Sb	SbH_3	(70)	1.71				
H—Te	H_2Te	57.4	(1.73)	Cl—Cl	Cl_2	57.87	2.002
H—I	HI	71.4	1.615	Cl—Ge	$GeCl_4$	81	2.08
				Cl—As	$AsCl_3$	70	2.16
C—C	Diamond	85	1.541	Cl—Br	BrCl	52.2	2.138
	C_2H_6	83	1.543	Cl—Sn	$SnCl_4$	76	2.30
C—N	CH_3NH_2	68.1	1.47	Cl—Sb	$SbCl_3$	74	2.37
C—O	$(CH_3)_2O$	74	1.42	Cl—I	ICl	50.3	2.32
C—F	CF_4	116	1.36				
C—Si	SiC	76	1.89	Ge—Ge	Ge	45	2.450
	$Si(CH_3)_4$	72	1.93	Ge—Br	$GeBr_4$	66	2.32
C—P	$P(CH_3)_3$	63	1.87	Ge—I	GeI_4	51	2.48
C—S	$(CH_3)_2S$	65	1.82				
C—Cl	CCl_4	78.2	1.761	As—As	Normal As_4	35	2.44
	$CHCl_3$	70	1.77	As—Br	$AsBr_3$	58	2.33
	CH_2Cl_2	70	1.77	As—I	AsI_3	43	2.54
	CH_3Cl	78.2	1.781				
C—Br	CBr_4	58	1.942	Se—Se	Se_6	41	2.32
N—N	N_2H_4	39	1.47	Br—Br	Br_2	46.1	2.286
N—O	NH_2OH	48	1.46	Br—Sb	$SbBr_3$	62	2.52
N—F	NF_3	65	1.37				
N—Cl	NCl_3	46	1.73				
O—O	H_2O_2	35	1.48	Sn—Sn	Sn	36	2.80
O—F	OF_2	45.3	1.41	Sn—I	SnI_4	(47)	2.64
O—Si	SiO_2	108	1.61				
O—P	P_4O_6	(80)	1.66	Sb—Sb	Sb	35	2.87

TABLE 2.14[a] — *Continued*

Bond	Molecule or crystal	Bond energy (kcal/mole)	Bond distance (Å)	Bond	Molecule or crystal	Bond energy (kcal/mole)	Bond distance (Å)
O—Cl	Cl_2O	49	1.68	Sb—I	SbI_3	44	2.67
F—F	F_2	36.6	1.435	Te—Te	Te	(34)	2.86
F—Si	SiF_4	135	1.54				
F—P	PF_3	117	1.52	I—I	I_2	36.1	2.666
F—Cl	ClF	60.6	1.628				
F—As	AsF_3	111	1.71				
F—Br	BrF	60.8	1.76				
F—Sb	SbF_3	108	2.03				
F—S	SF_6	68	1.58				

[a] Most values were taken from Cottrell, T. L., *The Strengths of Chemical Bonds* (2nd ed., London: Butterworths Scientific Publications, 1958). Values in parentheses are approximate.

Van der Waals Radii

The distance between atoms of neighboring molecules is determined by a balance between the van der Waals attraction and the repulsion caused by the interpenetration of the electron clouds. The shortest distance between chlorine atoms of adjacent molecules in CCl_4 or Cl_2 in the solid is essentially the same, about 3.6 Å. One-half of this distance is called the van der Waals radius of chlorine, 1.8 Å. The van der Waals radius is a nonbonded radius for an atom with a closed configuration. Hence it is not so surprising that the van der Waals radius of chlorine is essentially the same as the ionic radius. The ionic radii of nonmetals generally can be taken as reasonable values to be used as van der Waals radii. For a table of ionic radii see p. 109.

REFERENCES

Simple Interpretation of Covalent Bonding

Pauling, L., *The Nature of the Chemical Bond* (3rd ed.; Ithaca: Cornell University Press, 1960) Chapters 1 and 2.

Palmer, W. G., *Valency* (2nd ed.; London: Cambridge University Press, 1959) Chapters 1 and 2.

Wells, A. F., *Structural Inorganic Chemistry* (3rd ed.; Oxford: Oxford University Press, 1962) Chapters 1 and 2.

Gillespie, R. J., and R. S. Nyholm, "Inorganic Stereochemistry," *Quart. Rev.,* **11**, 339 (1957).

Gillespie, R. J., "The Valence-shell Electron-pair Repulsion Theory of Directed Valency," *J. Chem. Educ.,* **40**, 295 (1963).

Resonance

Pauling, L., *The Nature of the Chemical Bond* (3rd ed.; Ithaca: Cornell University Press, 1960) Chapters 1, 6, 8, and 14.

Theoretical Treatment of the Covalent Bond

Coulson, C. A., *Valence* (2nd ed.; Oxford: Oxford University Press, 1961) Chapters 1, 4–8.

Cartmell, E., and G. W. A. Fowles, *Valency and Molecular Structure* (2nd ed.; London: Butterworths Scientific Publications, 1961) Part II.

Liehr, A. D., "Molecular Orbital, Valence Bond and Ligand Field," *J. Chem. Educ., 39,* 135 (1962).

Carpenter, G. B., "The Use of *n*-Center Bonds," *J. Chem. Educ., 40,* 385 (1963).

Linnett, J. W., *The Electronic Structure of Molecules* (London: Methuen and Co., Ltd., 1964).

Gray, H. B., *Electrons and Chemical Bonding* (New York: W. A. Benjamin, Inc., 1964).

Ballhausen, C. J., and H. B. Gray, *Molecular Orbital Theory* (New York: W. A. Benjamin, Inc., 1964).

Electronegativity

Pauling, L., *The Nature of the Chemical Bond* (3rd ed.; Ithaca: Cornell University Press, 1960) Chapter 3.

Allred, A. L., "Electronegativity Values from Thermochemical Data," *J. Inorg. Nucl. Chem., 17,* 215 (1961).

Allred, A. L., and E. G. Rochow, "A Scale of Electronegativity Based on Electrostatics," *J. Inorg. Nucl. Chem., 5,* 264 (1958).

Pritchard, H. O., and H. A. Skinner, "The Concept of Electronegativity," *Chem. Rev., 55,* 745 (1955).

Sanderson, R. T., *Chemical Periodicity* (New York: Reinhold Publishing Corp., 1960) Chapter 2.

Sanderson, R. T., "Electronegativities in Inorganic Chemistry," *J. Chem. Educ., 29,* 539 (1952).

Weak Interactions in Covalent Substances

Rice, F. O., and E. Teller, *The Structure of Matter* (New York: John Wiley and Sons, Inc., 1949) Chapters 6 and 8.

Rice, O. K., *Electronic Structure and Chemical Binding* (New York: McGraw-Hill Book Co., Inc., 1940) Chapter 17.

Hagan, Sister M. M., *Clathrate Inclusion Compounds* (New York: Reinhold Publishing Corp., 1962).

Mandelcorn, L., "Clathrates," *Chem. Rev., 59,* 827 (1959).

Radii

Pauling, L., *The Nature of the Chemical Bond* (3rd ed.; Ithaca: Cornell University Press, 1960) Chapter 7.

Wells, A. F., *Structural Inorganic Chemistry* (3rd ed.; Oxford: Oxford University Press, 1962) Chapter 2.

Sutton, L. E., ed., *Tables of Interatomic Distances and Configuration in Molecules and Ions,* Special Publication No. 11 (London: The Chemical Society, 1958).

Problems

1.   Indicate the electronic configurations expected for the possible covalent states of Sn, At, and Ra. Assuming only σ bonding predict the geometry associated with each state.

2.   What ionic states are expected for the elements given in problem 1? What ionic states are expected for Ti, Pr, and Se?

3. Give the oxidation number, covalency, formal charge, and hybridization of the central atom in each of the following: NO_3^-, BF_4^-, $S_2O_3^{2-}$, ICl_2^+, ClO_3^-.

4. Select the reasonable electron dot structures for each of the following compounds. Indicate what is wrong with each incorrect or unlikely structure.

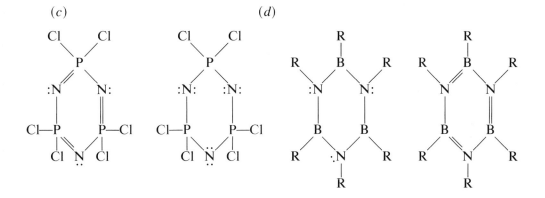

5. Give the expected hybridization of P, O, and Sb in Cl_3P—O—$SbCl_5$. The P—O—Sb bond angle is 165°.

6. Predict both the gross geometry (from the σ orbital hybridization) and the fine geometry (from bond–electron pair repulsion, etc.) of the following species: F_2SeO, $SnCl_2$, I_3^-, and $IO_2F_2^-$.

7. Which of the following in each pair will have the larger bond angle? Why? CH_4, NH_3; OF_2, OCl_2; NH_3, NF_3; PH_3, NH_3.

8. Trimethylphosphine has been reported by Holmes to react with $SbCl_3$ and $SbCl_5$ to form, respectively, $(Me_3P)(SbCl_3)$ or $(Me_3P)_2(SbCl_3)$ and $(Me_3P)(SbCl_5)$ and $(Me_3P)_2(SbCl_5)$. Suggest valence bond structures for each of these and indicate approximate bond anges around the Sb atom.

9. Indicate by a sketch the following hybrid orbitals (indicate the sign of the amplitude of the wave function on your sketch).
   (a) an *sd* hybrid   (b) a *pd* hybrid

10. The Ru—O—Ru bond angle in $(Cl_5Ru)_2O$ is 180°. What is the state of hybridization of the oxygen? Explain the reasons for the large bond angle. [Reference: Gillespie, *J. Am. Chem. Soc.*, **82**, 5978 (1960).]

11.   The bromine atom in BrF_5 is below the plane of the base of the tetragonal pyramid. Explain.

12.   Compare the expected bond orders of ClO_4^- and IO_4^-, and of IO_3^-, BrO_3^-, and ClO_3^-. [Reference, Nightingale, *J. Phys. Chem.*, **64**, 162 (1960).]

13.   The C—C bond distance in methyl acetylene is unusually short (1.46 Å) for a single bond. Show how this short bond can be rationalized in more than one way.

14.   Draw a reasonable structure for ClO_2 on the basis of the Double Quartet hypothesis. Is this representation consistent with the properties of ClO_2 (e.g., magnetic behavior, shape, and failure to dimerize)? Compare the D-Q representation of ClO_2 and ClO_2^- with the usual valence bond representations.

15.   Give the most probable arrangement for two electrons in a completed $1s$ shell, considering correlation effects. Compare the Linnett treatment of He_2^+ with the molecular orbital treatment.

16.   Show the Linnett electron dot formulas for the hypothetical molecules NeO, NeF, and NeN, and compare the bond orders with those predicted from a molecular orbital viewpoint. Do you feel that the bond orders predicted would show the same trend as stabilities? Why? Under what circumstances might you expect to find the above molecules?

17.   (*a*) Draw a molecular orbital energy diagram for the molecular orbitals that would arise in a diatomic molecule as a result of the combination of unhybridized d orbitals. Label the atomic orbitals being combined and the resulting molecular orbitals. Let the z axis lie along the bond. (*b*) Sketch the shape of these orbitals.

18.   Write the molecular orbital configurations and give the bond orders of NO^+, NO, and NO^-. Which of these species should be paramagnetic?

19.   (*a*) Draw the important resonance structures for NO_2. Show formal charges and indicate the relative importance of the various structures. (*b*) Give a molecular orbital description for NO_2. Sketch the molecular orbitals and give the population of the energy levels.

20.   Describe the expected structure of XeO_3. What approach to the description of the bonding do you think best?

21.   Calculate the dipole moment to be expected for the ionic structure H^+Cl^- using the same internuclear separation as for the HCl molecule. Calculate the dipole moment for HCl assuming 19% ionic character.

22.   Calculate the heats of formation (from electronegativities) for: H_2S, H_2O, SCl_2, NF_3, and NCl_3. Calculate the heats of formation of these compounds from the bond energies for comparison.

23.   Calculate the electronegativity differences from the bond energies for H—Cl, H—S, and S—Cl. Using Allred's electronegativity of H, compare the electronegativity values which can be obtained for S and Cl with those tabulated.

24.   Calculate the bond lengths from nonpolar radii and electronegativities and from constant energy radii and bond energies for: C—N in CH_3NH_2, S—Cl in S_2Cl_2, O—F in OF_2, Si—F in SiF_4, and Si—I in SiI_4.

25.   Allred and Rochow [*J. Inorg. Nucl. Chem.*, **5**, 264–8, 269–88 (1958)] have proposed the following empirical equation for the calculation of electronegativities:

$$\chi = 0.359\, \frac{Z_{eff}}{r^2} + 0.744$$

where Z_{eff} is calculated using Slater's rules (p. 32) and r is the covalent radius. Using the nonpolar radii given in Table 2.14, calculate the electronegativities of As and Br. Little and Jones used this equation to calculate a complete set of electronegativities [*J. Chem. Educ.*, **37**, 231 (1960)]. What advantages and disadvantages does this method of obtaining electronegativities have?

CHAPTER III

Ionic Substances

Crystals of simple inorganic salts consist of positive and negative ions packed in such a way as to allow a minimum distance between cation and anion, and to provide maximum shielding of ions of like charge from one another. This provides for the maximum attractive forces and the minimum repulsive forces. The number of ions of opposite charge around an ion in the crystal is the *coordination number* (C.N.) of that ion. For spherical ions there are no directed bonding forces. The arrangement in the crystal is determined by the relative sizes of the ions and coulombic forces between ions.

Common Structures of Ionic Crystals

A large number of simple ionic substances crystallize in one of six common structures shown in Figure 3.1. Most of the alkali halides, alkaline earth oxides, sulfides, etc., and some other 1:1 compounds crystallize in the face-centered cubic NaCl structure in which the cation and anion both have coordination numbers of six. Some of the larger alkali metal ions give the cubic CsCl structure where the cation and anion both have coordination numbers of eight. The structures encountered for some common ionic compounds are summarized in Table 3.1. The compounds CsCN, TlCN, and CsSH also have the NaCl structure. Although these anions are not spherical, they attain spherical symmetry by free rotation. Some other salts, which contain complex anions, give structures closely related to the NaCl structure. Thus the CaC_2 (calcium carbide) structure is face-centered with the linear C_2^{2-} ions all lined up in the same direction to extend the unit cell along one axis. The calcite ($CaCO_3$) structure occurs for several carbonates of divalent cations, for some nitrates such as $LiNO_3$ and $NaNO_3$, and for some borates such as $ScBO_3$, YBO_3, and $InBO_3$. The calcite structure is similar to the NaCl structure with the lattice expanded as required by the replacement of the Cl^- by the plane triangular carbonate ions.

Some of the substances of the MX type, which are appreciably covalent, give the zinc blende (the diamond structure differs only in that all sites are occupied by carbon atoms) or the wurtzite structure. These structures are found for the copper(I) halides, and the oxides, sulfides, etc., of Be and the Group IIB metals. In each of these structures the cations and anions are tetrahedrally surrounded by four ions of opposite charge. The S^{2-} ions are in a cubic close-packed arrangement in the zinc blende structure and in a hexagonal close-packed arrangement in wurtzite. The cubic and hexagonal

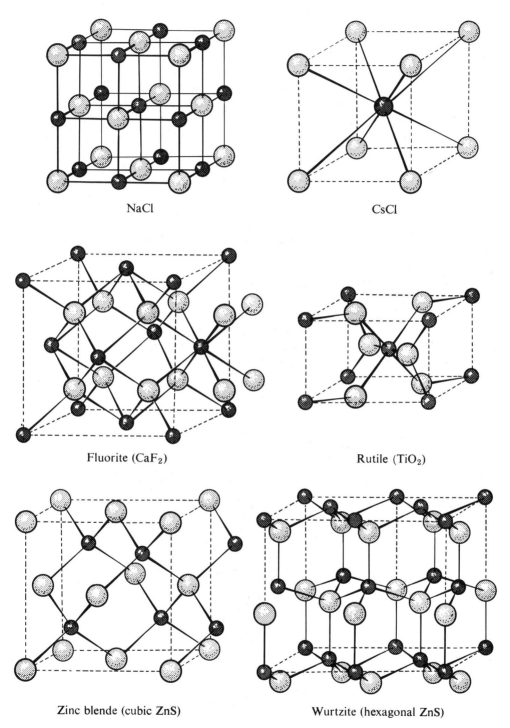

NaCl

CsCl

Fluorite (CaF$_2$)

Rutile (TiO$_2$)

Zinc blende (cubic ZnS)

Wurtzite (hexagonal ZnS)

FIGURE 3.1. *Some common ionic structures.*

TABLE 3.1
Structures[a] of Some Ionic Compounds of the Type MX

Ions	Halides				Ions	Oxygen Family			
	F	Cl	Br	I		O	S	Se	Te
Li	NaCl	NaCl	NaCl	NaCl	Be	W	Z	Z	Z
Na	NaCl	NaCl	NaCl	NaCl	Mg	NaCl	NaCl	NaCl	Z
K	NaCl	NaCl	NaCl	NaCl	Ca	NaCl	NaCl	NaCl	NaCl
Rb	NaCl	NaCl	NaCl	NaCl	Sr	NaCl	NaCl	NaCl	NaCl
Cs	NaCl	CsCl	CsCl	CsCl	Ba	NaCl	NaCl	NaCl	NaCl
Ag	NaCl	NaCl	NaCl	Z	Zn	WZ	WZ	Z	WZ
					Cd	NaCl	WZ	WZ	Z
					Hg	other	Z	Z	Z

[a] NaCl and CsCl structures are represented by the formulas. Zinc blende and wurtzite are represented by Z and W, respectively.

close-packed arrangements, which are commonly encountered for metals, are pictured in Figure 9.2.

The tetrahedral and octahedral holes are shown in Figure 3.2 for two layers of close-packed spheres. These sites are identical for cubic and hexagonal close-packed structures since any two adjacent layers are arranged in the same way and the structures differ only in the arrangement of a third layer relative to these two. In wurtzite and zinc blende half of the tetrahedral sites are occupied by cations (Zn^{2+}). The NaCl structure

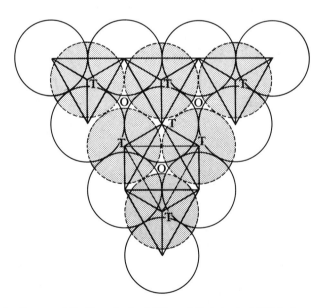

FIGURE 3.2. *Tetrahedral (T) and Octahedral (O) holes in a close-packed arrangement of spheres.*

can be regarded as a cubic close-packed arrangement of Cl^- with Na^+ ions in all of the octahedral sites.

Compounds of the type MX_2 commonly give the fluorite (CaF_2) or rutile (TiO_2) structures. In CaF_2 each Ca^{2+} is surrounded by eight F^- at the corners of a cube, and each F^- by four Ca^{2+} at the corners of a tetrahedron. The fluorite structure can be regarded as a close-packed arrangement of Ca^{2+} ions with F^- ions in all of the tetrahedral holes. The coordination numbers of Ti^{4+} and O^{2-} are six and three, respectively, in rutile. These structures are commonly encountered for fluorides and oxides, but not for the more covalent chlorides, bromides, iodides, sulfides, selenides, and tellurides. The antifluorite structure in which the positions of the cations and anions are reversed, as compared with fluorite, is encountered for alkali metal oxides, etc., of the type M_2X. Some compounds with these structures are shown in Table 3.2.

TABLE 3.2

Structures of Some Compounds of the Type MX_2 and M_2X

Fluorite (CaF_2)			Rutile (TiO_2)			Antifluorite			
CaF_2	CdF_2	ZrO_2	MgF_2	NiF_2	TiO_2	Li_2O	Li_2S	Li_2Se	Li_2Te
SrF_2	HgF_2	ThO_2	MnF_2	ZnF_2	MnO_2	Na_2O	Na_2S	Na_2Se	Na_2Te
BaF_2	PbF_2	CeO_2	FeF_2	PdF_2	MoO_2	K_2O	K_2S	K_2Se	K_2Te
	$SrCl_2$	UO_2	CoF_2		GeO_2		Rb_2S		
	$BaCl_2$				SnO_2				

The ionic structures in Tables 3.1 and 3.2 are determined largely by the charges on the ions and the relative sizes of the ions (see radius ratio, p. 110). The situation is altered when polarization effects become important or because of crystal field distortions (p. 353). Although ZnF_2 and MnF_2 have the rutile structure, the CuF_2 structure has lower symmetry because of the distorted (elongated) octahedral arrangement of the six fluorides around each Cu^{2+} ion.

Some Characteristic Properties of Ionic Substances

The ions of a salt are held fairly rigidly in place by strong coulombic forces. Because the ions are not free to move about, ionic crystals are usually very poor conductors of electricity. If the crystal lattice is broken down by melting the substance or by dissolving it in a polar solvent, the ions become quite free to migrate in an electrical field and hence carry current. The current flows with mass transfer as the ions travel through the melt or solution. The charge transfer processes at the electrodes require oxidation–reduction reactions involving the electrodes and/or the ions in a fused salt. In solution the electrode reactions also might involve oxidation and/or reduction of the solvent. The conductivity of the fused salt or of a solution of the salt is determined by the mobility of the ions, which is dependent on the size and charge of the ions. The mobility of ions of high charge is decreased by association with ions of opposite charge and with solvent molecules.

The strong electrostatic forces between ions cause ionic crystals to be relatively hard and to have high melting points and boiling points. The influence of ionic charge and interionic distance on hardness can be seen from the following comparisons.

(*1*)   Hardness increases with decreasing interionic distance for crystals with similar structures and the same ionic charge (Table 3.3).

TABLE 3.3

Variation of Hardness (Moh's Scale) with M–X (Cation–Anion) Distance for Some Crystals with the NaCl Structure[a]

Anion	Metal	Mg	Ca	Sr	Ba
O^{2-}	M–X distance (Å)	2.10	2.40	2.57	2.77
	Hardness	6.5	4.5	3.5	3.3
S^{2-}	M–X distance	2.59	2.84	3.00	3.18
	Hardness	4.5	4.0	3.3	3
Se^{2-}	M–X distance	2.74	2.96	3.12	3.31
	Hardness	3.5	3.2	2.9	2.7

[a] Data from Stilwell, C. W., *Crystal Chemistry* (New York: McGraw-Hill Book Company, 1938) pp. 28, 29 and 227. Used by permission.

(*2*)   Hardness increases with increasing ionic charge for crystals with similar structures and similar interionic distances (Table 3.4).

TABLE 3.4

Variation of Hardness with Ionic Charge for Some Crystals with the NaCl Structure[a]

	LiF	MgO	NaF	CaO	LiCl	SrO
M–X distance (Å)	2.02	2.10	2.31	2.40	2.57	2.57
Hardness	3.3	6.5	3.2	4.5	3	3.5
	LiCl	MgS	NaCl	CaS	LiBr	MgSe
M–X distance	2.57	2.59	2.81	2.84	2.75	2.73
Hardness	3	4.5–5	2.5	4.0	2.5	3.5
	CuBr[b]	ZnSe[b]	GaAs[b]	GeGe[b]		
M–X distance	2.46	2.45	2.44	2.43		
Hardness	2.4	3.4	4.2	6		

[a] See footnote *a* of Table 3.3.
[b] Zinc blende structure.

(*3*)   Hardness is greater for substances which contain inert gas type cations than for those which contain cations with pseudo-inert gas type or similar configurations. Other factors such as interionic distance, charge type, and crystal structure are assumed to be similar (Table 3.5).

TABLE 3.5
Variation of Hardness for Some Crystals Which Differ in Electronic Configurations of Cations[a]

	CaSe	PbSe	CaTe	PbTe
M–X distance (Å)	2.96	2.97	3.17	3.22
Hardness	3.2	2.8	2.9	2.3
	CaF_2	CdF_2	SrF_2	PbF_2
M–X distance	2.36	2.34	2.50	2.57
Hardness	6	4	3.5	3.2
	AlP	GaP	AlAs	GaAs
M–X distance	2.36	2.35	2.44	2.44
Hardness	5.5	5	5	4.2

[a] See footnote *a* of Table 3.3.

Ionic substances are usually only very slightly soluble in all but the most polar solvents. Water is a good solvent for ionic substances because of its large dipole moment, which contributes to the high hydration energies of ions, and its high dielectric constant, which reduces the attractive forces between cations and anions in solution. The solubility of ionic substances and specific consideration of water as a solvent will be discussed in greater detail later (p. 124).

Ionic Radii

The radius of a completely isolated atom or ion is difficult to define. It might be taken as infinite. The ionic radius refers to the distance of closest approach by another ion. One cannot identify the outer edge of an atom or ion, so the radius is evaluated from the observed distance between centers of nearest neighbors.

Several approaches have been used to evaluate the individual ionic radii. A method used by Landé[*] for obtaining the radius of the anion assumes that the anions will be in contact with one another when packed around a small cation such as Li^+ in LiI (see Figure 3.2). The radius of the iodide ion is taken as half of the I—I internuclear distance. In other crystals, such as KI, where the I—I distance is greater than that found in LiI, it is assumed that the anion and cation are in contact with each other. From the known radius of I^- (i.e., from LiI) and the internuclear distance in KI, the radius of K^+ may be calculated. Similarly, an estimate of the ionic radius of the oxide ion can be obtained from the O—O distance in silicates.[†] Wasastjerna used molar refractivities of ions as the basis for dividing the internuclear distances in alkali halides and alkaline earth oxides. The molar refractivity of an ion is roughly proportional to its volume. The ionic radii so obtained for fluoride ion (1.33 Å) and oxide ion (1.32 Å) were used by Goldschmidt[‡] as the basis for the first extensive table of ionic radii. Goldschmidt used

[*] Landé, A., *Z. Physik,* **1**, 191 (1920).
[†] Bragg, W. L., and J. West, *Proc. Roy. Soc. (London),* **A114**, 450 (1927).
[‡] Goldschmidt, V. M., *Skrifter Norske Videnskaps-Akad. Oslo,* No. 2, (1926); No. 8 (1927); *Trans. Faraday Soc.,* **25**, 253 (1929).

a substitutional procedure which permitted the evaluation of ionic radii of metal ions from observed interionic distances in fluorides or oxides, and radii for other anions from the ionic radii of these cations and observed interionic distances in other salts. By making such substitution for the oxide radius in sulfate and perchlorate ions, radii for S^{6+} and Cl^{7+} "ions" can be obtained, even though these hypothetical ions are not expected to have any independent existence.

Pauling Univalent Radii

One of the more widely used sets of ionic radii is that proposed by Pauling.* The entire set of radii is based on observed internuclear separations in four crystals — NaF, KCl, RbBr and CsI. These salts were selected because they have almost the same radius ratio ($r_+/r_- = 0.75$), about equal ionic character, and in each case the cation and anion are isoelectronic (same number of electrons) inert gas type ions. Except for CsI they all have the NaCl structure. The correction for a change in coordination number (8 for CsI and 6 for NaCl) is discussed later (p. 112). In order to assign radii to the individual ions, two assumptions are made: (*1*) The cation and anion are assumed to be in contact, i.e., $r_+ + r_- = R$ (R = internuclear separation). (*2*) For a given noble gas configuration, the radius is assumed to be inversely proportional to the effective nuclear charge, $r = C/Z_{eff}$, where C is the proportionality constant. The effective nuclear charges are evaluated by subtracting a screening constant from the actual nuclear charge. For the lighter elements the screening constants used by Pauling are similar to those obtained from Slater's rules (see p. 32). Once the proportionality constant has been evaluated it is possible to calculate the univalent radius for any isoelectronic ion. The following illustrates these calculations for Na^+, F^-, and "univalent oxygen."

The internuclear separation in sodium fluoride is 2.31 Å. Accordingly

$$r_{Na^+} + r_{F^-} = 2.31 \text{ Å}$$

Sodium ion and fluoride ion both have a neon configuration, $1s^2 2s^2 2p^6$, for which the Slater screening constant is $2 \times 0.85 + 8(0.35)$ or 4.5. This gives an effective atomic number for Na^+ of $11 - 4.5$ or 6.5 and for F^- of $9 - 4.5$ or 4.5. The proportionality constant C is obtained now from

$$\frac{C}{6.5} + \frac{C}{4.5} = 2.31$$

giving $C = 6.41$ for ions of the neon configuration. The radius of Na^+ is obtained from

$$r_{Na^+} = \frac{C}{Z_{eff}} = \frac{6.41}{6.5} = 0.95 \text{ Å}$$

Similarly for F^-

$$r_{F^-} = \frac{C}{Z_{eff}} = \frac{6.41}{4.5} = 1.36 \text{ Å}$$

---

* Pauling, L., *J. Am. Chem. Soc.*, **49**, 765 (1927); *Proc. Roy. Soc. (London)*, **A114**, 181 (1927); *The Nature of the Chemical Bond* (3rd ed., Ithaca: Cornell University Press, 1960) pp. 511–543.

For isoelectronic ions the screening constant will be the same. A univalent radius for oxide ion may be calculated from

$$r_0 = \frac{C}{Z_{eff}} = \frac{6.41}{8 - 4.5} = 1.76$$

Pauling Crystal Radii

Pauling's ionic radii for univalent ions agree quite well with observed interionic distances for salts containing univalent ions. However, if one attempts to calculate internuclear separation of O and Mg in MgO using the sum of the univalent radii the value obtained (2.58 Å) does not agree with the observed Mg—O distance (2.05 Å). Although all the ions involved in the calculation are isoelectronic, the Mg—O distance is much shorter than expected because of the higher charge on the ions. The calculated radii are *univalent radii*, the radii the ions would have if they had unit charge *without any change* in electronic configuration. The univalent radii can be converted into crystal radii, which will then agree with the observed interionic distances, by taking the charge on the ions into account. The ratio of the crystal radius, r_c, to the univalent radius, r_1, is given by the equation

$$\frac{r_c}{r_1} = Z^{-2/(n-1)} \tag{3.1}$$

where Z is the ionic charge, and n is a constant, called the Born exponent, which has a particular integral value for each type of electronic configuration (see p. 112). Values of crystal radii are listed in Table 3.6 for some common ions with a coordination number of six.

TABLE 3.6
Crystal Radii and Univalent Radii of Ions[a]

I	II	III	IV		V		VI		VII		O
									H^-		He
									2.08		
									(2.08)		(0.93)
Li^+	Be^{2+}	B^{3+}	C^{4+}	C^{4-}	N^{5+}	N^{3-}	O^{6+}	O^{2-}	F^{7+}	F^-	Ne
0.60	0.31	0.20	0.15	2.60	0.11	1.71	0.09	1.40	0.07	1.36	
(0.60)	(0.44)	(0.35)	(0.29)	(4.12)	(0.25)	(2.47)	(0.22)	(1.76)	(0.19)	(1.36)	(1.12)
Na^+	Mg^{2+}	Al^{3+}	Si^{4+}	Si^{4-}	P^{5+}	P^{3-}	S^{6+}	S^{2-}	Cl^{7+}	Cl^-	Ar
0.95	0.65	0.50	0.41	2.71	0.34	2.12	0.29	1.84	0.26	1.81	
(0.95)	(0.82)	(0.72)	(0.65)	(3.84)	(0.59)	(2.79)	(0.53)	(2.19)	(0.49)	(1.81)	(1.54)
K^+	Ca^{2+}	Sc^{3+}	Ti^{4+}		V^{5+}		Cr^{6+}		Mn^{7+}		Kr
1.33	0.99	0.81	0.68		0.59		0.52		0.46		
(1.33)	(1.18)	(1.06)	(0.96)		(0.88)		(0.81)		(0.75)		
Cu^+	Zn^{2+}	Ga^{3+}	Ge^{4+}	Ge^{4-}	As^{5+}	As^{3-}	Se^{6+}	Se^{2-}	Br^{7+}	Br^-	Kr
0.96	0.74	0.62	0.53	2.72	0.47	2.22	0.42	1.98	0.39	1.95	
(0.96)	(0.88)	(0.81)	(0.76)	(3.71)	(0.71)	(2.85)	(0.66)	(2.32)	(0.62)	(1.95)	(1.69)

TABLE 3.6 – *Continued*
Crystal Radii and Univalent Radii of Ions[a]

I	II	III	IV		V		VI		VII		O
Rb^+	Sr^{2+}	Y^{3+}	Zr^{4+}		Nb^{5+}		Mo^{6+}				
1.48	1.13	0.93	0.80		0.70		0.62				
(1.48)	(1.32)	(1.20)	(1.09)		(1.00)		(0.93)				
Ag^+	Cd^{2+}	In^{3+}	Sn^{4+}	Sn^{4-}	Sb^{5+}	Sb^{3-}	Te^{6+}	Te^{2-}	I^{7+}	I^-	Xe
1.26	0.97	0.81	0.71	2.94	0.62	2.45	0.56	2.21	0.50	2.16	
(1.26)	(1.14)	(1.04)	(0.96)	(3.70)	(0.89)	(2.95)	(0.82)	(2.50)	(0.77)	(2.16)	(1.90)
Cs^+	Ba^{2+}	La^{3+}	Ce^{4+}								
1.69	1.35	1.15	1.01								
(1.69)	(1.53)	(1.39)	(1.27)								
Au^+	Hg^{2+}	Tl^{3+}	Pb^{4+}		Bi^{5+}						
1.37	1.10	0.95	0.84		0.74						
(1.37)	(1.25)	(1.15)	(1.06)		(0.98)						

[a] Pauling, L., *The Nature of the Chemical Bond*, Third Edition © 1960 by Cornell University, p. 514. Used by permission of Cornell University Press. Univalent radii are in parentheses.

Just as the Mg—O distance is shorter than that calculated from univalent radii, the radius of a univalent ion is shorter when its neighbors have a charge greater than one. The correction for the charge of *neighboring ions* can be made by the relationship

$$r_{11} = r_{z_1 z_2} (Z_1 Z_2)^{1/(n-1)} \tag{3.2}$$

where r_{11} is the univalent radius (or the sum of univalent radii), $r_{z_1 z_2}$ is the radius (or the internuclear distance) in the salt with ions of charges Z_1 and Z_2, and n is the Born exponent. This equation reduces to Equation 3.1 for the special case where $Z_1 = Z_2$ and $r_{z_1 z_2}$ is the crystal radius.

Radius Ratio Effects

The arrangement of ions in a crystal depends on the relative sizes of the ions. The arrangements for the packing of spheres is given in Table 3.7. Ratios outside the ranges given are encountered without a change in structure, but in those cases the interionic distances no longer agree with the sum of the ionic radii. This can be seen from a consideration of a structure with a coordination number 6. The spatial relationship can be seen most clearly in a sectional view through any plane of 4 anions around the central cation. The stable arrangement, where there is cation–anion contact and the anions are almost in contact, is shown in Figure 3.3a. If the radius ratio is larger (Figure 3.3b, larger cation or smaller anion), the decreased anion repulsion would give an M—X distance shorter than the sum of the ionic radii. Actually, for an exaggerated situation as shown in Figure 3.3b, an increase in coordination number would be expected. If the radius ratio is smaller than in Figure 3.3a, the anion repulsion prevents anion–cation

TABLE 3.7
Stable Arrangements of Rigid Spheres X about Sphere M

Coordination number of M	Arrangement of X	Radius ratio $R_M:R_X$
2	Linear	To 0.15
3	Triangular	0.15–0.22
4	Tetrahedral	0.22–0.41
5	Planar	0.41–0.73
6	Octahedral	0.41–0.73
8	Cubic	Greater than 0.73

contact and the apparent M—X distance is increased beyond the sum of the ionic radii (Figure 3.3c). Where anion–anion repulsion is important, as for many lithium salts, a radius ratio correction must be applied to relate the ionic radii to the internuclear distance.

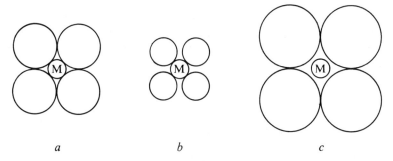

a *b* *c*

FIGURE 3.3. *Effect of variation of radius of cation to radius of anion.*

The effect of the radius ratio can be seen by comparison of substances of the type MX_2 which have the fluorite or rutile structures. The fluorite structure (C.N. of cation 8) is stable for a radius ratio greater than 0.73. The rutile structure (C.N. of cation 6) is usually encountered for smaller cations where the radius ratio is in the range 0.41–0.73 (see Table 3.7).

The alkali halides represent a series in which properties dependent on the stability of the ionic lattice might be expected to vary in a consistent way. The heats of fusion, melting points, boiling points, etc. might be expected to vary regularly with the M—X distance. These properties do follow a consistent pattern for salts of K^+, Rb^+, and Cs^+, but Li^+ salts and some Na^+ salts show significant deviations as shown by the melting points in Figure 3.4. The irregularities are eliminated when radius ratio corrections are applied, to allow for the lower stability of the salts for which anion–anion repulsion is important. Similar corrections are needed to remove irregularities in the boiling points.

Some salts crystallize in two or more modifications differing in coordination number. The anion–anion repulsion is always greater for the higher coordination number, re-

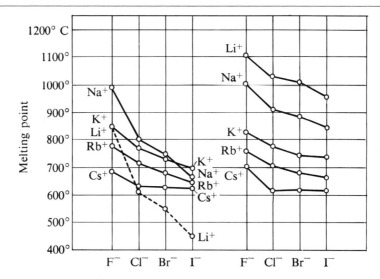

FIGURE 3.4. *The observed melting points of the alkali halogenides (left) and values corrected for the radius-ratio effect (right).* (Pauling, L., The Nature of the Chemical Bond, *Third Edition,* © 1960 by Cornell University, p. 528. Used by permission of Cornell University Press.)

sulting in an increase in the cation–anion distance. Rubidium halides (RbCl, RbBr, and RbI) normally show a coordination number of 6 (NaCl structure), but adopt a coordination number of 8 (CsCl structure) at high pressures. The radius for C.N. 8 (r_8) can be calculated from the radius for C.N. 6 (r_6 as given in Table 3.6) by the equation

$$\frac{r_8}{r_6} = \left(\frac{8A_6}{6A_8}\right)^{1/(n-1)} \tag{3.3}$$

where n is the Born exponent and A_6 and A_8 are the Madelung constants (see p. 113) for the NaCl structure (C.N. 6) and CsCl structure (C.N. 8), respectively. The Madelung constants for these structures are almost the same so that the ratio r_8/r_6 is approximately $(\frac{4}{3})^{1/(n-1)}$; for $n = 10$, $r_8/r_6 = (\frac{4}{3})^{1/9} = 1.032$.

Lattice Energy

The stability of an ionic lattice can be determined from the coulombic interactions among the ions. A pair of ions of opposite charge attract one another and the potential energy varies inversely with the first power of d, the internuclear separation. (The force between the ions would be Z_1Z_2/d^2.) As the ions come very close together they repel one another because of interpenetration of electron clouds. The repulsion energy is inversely proportional to the nth power of d. The Born exponent, n, increases with an increase in electron density around the ions ($n = 5$ for the He configuration, 7 for Ne, 9 for Ar or Cu^+, 10 for Kr or Ag^+, and 12 for Xe or Au^+; an average value for n is used if the cation and anion have different configurations.

The Born equation gives the potential energy for a pair of ions where Z_1 and Z_2 are

$$\text{PE} = \frac{Z_1Z_2e^2}{d} + \frac{be^2}{d^n} \tag{3.4}$$

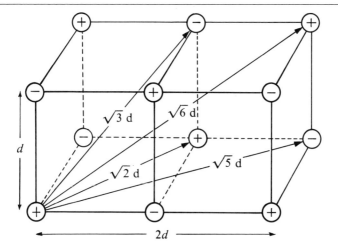

FIGURE 3.5. *Distances to neighboring ions in the* NaCl *lattice.*

integral charges (with appropriate signs), e is the charge on the electron, d is the internuclear separation, n is the Born exponent, and b is a repulsion coefficient. The potential energy is negative (corresponding to the release of energy) when d is greater than the internuclear separation, d_0, since the first term is negative for ions of opposite charge. The repulsion term increases and becomes the larger of the two for very small values of d. The potential energy is at a minimum at d_0 and becomes positive when d is very small.

Equation 3.4 gives the energy released when a cation and anion, separated by an infinite distance, are brought together until they are separated by the distance d. However, in a crystal of sodium chloride each sodium ion is surrounded by six chloride ions at a distance d, not one. Twelve other sodium ions are located at a distance of $\sqrt{2}d$, eight other chloride ions are located at a distance $\sqrt{3}d$, six more sodium ions at a distance $2d$, 24 chlorides at a distance $\sqrt{5}d$, and 24 sodium ions at a distance $\sqrt{6}d$, etc. (see Figure 3.5). The first term of the potential energy expression for the energy released in bringing a sodium ion from infinity to its stable position in the sodium chloride lattice is obtained by summing all of the interactions:

$$PE_{(1)} = -\frac{6e^2}{d} + \frac{12e^2}{\sqrt{2}d} - \frac{8e^2}{\sqrt{3}d} + \frac{6e^2}{2d} - \frac{24e^2}{\sqrt{5}d} + \frac{24e^2}{\sqrt{6}d} \cdots$$

or

$$PE_{(1)} = -\frac{e^2}{d}\left(6 - \frac{12}{\sqrt{2}} + \frac{8}{\sqrt{3}} - \frac{6}{2} + \frac{24}{\sqrt{5}} - \frac{24}{\sqrt{6}} \cdots\right) \tag{3.5}$$

The product Z_1Z_2 is omitted for simplicity since it is unity in this case; only the appropriate signs are carried. Equation 3.5 is the sum of an infinite series which converges toward 1.747558. This is the *Madelung constant* for the sodium chloride structure. It is used for any salt with this structure since it depends only on the geometrical arrangement of the ions. Values of the Madelung constant for other structures are evaluated similarly; values for some common structures are given in Table 3.8.

TABLE 3.8

Values of Madelung Constants[a]

Structure	Madelung constant	Structure	Madelung constant
Sodium chloride	1.747558	Rutile (TiO$_2$)	4.816
Cesium chloride	1.762670	Anatase (TiO$_2$)	4.800
Zinc blende (ZnS)	1.63806	Cadmium iodide	4.71
Wurtzite (ZnS)	1.641	β Quartz (SiO$_2$)	4.4394
Fluorite (CaF$_2$)	5.03878	Corundum (Al$_2$O$_3$)	25.0312

[a] Values given are for Z defined as the highest common factor of the ionic charges.

The second term in the potential energy expression for ions in a real crystal allows for the repulsive forces resulting from the interpenetration of electron clouds. This can be handled more simply than the first term since the repulsion varies inversely with d^n and hence only nearest neighbors need be considered. Each sodium ion is surrounded by six chloride ions, so the repulsion energy term becomes $6be^2/d^8$. The number of nearest neighbors times b is designated by B, the repulsion coefficient.

The potential energy of an ion in a crystal, considering the forces of all neighboring ions, becomes

$$PE = -\frac{Ae^2Z^2}{d} + \frac{Be^2}{d^n} \tag{3.6}$$

where A is the Madelung constant, B is the repulsion coefficient, and Z is the highest common factor of the ionic charges (1 for NaCl, Na$_2$O, MgCl$_2$, Al$_2$O$_3$, etc., and 2 for MgO, TiO$_2$, etc.). An additional repulsion term must be added where anion–anion repulsion is unusually great as in the case of many lithium salts.

The most stable equilibrium position of an ion will be achieved when attractive and repulsive forces are balanced; then the PE is a minimum and $d = d_0$. By differentiating the PE with respect to d and equating to zero, d_0 is found to be

$$d_0 = \left(\frac{nB}{AZ^2}\right)^{\frac{1}{(n-1)}} \tag{3.7}$$

and

$$B = \frac{d_0^{n-1}AZ^2}{n} \tag{3.8}$$

By substituting the value of B in Equation 3.6, the potential energy becomes

$$(PE)_0 = \frac{Ae^2Z^2}{d_0}\left(\frac{1}{n} - 1\right) \tag{3.9}$$

The lattice energy, U_0, is defined as the energy released in the formation of a mole of MX (crystal) from the gaseous ions separated from each other by infinite distances ($U_0 = -(PE)_0N$, where N is Avogadro's number).

$$U_0 = \frac{NAe^2Z^2}{d_0}\left(1 - \frac{1}{n}\right) \tag{3.10}$$

The lattice energy is very useful in correlating properties of ionic substances because the formation or the destruction of the crystal is frequently the most important step in reactions involving ionic substances.

The Born treatment assumes that the ions are hard spheres and are not distorted by the neighboring ions. Increasing distortion corresponds to increasing covalent character and hence the lattice energy calculated from Equation 3.10 would be expected to be in poor agreement with the experimental value where the covalent character of the bonds is appreciable (see p. 120).

The Born–Haber Cycle

Lattice energies have not been obtained by direct measurement until recently, but can be evaluated using the Born–Haber cycle which relates the lattice energy to other thermochemical quantities. The formation of a solid salt (MX) from the elements by two different paths is formulated as

$$
\begin{array}{ccc}
\text{MX(c)} & \xleftarrow{\;\;U_0(-)\;\;} & \text{M}^+(g) + \text{X}^-(g) \\
\Delta H_f(-) \uparrow & & \uparrow\; I + E(-) \\
\text{M(c)} + 1/2\text{X}_2(g) & \xrightarrow{\;\;S + 1/2D\;\;} & \text{M(g)} + \text{X(g)}
\end{array}
$$

where U_0 is the lattice energy, I the ionization potential of M(g), E the electron affinity of X(g), D the heat of dissociation of X_2(g), S the sublimation energy of the metal, and ΔH_f the heat of formation of MX(c) from the elements. The negative signs after ΔH_f, E, and U indicate that these processes correspond to the release of energy (as written). Since the change in energy is independent of the path, ΔH_f can be equated to the algebraic sum of the other thermochemical quantities. Similarly U_0 can be expressed as

$$U_0 = \Delta H_f + S + 1/2D + I - E \tag{3.11}$$

Thus the lattice energy is obtainable from other thermochemical quantities which can be evaluated experimentally. The lattice energy was calculated in early application from Equation 3.10 and used with the experimental thermochemical quantities to evaluate electron affinities, for which experimental values were not available. Where electron affinities are available, an experimental U_0 can be obtained from Equation 3.11 and compared with the theoretical value from Equation 3.10. The agreement is usually very good except for salts which contain ions of high charge or pseudo-inert gas type cations, for which the bonding has appreciable covalent character. The experimental value of U_0 is usually appreciably larger than the theoretical value for salts such as HgS, HgSe, and PbO_2.

If one compares the heats of formation of the alkali halides (Table 3.9) it is apparent that all of the thermochemical quantities involved must be considered in order to explain the variations. The heats of formation (ΔH_f) decrease in magnitude through the series MF, MCl, MBr, and MI, as anion repulsion increases and the coulombic energy decreases because of the increasing interionic distances. The relative contributions of the lattice energy (U_0), dissociation energy (D), and electron affinity (E) vary through the series. The ΔH_f values increase in magnitude with an increase in the size of M for the chlorides, bromides, and iodides, corresponding to a decrease in anion repulsion, but decrease for the fluorides. The anion repulsion is at a minimum for F⁻ because of its small size. The lattice energy of fluorides is greater with small cations because of the short M—X distance.

TABLE 3.9

Thermochemical Data and Electron Affinities $(0°K)^a$ (all values in kcal/mole)

	$-\Delta H_f$ 298°K (MX)	S 298°K (M)	$1/2D$ 298°K	$\Delta H_1{}^b$	$\Delta H_2{}^c$	I	U_0 (Theoretical)	E^d (From Born– Haber Cycle)
								Av.
LiF	145.7	38.4	18.9	3.0	1.5	124.4	246.8	79.1
NaF	136.3	25.9	18.9	3.0	1.9	118.4	218.7	79.7
KF	134.5	21.5	18.9	3.0	2.3	100.0	194.4	79.8
RbF	131.8	19.5	18.9	3.0	2.5	96.3	185.9	80.1
CsF	135.1	18.7	18.9	3.0	2.8	89.7	178.7	78.6
								79.5
LiCl	96.0	38.4	28.9	3.0	1.8	124.4	202.0	84.5
NaCl	98.2	25.9	28.9	3.0	2.5	118.4	185.9	85.1
KCl	104.2	21.5	28.9	3.0	2.8	100.0	169.4	85.1
RbCl	103.4	19.5	28.9	3.0	3.0	96.3	164.0	84.2
CsCl	106.9	18.7	28.9	3.0	3.3	89.7	155.9	88.7
								85.5
LiBr	83.7	38.4	26.8	3.0	2.0	124.4	190.7	81.6
NaBr	86.0	25.9	26.8	3.0	2.8	118.4	176.7	80.2
KBr	93.7	21.5	26.8	3.0	3.0	100.0	162.4	79.6
RbBr	93.	19.5	26.8	3.0	3.2	96.3	157.5	78.8
CsBr	97.7	18.7	26.8	3.0	3.5	89.7	151.1	82.3
								80.5
LiI	64.8	38.4	25.5	3.0	2.4	124.4	176.8	75.7
NaI	68.8	25.9	25.5	3.0	3.1	118.4	165.4	73.3
KI	78.3	21.5	25.5	3.0	3.2	100.0	153.0	72.5
RbI	79.0	19.5	25.5	3.0	3.3	96.3	148.7	71.9
CsI	83.9	18.7	25.5	3.0	3.5	89.7	143.7	74.6
								73.6

[a] Cubicciotti, D., *J. Chem. Phys.*, **31**, 1646 (1959); **34**, 2189 (1961).
[b] ΔH_1 to change M(g) and X(g) at 298° to 0°K.
[c] ΔH_2 to change MX(c) at 298° to 0°K.
[d] Recent experimental values of E are: F, 79.52 ± 0.12; Cl, 83.33 ± 0.07; Br, 77.56 ± 0.07; and I, 70.64 ± 0.07, taken from R. S. Berry and C. W. Reimann, *J. Chem. Phys.*, **38**, 1540 (1963).

Considering the individual steps for the formation of MX(c) from the elements, the only quantities corresponding to the release of energy are the lattice energy and the electron affinity. The electron affinity is the energy involved in the addition of an electron to a gaseous atom in its lowest energy state to form a gaseous anion. The electron affinity, for the addition of a single electron, is greater for each of the halogens than for the member of the oxygen family in the same period because of the greater nuclear charge, smaller size, and the formation of a closed electronic configuration. Within a family, the electron affinity usually decreases with increasing atomic size. Surprisingly the electron affinity of F(79.5) is slightly lower than that of Cl(83.3).* The very small size of the F atom with its high electron density makes the addition of an electron slightly less favorable energetically than for Cl. Fluorine is a better oxidizing agent than chlorine partly because of the much lower dissociation energy of F_2, which more than compensates for the difference in electron affinity. (The student might recalculate the dissociation energies from the recent electron affinities, see Problem 3.7.) In addition, the very high hydration energy of F^- and the high lattice energy of fluorides contribute greatly to the energy released in the formation of fluorides in solution or in the solid state.

The fact that the bond energy of F_2 is much lower than that of Cl_2 is not so unexpected if one considers the low single bond energies (in kcal/mole) for O(33) and N(32) compared with S(48) and P(51). The low values for N, O, and F might result from the greater repulsion among the nonbonding electrons of the two small atoms which have such high electron densities. In addition, the other members of the families have vacant *d* orbitals of the same quantum number, which might be hybridized with the *p* orbitals to some extent to contribute to the bonding and reduce repulsion. The increased polarizability of the larger atoms also helps to decrease repulsion.

The formation of the oxide ion and other anions with a charge greater than one is an endothermic process. The first electron gained by a gaseous oxygen atom is accompanied by the release of energy, but the addition of the second electron requires the expenditure of a greater amount of energy because it is repelled by the negative charge on the O^- ion. Because of the greater size of the sulfur atom, the charge density is less than for oxygen and the electron affinity for the formation of S^{2-} from S is less endothermic than for the formation of O^{2-} from O. Thus, for oxides and salts of other simple 2− or 3− ions, the only quantity involved in the formation of the solid which releases energy is the lattice energy. The only simple 3− ion encountered in ionic crystals is the nitride ion and then only when combined with the most electropositive metal ions. The formation of the N^{3-} ion from N would require 550 kcal/mole.†

Oxygen Compounds of the Alkali Metals

The oxygen compounds of the alkali metals demonstrate the delicate balance of the energy terms involved in the formation of the compounds. The compounds obtained by burning the metals in air are Li_2O, Na_2O_2, KO_2, RbO_2, and CsO_2, which contain O^{2-}, O_2^{2-} (peroxide ion), and O_2^- (superoxide ion), respectively (Table 3.10).

---

* The value of the electron affinity of fluorine used until recently was obtained from the Born–Haber cycle and was greatly in error because of the uncertainty in available values of the dissociation energy of F_2. Recent determinations of the electron affinity and dissociation energy of fluorine are quite consistent with the over-all heat of formation of F^- from F_2. The values for the electron affinities of the halogens given in the footnote to Table 3.9 are from recent direct determinations.

† Syrkin, Y. K., and M. E. Dyatkina, *Structures of Molecules and the Chemical Bond* (London: Butterworths Scientific Publications, 1950) p. 40.

TABLE 3.10

Thermodynamic Data for Oxycompounds of the Alkali Metals[a]

(kcal/2 moles of M, 25°C)

		M_2O	M_2O_2	$2MO_2$
Li	$-\Delta H^0$	142	152	—
	$-\Delta F^0$	134	135	—
Na	$-\Delta H^0$	99	121	124
	$-\Delta F^0$	90	103	93
K	$-\Delta H^0$	86	118	134
	$-\Delta F^0$	76	100	100
Rb	$-\Delta H^0$	79	102	126
	$-\Delta F^0$	70	84	95
Cs	$-\Delta H^0$	76	96	124
	$-\Delta F^0$	78	86	92

[a] Latimer, W. M., *Oxidation Potentials* (2nd Ed., Englewood Cliffs: Prentice-Hall, Inc., 1952) pp. 329–335.

The heats of formation decrease from Li to Cs for each type of compound, except for NaO_2 which is slightly out of line. The compounds KO_2, RbO_2, and CsO_2 have the tetragonal CaC_2 structure, but the modification of NaO_2 stable above $-50°C$ has a disordered pyrite structure.* The difference in structure may account for the apparently low ΔH value for NaO_2. The general decrease in ΔH with increasing size of M^+ is to be expected, because the lattice energy should decrease as the interionic distance increases. The decrease is greatest for the small O^{2-} ion and relatively slight for the larger O_2^- ion, which also has a lower charge.

The lattice energies would be expected to decrease for each metal with increasing size of the anion. The decrease in charge for O_2^- would also decrease the lattice energy. The decrease in lattice energy through the series of anions should be greatest for the small Li^+ ion, and much less for the larger cations. In spite of a decrease in lattice energy, the ΔH values increase in the order oxide, peroxide, and superoxide for each metal. The only other thermochemical quantities involved in the Born–Haber cycle which change in such a series (for the same metal) are those involved in the formation of the anion. The addition of two electrons to O_2 to form the O_2^{2-} ion requires less energy than the addition of two electrons to O to form O^{2-}, because the charge can be distributed over the two atoms in the latter case. The addition of a single electron to O_2 is an exothermic process. In addition, the formation of O_2^{2-} or O_2^- does not require the dissociation of O_2. The formation of the O^{2-} ion is endothermic to the extent of 215 kcal/mole, while the formation of the O_2^{2-} ion requires 112 kcal, and the formation of the O_2^- ion releases 20 kcal. The differences in the energies of formation of the anion are most important for the larger cations, where the changes in the lattice energy (which are in the opposite direction) are relatively small.

When the differences in heats of formation of the oxycompounds are relatively large, the one with the highest heat of formation is obtained when the metal is burned in air

* Pyrite (FeS_2) has a cubic structure (NaCl) with the S_2^{2-} ions arranged parallel to the 3-fold axes (diagonally with respect to the cube edges). In the disordered structure of NaO_2 the O_2^{2-} ions are arranged randomly.

KO_2, RbO_2, and CsO_2). The differences in the ΔH values for Li_2O and Li_2O_2 and for Na_2O_2 and NaO_2 are small and other factors are important in determining the relative stabilities. The free energies of formation include the heat changes and the entropy changes. We see that the free energy of formation of Na_2O_2 is considerably greater than that of NaO_2; the product obtained is Na_2O_2. The values for Li_2O and Li_2O_2 are nearly the same. When Li is burned in air some Li_2O_2 is formed, but the major product is Li_2O. The conditions prevailing at the site of the reaction during the combustion of a metal are likely to be very much different from those conditions to which the thermodynamic data refer. Reliable predictions of products cannot be made when the free energy values are nearly the same if equilibrium conditions do not prevail.

The Formation of $M^{n+}(g)$ from $M(c)$

The steps required for the formation of a gaseous metal ion involve the sublimation energy, to convert the solid metal in its standard state to the separate gaseous atoms, and the ionization potential. The ionization potential (I) is the energy required to remove the outermost electron from the gaseous atom (p. 6). The energy for the removal of the 2nd, 3rd, etc., electrons corresponds to the 2nd, 3rd, etc., ionization potentials, respectively, and the energy for the formation of $\dot{M}^{2+}$ is the sum of the 1st and 2nd ionization potentials. The ionization potential decreases with increasing atomic number within a family because of the increasing size of the atom and the more effective screening of the nucleus. There is a general increase in I with increasing atomic number within a period because of the decrease in size and increase in nuclear charge. The notable exceptions are encountered for p^1 and p^4 configurations where I is smaller than expected because of the greater ease of removal of an electron to give a stable configuration involving empty or half-filled orbitals. The variation in I indicates that the elements most likely to form simple ionic compounds (those with low I values) are to be found at the beginning of each period and particularly the lower members (higher atomic number) of a family.

The very great increase in successive ionization potentials is the major factor limiting the charge of cations in simple ionic substances to 1+ or 2+, with 3+ uncommon, and 4+ encountered only for very large ions, such as Th^{4+}. The other factor involves the increased covalent character of compounds containing ions of high charge. It is apparent from Equation 3.10 that the lattice energy increases greatly with increasing ionic charge. The lattice energy of a salt such as NaF_2 might be expected to be very large (the value for MgF_2 can be taken as an estimate), but if one calculates the energy for the reaction

$$NaF_2 \rightarrow NaF + \tfrac{1}{2}F_2$$

it is found to be highly exothermic, primarily because of the very high second ionization potential of Na. Similarly, the formation of MgF should be an exothermic process (the lattice energy of MgF should be about the same as that of NaF). However, the much greater lattice energy of MgF_2 makes the formation of solid MgF_2 much more favorable and the disproportionation of the solid MgF to give MgF_2 and Mg is exothermic.

EXAMPLE: Calculate the lattice energy, the heat of formation and the heat of disproportionation of CaCl.

Let us assume that CaCl has the NaCl structure. The crystal radius of Ca^{2+} is 0.99 Å and the univalent radius is 1.18 Å. We shall use 1.2 Å as an approximation. The value of e is 4.80×10^{-10} esu or $\sqrt{dyne}$ cm.

$$U_0 = \frac{(4.80 \times 10^{-10} \sqrt{dyne}\ cm)^2\ 1^2(6.02 \times 10^{23})\ 1.75}{3.0 \times 10^{-8}\ cm}\left(1 - \frac{1}{9}\right)$$

$$= \frac{7.15 \times 10^{12}\ erg}{mole} \times \frac{1\ joule}{10^7\ erg} \times \frac{1\ kcal}{4.18 \times 10^3\ joule}$$

$$= 172\ kcal/mole$$

Using $S = 48$ kcal, $1/2D = 29$ kcal, $IP = 141$ kcal, and $E = 83$, from Equation 3.11

$$\Delta H_f = 48 + 29 + 141 - 83 - 172 = -37\ kcal/mole\ CaCl$$

For the disproportionation reaction

$$2\ CaCl \rightarrow CaCl_2 + Ca$$
$$\Delta H = -191 + 0 + 2(37) = -117\ kcal/mole\ CaCl_2\ formed$$

The rate of evaporation of Al from liquid Al is greatly increased by passing a stream of $AlCl_3$ over the surface. Some AlCl is formed and carried along in the gas stream. On cooling, the AlCl disproportionates to deposit Al. This process has been patented (Gross, 1946) for the purification of Al.

The low heat of formation of some noble metal halides, compared to alkali metal halides, is largely the result of high ionization potentials, but frequently the differences in sublimation energy are also great. Consider the steps of the Born–Haber cycle which differ for NaCl and AgCl (energies in kcal/mole):

$$Ag(c) \xrightarrow[S]{68} Ag(g) \xrightarrow[I]{174} \begin{matrix} Ag^+(g) \\ Cl^-(g) \end{matrix} \xrightarrow[U_0]{-214} AgCl(c)\ \ \Delta H_f = -30$$

$$Na(c) \xrightarrow[S]{26} Na(g) \xrightarrow[I]{118} \begin{matrix} Na^+(g) \\ Cl^-(g) \end{matrix} \xrightarrow[U_0]{-184} NaCl(c)\ \ \Delta H_f = -98$$

Although the lattice energy is greater for AgCl, the heat of formation is much less. Both the ionization potential and sublimation energy contribute significantly to the "nobility" of Ag as compared to Na. (See p. 37 for a discussion of periodic variations in sublimation energies.) The heat of formation of AgCl would be even lower if it were not for the importance of polarization effects. Silver chloride is one of the compounds (p. 115) for which the polarization effects (or increased covalent character) cause the lattice energy obtained from the Born–Haber cycle (214 kcal) to be appreciably higher than that calculated using the Born equation and the ionic radii (203 kcal).

Deviations from Simple Ionic Structures

It has been pointed out that the calculated lattice energy disagrees with the observed value whenever the bonding is appreciably covalent in character. Substances generally fall somewhere between the extremes of ionic and covalent character. Those substances, which have the properties described earlier (high melting points, high boiling points, conductivity in the fused state and in polar solvents, etc.), are usually classified as ionic. Some salts possess these properties only to a limited extent. Layer structures of infinite chains or sheets are frequently encountered for salts in which the bonding is appreciably covalent in character. In $CdCl_2$ there are six Cl^- around each Cd^{2+}, but the $CdCl_6$ groups share corners to form infinite sheets. $CuCl_2$ and $PdCl_2$ form infinite chains by sharing Cl^- between planar MCl_4 groups (Figure 3.6).

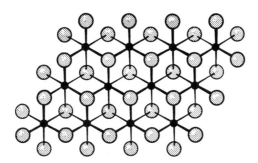

CdCl₂ Layer structure

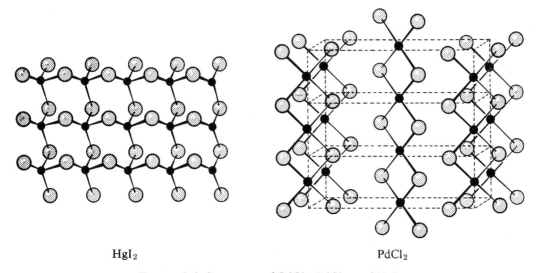

HgI₂   PdCl₂

FIGURE 3.6. *Structures of* $CdCl_2$, *$PdCl_2$, and* HgI_2.

The $CdCl_2$ structure can be regarded as a cubic close-packed array of Cl^- ions with Cd^{2+} ions in half of the octahedral sites to give layers. Adjacent layers are held together by the van der Waals' interactions between the Cl^- ions. Other salts having the $CdCl_2$ structure are $MnCl_2$, $FeCl_2$, $CoCl_2$, $NiCl_2$, NiI_2, $MgCl_2$, and $ZnBr_2$. The CdI_2 structure differs in that the Cl^- ions are in a hexagonal close-packed arrangement. Other compounds with the CdI_2 structure are $CdBr_2$, $FeBr_2$, $CoBr_2$, $NiBr_2$, MgI_2, CaI_2, ZnI_2, PbI_2, MnI_2, FeI_2, CoI_2; hydroxides of divalent Mg, Ca, Cd, Mn, Fe, Co, and Ni, and sulfides of quadrivalent Zr, Sn, Ti, and Pt. The $CrCl_3$ layer structure is similar to that of $CdCl_2$ with only one-third of the octahedral sites filled, i.e., two-thirds of the sites in each layer.

The mercury(II) halides are unique in their structural variation. HgF_2 has the typically ionic fluorite structure. The $HgCl_2$ structure consists of discrete $HgCl_2$ molecules.

HgBr₂ gives a layer type lattice similar to that of CdCl₂. However, the octahedral arrangement is distorted with two Br atoms much closer than the other four. HgI₂ crystallizes in a layer lattice in which each Hg atom is surrounded tetrahedrally by four equivalent iodide ions (Figure 3.6). The HgI₂ structure can be regarded as a cubic close-packed arrangement of I⁻ ions with Hg²⁺ ions in one-half of the sites (in alternate layers).

Defect Structures

Thus far, we have treated crystals as being made up of a perfectly repeating array of atoms. The extent of perfection in crystals is far less than has been assumed. Imperfections occur in crystals as a result of dislocation of ions, ion vacancies in the lattice, nonstoichiometric proportion of the ions present, or simply due to foreign ions or "impurities" in the lattice.*

In stoichiometric crystals two types of lattice defects may exist. Vacancies of anions and cations, which are equal in number, may exist; these defects are termed Schottky defects. A single layer sketch representation of a sodium chloride crystal containing Schottky defects and a schematic representation are shown in Figure 3.7.

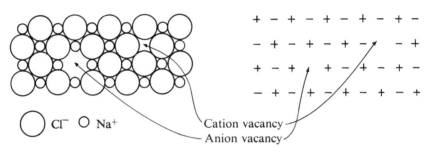

FIGURE 3.7. *Schottky defects in sodium chloride.*

If an ion occupies an interstitial site and leaves its normal site vacant, the defect is termed a Frenkel defect. Frenkel defects are most likely in crystals in which the anion and cation differ greatly in size. Frenkel defects in silver bromide are indicated in Figure 3.8.

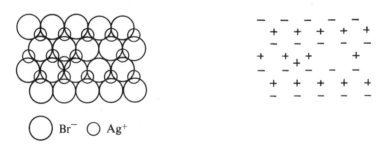

FIGURE 3.8. *Frenkel defects in silver bromide.*

* Rohmer, R., *Bull. Soc. Chim. France,* **1955**, 159; H. W. Etzel, *J. Chem. Educ.,* **38**, 225 (1961).

Both Frenkel and Schottky defects exist in pure stoichiometric crystals due to a balance in enthalpy and entropy terms as discussed below. Stoichiometric CrO has 8% vacancies in the anion and the cation lattices. In stoichiometric solids, such as Fe_3O_4, where there exist two oxidation states for the cation, further disorder may be introduced. (In Fe_3O_4 the Fe^{3+} occupies both tetrahedral and octahedral holes, while the Fe^{2+} occupies only octahedral holes.)

The large amount of heat released in the formation of a crystal lattice from gaseous ions is accompanied by a large unfavorable entropy change because of the formation of the rigid well-ordered crystal lattice. The introduction of vacancies or dislocations in the crystal lattice will certainly decrease the heat of formation of a crystal, but the increase in entropy accompanying the decrease in order favors the process. Obviously a balance will be achieved between entropy and enthalpy and defects will be more abundant in crystals where the enthalpy needed to create a defect is low. Defects are less likely for crystals of the extreme ionic type where the balance of coulombic forces is critical. They are more likely for partially covalent substances.

Nonstoichiometric compounds often result when a cation can have different oxidation states, as in FeS, FeO, Cu_2O, NiO, CuO, CuI, etc. These might better be represented by formulas such as $Fe_{1-\delta}S$ where δ would represent the fraction of vacant cation sites per formula weight. Electrical neutrality can be maintained by oxidation of the equivalent number of Fe^{2+} to Fe^{3+} giving the composition $Fe^{2+}_{1-\delta} Fe^{3+}_{2\delta} S^{2-}$. The lattice of $Fe_{1-\delta}S$ may be represented as in Figure 3.9.

$$
\begin{array}{cccc}
Fe^{3+} & S^{2-} & Fe^{2+} & S^{2-} \\
S^{2-} & \square & S^{2-} & Fe^{3+} \\
Fe^{2+} & S^{2-} & Fe^{2+} & S^{2-}
\end{array}
$$

FIGURE 3.9. *Defects in FeS.*

Nonstoichiometric compounds may occur even if the metal is not present in two or more oxidation states, as in the case of zinc oxide which loses oxygen on heating to give $Zn_{1+\delta}O$ or sodium chloride, which reacts with sodium vapor to give $Na_{1+\delta}Cl$. In these cases an electron or an electron pair may occupy the vacant anion site (Figure 3.10).

$$
\begin{array}{ccccc}
Na^+ & Cl^- & Na^+ & Cl^- & Na^+ \\
Cl^- & \square & Cl^- & Na^+ & Cl^- \\
Na^+ & \boxed{e} & Na^+ & Cl^- & Na^+
\end{array}
$$

Schottky defects

"trapped electron" or "F" center

FIGURE 3.10. *Defects in NaCl.*

Chemical defects, or impurities, also give rise to imperfections in the lattice. A simple solution results for Cu contained in Ag with random substitution of Cu for Ag. With germanium containing a trace amount of gallium, the gallium goes into the germanium lattice (diamond structure) but lacks one electron, thus creating an electron hole. Movement of electrons into this hole is the equivalent of movement of the hole about the lattice. Such a hole behaves as if it were a positive charge when placed in an electric field. A sample of germanium "doped" with gallium is called a p-type semiconductor because it behaves as if it had mobile positive centers in it. Contrariwise a sample of germanium "doped" with arsenic adds electrons to the conduction band of germanium (see section on metals) and is called an n-type semiconductor since it behaves as if it has negative charge carriers in it (as indeed it does) (see p. 293). In $Fe_{1-\delta}S$ and $Fe_{1-\delta}O$, electron transfer from Fe^{2+} to Fe^{3+} makes the Fe^{3+} appear to move through the lattice, hence, these solids are p-type semiconductors, while $Na_{1+\delta}Cl$ and $Zn_{1+\delta}O$ are n-type semiconductors due to the mobility of the "trapped electrons."

Occasionally impurities are added to reduce semiconduction rather than to promote it, as in the case of TiO_2 ceramic insulators where pentavalent impurities are added to reduce the effect of Ti^{3+} ions.

In addition to applications to semiconductors (transistors, etc.) lattice defect compounds are important in catalysis, luminescence (especially color TV), photography, and are being studied with regard to radiation damage in materials, and corrosion phenomena.

Solubility of Ionic Substances

Ionic substances are only very slightly soluble in most common solvents, except for those that are quite polar. The strong attractive forces between ions in the crystal must be overcome and this can be accomplished only if the attractive forces between the ions and solvent molecules are at least comparable to the lattice energy. The energy, which must be provided for the separation of the ions from the crystal, comes from the solvation of the ions. The attractive forces between nonbonded neutral molecules is usually very weak and the forces between an ion and a neutral molecule are not much stronger unless the molecule has a fairly high dipole moment and/or high polarizability. The greater the dipole moment, the stronger the attraction by an ion, and usually the greater the solvation energy. Solvation energies also increase with the polarizability of the solvent molecules. The energy required to separate ions or keep them apart is diminished if the forces between ions are decreased. The forces between ions are dependent on the *dielectric constant** of the medium. The dielectric constant of water is 78.54 (25°C), so that the attractive forces between two ions in water is 1/78.54 of the force between the ions separated by the same distance in a vacuum. Good solvents for ionic substances usually have high dipole moments and high dielectric constants, although few solvents have dielectric constants as high as that of water.

Water is a much better solvent for ionic substances than other solvents with high dielectric constants (e.g., HF). The water molecules might be considered to donate electron pairs to the metal ions, but the interaction can be interpreted quite satisfactorily for many metal ions in terms of electrostatic forces (see Ligand Field Theory,

---

* The dielectric constant of a medium is defined as the ratio of a condenser's capacity with the medium between the plates to its capacity with the space between the plates evacuated.

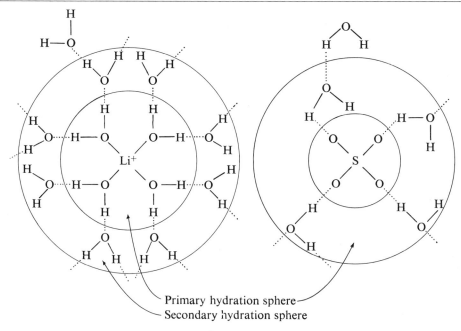

FIGURE 3.11. *Hydrated* Li^+ *and* SO_4^{2-} *ions.*

p. 348). According to either interpretation, a metal ion interacts strongly with a layer of water molecules referred to as the primary hydration sphere. The water molecules in the primary hydration sphere form stronger hydrogen bonds to other water molecules than they would otherwise, giving rise to a secondary hydration sphere. The water molecules in the secondary hydration sphere, in turn, are hydrogen bonded to other water molecules. These hydrogen bonds are weaker than those formed by water in the primary hydration sphere, but stronger than in water itself. Anions, particularly oxyanions, can be strongly hydrogen bonded to water also (see Figure 3.11). HF is a poorer solvent for salts, in spite of its high dipole moment and ability to form strong hydrogen bonds, because it is a much weaker base than water and hence a poorer electron donor.

The energy changes involved in the dissolution of a salt can be handled conveniently by a Born–Haber type cycle:

$$MX(c) \xrightarrow{-U_0} M^+(g) + X^-(g)$$
$$L \searrow \quad \downarrow H_+ \quad \searrow H_-$$
$$M^+(solv.) + X^-(solv.)$$

where U_0 is the lattice energy of the crystal MX, H_+ and H_- are the energies released as a result of the solvation of the gaseous positive and negative ions, and L is the observed heat of solution at infinite dilution. Since the total energy change in going from MX(c) to the solvated ions is independent of the path, the heat of solution is given by

$$L = H_+ + H_- - U_0$$

The heat of solution can be positive or negative depending on the relative magnitude of the lattice energy and the heats of solvation of the ions. The heat of solution is often negative (exothermic) for very soluble substances, but not always. The other factor, which can account for high solubility, even though the process is endothermic, is the entropy change which accompanies dissolution. The destruction of the well-ordered crystal lattice is accompanied by a large favorable entropy change, but the ions orient the solvent molecules causing a decrease in entropy. Using the thermodynamic relationships $\Delta F° = \Delta H° - T\Delta S°$ and $\Delta F° = -RT \ln K$, the heat of solution, L, can be related to the solubility product constant, K, and the change in entropy, $\Delta S°$, when one mole of solute dissolves to give an ideal 1 molar solution:

$$RT \ln K = -L + T\Delta S° \qquad (3.12)$$

where R is the gas constant and T the absolute temperature. Care must be exercised in obtaining thermodynamic quantities from solubility products because of complications caused by nonideal behavior and competing equilibria, e.g., complex formation.

The effects of size and charge on lattice energy are given by Equation 3.10. The solvation energy, H, of an ion is given by the Born equation

$$H = \frac{z^2}{2r}\left(1 - \frac{1}{\epsilon}\right) \qquad (3.13)$$

where z is the charge on the ion, r the radius,* and ϵ the dielectric constant of the solvent. The solvation energies and solubilities of salts usually increase with increasing dielectric constant of the solvent. The solvation energy and lattice energy are both inversely proportional to the ionic radii. The solubilities of salts usually increase with increasing size of cations or anions, presumably because of more favorable entropy changes on solvation and also possibly because of polarization effects in some cases. The effect of charge is usually considerably greater than the size effect. The lattice energy increases more than the solvation energy with increasing ionic charge whenever there is an accompanying increase in the Madelung constant. The entropy change accompanying the dissolution of a salt is usually less favorable for small ions and particularly for ions of high charge. Ions of high charge density cause a great deal of ordering of the solvent molecules as a result of solvation.

Polarization effects are not taken into account in Equation 3.13 for the evaluation of solvation energies and the only allowance for the greater polarization of cations with pseudo-inert gas type configurations is in the value of the Born exponent used in Equation 3.10 for the calculation of lattice energy. Solubility is dependent on the relative polarizability of the anion and of the solvent molecules. Unless the solvent molecules are easily polarizable, the solubility of the salt is usually low if the cation is strongly polarizing and the anion is easily polarizable. The solubilities of salts containing pseudo-inert gas type cations, e.g., $AgCl$, $PbCl_2$, $HgCl_2$, are usually lower in water than those containing inert gas type cations, e.g., alkali and alkaline earth halides, because of the greater anion polarization. Ammonia has a lower dipole moment than water, but it is

---

* Latimer, Pitzer, and Slansky [*J. Chem. Phys.*, 7, 108 (1939)] showed that the Born equation gives poor results unless an empirical adjustment of the radius is made. Reasonable results are obtained if the effective cationic radius is taken to be the ionic radius plus 0.85 Å and the effective anionic radius is 0.10 Å larger than the ionic radius. Probably the major factor requiring some adjustment is the expected decrease in ϵ in the immediate vicinity of an ion.

more polarizable. Hence, ammonia is a poorer solvent than water for substances of the extreme ionic type, but better than water for salts of strongly polarizing cations and for salts of anions which are easily polarized. Salts of pseudo-inert gas type cations are commonly more soluble in ammonia than in water because of the greater polarizability and basicity of ammonia, giving stable complexes. The solubilities of the silver halides in liquid ammonia increase with increasing anion size (and polarizability) whereas the reverse order is observed in water.

Equation 3.13 also neglects specific solvent interactions such as hydrogen bonding. The hydration energy of F^- is much higher than that of K^+ even though the ionic radii are about the same. The unusually high hydration energy of F^- (and OH^-) results from the formation of strong hydrogen bonds (see Chapter V).

Complex Ionic Crystals

The same principles apply to simple and complex ionic crystals. However, the assumptions on which the Born equation is based apply less rigorously to crystals which contain large aggregates. The complex ionic crystals include salts of the isopoly and heteropoly acids, and complex minerals such as the silicates.

Pauling's Rules

The consideration of the structure of complex ionic crystals is simplified by a set of empirical rules proposed by Pauling.* These rules will be discussed briefly, with a few examples, before going into a more systematic discussion of silicates.

Pauling's first rule is a restatement of a principle which was applied in the earlier discussion of simple ionic substances. It states: *a coordinated polyhedron of anions†* *is formed about each cation, the cation–anion distance being determined by the sum of* *the radii and the coordination number by the radius ratio.* The importance of radius ratio in determining structure was discussed earlier (p. 110).

The second rule is known as the *electrostatic valence rule.* This rule states that *the* *charge of each anion (with changed sign) is exactly or nearly equal to the sum of the* *strengths of the electrostatic bonds to it from the adjacent cations.* The strength of an electrostatic bond is defined as the charge on the cation divided by the number of coordinated anions (z/n). Thus the strength of each bond in a tetrahedral AlO_4 group‡ is $\frac{3}{4}$ and in an octahedral AlO_6 group it is $\frac{3}{6}$ or $\frac{1}{2}$. The rule leads to the expectation that AlO_6 groups will be joined in such a way that the oxygens will be bonded to four Al^{3+} ions in order to neutralize the charge ($\frac{1}{2} \times 4 = 2$). MgO has the NaCl structure in which each magnesium ion is surrounded by six oxygens (bond strength $\frac{1}{3}$), and each oxygen is surrounded by six magnesium ions ($\frac{1}{3} \times 6 = 2$). The charge on an oxide ion is neutralized by being shared between two SiO_4 groups (bond strength 1). In the mineral for-

---

* Pauling, L., *The Nature of the Chemical Bond* (3rd ed., Ithaca: Cornell University Press, 1960) pp. 544–562.
† Coordination of the anions is used in the crystallographic sense of nearest neighbors. There is no implication that coordinate covalent bonds are involved.
‡ The units AlO_4, SiO_4, etc., have the central atom in the usual oxidation state. The charge distribution depends on the number of oxygen atoms shared.

sterite, Mg_2SiO_4, each oxygen is shared among three MgO_6 groups and one SiO_4 group $(3 \times \frac{1}{3} + 1 = 2)$.

Pauling's third rule states that *the presence of shared edges and especially of shared faces of coordinated polyhedra decreases the stability of the structure; this effect is large for cations with high charge and small coordination number.* Shared faces are very rare in stable crystals and can be taken as an indication of covalent character. The ions $Tl_2Cl_9{}^{3-}$, $Cr_2Cl_9{}^{3-}$, and $W_2Cl_9{}^{3-}$ can be represented as two octahedra sharing a face (see p. 326). The bonding is probably appreciably covalent in these ions. In $W_2Cl_9{}^{3-}$ the tungsten atoms are displaced from the center of the octahedra toward one another to give a W—W distance shorter than that in metallic tungsten, indicating the presence of a W—W bond. Shared edges are fairly common for octahedra, but less common for tetrahedra. The cation–cation distance is shortened more for a shared edge involving two tetrahedra than for two octahedra. Edges are shared between TiO_6 octahedra in rutile and between AlO_6 octahedra in a variety of compounds. Edges or faces of SiO_4 tetrahedra are never shared in naturally occurring silicates. Edges of SiS_4 tetrahedra are shared in SiS_2 to give long chains. The larger S^{2-} ions can shield the Si^{4+} ions from one another more effectively than O^{2-} does, diminishing the repulsion between the cations. It is also to be expected that the bonding will be appreciably covalent. The cation–cation repulsion in polyhedra sharing an edge tends to shorten the length of the shared edge in order to increase the distance between cations. Thus in Al_2Cl_6 the edge shared between the two $AlCl_4$ tetrahedra is shorter than the unshared edges.

The third rule can be applied to oxyanions regardless of whether the anion is part of a crystal. Aluminum shares polyhedral edges in many of its oxycompounds. Silicon does not share edges in silicates, but almost always shares corners. Phosphorus gives a number of polymeric oxy acids and oxyanions (isopoly acids and their salts), but these tend to convert to the orthophosphates in aqueous solution. Sulfur gives a disulfate and some higher polymers, but these are unstable in aqueous solution relative to the simple sulfate ion. The perchlorate ion with its high oxidation state on the central atom $(+7)$ does not dimerize. Although the oxidation states are the same in nitrates and phosphates, the nitrates (with lower coordination number) do not give stable compounds corresponding to the polyphosphates.

Pauling's fourth rule states that *in a crystal containing different cations those with large charge and small coordination number tend not to share polyhedron elements with each other.* This rule is the consequence of an increase in cation–cation repulsion as the charges on the cations increase and as the coordination number decreases. In aluminum silicates the AlO_6 octahedra sometimes share edges, but the SiO_4 tetrahedra do not. Shared edges are usually necessary to satisfy rule two for cations with low charge, particularly if the coordination number is high.

Structures of Silicates

Silicates provide an interesting array of structural types, showing greater variety than usually encountered for compounds of other elements. The silicates are also of great technical importance. The crust of the earth is made up primarily of metal silicates. Silicon and oxygen account for almost 75% by weight of the earth's crust. On a volume basis, oxygen alone accounts for 92% of the earth's crust. The eight most abundant elements in the earth's crust* are the ones which usually occur in silicates. The ubiquitous silicates occupy a unique position in minerology.

The composition of the silicate minerals used to be given in terms of mole ratios of oxides, e.g., forsterite, $2MgO \cdot SiO_2$ for Mg_2SiO_4; and orthoclase, $K_2O \cdot Al_2O_3 \cdot 6SiO_2$ for $KAlSi_3O_8$. The mixed oxide formulations were used partly because the structures or manner of chemical combination were not known in many cases. Also, most minerals are not pure chemical compounds which can be represented accurately by simple chemical formulas. The formulas given are idealized formulas; the actual composition might vary to a considerable extent.

The greatest cause of variation in the composition of minerals is the isomorphous replacement of one ion by another. The extent of isomorphous replacement of ions of the same charge is determined by the relative sizes of the ions. If the sizes are very similar (i.e., if the radius of the larger ion is within 15% of the radius of the smaller ion) complete isomorphous replacement can occur. Mg^{2+} (0.65 Å) and Fe^{2+} (0.75 Å) can combine in any proportion in a mineral of the type $M_2''SiO_4$. If little iron is present the mineral is called forsterite and is represented as Mg_2SiO_4. In the less common occurrence where little magnesium is present the mineral is called fayalite, Fe_2SiO_4. Most often the mineral encountered contains varying proportions of Mg and Fe and is known as olivine. The nonstoichiometric replacement of Mg^{2+} by Fe^{2+} is represented by $(Mg,Fe)_2SiO_4$.

Ions which are of comparable size can replace one another even if the charges differ. The feldspars can be represented by the general formula $M(Al,Si)_4O_8$ where M can be Na, K, Ca, or Ba and the ratio of Si to Al varies from 3:1 to 2:2. For each Ca^{2+}, which substitutes for Na^+ in albite, $NaAlSi_3O_8$, an additional Al^{3+} ion substitutes for Si^{4+}. In the mineral anorthite, $CaAl_2Si_2O_8$, the substitution of Ca^{2+} for Na^+ is complete. Actually the formulas for albite and anorthite are idealized and the presence of small amounts of the other cation (Na^+ or Ca^{2+}) does not make it necessary to change the name of the mineral. Nevertheless, many of the minerals of intermediate composition ranges are characterized and given their own names.

The silicate minerals have a number of essential features, which should be kept in mind. All of the silicates contain tetrahedral SiO_4 units, which may be linked together by sharing corners, never by sharing edges or faces. When other cations (alkali or alkaline earth metal ions, Fe^{2+}, etc.) are present in the structure, they usually share oxygens of the SiO_4 groups to give an octahedral configuration around the cation. Aluminum can replace Si in the SiO_4 tetrahedra, requiring the addition of another cation or the replacement of one by another of higher charge to maintain charge balance. Aluminum can also occupy the octahedral sites of other cations.

SILICATES CONTAINING "DISCRETE" ANIONS

The term "discrete" ion, in discussing silicates, is used when the oxygen atoms belonging to one silicate anion are not shared with another silicate anion. The silicate ions are not discrete in the sense of independent rotation as are the perchlorate ions in alkali metal perchlorates at temperatures above *ca.* 300°C. The most simple discrete silicate anion is the orthosilicate ion, SiO_4^{4-}. In the orthosilicates forsterite, $Mg_2[SiO_4]$,

* These eight elements account for 98.6% by weight of the crust: O, 46.60%; Si, 27.72%; Al, 8.13%; Fe, 5.00%; Ca, 3.63%; Mg, 2.09%; Na, 2.83%; and K, 2.59%.

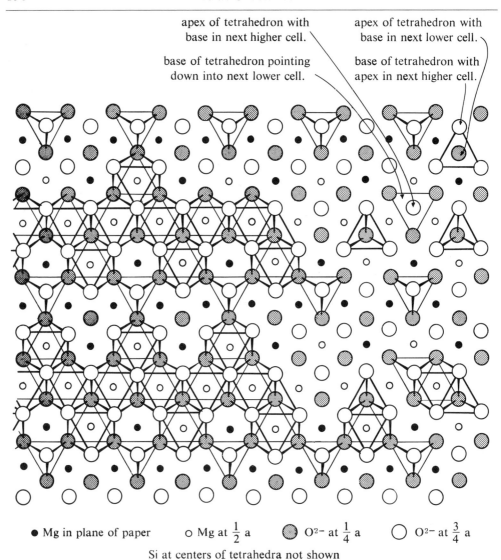

apex of tetrahedron with
base in next higher cell.

apex of tetrahedron with
base in next lower cell.

base of tetrahedron pointing
down into next lower cell.

base of tetrahedron with
apex in next higher cell.

● Mg in plane of paper   ○ Mg at $\frac{1}{2}$ a   ◉ O^{2-} at $\frac{1}{4}$ a   ○ O^{2-} at $\frac{3}{4}$ a

Si at centers of tetrahedra not shown

FIGURE 3.12. *Forsterite (or olivine) structure of close-packed oxide layers with* Si *in tetrahedral holes and* Mg *in octahedral holes (projection on bc plane).*

and olivine, $(Mg,Fe)_2[SiO_4]$, the SiO_4 tetrahedra are stacked around the divalent cation to give it an octahedral configuration. The structure (see Figure 3.12) can be regarded as an array of close-packed layers of oxide ions with Si^{4+} ions in tetrahedral voids ($\frac{1}{8}$ occupied) and M^{2+} ions in octahedral voids ($\frac{1}{2}$ occupied). The SiO_4^{4-} discrete ion gives the most compact structures for silicates. Sharing oxygen atoms by two or more Si atoms actually opens up the structure.

The uncommon mineral phenacite, $Be_2[SiO_4]$, contains the very small Be^{2+} ions in tetrahedral sites. In zircon, $Zr[SiO_4]$, the large Zr^{4+} ion has a coordination number of eight. The garnets, $M_3^{II}M_2^{III}[SiO_4]_3$, where M^{II} is Ca, Mg, or Fe and M^{III} is Al, Cr, or

Fe, have a more complex structure which gives a coordination number of eight to the M^{II} ions and a coordination number of six to the M^{III} ions. These minerals can be seen to conform to Pauling's second rule. Each oxygen is shared by one Si and three Mg in forsterite, by one Si and two Be in phenacite, by one Si and two Zr in zircon, and by one Si, one Al, and two Ca in garnet. Pauling's rules would not have predicted these unambiguously, but may be thought of as an aid in guiding structure determination.

Discrete anions containing short chains of SiO_4 tetrahedra might be expected, but these are rare. The $Si_2O_7^{6-}$ anion is encountered in thortveitite, $Sc_2[Si_2O_7]$, and in a few other minerals of greater complexity. These are very few examples of short chains containing more than two SiO_4 groups. Discrete anions consisting of rings of SiO_4 groups are more commonly encountered. Rings of three tetrahedra (to give six-membered rings) containing the anion $[Si_3O_9]^{6-}$ are encountered in wollastonite, $Ca_3[Si_3O_9]$, and benitoite, $BaTi[Si_3O_9]$. The anion $[Si_6O_{18}]^{12-}$, consisting of a ring of six tetrahedra, is found in the emerald, which is the mineral beryl, $Al_2Be_3[Si_6O_{18}]$. In beryl an oxygen is shared by one Si, one Al (coordination number six), and one Be (coordination number four) in accordance with Pauling's second rule. One Al is substituted for an Si in the ring in cordierite, $Mg_2Al_3[AlSi_5O_{18}]$ (Figure 3.13).

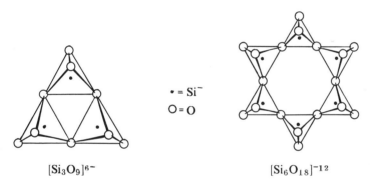

$$[Si_3O_9]^{6-} \qquad \bullet = Si^- \qquad O = O \qquad [Si_6O_{18}]^{-12}$$

FIGURE 3.13. *Cyclic silicate anions.*

SILICATES CONTAINING INFINITE CHAINS

Single Chains. Each SiO_4 tetrahedron can share two oxygens to give single chains of indefinite length (Figure 3.14). The anion can be represented by the formula of the repeating unit, SiO_3^{2-}. Minerals of this type are called the *pyroxenes*. These include enstatite, $Mg[SiO_3]$, diopside, $CaMg[SiO_3]_2$, and spodumene, $LiAl[Si_2O_6]$. The non-bridging oxygens in enstatite are shared with magnesium to give it a coordination number of six. In diopside the Mg has a coordination number of six and the Ca has a coordination number of eight. Both Li and Al are six-coordinate in spodumene.

Double Chains. A class of minerals known as the amphiboles contain double chains of SiO_4 tetrahedra (Figure 3.14). The chains are joined to form rings of six tetrahedra. The repeating unit is $Si_4O_{11}^{6-}$ with half of the silicon atoms sharing three oxygens with other Si atoms and half of them sharing only two oxygens with other Si atoms. The amphiboles always contain some OH^- groups associated with the metal ion. Tremolite,

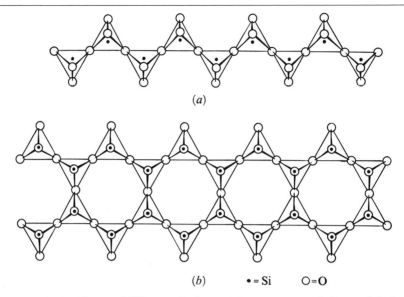

(a)

(b)   • = Si   ○ = O

FIGURE 3.14. *Chains of* SiO_4 *tetrahedra in (a) pyroxenes and (b) amphiboles.*

$Ca_2Mg_5[(OH)_2|(Si_4O_{11})_2]$, is a typical amphibole. The vertical bar is used in the formula to indicate that the OH is not a part of the silicate framework.

The asbestos minerals are related to the amphiboles, but the structures are more complex.

Silicates Containing Sheets. Each silicon atom can share three oxygen atoms with other Si atoms to give large sheets. Crosslinking similar to that in the amphiboles, but extending indefinitely in two dimensions, gives rings of six Si in talc, $Mg_3[(OH)_2|Si_4O_{10}]$, and biotite, $K(Mg,Fe)_3[(OH)_2|AlSi_3O_{10}]$. Biotite is one of the mica minerals. The SiO_4 (and AlO_4) tetrahedra form sheets of interlocking rings with the unshared oxygens pointed in the same direction. Two of these sheets are arranged parallel with the unshared oxygens pointed inward. These oxygens and the OH$^-$ ions are bonded to the Mg^{2+} and Fe^{2+}, which are between the sheets. The double sheets are weakly bonded together by the K^+ ions, accounting for the characteristic cleavage into thin sheets.

Apophyllite, $Ca_4K[F|(Si_4O_{10})_2]\cdot 8H_2O$, contains sheets made up of SiO_4 tetrahedra linked to form alternating 4- and 8-membered rings. The sheets are not doubled in this case because the oxygens not shared between Si atoms do not all point in the same direction. The K^+ and Ca^{2+} ions lie between the sheets associated with the oxygens that are not part of the interlocking network of the sheets.

Framework Silicates. If SiO_4 tetrahedra are linked by the sharing of all four oxygens to give a three-dimensional framework, one of the modifications of SiO_2 results. The replacement of Si by Al requires the addition of another cation to give the framework silicates. Three groups of framework silicates are encountered: the feldspars, the zeolites, characterized by a very open structure so that the minerals are effective cation exchangers, and the ultramarines, which have a basket-like framework, are commonly colored, and hence are used as pigments.

The feldspars are the most important of the framework silicates from the standpoint of abundance. They make up about two-thirds of the igneous rocks, and thus are the most important of the rock-forming minerals. The general formula for the feldspars was given (p. 129) as $M(Al,Si)_4O_8$. When the ratio of Si:Al is 3:1, M is Na or K, and when it is 2:2, M is Ca or Ba. The two classes of feldspars are not based on the charge on the cation, but on the crystal symmetry. The monoclinic feldspars, including orthoclase, $K[AlSi_3O_8]$, and celsian, $Ba[Al_2Si_2O_8]$, contain the larger cations. The substitution of Na^+ for K^+ or Ca^{2+} for Ba^{2+} does not occur extensively. The triclinic feldspars are referred to as the plagioclase feldspars. A number of minerals in this series are known, varying in composition from albite, $Na[AlSi_3O_8]$, to anorthite, $Ca[Al_2Si_2O_8]$, corresponding to the isomorphous substitution of Ca^{2+} for Na^+.

REFERENCES

Wells, A. F., *Structural Inorganic Chemistry* (3rd ed.; Oxford: Oxford University Press, 1962) Chapters 3, 4 and 5.

Ketelaar, J. A. A., *Chemical Constitution* (Amsterdam: Elsevier Publishing Co., 1958).

van Arkel, A. E., *Molecules and Crystals* (2nd ed.; New York: Interscience Publishers, Inc., 1956).

Pauling, L., *The Nature of the Chemical Bond* (3rd ed.; Ithaca: Cornell University Press, 1960) Chapter 13.

Rice, F. O., and E. Teller, *The Structure of Matter* (New York: John Wiley and Sons, Inc., 1949) Chapter 8.

Rice, O. K., *Electronic Structure and Chemical Binding* (New York: McGraw-Hill Book Co., Inc., 1940) Chapters 14 and 19.

Stillwell, C. W., *Crystal Chemistry* (New York: McGraw-Hill Book Co., Inc., 1938) Chapters 2, 5–8, and 10.

Waddington, T. C., "Lattice Energies," in *Advances in Inorganic Chemistry and Radiochemistry*, Vol. I, H. J. Emeleus and A. G. Sharpe, eds. (New York: Academic Press, Inc., 1959).

Dunitz, J. D., and L. E. Orgel, "Stereochemistry of Inorganic Solids," in *Advances in Inorganic Chemistry and Radiochemistry*, Vol. II, H. J. Emeleus and A. G. Sharpe, eds. (New York: Academic Press, Inc., 1959).

Kapustinskii, A. F., "Lattice Energy of Ionic Crystals," *Quart. Rev.*, **10**, 283 (1956).

Stern, R. H., and E. S. Amis, "Ionic Size," *Chem. Rev.*, **59**, 1 (1959).

Etzel, H. W., "Ionic Crystals," *J. Chem. Educ.*, **38**, 225 (1961).

Honig, J. M., "Imperfections in Crystals," *J. Chem. Educ.*, **34**, 224, 343 (1957).

Problems

1. Rubidium chloride assumes the CsCl structure at high pressures. Calculate the Rb—Cl distance in the CsCl structure from that for the NaCl structure (from ionic radii).

2. Calculate the M—X distances for LiF, BeO, and BN as the sum of the ionic radii and considering the charge effects.

3. By using plane geometry calculate the cation/anion radius ratio for a triangular arrangement in which the cation is in contact with the anions but does not push them apart.

4.   Compare the thermochemical data for the alkali halides. What factors are important in establishing the order of increasing heats of formation within each group of halides (fluorides, chlorides, etc.)?

5.   Calculate the heat of formation of NaF_2 and the heat of reaction to produce $NaF + \frac{1}{2}F_2$. (Check result with Waddington, see references).

6.   Calculate the heats of formation of Ne^+F^- and Na^+Ne^-. What factors prohibit the formation of these compounds in spite of favorable lattice energies? (Check result with Waddington, see references).

7.   The recent values for the bond energy of F_2 and the electron affinity of F are quite different from those used in texts until very recently. Calculate the dissociation energy of F_2 from the other thermochemical quantities for NaF using 93 kcal as the electron affinity for F (old value).

8.   From spectral data the dissociation energy of ClF has been determined to be 58.9 kcal. The ΔH_f^0 of ClF(g) is -13.4 kcal/mole. The dissociation energy of Cl_2 is 57.0 kcal/mole. Calculate the dissociation energy of F_2.

9.   For each of the following pairs indicate which substance is expected to be:

    (*a*) More covalent (Fajans' Rules):

$MgCl_2$	or	$BeCl_2$	$SnCl_2$	or	$SnCl_4$
$CaCl_2$	or	$ZnCl_2$	$CdCl_2$	or	CdI_2
$CaCl_2$	or	$CdCl_2$	ZnO	or	ZnS
$TiCl_3$	or	$TiCl_4$	NaF	or	CaO

    (*b*) Harder:

NaF	or	$NaBr$	MgF_2	or	TiO_2
Al_2O_3	or	Ga_2O_3			

10.   Calculate the energy released when a mole of gaseous sodium chloride molecules form (*a*) dimers; (*b*) tetramers; (*c*) solid NaCl.

11.   Compare the ionic radii of Na^+ and Mg^{2+} and also those of S^{2-} and Cl^-. Explain the causes of the variations.

12.   Calculate the crystal radii of P^{5+} and P^{3-} starting with the internuclear separations of 3.14 Å for KCl and 2.31 Å for NaF.

13.   If Ge is added to GaAs, the Ge is about equally distributed between the Ga and As sites. Which sites would the Ge prefer if Se is added also? Would GaAs doped with Se be an *n*-type or a *p*-type semiconductor?

CHAPTER IV

Thermodynamic Considerations

One of the most compact ways of storing chemical information is in the form of tables of thermodynamic properties of substances. A single entry may be the summary of months of investigation. Thermodynamic data may be used not only to reconstruct much of the information from which the data came, but also to make predictions about unknown reactions. Extensive tables giving standard free energies and heats of formation, and entropies; free energy functions, and half-cell electromotive force data are available.*

Of particular interest to the chemist is the free energy change accompanying a reaction under a given set of conditions for this indicates the direction of the reaction in approaching equilibrium.

Conventions Regarding Standard States

At equilibrium the free energy change accompanying a reaction at a fixed temperature and pressure is zero. Thus, from the equilibrium partial pressures at $1000°K$ of 0.564 atm SO_2, 0.102 atm O_2, and 0.333 atm SO_3, one may write

$$2SO_2(0.564 \text{ atm}) + O_2(0.102 \text{ atm}) \rightarrow 2SO_3(0.333 \text{ atm}) \quad \Delta F_{1000°K} = 0$$

Assuming ideal gas behavior for the above system one may write

$$K_p = \frac{(P_{SO_3})^2}{(P_{SO_2})^2(P_{O_2})} = 3.42 \text{ atm}^{-1} \quad \text{or} \quad 4.5 \times 10^{-3} \text{ mm}^{-1}$$

The ΔF value for the above reaction may be found under conditions other than the equilibrium value by means of an equation known as the van't Hoff reaction isotherm:

$$\Delta F_T = RT \ln \frac{Q}{K} \tag{4.1}$$

where Q is an activity quotient having a form similar to the equilibrium constant but in which the activity values may be arbitrary. Thus at $1000°K$ and with $P_{SO_2} = 5$ atm, $P_{O_2} = 2$ atm, and $P_{SO_3} = 10$ atm

* See the general references listed at the end of the chapter.

$$Q = \frac{(10)^2}{(5)^2(2)} = 2 \text{ atm}^{-1}$$

$$K = 3.42 \text{ atm}^{-1}$$

and

$$\Delta F_{1000°K} = 2.303 \times 1.982 \times 1000(\log 2 - \log 3.42) = -1057 \text{ cal}$$

Under the stated conditions, equilibrium would be approached by formation of SO_3.

The units used in expressing Q and K must, of course, be the same. When the arbitrary activity of unity is selected for both the reactants and products the free energy change for the reaction is called the "standard" free energy change and is designated by superscript zero, i.e., ΔF^0.

From the relationship $\Delta F^0 = -RT \ln K$ one may calculate a "standard" free energy change for the SO_2 oxidation as follows:

$$2SO_2 \text{ (1 atm)} + O_2 \text{ (1 atm)} \longrightarrow 2SO_3 \text{ (1 atm)} \quad \Delta F^0{}_{1000°K} = -2440 \text{ cal}$$

or

$$2SO_2 \text{ (1 mm)} + O_2 \text{ (1 mm)} \longrightarrow 2SO_3 \text{ (1 mm)} \quad \Delta F^0{}_{1000°K} = +10750 \text{ cal*}$$

From this example it may readily be seen that the equilibrium constant and the standard free energy change are dependent upon the standard states selected for the reactants and products.

For thermodynamic equilibrium constants the quantities used in the equilibrium product should be activities rather than concentrations. The standard state of any substance is defined as a state of unit activity. Convention is as follows: for *gases* the standard state is unit fugacity, i.e., the gas behaving ideally at 1 atm pressure. For most gases the standard state may thus be taken as 1 atm. For *pure liquids* and *solids*, which occur as separate phases in reactions, the standard state is conventionally defined as the pure solid or pure liquid at 1 atm pressure. Conventions regarding *solutions* are not as uniform as those for gases and pure liquids or solids. The standard state for the solvent is usually taken as that of the pure liquid. For the solute the standard state may be taken as an *activity* (a) (thermodynamic concentration) of one molal. For approximate calculations *concentration* (m) in units of molality may be used instead of activities. These two quantities may be related to each other through the use of activity coefficients (γ)

$$a = \gamma m$$

At high dilution γ approaches 1. It should be noted that the use of activities in terms of molarities or mole fractions involves different standard states from those selected by the use of molalities.

EXAMPLES: 1. A standard free energy change of 10900 cal is calculated from the K_{sp} for $PbSO_4$. Write the reaction for which this ΔF^0 applies.

$$PbSO_4(s) \longrightarrow Pb^{2+} \ (\gamma^{\pm}m = 1) + SO_4{}^{2-} \ (\gamma^{\pm}m = 1)$$

---

* The standard state assumed here is not the conventional one and this ΔF would normally not be designated as ΔF^0, *vide infra*.

2. At 20°C K_N is 4 for the esterification reaction of acetic acid with ethanol. Mole fractions are used as concentrations in the expression for K_N. Calculate ΔF^0 and write the hypothetical reaction to which it applies. What data would be needed to calculate K_p?

$$\Delta F^0 = -RT \ln K_N = -820 \text{ cal}$$

for the reaction

$$CH_3CO_2H(l) + C_2H_5OH(l) \longrightarrow CH_3CO_2C_2H_5(l) + H_2O(l)$$

This must also be the free energy change for the above reaction when each of the substances is in the gas phase with a partial pressure equal to the vapor pressure of the pure liquid. K_p may thus be found by using the ΔF^0 as ΔF in Equation 4.1 and evaluating Q from the vapor pressures.

Methods of Determining Changes in Free Energy

Changes in free energy, enthalpy, and entropy are related through the equation

$$\Delta F = \Delta H - T\Delta S$$

Knowledge of any two of these quantities allows the other to be calculated, while knowledge of all three provides a check on the assumptions involved in the calculation and/or in the experimental methods. The more common methods used to obtain one or more of these pieces of information are:

(1) Direct calorimetric measurement of heats of reaction
(2) Heat capacity measurements
(3) Direct determination of equilibrium constants
(4) Galvanic cell potentials
(5) Statistical mechanics and appropriate spectral data
(6) Approximation methods

Calorimetric Data

The enthalpy, entropy, or free energy change accompanying a reaction is independent of the reaction path. Accordingly, if ΔH (or ΔF or ΔS) values are known for all but one step in a cycle, the value for the last step may be readily obtained. Thus from the knowledge of the enthalpy changes for the combustion of C to CO_2 and CO to CO_2 one may calculate the heat of combustion of C to CO, i.e.,

(1) $O_2(g) + C(s) \longrightarrow CO_2(g)$ $\qquad \Delta H^0 = -94.05 \text{ kcal}$
(2) $\frac{1}{2} O_2(g) + CO(g) \longrightarrow CO_2(g)$ $\qquad \Delta H^0 = -67.63 \text{ kcal}$
$\overline{\quad \frac{1}{2} O_2(g) + C(s) \longrightarrow CO(g) \quad \Delta H^0{}_3 = \Delta H^0{}_1 - \Delta H^0{}_2 = -26.42 \text{ kcal}}$

It is convenient *to define* the standard heat of formation at a particular reference temperature as the heat of reaction of the elements to form a compound, both reactants and product being in their standard states. By this definition the elements in their stable form at a particular reference temperature have $\Delta H^0{}_f$ values of zero. Extensive tables of heats of formation are available and allow the calculation of ΔH^0 at 25°C by the simple equation

$$\Delta H^0 = \Sigma \; \Delta H^0_f \; \text{(products)} - \Sigma \; \Delta H^0_f \; \text{(reactants)}$$

Coupled with heat capacity data and heats of transition for phase changes, ΔH^0 may be calculated at other temperatures.

The standard enthalpy of a solute includes not only the heat of formation of the isolated solute, but also its heat of solution. By adopting the *convention* that the H^+ ion in aqueous solution at 25°C be assigned a ΔH^0_f of zero it is possible to assign ΔH^0_f values to other ions in aqueous solution.

PROBLEM: Calculate the heat of reaction of

$$\text{AgNO}_3 \; (1 \; \text{molar}) + \text{NaCl (solid)} \longrightarrow \text{AgCl (solid)} + \text{NaNO}_3 \; (1 \; \text{molar})$$

$$\Delta H = \Delta H^0_{\text{AgCl}} + \Delta H^0_{\text{Na}^+\text{(aq)}} - \Delta H^0_{\text{Ag}^+\text{(aq)}} - \Delta H^0_{\text{NaCl}}$$

Using values from Latimer:

$$\Delta H = -30.36 - 57.28 - (+25.31) - (-98.23)$$
$$= -14.72 \; \text{kcal}$$

Standard free energies of formation of compounds and ions follow the same conventions as ΔH^0_f. If standard free energies of formation are known for both reactants and products the standard free energy change of the reaction may be calculated

$$\Delta F^0 = \Sigma \; \Delta F^0_f \; \text{(products)} - \Sigma \; \Delta F^0_f \; \text{(reactants)}$$

PROBLEM: Calculate ΔF^0 for

$$\text{AgNO}_3 \; (1 \; \text{molar}) + \text{NaCl (solid)} \longrightarrow \text{AgCl (solid)} + \text{NaNO}_3 \; (1 \; \text{molar})$$
Using values from Latimer:

$$\Delta F^0 = -26.22 + (-62.59) - (18.43) - (-91.78)$$
$$\Delta F^0 = -15.47 \; \text{kcal}$$

The convention regarding entropy differs from the convention for enthalpy and free energy in that most pure crystalline substances are assigned an entropy of zero at 0°K. The substances not assigned zero values at absolute zero are those having a degree of randomness in their crystalline lattice and hence a residual entropy. This convention is based on the third law of thermodynamics. Entropies for the substance at temperatures above 0°K may be obtained from heat capacity data coupled with heats of transition and the entropy at 0°K.

$$S_T = \int_0^T C_p \, d \ln T + \Sigma \left(\frac{\Delta H_{tr}}{T_{tr}} \right) + R \, \ln \sigma \qquad (4.2)$$

The integral may be evaluated graphically, the $\ln \sigma$ term gives the 0° entropy (σ is the number of distinguishable orientations of the molecule in the crystal at 0°K). An exception to the above convention is the hydrogen ion, which is assigned a molal entropy of zero at 25°C at infinite dilution in aqueous solution. This allows entropy values to be assigned to other ions.

Values of $\Delta H^0{}_f$, $\Delta F^0{}_f$, and S^0 at 25°C have been tabulated for many substances. These tabulations permit predictions to be made about reactions occurring at 25°C and 1 atm. $\Delta H^0{}_f$ and $\Delta F^0{}_f$ values at higher temperatures are becoming increasingly available.*

PROBLEM: Calculate the equilibrium constant at 2500°K for

$$SiO_2(l) + Si(l) \rightarrow 2SiO(g)$$

From Elliott and Gleiser the $\Delta F^0{}_f$ values at 2500°K are $-63,900$ and $-101,500$ cal/mole, respectively,

$$\Delta F^0 = 2(-63,900) - (-101,500) = -26,300$$
$$K_p = \exp_{10}\left(-\frac{\Delta F^0}{2.3RT}\right) = \exp_{10}\left(\frac{26,300}{2.3 \times 1.98 \times 2500}\right) = 10^{2.31} = 204 \text{ atm}^2$$

SiO is thermodynamically unstable at room temperature, but a quenched sample is kinetically stable. SiO condensed from the gas on optical parts provides a protective coating.

Approximate values for ΔF at temperatures other than 25°C may be obtained by assuming ΔH and ΔS are temperature-independent. ΔF may then be obtained by $\Delta F_T = \Delta H_{298°K} - T\Delta S_{298°K}$. This is equivalent to the assumption that ΔC_p for the reaction is zero. More accurate values for ΔF at temperatures other than 298°K may be made from free energy function data (see p. 153).

Displacement reactions of the type

$$AB_x + yC \rightleftharpoons AC_y + xB$$

generally occur if ΔH_f of AC_y per equivalent is much greater than that of AB_x per equivalent (i.e., the reaction is exothermic). When the heats of formation are almost the same, entropy effects may cause endothermic reactions to occur, as in the case of

$$Ag(s) + Hg_2Cl_2(s) \rightleftharpoons AgCl(s) + Hg(l)$$

Van Arkel† has generalized on data such as that in Table 4.1 to construct the following displacement chart for the nonmetals in ionic compounds shown in Figure 4.1.

* See particularly Elliott and Gleiser under general references. This volume contains such data for carbides, nitrides, oxides, phosphides, silicides and sulfides as well as C_p, S, free energy functions and enthalpy functions for a number of elements.
† Van Arkel, A. E., *Molecules and Crystals in Inorganic Chemistry*, translated by J. C. Swallow, (New York: Interscience Publishers, A Division of John Wiley and Sons, Inc., 2nd ed., 1946) Chapter 5.

TABLE 4.1
Some Heats of Formation in kcal per Equivalent

LiF	Li$_2$O	Li$_3$N
145.5	71	15
NaF	Na$_2$O	Na$_3$N
136	49.5	0
CaO	CaS	CaSe
76	57	44

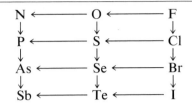

FIGURE 4.1. *Displacement chart for the nonmetals.*

Except for halogen displacement, these reactions are generally slow at room temperature. At higher temperatures more complex reactions might occur. Free energy functions are used to make better predictions since (*1*) entropy changes are not ignored, (*2*) data are available in this form for many materials at high temperatures.

Schematic Representation of Galvanic Cells

Electrodes—An electrode consists of a metallic conductor in contact with (or a part of) a phase boundary across which a difference in electrical potential occurs. The phase boundary is represented by a single vertical line |. The composition of the phases is indicated on the two sides of the vertical line. The schematic representation of the electrode signifies a half-reaction in which positive ions move from left to right and negative ions move from right to left. The representations below thus imply the half-reactions which follow.

Electrode	Half-Reaction
$Ag \mid Ag^+(aq)$	$Ag(s) \rightarrow Ag^+(aq) + e$
$Ag^+(aq) \mid Ag(s)$	$Ag^+(aq) + e \rightarrow Ag(s)$
$Pt(s) \mid Fe^{2+}(aq), Fe^{3+}(aq)$	$Fe^{2+}(aq) \rightarrow Fe^{3+}(aq) + e$
$Ag(s), AgCl(s) \mid Cl^-(aq)$	$Ag(s) + Cl^-(aq) \rightarrow AgCl(s) + e$
$Pt(s), H_2(g) \mid H^+(aq)$	$\frac{1}{2}H_2(g) \rightarrow H^+(aq) + e$

The last electrode listed above is called the hydrogen electrode and under standard conditions has a defined electrical potential of zero. It consists of a platinum electrode coated with platinum black in contact with a solution saturated with hydrogen. An early design by Hildebrand, which is still widely used, is shown in Figure 4.2.

Conventions Regarding Cells

In order to construct a galvanic cell one must be able to carry out an oxidation half-reaction and a reduction half-reaction in separate places (i.e., at the electrodes). Electrolytic conduction (current carried by ions) must be possible internally and metallic conduction (current carried by electrons) externally. For some systems the electrolyte may be the same throughout the cell and the cell represented by the appropriate combination of electrodes as in the following example:

CELL $Pt, H_2(g) \mid HCl(aq) \mid AgCl(s), Ag$

REACTION $AgCl(s) + \frac{1}{2}H_2 \rightarrow Ag(s) + HCl(aq)$

To construct a cell in which the reaction $Zn + 2HCl \rightarrow H_2 + ZnCl_2$ may be carried out reversibly it is necessary to prevent the hydrogen ion from coming into direct con-

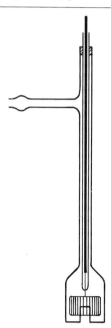

FIGURE 4.2. *The hydrogen electrode [from J. H. Hildebrand,*
J. Am. Chem. Soc., *35, 847 (1913)]*.

tact with the Zn. One technique by which this may be done is to insert a salt bridge which prevents the direct mixing of the electrolytes of the two electrodes. The salt bridge may be designated by two parallel vertical lines ||. It may introduce liquid junction potentials, which will not be discussed here. The reaction of hydrogen ion and Zn could thus be reversibly carried out in the following cell

$$Zn(s) \mid ZnCl_2(aq) \parallel HCl(aq) \mid H_2(g), Pt(s)$$

Electrode Potentials

When two electrodes are coupled to make a cell the voltage developed by the cell will simply be the difference in the electrical potential of the two electrodes. If the hydrogen electrode under standard conditions is assigned a potential of zero then the potential of any electrode relative to hydrogen may be assigned. By this convention the potential of the Zn electrode in contact with Zn ions under standard conditions is −0.76 V. It may be noted that the sign of the *potential* of the Zn electrode is independent of the cell in which the Zn electrode occurs whether oxidation or reduction takes place at the Zn electrode.

Half-Cell emf Values

By the conventions stated earlier the electromotive force for the reversible operation of the cell

$$Zn(s) \mid Zn^{2+}(aq) \parallel H^+(aq) \mid H_2(g), Pt(s)$$

is related to the free energy change for the reaction

$$Zn(s) + 2H^+(aq) \rightarrow Zn^{2+}(aq) + H_2(g) \tag{4.3}$$

through the relationship

$$\Delta F^0 = -n \mathcal{F} E^0$$

where $\mathcal{F}$ is the Faraday electrochemical constant 23.06 kcal/abs Vg equiv and n is the number of Faradays passed by the external circuit of the cell in carrying out the chemical reaction as written.

Since the conventions assign ΔF^0_f values of zero for hydrogen and hydrogen ion the ΔF^0_f value obtained may be assigned entirely to the free energy change for the oxidation half-reaction

$$Zn \rightarrow Zn^{2+} + 2e \qquad E^0 = +0.76$$

Since reaction (4.3) occurs spontaneously under standard conditions, ΔF^0 must be negative and accordingly E^0 positive. For the reverse of reaction (4.3)

$$H_2(g) + Zn^{2+}(aq) \rightarrow Zn(s) + 2H^+(aq)$$

the signs on ΔF^0 and E^0 will be reversed and accordingly E^0 for the reduction half-reaction

$$Zn^{2+}(aq) + 2e \rightarrow Zn(s) \qquad E^0 = -0.76$$

will be reversed. It may be noted that the standard emf for a reduction half-reaction is identical in sign and magnitude to the value of the standard potential for the electrode at which the half-reaction may be carried out. It has already been noted that the electrode potential is independent of whether an oxidation or reduction reaction is taking place at the electrode. Accordingly, terms such as oxidation potentials or reduction potentials are inappropriate when one is talking about electromotive force values for half-cell oxidation or reduction reactions. Nevertheless, the International Union of Pure and Applied Chemistry has agreed to the use of the word "potential" as synonymous with the emf value for the *reduction* half-cell reaction. Due to the general lack of adherence to a single convention in many sources of emf data the reader is well advised to remember the sign of a half-cell emf reaction such as given in Equation (4.3) and to check the sign given this half-reaction in any tabulation which he may use.

Calculations Using emf Diagrams

Given below is an emf diagram for the standard half-cell oxidation reactions in acid solution at 25°C.

$$E^0_A \quad Mn \xrightarrow{1.19} Mn^{2+} \xrightarrow{-1.51} Mn^{3+} \xrightarrow{-0.95} MnO_2 \xrightarrow{-2.26} MnO_4{}^{2-} \xrightarrow{-0.564} MnO_4{}^-$$

Except for the use of the arrows to designate the direction of the half-cell reaction the above diagram is identical with those given by Latimer* in his extensive treatment. The above diagram abbreviates the half-reactions by showing only the substances which

---

* Latimer, W. M., *The Oxidation States of the Elements and Their Potentials in Aqueous Solution* (2nd ed., New York: Prentice-Hall, Inc., 1952).

change in oxidation number. Thus the E^0 of -2.26 is for the half-reaction*

$$2H_2O + MnO_2 \rightarrow MnO_4{}^{2-} + 4H^+ + 2e \qquad E^0 = -2.26$$

The super zero implies that all substances shown in the equation are in their standard states; $E^0{}_A$ specifically indicates that the hydrogen ion activity is unity, while $E^0{}_B$ indicates the hydroxide ion activity is unity. For many practical purposes the prediction of a reaction without evaluating activity coefficients can be made directly using *formal emf values*. The formal emf, E^0, is the emf of a half-reaction with the *concentrations* of oxidant and reductant equal to unity, and with arbitrarily chosen concentrations of other electrolytes, including acids. A disadvantage for formal emf values is that they vary with the ionic strength of the solution and a given list applies to one ionic strength only. The emf for the reduction of an oxyanion such as $Cr_2O_7{}^{2-}$ varies tremendously with changes in acidity. If formal emf values are available for a particular medium, reaction predictions based on them can be made conveniently. In many practical situations the necessary activity coefficients are not easily available to permit the use of the standard emf data. Formal emf values in $1M$ perchloric acid solution are often used as close approximations of $E^0{}_A$ values.

Combination of Half-Cell emf Values to Obtain Other Half-Cell emf Values
(the use of volt equivalents)

From the emf diagram given for manganese one may find the half-cell emf values for any half-reaction that occurs between a pair of the species given in the diagram. Since the E^0 refers to the voltage per electron the evaluation of the E^0 for the new half-reaction corresponds to calculating a weighted average. Volt equivalents, that is, the product of the number of electrons involved in the half-reaction and the E^0 of the half-reaction are used. That this gives the same E^0 as the use of the more familiar handling of ΔF^0 values may be seen from the following example.

Reaction	E^0	$\Delta F^0 = -n\mathscr{F}E^0$	nE^0 (volt equivalent)
$Mn \rightarrow Mn^{2+} + 2e$	1.19	$-2\mathscr{F}1.19$	2.38
$Mn^{2+} \rightarrow Mn^{3+} + e$	-1.51	$\mathscr{F}1.51$	-1.51
$Mn \rightarrow Mn^{3+} + 3e$	$\Delta F^0 = -0.87\mathscr{F}$ $\qquad E^0 = \dfrac{-(-0.87\mathscr{F})}{3\mathscr{F}} = 0.29$		0.87

Summarizing, the E^0 for a couple may be obtained as the sum of the E^0 values of intervening couples each multiplied by the number of electrons involved, divided by the total number of electrons involved in the new half-reaction. Thus the $E^0{}_A$ value for $Mn^{2+} \rightarrow MnO_4{}^-$ is given by

$$\frac{(1)(-1.51) + (1)(-0.95) + (2)(-2.26) + (1)(-0.564)}{5} = -1.51 \text{ V}$$

---

* The half-reactions may readily be written by the following sequence: (*1*) The equation is balanced with respect to the atoms undergoing change in oxidation number. (*2*) A balance of oxygen atoms is obtained by adding H_2O to the appropriate side of the equation. (*3*) The equation is balanced with respect to hydrogen atoms by adding H^+ to the appropriate side of the equation. (*4*) The equation is balanced with respect to charge by adding electrons to the appropriate side of the equation.

Effect of pH on Half-Cell emf Values

The effect of variation of activity (thermodynamic concentration) on the emf of a cell or half-cell is given by the Nernst equation

$$E = E^0 - \frac{RT}{n\mathfrak{F}} \ln Q$$

where Q is an activity product having the same form as the equilibrium constant, but in which the activities need not represent equilibrium values. If there are no changes in the species involved, the Nernst equation readily permits the effect of pH on the emf values to be calculated.

PROBLEM: Given E^0_A for the couple $MnO_2(s) \rightarrow MnO_4^{2-}$ calculate the standard emf value in base.

From the Nernst equation and the balanced half-reaction we may write

$$E = E^0_A - \frac{0.059}{2} \log (H^+)^4 (MnO_4^{2-})$$

For the standard emf value in base the activity of (MnO_4^{2-}) would be unity and that of *hydroxide* ion would be unity. Accordingly the hydrogen ion activity would be 10^{-14} since $(H^+)(OH^-) = K_w = 10^{-14}$. Accordingly

$$E^0_B = -2.26 - \frac{0.059}{2} \log (10^{-14})^4 = -0.60 \text{ V}$$

PROBLEM: Given E^0_A for the couple $MnO_4^{2-} \rightarrow MnO_4^-$ what is E^0_B?

Since hydrogen ion is not involved in the half-reaction E^0_B and E^0_A will be identical.

When a change of pH results in the formation of an insoluble hydroxide the emf value for the half-cell at the new pH may be calculated if the value of K_{sp} is known by application of the Nernst equation. This may be seen from the following free energy cycle

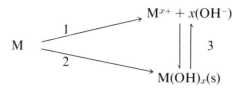

If M^{x+} exists in a solution in contact with $M(OH)_x$ (that is to say, in equilibrium) ΔF for step 3 must be zero and ΔF for steps 1 and 2 must be identical.

PROBLEM: Given $E^0_A = 1.19$ for $Mn \rightarrow Mn^{2+} + 2e$ and K_{sp} for $Mn(OH)_2 = 2 \times 10^{-13}$, what is E^0_B for the $Mn \rightarrow Mn(OH)_2(s)$ couple? K_{sp} is the equilibrium constant for the reaction

$$Mn(OH)_2(s) \rightleftharpoons Mn^{2+} + 2(OH^-)$$
$$K_{sp} = (Mn^{2+})(OH^-)^2$$

In 1 normal base $(OH^-) = 1$ and thus $Mn^{2+} = K_{sp} = 2 \times 10^{-13}$. From the Nernst equation

$$E = E^0 - \frac{0.059}{2} \log Mn^{2+}$$

$$= 1.19 - \frac{0.059}{2} \log 2 \times 10^{-13}$$

$$= 1.56$$

The result for the calculation is that expected qualitatively on the basis of LeChatelier's principle. As the metal ion concentration is decreased, it becomes easier to form the ion from the metal. Similar considerations apply to the effect of complexing of metal ions by ligands such as cyanide, chloride, ammonia, etc. The relative effectiveness of such ligands in decreasing the free metal ion concentration in solution may be seen from the following emf values.

$$Zn + H_2O \rightarrow Zn(H_2O)_w^{2+} + 2e \qquad E^0 = 0.76$$
$$Zn + 4NH_3 \rightarrow Zn(NH_3)_4^{2+}(aq) + 2e \qquad E^0 = 1.03$$
$$Zn + 4CN^- \rightarrow Zn(CN)_4^{2-}(aq) + 2e \qquad E^0 = 1.26$$

The use of emf data to obtain both stoichiometries and stability constants of complex ions is further discussed on page 152.

The Use of Half-Cell emf Data in the Prediction of Chemical Reactions

Since $\Delta F = -n\mathfrak{F}E$ a positive value of E means that the reaction will be "spontaneous" in a thermodynamic sense, that is to say, that the reactants and products are not in equilibrium and equilibrium will be approached by the formation of more product. The major advantage of the use of emf data as compared to free energy data is that in using emf data the stoichiometries need not be taken into account. This is due to the fact that the half-cell emf data are in terms of volts per electron transferred. Thus the sum of the emf values for any oxidation half-reaction and any reduction half-reaction gives an answer as to whether such a reaction may occur "spontaneously."

When a substance is added to water it may be unstable due to one of the following reactions: it may undergo disproportionation, or auto-oxidation–reduction, in which species of higher and lower oxidation states are produced; it may react with water to evolve hydrogen; or it may react with water to evolve oxygen.

PROBLEM: Is Mn^{2+} stable in solution in water?

Referring to the emf diagram for manganese we may obtain a sum for the half-reactions as follows:

	E^0
$Mn^{2+} + 2e \longrightarrow Mn$	-1.19
$2(Mn^{2+} \longrightarrow Mn^{3+} + e)$	-1.51
$3Mn^{2+} \longrightarrow Mn + 2Mn^{3+}$	-2.70

Since E^0 is negative the reaction does not occur and Mn^{2+} does not disproportionate. Note that the emf for the reduction half-reaction

$$2e + Mn^{2+} \longrightarrow Mn$$

is simply the negative of the emf for the oxidation half-reaction given on the emf diagram. In this case it is unnecessary to consider disproportionation to higher oxidation states than Mn^{3+} since inspection of the diagram shows that the half-cell emf for the oxidation of Mn^{2+} to any higher state will be negative. The reader may verify by calculations similar to those given above that Mn^{3+} or MnO_4^{2-} would be unstable with respect to disproportionation in acid solution. In order to determine whether Mn^{3+} and MnO_4^{2-} would be stable in water a new emf diagram should be calculated for pH = 7. For

$$2H_2O + Mn^{3+} \longrightarrow MnO_2(s) + 4H^+ + e$$

$$E = E^0{}_A - \frac{0.059}{1} \log (10^{-7})^4 = 0.73$$

Similar calculations should be made for the $MnO_2 \rightarrow MnO_4^{2-}$ couple. These new emf values are the emf values in neutral water, E_N. The E_N diagram for Mn is as follows:

$$E_N \ Mn \xrightarrow{1.19} Mn^{2+} \xrightarrow{-1.51} Mn^{3+} \xrightarrow{0.73} MnO_2 \xrightarrow{-1.43} MnO_4^{2-} \xrightarrow{-0.564} MnO_4^-$$

$$(-2.86 - 0.56)/3$$

Inspection of this diagram indicates that MnO_4^{2-} will disproportionate in water ($E_N = 1.43 - 0.564$) and Mn^{3+} will disproportionate ($E_N = 1.51 + 0.73$). All other species are stable with respect to disproportionation in water. Disproportionation cannot occur for terminal species (Mn, or MnO_4^-) since such species cannot undergo both oxidation and reduction.

HYDROGEN EVOLUTION

$E^0{}_A$ for the half-reaction

$$H_2 \longrightarrow 2H^+ + 2e$$

is by convention given a value of zero. Using the Nernst equation one obtains $E_N = 0.414$ and $E^0{}_B = 0.828$. For the reaction of manganese with acid an $E^0{}_A$ of 1.18 is obtained. For gas evolution reactions to occur at reasonable rates, the emf for the reaction must generally be of the order of +0.4 V or more due to overvoltage effects, which are specific for both the metal and the gas evolved. Since the $E^0{}_A$ for the reaction of manganese with acid exceeds the gas evolution overvoltage, reaction may be expected to take place. Similarly, E_N for hydrogen evolution by manganese is +0.77 and hydrogen evolution may be expected.

OXYGEN EVOLUTION

The following half-cell emf value may be written for oxygen

$$2H_2O = O_2 + 4H^+ + 4e^- \qquad E^0{}_A = -1.229$$

From this we may obtain $E_N = -0.815$ and $E^0{}_B = -0.401$.

PROBLEM: Will permanganate evolve oxygen in acid solution?
For the reaction

$$2MnO_4^- + H_2O \longrightarrow 2MnO_4^{2-} + \tfrac{1}{2}O_2 + 2H^+$$
$$E^0{}_A = +0.564 - 1.229 = -0.665$$

hence the reaction does not occur. However, for the reaction

$$2MnO_4^- + 2H^+ \longrightarrow 2MnO_2 + H_2O + \tfrac{3}{2}O_2$$
$$E^0_A = 1.695 - 1.229 = 0.466 \text{ V}$$

This value is just barely in excess of the overvoltage needed for oxygen evolution and it is accordingly found that oxygen evolution of permanganate solutions does take place very slowly in acid. The E_N value shows that oxygen evolution will not take place unless a suitable catalyst, such as platinum, is present to reduce the overvoltage.

Overvoltage

In order to carry out an electrolytic reaction resulting in gas evolution, a potential difference, which exceeds that calculated for a reversible galvanic cell, has to be applied to the electrodes. This excess potential is called overvoltage and increases as the current density at the electrodes increases. The overvoltage is dependent on the gas evolved and on the material used for the electrode. Thus at a current density of 0.01 A/sq cm, shiny platinum has a hydrogen overvoltage of 0.07 V, while the oxygen overvoltage is 0.40 V. Under the same conditions nickel has a hydrogen overvoltage of 0.56 V, while the oxygen overvoltage is 0.35 V. Metal deposition does not show an overvoltage effect. Hence, by working at high current density and low temperatures (where overvoltages are highest), it is possible to electroplate from aqueous solution metals, such as nickel, which lie above hydrogen in the activity series.

The overvoltage effect is not limited to reactions carried out in an electrolytic cell, but is present in many reactions producing a gas in solution, particularly those producing hydrogen and oxygen as already noted above.

Use of Approximation Methods in Establishing Half-Cell emf Values

Much of the chemistry of the transuranium elements, and other radioactive elements, has been studied with minute amounts of the radioactive element which go along with workable amounts of an added substance termed a carrier. The presence or absence of the radioactive species is determined by counting techniques. Approximation methods of estimating E^0 values from chemical reactions are extremely useful in this type of chemistry. Thus during the discovery of plutonium it was found that the radioactivity due to plutonium could be separated from solution by precipitating a thorium or rare earth fluoride which carried with it the radioactivity. However, when peroxydisulfate was added to the original solution, the plutonium did not appear in the precipitate indicating that it had been oxidized to a higher oxidation state. Addition of bromate to the original solution did not prevent the plutonium from being precipitated as the fluoride; the bromate did not oxidize the plutonium species.* From this the following emf values may be deduced.

$$\begin{array}{ll} Pu_{red} \longrightarrow Pu_{ox} + ne & E^0 = x \\ 6e + 3H_2O + BrO_3^- \longrightarrow Br^- + 6(OH^-) & E^0 = +0.61 \text{ (known emf)} \\ \hline Pu_{red} + BrO_3^- \longrightarrow Pu_{ox} + Br^- & x + 0.61 < 0 \\ & x < -0.61 \end{array}$$

* Seaborg, G. T., *The Transuranium Elements* (New Haven: Yale University Press, 1958).

From this reaction E^0 is less than (more negative than) -0.61. From the reaction with $S_2O_8^{2-}$

$$\begin{array}{ll} Pu_{red} \longrightarrow Pu_{ox} + ne & E^0 = x \\ \underline{2e + S_2O_8^{2-} \longrightarrow 2SO_4^{2-}} & E^0 = 2.01 \text{ (known emf)} \\ Pu_{red} + S_2O_8^{2-} \longrightarrow Pu_{ox} + SO_4^{2-} & x + 2.01 > 0 \\ & x > -2.01 \end{array}$$

Therefore, $-2.01 < E < -0.61$.

Using other reactions the E^0 value was set at $-1.4 < E < -1$. These E^0 values were useful in suggesting a redox cycle for purifying plutonium.

Approximation methods are not restricted to trace elements but have greatest application here.

PROBLEM: Americium(III) (Am^{3+}) in solution (assume unit molar concentrations) is oxidized by peroxydisulfate ion to Am(VI). Am(VI) is reduced by excess ferrous ion. The ferrous ion is back titrated using cerium(IV) sulfate without removing the Am activity from solution and it is found from the amount of ferrous ion consumed in the reduction that the Am has been reduced to Am(III) by ferrous ion. That Am is in the III state after treatment is then confirmed by demonstration of a known reaction of Am(III). The Am(V)– Am(VI) couple has been measured in acid solution as $E^0 = -1.64$ V. Write the limits for E^0 values of the couples Am(III) $\rightarrow$ Am(V) and Am(III) $\rightarrow$ Am(VI) in acid. If Am is a stronger reducing agent than Zn, are Am(III) and Am(V) stable, unstable, or maybe stable? Explain.

$$\begin{array}{ll} Fe^{2+} = Fe^{3+} + e & E^0 = -0.76 \\ 2SO_4^{2-} = S_2O_8^{2-} + 2e & E^0 = -2.05 \\ Ce(III) = Ce(IV) + e & E^0 = -1.61 \end{array}$$

Solution

$$\begin{array}{ll} Am^{3+} \longrightarrow Am(VI) + 3e & E^0_x \\ \underline{2SO_4^{2-} \longrightarrow S_2O_8^{2-} + 2e} & E^0 = -2.05 \\ 3S_2O_8^{2-} + 2Am^{3+} \longrightarrow 2Am(VI) + 6SO_4 & \quad E^0_x + 2.05 > 0 \\ & \quad E^0_x > -2.05 \end{array}$$

$$\begin{array}{ll} Am^{3+} \longrightarrow Am(VI) + 3e & E_x \\ \underline{Fe^{2+} \longrightarrow Fe^{3+} + e} & E^0 = -0.76 \\ Am(VI) + 3Fe^{2+} \longrightarrow Am^{3+} + 3Fe^{3+} & \quad -E_x - 0.76 > 0 \\ & \quad E_x + 0.76 < 0 \\ & \quad E_x < -0.76 \end{array}$$

$$\begin{array}{ll} Am^{3+} \longrightarrow Am(VI) + 3e & E_x \\ \underline{Ce^{3+} \longrightarrow Ce^{4+} + e} & -1.61 \\ Am^{3+} + Ce(IV) \longrightarrow Ce(III) + Am(VI) & \quad 1.61 + E_x < 0 \\ & \quad E_x < -1.61 \end{array}$$

These limits give

$$\text{Am} \longrightarrow \text{Am}^{3+} \xrightarrow{\ E_y\ } \text{Am(v)} \xrightarrow{-1.64} \text{Am(vi)}$$

$$-2.05 < E_x < -1.61$$

From the interrelationship of E_x and E_y the limits of E_y may be obtained.

$$-2.05 < E_x = \frac{2E_y + 1(-1.64)}{3} < -1.61$$

$$\frac{3(-2.05) + 1.64}{2} < E_y < \frac{3(-1.61) + 1.64}{2}$$

$$-2.25 < E_y < -1.59$$

The last statement of the problem assumes $\text{Am} \xrightarrow{E > 0.76} \text{Am}^{3+}$ and the emf diagram is thus

$$\text{Am} \xrightarrow{E^0 > 0.76} \text{Am}^{3+} \xrightarrow{-2.25 < E^0 < -1.59} \text{Am(v)} \xrightarrow{-1.64} \text{Am(vi)}$$

$$-2.05 < E^0 < -1.61$$

The diagram indicates Am would dissolve in acid solution to form the stable Am(III) species. The Am(v) species may be stable with respect to disproportionation if the upper limit of E_y is attained but it will probably evolve oxygen slowly even if this limit is attained. Am(vi) should decompose water liberating oxygen.

Chemical Reactions

The chemistry of inorganic species in aqueous solution can often be understood from a consideration of emf data. Consider the following data for Cl_2 taken from Latimer.

$$E^0{}_A \ Cl^- \xrightarrow{-1.3595} Cl_2 \xrightarrow{-1.63} HClO \xrightarrow{-1.645} HClO_2 \xrightarrow{-1.27} ClO_2 \xrightarrow{-1.15} ClO_3{}^- \xrightarrow{-1.19} ClO_4{}^-$$

$$E^0{}_B \ Cl^- \xrightarrow{-1.3595} Cl_2 \xrightarrow{-0.40} ClO^- \xrightarrow{-0.66} ClO_2{}^- \xrightarrow{-1.16} ClO_2 \xrightarrow{0.50} ClO_3{}^- \xrightarrow{-0.36} ClO_4{}^-$$

In the laboratory elemental chlorine may be produced from Cl^- sources using a variety of oxidizing agents in acid solution—$KMnO_4$, $K_2Cr_2O_7$, $KClO_3$, MnO_2, PbO_2, etc. Pertinent $E^0{}_A$ values are

$$Mn^{2+} \xleftarrow{1.51} MnO_4{}^- \qquad Cl_2 \xleftarrow{1.47} ClO_3{}^-$$

$$E^0{}_A \qquad Mn^{2+} \xleftarrow{1.23} MnO_2 \qquad Pb^{2+} \xleftarrow{1.455} PbO_2$$

$$Cr^{3+} \xleftarrow{1.33} Cr_2O_7{}^{2-}$$

With MnO_2 and $K_2Cr_2O_7$, a concentrated acid having a hydrogen ion activity greater than 1 is required. The acid usually used is sulfuric acid. Sulfuric acid itself is too weak an oxidizing agent to oxidize the Cl^- ion and thus serves, if used by itself, simply to form hydrogen chloride.

$$E^0_A \qquad S \xleftarrow{+0.45} H_2SO_3 \xleftarrow{+0.17} SO_4^{2-}$$

Although Cl_2 is produced by the action of concentrated nitric acid on chlorides, lower oxides of nitrogen are also produced. A mixture of concentrated nitric and hydrochloric acids (aqua regia) does serve as a strong oxidizing medium for many metals due to the complexing action of the chloride ion with the metal ion produced.

Commercially the electrolysis of brine solutions is used to produce chlorine. Although the evolution of oxygen would be expected to take place at lower voltages than needed for chlorine

$$E_N \qquad H_2O \xrightarrow{-0.815} O_2$$

the overvoltage for oxygen at high current densities is much greater than that for chlorine.

Chlorine reacts slowly with water to liberate oxygen

$$Cl_2 + H_2O \longrightarrow 2HCl + O_2 \qquad E_N = 0.545$$

The more immediate reaction, however, is a disproportionation reaction which is self-repressed by the hydrogen ion formed

$$Cl_2 + H_2O \longrightarrow HOCl + H^+ + Cl^- \qquad E_N = +0.14$$
$$E_{pH4.5} = 0$$

In basic solution hydrolysis is complete ($E^0_B = +0.96$) to give hypochlorite and chloride ions. In one commercial procedure a brine solution is stirred during electrolysis, so that the anode and cathode products mix, and hypochlorite ions are formed. More commonly chlorine is reacted directly with "slaked lime" to form bleaching powder or "chloride of lime"

$$Cl_2 + Ca(OH)_2 \longrightarrow CaCl(OCl) + H_2O$$

Although the couples $Cl^- \xrightarrow{-1.36} Cl_2$ and $H_2O \xrightarrow{-1.23} O_2$ indicate that in acid solution chlorine and oxygen should have about the same ability as oxidizing agents, chlorine is actually much stronger. This is because hydrogen peroxide is an intermediate when oxygen is reduced to water and the $H_2O_2 \rightarrow O_2$ couple is the effective emf available in oxygen oxidations.

$$E^0_A \qquad H_2O \xrightarrow{-1.77} H_2O_2 \xrightarrow{-0.69} O_2$$
$$\underset{-1.23}{\rule{6cm}{0pt}}$$

Accordingly O_2 cannot be used to displace bromine from bromides. Instead Cl_2 is used to displace bromine from bromide in sea water with the pH adjusted to 3.5. The pH adjustment is to prevent disproportionation of Cl_2 or Br_2 to the halide and hypohalite.

As the emf data indicate, chlorous acid is unstable with respect to disproportionation in acid solution. In base a mixture of chlorites and chlorates is obtained from the disproportionation of ClO_2

$$2ClO_2 + 2OH \longrightarrow ClO_2^- + ClO_3^- + H_2O \qquad E^0{}_B = 1.56$$

Reaction of ClO_2 with sodium peroxide in aqueous solution produces pure chlorites.

$$OH^- + 2ClO_2 + O_2H^- \longrightarrow 2ClO_2^- + O_2 + H_2O \qquad E^0{}_B = 1.24$$

Chlorine dioxide may be obtained from the reaction of oxalic acid with a chlorate in dilute sulfuric acid.

$$(CO_2H)_2 + 2ClO_3^- + 2H^+ \longrightarrow 2H_2O + 2CO_2 + 2ClO_2$$

It is also produced by the action of concentrated sulfuric acid on potassium perchlorate, but this reaction is difficult to control.

$$3H_2SO_4 + 3KClO_3 \longrightarrow 3KHSO_4 + HClO_4 + H_2O + 2ClO_2$$

Chlorine dioxide is explosive in air when its partial pressure exceeds 70 mm. Even so, it has found use as a commercial bleaching agent, particularly in making white wheat flour.

In hot basic solution the disproportionation of chlorine yields chlorates and chlorides.

$$3Cl_2 + 6(OH^-) \longrightarrow 5Cl^- + ClO_3^- + 3H_2O \qquad (E^0{}_B = +0.89 \text{ at } 25°)$$

This reaction may also be carried out by allowing mixing of the anode and cathode compartments during electrolysis of a hot brine solution.

Perchlorates are prepared from chlorates by disproportionation of the dry alkali metal salt.

$$4KClO_3 \xrightarrow[\Delta]{} 3KClO_4 + KCl$$

On heating above 400° the $KClO_4$ decomposes to O_2 and KCl. Perchlorates may be prepared in solution by electrolytic oxidation. Perchloric acid may be obtained from perchlorates by acidifying. If concentrated $NaClO_4$ and HCl are used, NaCl is precipitated and the excess HCl removed by warming. Sulfuric acid may be used and the perchloric acid purified by vacuum distillation. Hot concentrated perchloric acid is an extremely explosive oxidizing agent. In basic media the perchlorates are mild oxidizing agents. Magnesium perchlorate is commonly used as a drying agent. Great care should be taken when using magnesium perchlorate as a drying agent to assure nonacidic conditions.

Numerical Calculations Using emf Data

In addition to qualitative predictions about the spontaneity of a reaction, the E^0 value for a reaction permits the calculation of the equilibrium constant for the reaction. At equilibrium, $E = O$ and $Q = K_{eq}$ the Nernst equation then gives

$$E^0 = \frac{0.059}{n} \log K_{eq}$$

PROBLEM: Calculate the equilibrium constant for the reaction

$$Pb + Sn^{2+} \longrightarrow Pb^{2+} + Sn$$

From the emf data we calculate $E^0 = 0.126 - 0.136 = -0.01$ and hence $K_{eq} = 10^{-2(0.010)/0.059} = 0.999$.

PROBLEM: Utilizing standard emf data calculate K_p for the reaction

$$2PbO(s) \longrightarrow 2Pb(s) + O_2$$

$$
\begin{array}{ll}
4e + 2PbO + 2H_2O \longrightarrow 2Pb + 4(OH^-) & E^0{}_B = -0.54 \\
4(OH^-) \longrightarrow O_2 + 2H_2O + 4e & E^0{}_B = -0.40 \\
\hline
2PbO(s) \longrightarrow 2Pb(s) + O_2 & E^0{}_B = -0.94
\end{array}
$$

$$K_p = 10^{4(-0.94)/0.059} = 10^{-63.6} = 2.5 \times 10^{-64} \text{ atm at } 25°C$$

Solubility products of slightly soluble substances are often obtained by the use of cell measurements by reversing the calculation procedure indicated on page 144.

PROBLEM: Utilizing the E^0 value for $Ag(s) \rightarrow AgCl(s)$ and $Ag(s) \rightarrow Ag^+(aq)$ calculate K_{sp} for AgCl.

Stability constants can often be evaluated from emf data by procedures very much like those used to obtain solubility products.

PROBLEM: Calculate the equilibrium constant (β_6) for $Fe^{2+}(aq) + 6CN^-(aq) \rightarrow [Fe(CN)_6]^{4-}(aq)$ from the E^0 values

$$Fe \xrightarrow[E^0]{0.41} Fe^{2+}$$

and

$$Fe \xrightarrow[E^0{}_C]{1.5} [Fe(CN)_6]^{4-}$$

The $E^0{}_C$ value is the *standard* emf for

$$Fe(s) + 6CN^-(aq) \longrightarrow [Fe(CN)_6]^{4-}$$

i.e., for a solution containing CN^- and $[Fe(CN)_6]^{4-}$ at unit activity. The Fe^{2+} activity will accordingly be

$$(Fe^{2+}) = \frac{1}{\beta_6} \frac{(Fe(CN)_6{}^{4-})}{(CN^-)^6} = \frac{1}{\beta_6}$$

Iron in equilibrium with $[Fe(CN)_6]^{4-}$ and CN^- ion at unit activity is thus also in equilibrium with Fe^{2+} at an activity of $\frac{1}{\beta_6}$, and from the Nernst equation we may write

$$E^0{}_C = E^0 - \frac{0.059}{n} \log(Fe^{2+})$$

$$1.5 = +0.41 - \frac{0.059}{2} \log\frac{1}{\beta_6}$$

$$\beta_6 = 10^{37}$$

If the stoichiometry of the complex had not been known it could be found by measuring E_C at several different CN^- concentrations provided the total cyanide concentration exceeds that required by the stoichiometry of the complex. Under these conditions the Nernst equation becomes

$$E_c = E^0 + \frac{0.059}{n} \log \beta + \frac{0.059}{n} c \log (CN^-)$$

where c is the number of ligands per metal atom. Taking derivatives yields

$$\frac{d(E_c)}{d \log (CN^-)} = \frac{0.059}{n} c$$

$d(E_c)/d \log (CN^-)$ is simply the slope of E_c plotted against $\log (CN^-)$. If complexes of other stoichiometries are present over the ligand concentration studied a plot of E_c versus log (ligand concentration) will not be linear.

Free Energy Functions*

The use of emf data in the prediction of chemical reactions is largely restricted by the available data to reactions occurring in aqueous solution at 25°C. This can be extended somewhat by the tabulated temperature coefficients for electrode potentials.† Free energy functions are tabulated for many materials at temperatures up to several thousand degrees and have been calculated for the unipositive ions at temperatures up to 50,000°K.‡ These data permit predictions of reactions in plasmas, flames, or even at moderate temperatures.

The free energy function, abbreviated as fef, is defined through the relationship

$$\text{fef}_T = \left(\frac{F^0{}_T - H^0{}_{T\text{ref}}}{T} \right) = \left(\frac{H^0{}_T - H^0{}_{T\text{ref}}}{T} \right) - S^0{}_T \tag{4.4}$$

These terms may conveniently be evaluated for solids and liquids§ from heat capacity data — see Equation 4.2 for the entropy term. The enthalpy term is obtained from

$$H^0{}_T - H^0{}_{T\text{ref}} = \int_{T\text{ref}}^{T} C_p dT + \Delta H_{\text{phase transitions}}$$

Two reference temperatures are in common usage, 0°K and 298.1°K, the former being favored for theoretical reasons, the latter for experimental convenience. For gases the free energy function may be calculated from the partition function, Q, which may be evaluated from spectroscopic data and statistical mechanics.

$$\left(\frac{F^0 - H^0{}_0}{T} \right) = R \ln \frac{N}{Q}$$

where R is the gas constant and N is Avogadro's number. The free energy function changes slowly with temperature permitting ready interpolation and extrapolation of data at different temperatures. The free energy function can often be estimated with fair accuracy for unknown compounds by the use of empirical procedures.‖

* Margrave, J. L., *J. Chem. Educ.*, **32**, 520 (1955).
† Salvi, G. R., and A. J. de Bethune, *J. Electrochem. Soc.*, **108**, 672 (1961); A. J. de Bethune, T. S. Licht, and N. Swendeman, *ibid.*, **106**, 616 (1959).
‡ Green, J. W., D. E. Poland, and J. L. Margrave, *J. Chem. Phys.*, **33**, 35 (1960).
§ For details see E. F. Westrum, *J. Chem. Educ.*, **39**, 443 (1962).
‖ Janz, G. J., *Estimation of Thermodynamic Properties of Organic Compounds* (New York: Academic Press, Inc., 1958).

The free energy change for a reaction is found from Equation 4.5

$$\Delta\text{fef} = \frac{\Delta F^0}{T} - \frac{\Delta H^0_{T\text{ref}}}{T}$$ (4.5)

and

$$\Delta\text{fef} = \Sigma \text{ fef products} - \Sigma \text{ fef reactants}$$

PROBLEM: Using data obtained from the general references of this chapter calculate ΔF^0 at 1000°K for the reaction

$$CrCl_3(s) + \frac{1}{2}H_2(g) \longrightarrow CrCl_2(s) + HCl(g)$$

Solution

Data	$\dfrac{F^0 - H^0_{298}}{1000}$	ΔH^0_{f298}
$CrCl_2$	-36.7	-97
HCl	-46.2	-21.8
H_2	-32.8	0
$CrCl_3$	-43	-132

Calc. $\Delta H^0_{298} = -97 - 21.8 + 132 = 13$ kcal

$$\Delta\text{fef} = -36.7 - 46.2 + \frac{1}{2}(32.8) + 43 = -23.5$$

$$\frac{\Delta F^0}{T} = \Delta\text{fef} + \frac{\Delta H_{298}}{T} = -23.5 + \frac{13000}{1000} = -20.5$$

$$\Delta F^0 = -20,500 \text{ cal/mole}$$

As seen from the large negative free energy change the reaction should occur. It does — a mixture of H_2 and HCl is used at about the temperature cited in this problem to reduce $CrCl_3$ to $CrCl_2$.

Periodic Trends in Half-Cell emf Values and Extrathermodynamic Relationships

The heat released (Q) during the oxidation of an element to its monatomic ion in aqueous solution can be considered to be the difference between the heat of solution of the gaseous ion and the sum of its sublimation energy and ionization potentials.

$$\begin{array}{ccc}
& I_1 + I_2 + \ldots I_x & \\
M(g) & \xrightarrow{\hspace{2cm}} & M^{x+}(g) + xe \\
\Big\uparrow S & & \Big\downarrow H_+ \\
& Q & \\
M(s) & \xrightarrow{\hspace{2cm}} & M^{x+}(aq) + xe
\end{array}$$

$$Q = (-\Delta H) = -S - \underset{x}{\Sigma I} + H_+$$

Assuming the free energy change to be proportional to the enthalpy change then E^0 will parallel Q/x, i.e., the emf for the oxidation will increase as the reaction becomes more exothermic. The heat of solution and the ionization potential will usually vary in a parallel fashion. In most cases the variations in I and S will determine the major variation in E^0. An exception to the preceding generalization is provided by lithium ion, which has a very high heat of solution causing the $Li \rightarrow Li^+$ couple to have a higher voltage than the $Na \rightarrow Na^+$ or $K \rightarrow K^+$ couples.

The decrease in emf for M/M^{x+} with increasing x within a period can be attributed almost entirely to the $\Sigma I/x$ factor. Crossing the first transition series in going from M to M^{x+} the increased penetration of the $4s$ electrons is reflected in the decreasing E^0 values. Within a transition metal family both S and I increase with atomic number, resulting in a decrease in ease of oxidation of M to M^{x+}.

			Increasing emf for oxidation half-reaction							
Na/Na⁺	Mg/Mg²⁺	Al/Al³⁺	Ti/Ti²⁺	V/V²⁺	Cr/Cr²⁺	Mn/Mn²⁺	Fe/Fe²⁺	Co/Co²⁺
K/K⁺	Ca/Ca²⁺	Sc/Sc³⁺						
Rb/Rb⁺	Sr/Sr²⁺					Tc/Tc²⁺	Ru/Ru²⁺	
						Re/Re²⁺	Os/Os²⁺	

With the actinides there is a regular decrease in the formal emf for the oxidation of M^{3+} to M^{4+}; the values for U, Np, Pu, and Am are, respectively, $0.631, -0.155, -0.982$, and -2.6 V. Curium can be oxidized to $Cm(IV)$ in aqueous solution only if a high concentration of fluoride ion is present to complex the product. The high stability of $Cm(III)$ may be associated with the stability of a half filled f shell. Oxyanions utilizing outer d orbitals (SO_4^{2-}, SeO_4^{2-}) show an increase in ability to serve as oxidizing agents with increasing atomic number, while those using inner d orbitals (MnO_4^-, TcO_4^-) show a decrease with increasing atomic number.

The coupling reaction

$$HX \longrightarrow \frac{1}{2}X_2 + H^+ + e$$

may be related to electronegativity if the hydrogen half-reaction is added to give

$$HX \longrightarrow \frac{1}{2}X_2 + \frac{1}{2}H_2$$

for which $\Delta H = -23.060 (\chi_L - \chi_H)^2$ if solvation is ignored. (χ is the electronegativity.) Further, if entropy changes are ignored, then

$$-E^0 = (\chi_L - \chi_H)^2 \tag{4.6}$$

This may be used to rationalize the trends shown below.

H₂NNH₂	H₂O₂	F₂	
H₂PPH₂	H₂S₂	Cl₂	Oxidizing ability
		Br₂	
		I₂	

CH₄	NH₃	H₂O	HF	
SiH₄	PH₃	H₂S	HCl	Reducing ability
	AsH₃	H₂Se	HBr	
			HI	

Equation 4.6 has been used to evaluate group electronegativities from E^0 data (i.e., χ for $HO_2CO—$, $HO—$, $O_2NO—$, etc.)[*]

Mechanisms of Redox Reactions

Complementary and Noncomplementary Reactions

When several reactions are possible, the *thermodynamically* favored one is that which has the greater E^0 value (or, equivalently, the more negative free energy change). However, the reaction which occurs may be determined by the relative *rates of reactions* rather than the free energy change.

A generalization has been made that redox reactions are usually faster when the oxidizing and reducing agents undergo the same net change in oxidation states.[†] Such reactions are termed "complementary." Examples of fast complementary and slow noncomplementary reactions are

$$Ce(IV) + Ti(III) \longrightarrow Ti(IV) + Ce(III) \quad \text{complementary, fast}$$
$$Tl(III) + Fe(II) \longrightarrow Tl(I) + Fe(III) \quad \text{noncomplementary, slow}$$

In some cases the reaction products actually differ when oxidation is carried out by 1-equivalent oxidants, Cu(II), Fe(III), Ag(II), Co(III) or by 2-equivalent oxidants, H_2O_2, Tl(III), Cl_2, Mo(VI), etc.[‡] Some examples of differing behavior with 1- and 2-equivalent oxidants are:

$$Cr(II) \begin{cases} \xrightarrow{-e} Cr(III)(aq) \\ \xrightarrow{-2e} \frac{1}{2}CrOCr^{4+}(aq) \end{cases}$$

$$N_2H_4 \begin{cases} \xrightarrow{-e} N_2H_3 \longrightarrow \frac{1}{2}N_2H_6 \longrightarrow \frac{1}{2}N_2 + NH_3 \\ \xrightarrow{-2e} N_2H_2 \xrightarrow{-2e} N_2 \end{cases}$$

$$SO_3^{2-} \begin{cases} \xrightarrow{-e} SO_3^- \longrightarrow \frac{1}{2}S_2O_6^{2-} \\ \xrightarrow{-2e} SO_3(SO_4^{2-}) \end{cases}$$

$$[(NH_3)_5Co^{III}C_2O_4]^+ \begin{cases} \xrightarrow{-e} Co(II)(aq) + 2CO_2 + 5NH_4^+ \\ \xrightarrow{-2e} [(NH_3)_5Co^{III}OH_2]^{3+} + 2CO_2 \end{cases}$$

---

[*] McDaniel, D. H., and A. Yingst, *J. Am. Chem. Soc.*, **86**, 1334 (1964).
[†] Shaffer, P. A., *J. Am. Chem. Soc.*, **55**, 2169 (1933); *J. Phys. Chem.*, **40**, 1021 (1936).
[‡] Halpern, J., *Quart. Rev.*, **15**, 207 (1961).

In the last example the oxalato group gives up two electrons regardless of the oxidant but with 1-equivalent oxidants the Co(III) atom accepts the second electron.* An indication that this reaction is a stepwise reaction with 1-equivalent oxidants is provided by a closely similar oxidation of the formato complex.† In this case permanganate is used, with a rate determining 1-equivalent electron transfer, and both Co(II) and Co(III) result presumably from a common intermediate.

$$[(NH_3)_5Co^{III}(OCHO^-)]^{2+} + MnO_4^- \longrightarrow [(NH_3)_5Co^{III}(CO_2^-)]^{2+} + HMnO_4^-$$

$$Co(II) + CO_2 \qquad (NH_3)_5Co^{III}OH_2^{3+} + CO_2$$

Deuterium substitution on the formato ligand reduces the over-all rate by a factor of 10.5 but does not alter the product ratio.

Electron Transfer Through Bridging Groups

The deuterium isotope effect on the above reaction suggests that the initial electron transfer takes place via an atom transfer which differs from those discussed on pages 416–417 only in that the atom transferred is assumed to be accepted by oxygen rather than the central metal atom. Due to the electronegativity difference of the atoms, the electron transfer is considered to be in the same direction as the atom transfer, in contrast to the second reaction considered below.

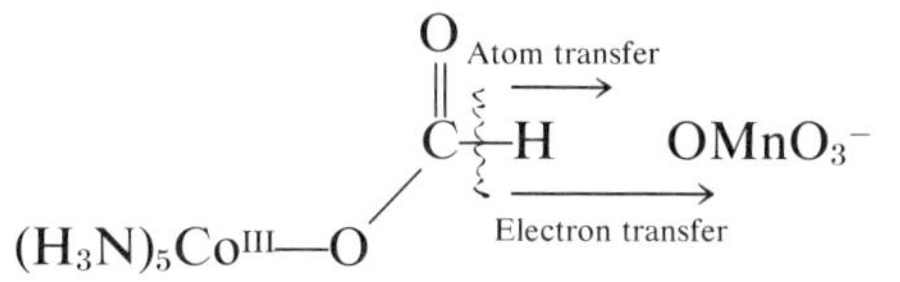

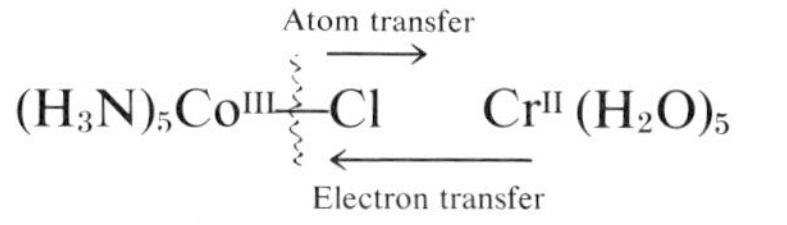

$$(H_3N)_5Co^{III}-O \quad \overset{O}{\underset{}{\overset{\|}{C}}}-H \quad \xrightarrow{\text{Atom transfer}} \quad OMnO_3^-$$
$$\xrightarrow{\text{Electron transfer}}$$

$$(H_3N)_5Co^{III}-Cl \quad \xrightarrow{\text{Atom transfer}} \quad Cr^{II}(H_2O)_5$$
$$\xleftarrow{\text{Electron transfer}}$$

Hydrogen atom transfer may also provide a mechanism for electron exchange between Fe(II) and Fe(OH)$^{2+}$

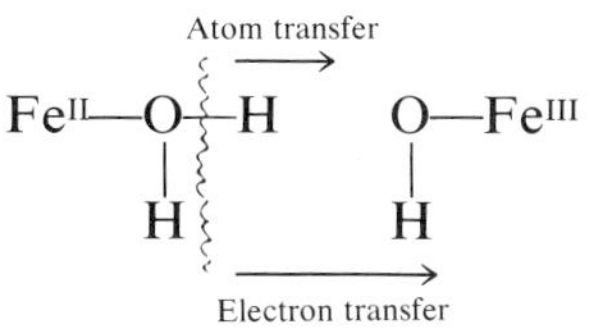

$$Fe^{II}-O-H \quad \xrightarrow{\text{Atom transfer}} \quad O-Fe^{III}$$
$$\overset{|}{H} \qquad \qquad \overset{|}{H}$$
$$\xrightarrow{\text{Electron transfer}}$$

However, in this case hydrogen bonding may simply serve to reduce the repulsion between Fe(II)(aq) and FeOH^{2+}(aq), allowing a direct transfer of electrons from Fe(II) to Fe(III) through the weakly interacting orbitals on the two atoms.

* Saffir, P., and H. Taube, *J. Am. Chem. Soc.*, **82**, 13 (1960).
† Candlin, J. P., and J. Halpern, *J. Am. Chem. Soc.*, **85**, 2518 (1963).

When the bridging group is transferred as a singly charged ion a two-electron transfer occurs

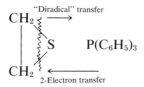

A "diradical" transfer may also result in a two-electron transfer.*

$$
\begin{array}{c}
\text{CH}_2 \\
| \\
\text{CH}_2
\end{array}
\quad S \quad P(C_6H_5)_3
$$

"Diradical" transfer

2-Electron transfer

GENERAL REFERENCES

Sources of Thermodynamic Data

See Appendix E for a summary of half-cell emf data.

Latimer, W. M., *The Oxidation States of the Elements and Their Potentials in Aqueous Solution* (2nd ed., New York: Prentice-Hall Inc., 1952).

Landolt-Bornstein. Zahlenwerte und Funktionen aus Physik, Chemie, Astronomie, Geophysik und Technik. 6th Auflage. II Band. Eigenschaften der Materie in Ihren Aggregatzustanden. 4 Teil. Kalorische Zustandsgrossen, edited by K. Schafer and E. Lax (West Berlin: Springer-Verlag, 1961).

Rossini, F. D., et al, "Selected Values of Chemical Thermodynamic Properties," National Bureau of Standards Circular 500, U.S. Government Printing Office, Washington, D.C., 1952.

Elliott, J. F., and M. Gleiser, *Thermochemistry for Steelmaking* (Reading: Addison-Wesley Publishing Co., 1960).

International Critical Tables (New York: McGraw-Hill Book Company, Inc., 1929).

National Nuclear Energy Series Vol. 19B, *The Chemistry and Metallurgy of Miscellaneous Materials,* edited by L. L. Quill (New York: McGraw-Hill Book Company, Inc., 1950).

Charlot, G., *Selected Constants Tables No. 8: Oxydo-Reduction Potentials* (New York: Pergamon Press, 1958).

de Bethune, A. J., and N. A. S. Loud, *Standard Aqueous Electrode Potentials and Temperature Coefficients at 25°C* (Skokie, Illinois: Clifford A. Hempel, 1964).

Problems

1. Write balanced ionic half-reactions for:

    (a) $CN^- \xrightarrow{\text{base}} CNO^-$

    (b) $Cr(OH)_4^{2-} \xrightarrow{\text{base}} CrO_4^{2-}$

---

* These and further group transfer reactions are discussed by E. M. Kosower in *Molecular Biochemistry* (New York: McGraw-Hill Book Company, Inc., 1962) pp. 158-166. A broad treatment of organic reactions is given by R. Stewart, *Oxidation Mechanisms* (New York: W. A. Benjamin Inc., 1964).

(c) $S_2O_3^{2-} \longrightarrow S_4O_6^{2-}$

(d) $SCN^- \xrightarrow{\text{acid}} SO_4^{2-} + CO_2 + N_2$

(e) $AsH_3 \xrightarrow{\text{base}} AsO_2^-$

(f) $H_3VO_4 \xrightarrow{\text{acid}} VO^{2+}$

2. Would the value of the heat of a reaction calculated from the variation of K_p with temperature be expected to be affected by the units in which K_p is expressed? Under what circumstances would ΔH be unaffected and under what circumstances would ΔH be affected by the selection of units for the K_{eq}?

3. Calculate E^0 values for the following cells and write the reactions for which these apply:

(a) $Pt, H_2 \mid HCl \parallel KCl \mid Hg_2Cl_2(s), Hg$

(b) $Cu \mid Cu^{2+} \parallel I^-, CuI(s) \mid Cu$

(c) $Pt, CuI(s) \mid Cu^{2+} \parallel I^- \mid CuI(s), Cu$

From parts (b) and (c), comment on the necessity of knowledge of the half-cells involved in making predictions of (a) the spontaneity of a reaction, (b) the free energy change of a reaction.

4. Calculate the emf values for the following cells:

(a) $Pt, H_2 \mid H^+(a = 0.1) \parallel H^+(a = 10^{-7}) \mid H_2, Pt$

(b) $Zn \mid Zn^{2+}(a = 1) \parallel Cu^{2+}(a = 10^{-4}) \mid Cu$

(c) $Fe, Fe(OH)_2 \mid OH^-(a = 0.1) \parallel Fe^{2+}(a = 1) \mid Fe$

5. Calculate the approximate half-cell emf values for the following reactions from known electronegativities and Equation 4.6.

$$H_2O \longrightarrow H_2O_2 + 2H^+ + 2e$$
$$HF \longrightarrow F_2 + 2H^+ + 2e$$
$$PH_3 \longrightarrow H_2PPH_2 + 2H^+ + 2e$$

Use Huggins' assignment of 2.2 for the electronegativity of hydrogen.

6. Describe the conditions of acidity which would be most appropriate for the following processes:

(a) $Mn^{2+} \longrightarrow MnO_4^-$ (e) $C_2O_4^{2-} \longrightarrow 2CO_2$

(b) $CrO_4^{2-} \longrightarrow Cr_2O_7^{2-}$ (f) $H_2O_2 \longrightarrow H_2O$

(c) $Fe^{3+} \longrightarrow FeO_4^{2-}$ (g) $H_2O_2 \longrightarrow O_2$

(d) $ClO_4^- \longrightarrow ClO_3^-$

7. (a) Draw a general conclusion about the effect of pH on the ease of oxidation of M to MO_x. (b) Balance the half-reaction $M \rightarrow MO_x$ on a scheme appropriate for the Lux–Flood acid–base approach. From your balanced half-reaction and the Nernst equation draw a general conclusion about the effect of oxide donors or oxide acceptors on the ease of oxidation of M to MO_x. Explain what might be expected from the fusion of a transition metal with an alkali metal carbonate in air.

8. By extrapolation from known data for Cr, W, and Mo, Seaborg estimates the following emf values for the couples involving possible species for the currently unknown element 106: E^0_A $M \xrightarrow{0.0} M^{3+} \xrightarrow{0.7} MO_2 \xrightarrow{0.2} M_2O_5 \xrightarrow{0.5} MO_3$.

Predict the results of the following:

(a) M is placed in $1N$ HCl;

(b) MCl_3 is placed in an acidic solution containing $FeSO_4$;

(c) MO_2 and M are in contact in acid solution;

(*d*) M^{3+} and MO_3 are in contact in acid solution;

(*e*) M is treated with excess HNO_3.

9. Latimer gives the following half-cell emf diagram for osmium:

$$E^0_A \qquad Os \xrightarrow{-0.85} Os^{2+} \xrightarrow{-0.4} OsCl_6^{3-} \xrightarrow{-0.85} OsCl_6^{2-} \xrightarrow{-1.0} OsO_4(s)$$

(*a*) Which of the above species, if any, would be unstable in $1N$ HCl? Give balanced equations for any reactions that occur. (*b*) Which couple(s) would remain unchanged in their emf value on altering the pH? (*c*) Which couple(s) would remain unchanged in their emf value on altering the chloride ion concentration? (*d*) Calculate the value of E^0_A for Os $\rightarrow$ $OsO_4(s)$. (*e*) Predict the results of mixing excess osmium with solid OsO_4 in contact with $1N$ HCl.

10. Appleman [*J. Am. Chem. Soc.*, **83**, 805 (1961)] reports the following data for astatine: Astatide is oxidized to At(0) by the As(III)–As(V) couple at pH 4. At pH 4 the As(III)–As(V) couple reduces At(0) to At$^-$. The bromide–bromine couple oxidizes At(0) to At(X+) (an unknown oxidation state between zero and 5+) while the VO^{2+}– VO_2^+ couple reduces At(X+) to At(0). The iodate–periodate couple oxidizes At(X+) to AtO_3^-. The Cl$^-$–Cl$_2$ couple reduces AtO_3^- to At(X+). All data, except as noted, were obtained at pH $\approx$ 1. From these data set the emf limits on the following couples:

$$At^- \longrightarrow At(0) \longrightarrow At(X+) \longrightarrow AtO_3^- \longrightarrow H_5AtO_6$$

Latimer gives the following half-cell emf values for $1N$ acid:

$$HAsO_2 \xrightarrow{-0.56} H_3AsO_4$$
$$VO^{2+} \xrightarrow{-1.0} VO_2^+$$
$$Br^- \xrightarrow{-1.07} Br_2$$
$$Cl^- \xrightarrow{-1.36} Cl_2$$
$$IO_3^- \xrightarrow{-1.7} H_5IO_6$$

11. Latimer gives the following E^0_B values for Ag:

$$Ag \xrightarrow{-0.344} Ag_2O \xrightarrow{-0.57} AgO \xrightarrow{-0.74} Ag_2O_3$$

(*a*) Calculate the equilibrium pressure at 25°C of O_2 above a system containing AgO and Ag_2O. (*b*) From the ΔH^0_f for AgO of -3.0 kcal/mole and for Ag_2O of -7.3 kcal/mole calculate ΔH_{298} for the reaction in part (*a*), and ΔS_{298}. (*c*) Assuming, as a first approximation, that ΔH and ΔS are independent of temperature, calculate the equilibrium pressure of the reaction in part (*a*) at 500°K.

12. Latimer gives the following emf diagrams in acid solution:

$$E^0_A \qquad SbH_3 \xrightarrow{0.51} Sb \xrightarrow{-0.212} Sb(III) \xrightarrow{-0.68} Sb_2O_4(s) \xrightarrow{-0.48} Sb_2O_5(s)$$
$$H_2O \xrightarrow{-1.23} O_2$$

(*a*) At a pH of 4 the Sb $\rightarrow$ Sb(III) emf is -0.052. From these data determine whether the predominate species for Sb(III) in the pH range of zero to 4 is Sb_2O_3, SbO_2^-, SbO^+, or Sb^{3+}. (*b*) Which of the oxidation states of Sb are unstable in acid solution? Write balanced equations for all reactions of the unstable species occurring spontaneously in acid. (*c*) What is the equilibrium pressure of oxygen in contact with Sb_2O_4 and Sb_2O_5? (*d*) What is the emf for $SbH_3 \rightarrow Sb_2O_5$ in acid solution?

13. The emf is more positive for the Fe(II)–Fe(III) couple in the presence of *o*-phenanthroline and more negative in the presence of F^- as compared to the value for the hydrated ions. What do these values tell us about the tendency of these ligands to stabilize Fe^{2+} or Fe^{3+}?

14. The half-cell emf for $Zn \rightarrow Zn^{2+}$ is +0.763 V. Calculate the number of groups coordinated and the formation constant for the zinc–ammonia complex $[Zn(NH_3)_p{}^{2+}]$ from the following data:

Concentration of NH_3(aq)	Formal emf
0.1*M*	+0.92
0.2	+0.96
0.4	+0.99
0.6	+1.01

15. K_{sp} for $Cu(OH)_2$ is 1.6×10^{-19}. Calculate the emf for $Cu–Cu(OH)_2$ in 1*M* base. What information other than the emf values for Fe(II)–Fe(III) in acid and in base is needed to calculate the K_{sp} values for both $Fe(OH)_2$ and $Fe(OH)_3$?

16. Elliott and Gleiser give the following free energies of formation at 1000°K: SiH_4, +28,800; SiO_2, −166,800; H_2O, −46,030 calories per mole. Calculate the equilibrium constant for the reaction $SiO_2(s) + 4H_2(g) \rightleftharpoons SiH_4(g) + 2H_2O(g)$ at 1000°K. What other reactions might be possible if reactions between SiO_2 and H_2 are being considered? Look up any necessary data and calculate equilibrium constants for the other possibilities.

17. The standard heat of formation at 298°K of $CrCl_2$ is −97 kcal/mole and of $CrCl_3$ is −132 kcal/mole. The value of $(F^0 - H^0{}_{298})/T$ in units of cal/mole/°K at 1000° is −8.87 for Cr, −36.7 for $CrCl_2$, and −43 for $CrCl_3$. For Cl_2 the following data are available: $(F^0 - H^0{}_0)/T = -55.45$ cal/mole/°K at 1000°K and $H^0{}_{298} - H^0{}_0 = 2192$ cal/mole. From these data calculate ΔF^0 at 1000°K for the following reactions:

(*a*) $CrCl_2 \longrightarrow Cr + Cl_2$

(*b*) $CrCl_2 + \frac{1}{2}Cl_2 \longrightarrow CrCl_3$

(*c*) $3CrCl_2 \longrightarrow 2CrCl_3 + Cr$

Which, if any, of the above reactions would occur on heating $CrCl_2$ to 1000°K in Cl_2 at 1 atm pressure?

18. The ionization potentials and sublimation energies of Li and Be are regular for their families. The emf for the oxidation of Li is very much out of line for the family, but Be is not. Explain.

19. The oxidation of $C_2O_4{}^{2-}$ by $MnO_4{}^-$ in acid solution is usually very slow initially, but it can be speeded up by the addition of Mn^{2+}. Explain how the Mn^{2+} might speed the process.

CHAPTER V

The Hydrogen Bond

By 1900 much data had accumulated on molecular association. Interpretation of vapor pressures, osmotic pressures, surface tension, freezing point depressions and boiling point elevations, Trouton constants, and similar data pointed to the existence of a class of associated molecular substances such as water, formic acid, formamide, and hydrogen cyanide. However, one of the earliest proposals for the hydrogen bond came not from data on association, but rather from dissociation data. In 1907 Moore* published a paper on the equilibrium constants in the system

$$\overset{K_h}{} \qquad \overset{K_b}{}$$
$$NH_3 \rightleftharpoons H_3NHOH \rightleftharpoons NH_4{}^+ + OH^-$$

and the related system of the ethylamines. K_h was obtained from experiments on the distribution of ammonia (or the amine) between water and an organic solvent. The product of K_h and K_b was obtained by conductivity studies. Moore's comments in 1907 were as follows:

> . . . The introduction of three ethyl groups into ammonia increases the constant (K_b) only twelve-fold. Now the introduction of a fourth ethyl group gives tetraethylammonium hydroxide, the degree of ionization of which is comparable with that of sodium hydroxide. It is difficult to imagine that this large change of ionization is produced solely by the introduction of the fourth ethyl group when the first three have produced a comparatively small effect. These results point rather to a difference in constitution between the quaternary ammonium hydroxides and the hydroxides of primary, secondary, and tertiary amines.

Five years later he published a clear picture of this difference:†

> "The following formulae, where thick strokes mean strong unions and thin strokes weak unions, show roughly the difference between trimethylammonium hydroxide and tetramethylammonium hydroxide."

* Moore, T. S., *J. Chem. Soc.*, **91**, 1379 (1907).
† Moore, T. S., and T. F. Winmill, *J. Chem. Soc.*, **101**, 1635 (1912).

However, Moore did not generalize his idea to cover other phenomena. Latimer and Rodebush, in 1920, introduced the term "hydrogen bond" to describe the nature of association in the liquid state of water, hydrogen fluoride, etc.† Furthermore, they pointed out the necessity for a slightly acidic hydrogen and a nonbonding electron pair in order to form a hydrogen bond, which they formulated as A:H:B. On the basis of this picture they were able to account for the high dielectric constant of water, the mobility of the hydrogen ion in water, the weakness of ammonium hydroxide as a base (apparently without knowledge of Moore's publications), as well as melting points and boiling points of liquids capable of hydrogen bonding. Within the next decade or so, the importance of hydrogen bonding in determining crystal structures, solubilities, and spectra had been pointed out. Some of these effects, as well as some theoretical aspects of the hydrogen bond, will be discussed in the sections to follow.

Influence on the Vaporization Process of Pure Liquids

Some of the most striking effects of hydrogen bonding on the physical properties of substances may be found by contrasting the properties of water with those of methyl ether (Table 5.1). As Figure 5.1 indicates, the dimethyl derivatives of the Group VI elements usually boil about 80 to 100°C higher than the hydrides. Accordingly, from Figure 5.1, it may be said that water boils about 200 degrees higher than it would in the absence of hydrogen bonding. Replacing a hydroxylic hydrogen with a methyl group in other compounds produces a similar decrease in boiling point. Thus dimethylsulfate boils at 188°C, trimethylphosphate at 193°C, and methylborate at 65°C; the corresponding hydrogen bonded compounds, sulfuric acid, phosphoric acid, and boric acid do not boil but decompose with the loss of water at considerably higher temperatures (340, 213, and 185°C, respectively). Boric acid does not melt before decomposing.

Hydrogen bonding is not restricted to hydroxylic compounds although it is most common in this class of compound. Hydrogen fluoride boils at 19.5°C, while methyl-

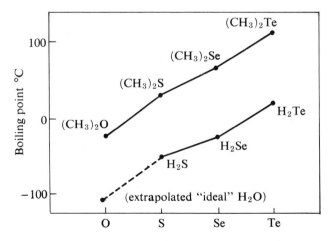

FIGURE 5.1. *Boiling points of hydrogen- and methyl-derivatives of the Group VI elements.*

† Latimer, W. M., and W. H. Rodebush, *J. Am. Chem. Soc.,* **42**, 1419 (1920).

fluoride boils at −78°C. Hydrazoic acid, HN_3, boils at 37°C, while methylazide boils at 20 to 21°C. The heat of vaporization of hydrogen bonded substances is also greater than that of their methyl derivatives.

TABLE 5.1
Some Physical Properties of Water, Methanol, and Dimethyl Ether

	H_2O	CH_3OH	$(CH_3)_2O$
Critical Temperature (°C)	374.2	240.6	126.7
Boiling Point (°C)	100	64.7	−23.7
Melting Point (°C)	0	−97.8	−138.5
Heat of Vaporization (kcal/mole)	9.72	8.42	5.14
Heat of Fusion (kcal/mole)	1.44	0.52	1.18
Trouton Constant (ΔH_v/b.p. °K) in entropy units	26.1	24.3	20.6
Dielectric Constant	78.54	32.63	5.02
Dipole Moment (Debye units)	1.84	1.68	1.30
Viscosity at 20°C (centipoise)	1.005	0.597	(0.2332 for ethyl ether)

Intermolecular hydrogen bonding in pure substances increases the heat of vaporization in two ways. (*1*) It adds to the attraction between molecules. This attraction must either be overcome on vaporization (as in the case of H_2O) and/or small polymeric molecules of the liquid must be vaporized (as in the case of HF at its normal boiling point). In the latter event the heat of vaporization is higher than normal due to the greater dispersion forces between the polymeric units than between the monomeric units. (*2*) Hydrogen bonding in the liquid restricts rotation of the molecules in the liquid. Such rotation is possible in the gas and the energy absorbed in exciting this rotation adds to the heat of vaporization. However, the additional degrees of freedom, which such rotation allows the molecules, are reflected in an increase in the entropy of vaporization. Accordingly, the extra heat of vaporization from the rotational contribution does not give rise to a further increase in the boiling point of the substance. Hydrogen bonding thus (*1*) increases the boiling point of a liquid beyond that expected from a consideration of dispersion forces alone (i.e., expected from comparison with comparable non-hydrogen bonded liquids) and (*2*) gives rise to a greater entropy of vaporization (i.e., Trouton constant when the temperature is the boiling point) than that of unassociated liquids.

Heats of vaporization and heats of sublimation are sometimes used to estimate the energy of the hydrogen bond involved. For water, the hydrogen bonds have an energy of about −6 kcal/mole H-bond. For substances such as HF and acetic acid, which are partially associated in the gas phase, the hydrogen bond energy is not obtained from ΔH_v, but directly from the variation of the degree of association of a gaseous sample with temperature. This in turn is obtained from PVT data with appropriate assumptions about the dissociating species.

The boiling point of ammonia is higher than might be expected from a comparison with phosphine, etc., but unlike the oxygen compounds, the boiling point of ammonia

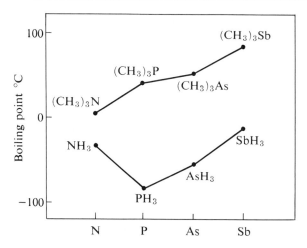

FIGURE 5.2. *Boiling points of hydrogen- and methyl-derivatives of the Group V elements.*

is lower than the completely methylated compound, trimethylamine (see Figure 5.2). X-ray studies of solid ammonia indicate that the lone pair of electrons has three hydrogen atoms from different nitrogen atoms pointed toward it. Thus a normal hydrogen bond is not formed. From heats of sublimation the energy of interaction with the lone pair is about −1.3 kcal/g-atom of hydrogen.

Energies of Hydrogen Bonds Formed between Molecules

In general, hydrogen bond energies determined from measurements of gas phase association equilibria tend to give energies somewhat higher than values determined for similar equilibria in solution. Table 5.2 contains a number of hydrogen bond energies evaluated from gas phase association, as well as some data obtained in solution studies.

Some Weak Hydrogen Bonds Involving Methyl Hydrogens

The assumption has been made up to this point that a hydrogen atom attached to a methyl group does not participate in hydrogen bonding. Yet CH_3CN, (b.p. 82°C) acetonitrile, has an even higher boiling point than HCN (b.p. 25°). It seems likely that the polar nature of the methyl C—H bond in this case is enhanced greatly by the strong electron withdrawing inductive effect of the CN group and also by hyperconjugative interactions with the CN group. The moderately high dielectric constant (38.8) of CH_3CN supports the notion of hydrogen bonding here. A *weak* hydrogen bond may also exist in acetone, $CH_3\overset{\|}{\underset{O}{C}}CH_3$, dimethylcarbonate, ethylene carbonate, and other places where a basic center exists in the molecule and the methyl group is attached to a relatively positive center. (See further under dielectric constant.)

TABLE 5.2
Some Energies of Hydrogen Bonds Formed by Neutral Molecules

Bond	ΔH kcal/ mole-H bond	Formed by	Ref
F—H···O	11	$(C_2H_5)_2O$, CH_3OH, $(CH_3)_2CO$ and HF	a
F—H···F	6.8	HF(g)	b
Cl—H···O	6-7	$CH_3OH(g)$, Diphenylcylopropanone and HCl	c
O—H···O	7	$CH_3CO_2H(g)$	b
	5	$H_2O(g)$	b
	4.5	$CH_3OH(g)$	b
O—H···O	6	C_6H_5OH, $(n\text{-}C_4H_9)_2O$ in CCl_4	d
O—H···S	4.2	C_6H_5OH, $(n\text{-}C_4H_9)_2S$ in CCl_4	d
O—H···Se	3.7_2	C_6H_5OH, $(n\text{-}C_4H_9)_2Se$ in CCl_4	d
O—H···F	3.1_3	C_6H_5OH, cyclohexyl fluoride in CCl_4	d
O—H···Cl	2.2_1	C_6H_5OH, cyclohexyl chloride in CCl_4	d
O—H···Br	2.0_5	C_6H_5OH, cyclohexyl bromide in CCl_4	d
O—H···I	1.7_2	C_6H_5OH, cyclohexyl iodide in CCl_4	d
N—H···N	3.4	$CH_3NH_2(g)$	b
	4.4	$NH_3(g)$	b
	5.8	$C_4H_9NH_2(g)$	e
N—H···O	> 5.8	$C_4H_9NH_2(g)$, $C_4H_9OH(g)$	e
	3.9	$CH_3CONHCH_3$ in CCl_4	b
C—H···N	3.3	HCN(g)	b
	4.6	HCN(l)	b
C—H···O	6.0	$(C_2H_5)_2O(g)$, $HCCl_3(g)$	b

[a] Smith, D. F., *Proc. U. N. Intern. Conf. Peaceful Uses At. Energy, 2nd, Geneva*, **28**, 130 (1958).
[b] Pimentel and McClellan, see General References.
[c] Gladishev, A. T., and Y. K. Syrkin, *Compt. Rend. acad. sci. U.R.S.S.*, **20**, 145 (1938); *Chem. Abst.*, **33**, 1578².
[d] West, R., et al, *J. Am. Chem. Soc.*, **84**, 3221 (1962).
[e] Cracco, F., and P. Huyskens, *Bull. Soc. chim. Belg.*, **69**, 255 (1960).

Azeotropic Behavior*

When two substances are mixed, if the molecules cannot distinguish between solute and solvent molecules (i.e., the intermolecular forces between solute and solvent are the same as between solvent and solvent or solute and solute and the molecules are of the same size) then an ideal solution results. In such cases the partial pressure of each component, P_i, is given by the product of the mole fraction of the component, N_i, and its vapor pressure in the pure state, P^0_i, i.e., the solution obeys Raoult's law $P_i = N_i P^0_i$. For an ideal two component system the total pressure, P_T, is a linear function of the mole fraction composition, i.e., $P_T = N_i P^0_i + (1 - N_i) P^0_j = P^0_j + N_i (P^0_i - P^0_j)$. Solutions having a total pressure greater than the ideal pressure are said to show positive deviation from Raoult's law and vice versa.

* Ewell, R. H., S. M. Harrison, and Lloyd Berg, "Azeotropic Distillation," *Ind. Eng. Chem.*, **36**, 871 (1944).

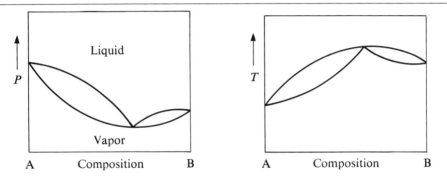

FIGURE 5.3. *Maximum boiling mixture.*

A negative deviation from Raoult's law is usually interpreted as due to a greater interaction between unlike molecules than between like molecules. If the negative deviation is very large then there will be a minimum in the total vapor pressure at some particular composition for a given temperature. Such solutions give rise to maximum boiling mixtures. (See Figures 5.3 and 5.4.) When liquids, which themselves show no strong hydrogen bonds but which together may form strong hydrogen bonds, are mixed, then negative deviation from Raoult's law follows and often results in maximum boiling mixtures. Some examples are found with mixtures containing highly halogenated hydrocarbons (thus making the remaining C—H bonds more polar) and ketones or esters— chloroform + acetone, cyclohexanone + bromoform, butylacetate + 1,2,3-trichloropropane, and pyridine + chloroform.

Positive deviation from Raoult's law indicates that the like molecules have greater attraction for each other than the unlike molecules. This often occurs when solutions are made with liquids, only one of which contains strong hydrogen bonds in the pure state. Thus mixtures of carbon disulfide or hydrocarbons (which have no hydrogen bonding capacity) with alcohols or primary or secondary amines will give positive deviations from Raoult's law and often give minimum boiling mixtures. If the deviation is extreme, separation of the system into two phases will result, as in the case of water and hydrocarbons. In codistillation processes use is made of the fact that immiscible liquids produce minimum boiling mixtures—steam distillation being the most common of these codistillations.

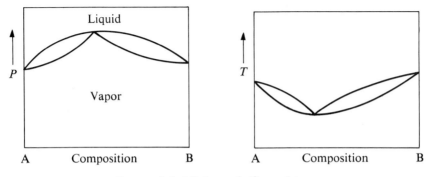

FIGURE 5.4. *Minimum boiling mixture.*

Solubility

When an uncharged organic compound dissolves to any appreciable extent in water, the solubility may be attributed to hydrogen bonding. Thus dimethylether is completely miscible with water, whereas dimethylsulfide is only slightly soluble in water.

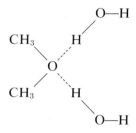

Benzene is only slightly soluble in water, while pyridine is completely miscible with water. The number of carbon atoms in a molecule that is still soluble in water is strongly dependent on the number of atoms per molecule capable of forming hydrogen bonds with water. About three carbon atoms per oxygen atom will usually give a highly water soluble compound. Thus dioxane, $C_4H_8O_2$, is completely miscible with water, whereas diethyl ether, $(C_2H_5)_2O$, is only moderately soluble (7.5 g/100). Sugars are water soluble due to hydrogen bonding with water. The solution of ionic compounds in water is also strongly dependent on hydrogen bonding. (See Chapter III, p. 125.)

Hydrogen bonding plays a role in many nonaqueous solvents also. Chloroform is a good solvent for fatty acids due to its polar C—H bond, which may engage in hydrogen bonding. Ethers can serve as solvents for hydrogen chloride due to the ability to form hydrogen bonds.

Acetylene is very soluble in acetone due to hydrogen bond formation. Since acetylene itself under pressure is dangerous to handle due to its sensitivity to shock, it is handled commercially by dissolving it in acetone under pressure. It does not dissolve appreciably in water since the hydrogen bonding interaction between water molecules is much stronger than that between acetylene and water molecules.

Some further solubility effects are mentioned in the section dealing with intramolecular hydrogen bonds.

Intramolecular Hydrogen Bonding

With many organic compounds there is a possibility of intramolecular hydrogen bonding (i.e., within the molecule) and in such cases intramolecular hydrogen bonding will be favored over intermolecular hydrogen bonding due to the more unfavorable entropy change associated with intermolecular hydrogen bonding. Changes from *inter* to *intra*molecular hydrogen bonding in going from *meta* and *para* to *ortho* aromatic compounds may cause large differences in the melting points, boiling points, and solubilities of these isomers. Intramolecularly hydrogen bonded substances are more soluble in organic solvents and have lower melting and boiling points than their intermolecularly hydrogen bonded isomers.

These differences are illustrated by the physical properties of the isomers of hydroxy-benzaldehyde listed below.

	m.p. (°C)	b.p. (°C)	Sol. in H_2O	Sol. in ether
o-hydroxybenzaldehyde	−7	196.5	sl. sol.	∞
m-hydroxybenzaldehyde	106–108	240	sol. hot	sol.
p-hydroxybenzaldehyde	116–117	−	sol. hot	4/100

The differences in melting points, boiling points, and solubility in ether are readily understood on the basis of o-hydroxybenzaldehyde acting as a discrete molecular unit (due to intramolecular hydrogen bonding) but the *meta* and *para* isomers behave as polymeric units which partially depolymerize on melting, boiling, or going into solution.

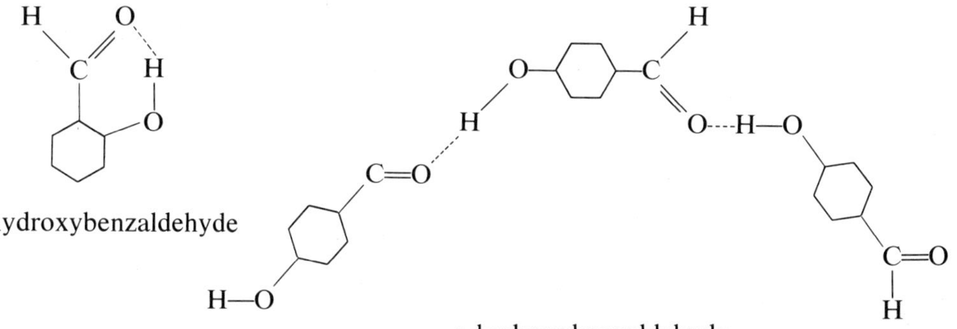

o-hydroxybenzaldehyde

p-hydroxybenzaldehyde

The lower water solubility of the *ortho* isomer is due to persistence of the intramolecular hydrogen bond even in aqueous solution, due in part to entropy considerations, whereas the *meta* and *para* isomers form hydrogen bonds with water.

Dielectric Constants

In Table 5.1 the decrease in dielectric constant on successively substituting methyl groups for hydrogen in H_2O may be noted. Other cases of a decrease in dielectric constant on replacing hydrogen by methyl may be noted: N-methylacetamide,* dielectric constant of 175.7 (25°C); N,N-dimethylacetamide,† 37.8; HCN, 120; CH_3CN, 38.8.

The unusually high dielectric constants of the hydrogen bonded materials may be ascribed to the existence of polymeric molecules having an enhanced electric dipole moment, which is greater than the sum of the dipole moments of the monomers of which it is composed. The polymeric species have structures similar to the solids but, of course, with fewer molecules per unit.

An apparent anomaly is found with acetamide which has a dielectric constant of 74, much less than its N-methyl derivative. This is believed to be due to the formation by acetamide of a randomly oriented polymer rather than a linear polymer as in the case of N-methylacetamide.

* Leader, G. R., and J. F. Gormley, *J. Am. Chem. Soc.*, **73**, 5731 (1951).
† Leader, G. R., *J. Am. Chem. Soc.*, **73**, 856 (1951).

In dealing with dielectric constants the assumption has been made that hydrogen bonding in the methyl derivatives is absent. Certainly it will be less than in the parent hydrogen compound, but it probably contributes appreciably to the dielectric constant in acetonitrile, CH_3CN, and also in compounds such as malononitrile, $NCCH_2CN$ (dielectric constant = 66.6 at 23°C), nitromethane (39 at 20°C), dimethylsulfate (55 at 20°C), and ethylene carbonate (73 at 50°C).

Infrared Spectra*

Various absorption bands in the infrared spectrum of a compound may often be associated with particular vibrational modes of the molecule or of functional groups in the molecule. Hydrogen bonding of a group such as the —O—H group will affect the frequency, band width, and intensity of the infrared absorption bands that may be assigned to the —O—H stretching vibration and —O—H bending vibration. Dilute solutions of an alcohol (or other substance capable of association through hydrogen bonding) in an inert solvent such as carbon tetrachloride will show an absorption band characteristic of the stretching vibration of a free —O—H group, while more concentrated solutions will have a new absorption band at a lower frequency and with a

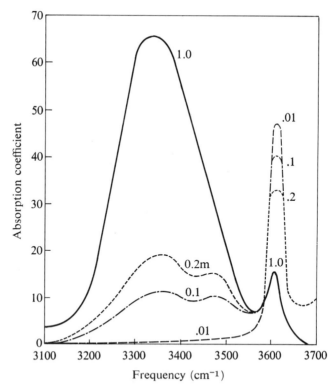

FIGURE 5.5. *Absorption spectra of tert-butanol in* CCl_4 *at various concentrations at 25°C.* [*from U. Liddel and E. D. Becker,* Spectrochim. Acta, *10, 70 (1957)*].

* See G. C. Pimentel and A. L. McClellan, *The Hydrogen Bond* (San Francisco and London: W. H. Freeman and Co., 1960) for an extensive treatment of this topic.

greater absorption. This new band is due to the absorption of a hydrogen bonded species, (see Figure 5.5). Information on the equilibria between monomeric and polymeric species may be obtained from this type of spectral data. From studies of the effect of temperature on these equilibria it is possible to evaluate the enthalpy, entropy, and free energy changes associated with the hydrogen bond formation in these cases. It has been found that the enthalpy change for hydrogen bond formation often parallels the shift in the —O—H (or —N—H) absorption frequency that takes place on going from the free O—H to the hydrogen bonded O—H.

Crystal Structure*

When hydrogen bonding is possible in molecular crystals, the structure will be such that the maximum number of hydrogen bonds will be formed. This gives rise to structures in which the individual molecules are connected through hydrogen bonds to form chains, sheets, or 3-dimensional networks. In some cases the crystals may be made of units consisting of dimeric or trimeric hydrogen bonded species.

Polymeric hydrogen bonded chains are found in the linear HCN polymer.

Zigzag chains are more common and occur in solid HF, CH_3OH, formic acid, acetanilide, and probably *N*-methylamides.

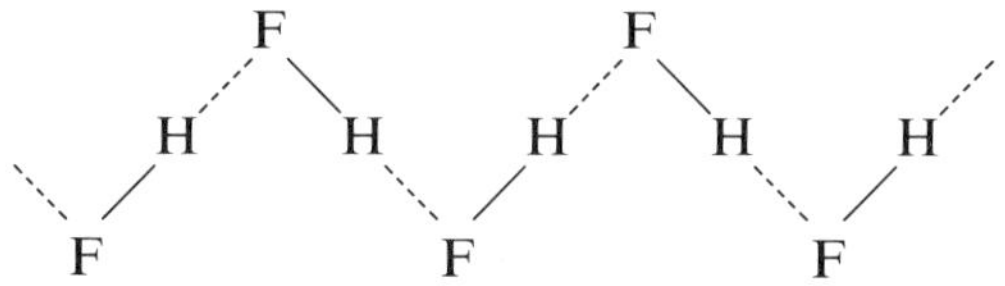

solid HF

Oxalic acid may form a maximum number of hydrogen bonds by forming either chains or sheet structures. Both modifications actually are known (see Figure 5.6).

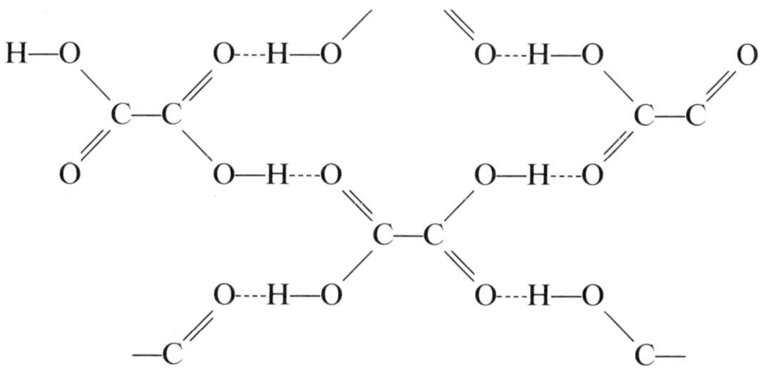

FIGURE 5.6. *α-Oxalic acid.*

The sheet and three-dimensional structures are typical in cases where each molecule has several hydrogens for hydrogen bonding and also several lone electron pairs. Boric acid is another example of a compound having a sheet structure. Three-dimensional networks occur in such compounds as water and telluric acid.

* Ubbelohde, A. R., and K. J. Gallagher, *Acta Cryst.,* **8**, 71 (1955).

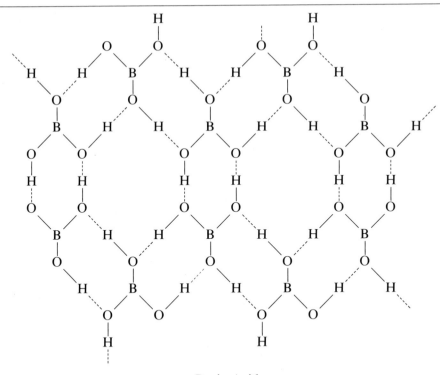

Boric Acid

Hydrogen bonding is very important in polypeptides and cellulose structures.

In ionic substances hydrogen bonding may also play a major role in determining the structure. Discrete hydrogen bonded ions may exist in acid salts such as KHF_2 (discussed in a later section). Other acid salts such as sodium hydrogen carbonate may form polyanion chains or three-dimensional networks as in KH_2PO_4.

The difference in structure between NH_4F and NH_4Cl is due to the greater strength of the N—HF bond than the N—HCl bond.

Theory

Coulson* has estimated the various contributions to the energy of the hydrogen bond in ice as follows:

Type of Energy

Electrostatic	−6	kcal
Delocalization	−8	
Repulsive	+8.4	
Dispersion	−3	
Total	Theoretical −8.6	Experimental −6.1

As Coulson has stated these factors may be of greater or lesser importance in other hydrogen bonded systems. Let us examine each of these factors.

* Coulson, C. A., *Research* (London), **10**, 149 (1957).

REPULSION AND DISPERSION

In most molecular compounds the closest interatomic distance between atoms of neighboring molecules is set by the balance of dispersive forces and repulsive forces due to interpenetration of the electron clouds. In cases where a hydrogen bond is formed, the forces due specifically to hydrogen bonding, i.e., the electrostatic force and the force due to delocalization, will cause the two atoms sharing the hydrogen atom to have an internuclear separation less than the sum of their van der Waals' radii. Indeed, this is one of the most reliable experimental criteria for hydrogen bond formation. This relationship does not hold for intramolecular hydrogen bonds since the approach of A and B may affect other bond energies in the molecule due to the distortions introduced in the molecule as A and B approach each other.

If two groups that may hydrogen bond are forced into close proximity due to other steric factors that are present in the molecule, then not all of the increase in repulsion, due to the close approach of atoms, will be at the expense of the H-bond energy and a very strong H-bond may be formed. This occurs in highly alkylated malonic acids, gem-dimethylcaronic acid, nickel dimethylglyoxime and some other compounds (Figure 5.7).

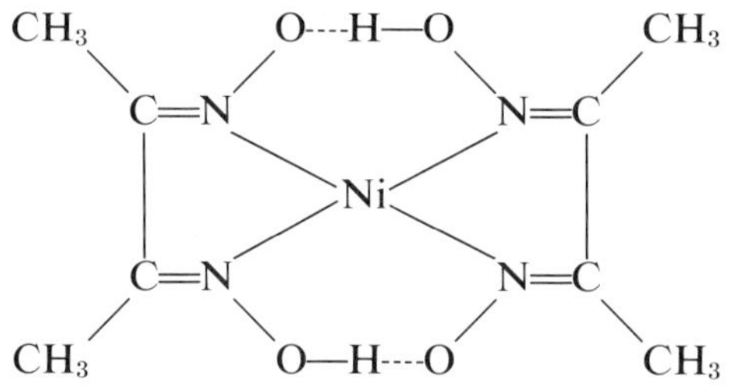

FIGURE 5.7. *Nickel dimethylglyoxime.*

ELECTROSTATIC TERM

In neutral molecules the electrostatic term may be thought of as arising from a unique type of dipole–dipole interaction. The uniqueness lies in the fact that the hydrogen has no underlying shell of electrons; this permits an unusually close approach of the positive end of the dipole to the negative end of a neighboring dipole. Also, a major component of the negative end of the dipole may reside in a free pair of electrons, relatively near the surface of the molecule, and with directional orientation in space. These factors could prevent even diatomic molecules that possess H-bonds from behaving like simple point dipoles. The structure of HF (p. 171) is thus not inconsistent with an electrostatic model of the hydrogen bond.

Since the interaction of an *ion* with a dipole is much greater than dipole–dipole interaction, it is expected that the electrostatic contribution to the energy of the hydrogen bond will be much greater in ion–molecule interactions, i.e., FHF^-, $ClHCl^-$, $HOHOH^-$, etc. Such interactions would decrease with increasing size of the ion. It would also decrease as the charge density is drained from the surface of a polyatomic

ion by π bonding between the outer atoms and the central atoms. Thus, Nightingale*
explains the greater interaction of iodates with water, as compared to the interaction of
chlorates with water, as due to a greater degree of π-bonding between O and Cl than
between O and I.

DELOCALIZATION

In terms of resonance the following will be contributing structures of the resonance
hybrid of the hydrogen bond AHB:†

$$A—H \quad B \qquad\qquad A^-H^+\cdots B \qquad\qquad A^-H—B^+$$
$$\textit{(1)} \qquad\qquad\qquad \textit{(2)} \qquad\qquad\qquad \textit{(3)}$$

$$A^+H^- \quad B \qquad\qquad\qquad \overline{A \quad H^- \quad B^+}$$
$$\textit{(4)} \qquad\qquad\qquad\qquad \textit{(5)}$$

Structure (1) represents no interaction, (2) and (4) electrostatic interaction, (3) and (5)
represent charge delocalization and might be said to represent the covalent character
of the hydrogen bond. To the extent that A—H has partial ionic character, charge
delocalization becomes more important. When A—H is a positive ion, or B a negative
ion, i.e., when there is a full unit charge, charge delocalization may become quite important. One would expect that the importance of charge delocalization would decrease
with increasing size of ions involved in hydrogen bonding.

Other Viewpoints and Further Considerations

The possibility of covalence contributing appreciably to the stability of the hydrogen
bond was rejected by Pauling on the basis that "the hydrogen atom, with only one
stable orbital (the $1s$ orbital), can form only one covalent bond . . . ." Pimentel‡ has
given a molecular orbital description of the hydrogen bond, which surmounts this objection to covalency. From the three atomic orbitals, the $1s$ of hydrogen and the two p
orbitals of A and B, three molecular orbitals are constructed—a bonding orbital, a nonbonding orbital, and an antibonding orbital. The four electrons then occupy the bonding and nonbonding orbitals. On this basis, the bridge bond in diborane may be considered to be a hydrogen bond in which the nonbonding orbitals are not occupied.
Pimentel's picture indicates the necessity that atoms A and B have nearly the same
electronegativity—otherwise the nonbonding orbital would be virtually the p orbital of
the highly electronegative atom and the bonding orbital would be virtually a two center
covalent bond A—H, and the hydrogen bond would lose its covalent character.

Another useful viewpoint is the notion that hydrogen bond formation involves acid–
base reactions in which proton transfer is incomplete. According to this view, factors
that increase the basicity of the proton acceptor will increase the strength of hydrogen
bond formation. Gordy§ has pointed out a relationship between the shift of the O—D
stretching frequency of CH_3OD in different solvents and the base strengths of these

* See p. 59.
† Pimentel, G. C., and A. L. McClellan, *The Hydrogen Bond* (San Francisco and London: W. H. Freeman
and Company, 1960) p. 234.
‡ Pimentel, G. C., *J. Chem. Phys., 19,* 446 (1951).
§ Gordy, W., *J. Chem. Phys., 7,* 93 (1939).

solvents in water. Ubbelohde and Gallagher* emphasize the "incomplete" in the proton transfer process. They point out that if A and B in A—H—B differ greatly in basicity then hydrogen bond formation will be negligible. If A is a strong base relative to B then essentially no proton transfer occurs, if A is a weak base relative to B proton transfer will be essentially complete. In the latter case the interaction of AH and B would be large, but it would produce A and BH, which would give negligible hydrogen bonding. When A and B are of equal basicity an ideal situation for hydrogen bonding results. This situation occurs when A and B are the same, i.e., in ion–molecule interactions such as FHF^- or $H_2OHOH_2^+$. These cases are discussed in the next sections.

Anion–Molecule Interactions

When hydrogen fluoride comes into contact with an alkali metal fluoride at room temperature, an exothermic reaction occurs and an acid salt is formed. Use is made of this reaction for the removal of HF from gas streams, particularly in the commercial production of F_2 where HF is almost always a contaminant.

$$NaF(s) + (HF)_x(g) \longrightarrow NaHF_2(s) + 16.5 \text{ kcal}$$

Reversal of the reaction, i.e., thermal decomposition of KHF_2, serves as a convenient source of anhydrous HF. The heat released in reacting with HF is least with LiF (10.2 kcal per mole) and increases with the size of the cation, being 21.1 kcal with KF, 22.2 with RbF, 23.4 with CsF, and 37 kcal† with tetramethylammonium fluoride. X-ray diffraction studies indicate that the alkali metal hydrogendifluorides are salts having a positive metal cation and $(FHF)^-$ as an anion. (See Figure 5.8). The F—F distance in KHF_2 is only 2.25 Å with the hydrogen nucleus equidistant from the fluorine nuclei (see Chapter XII for a discussion of an NMR investigation of this species).

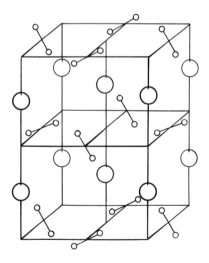

FIGURE 5.8. KHF_2 *structure according to R. M. Bozorth,* J. Am. Chem. Soc., **45**, *2128 (1923). This is a distorted CsCl structure.*

* Ubbelohde, A. R., and K. J. Gallagher, *Acta Cryst.,* **8**, 71 (1955).
† Harrell, S. A., Ph.D. thesis, University of Cincinnati, 1964.

As the HF is absorbed the crystal lattice of KF must expand to accommodate the $(FHF)^-$ ion. The energy necessary for this expansion will be greatest for $LiHF_2$ and least for $CsHF_2$. The loss of lattice energy on going from the halide to the HF adduct is reflected in a decrease in m.p. — the m.p. of KF is 846°C whereas that of KHF_2 is 239°C. The larger alkali metal ions permit the formation of even higher adducts such as KH_2F_3 and KH_3F_4, CsH_2F_3, etc., having still lower melting points. Advantage is taken of the low melting points of these compounds in the production of fluorine by the electrolysis of fused KHF_2, KH_3F_4, etc. Liquid HF (b.p. 19°C) is also used for this purpose, but the volatility of HF and its corrosive nature introduce technical difficulties.

The energy of the reaction

$$HF + F^- \longrightarrow FHF^-$$

has been estimated by Ketelaar from the cycle

$$K^+(g) + F^-(g) \; + \; HF(g) \xrightarrow{\text{(ii)}} K^+(g) + HF_2^-(g)$$

$$(i) \uparrow \qquad\qquad\qquad \downarrow (iii)$$

$$KF(s) + HF(g) \xrightarrow[\text{(iv)}]{} KHF_2(s)$$

Step (ii) corresponds to the hydrogen bond formation in FHF^- and has been estimated to release 30 to 50 kcal per g-ion of HF_2^-.[*] The uncertainty in the energy is due to the uncertainty in the lattice energy of KHF_2 (step iii). Waddington[†] has done some more refined calculations of the lattice energies of KHF_2, $RbHF_2$, and $CsHF_2$ and combined these with thermochemical data to obtain a value of -58 ± 5 kcal per g-ion of HF_2^- for the hydrogen bond energy. This value is 21 kcal higher than the highest experimentally observed value of -37 kcal in $(CH_3)_4NFHF$, a compound in which lattice expansion effects are expected to be negligible.

The solubility of many fluorides in liquid HF is undoubtedly due to the high degree of solvation of the fluoride ion through hydrogen bonding, i.e., $F(HF)_n^-$. The strong acid behavior of liquid HF, as contrasted with aqueous solutions of HF, indicates that the solvation energy of the fluoride ion is much higher in HF than in water.

Although all of the alkali metal fluorides will form MHF_2 type compounds with HF, $CsHCl_2$ is the only alkali metal hydrogen dichloride which has been made, and it is stable only at low temperatures or high HCl pressures.[‡] The heavier halogens form no MHX_2 compounds with the alkali metal halides. This indicates that the energy necessary to expand the crystal lattice is greater than that given up by the formation of the $[XHX^-]$ ion. When the halide ion is present in a lattice with a very large cation, as in tetraalkyl ammonium salts or even some amine hydrohalides, the hydrogen dihalide ion may be formed. Thus N-dimethylaniline will react with two moles of HCl, HBr, or HI. When the cation is quite large still more hydrogen halide may be taken up. Thus, with a tetraethylammonium cation one may obtain a solid with the anion $H_3Cl_4^-$, or $H_2Br_3^-$, or $H_2I_3^-$.

* Ketelaar, J. A. A., *Rec. trav. chim.*, **60**, 523 (1941).
† Waddington, T. C., *Trans. Faraday Soc.*, **54**, 25 (1958).
‡ Valleé, R. E., and D. H. McDaniel, *J. Am. Chem. Soc.*, **84**, 3412 (1962).

The species HX_2^- and possibly higher polymers $H_2X_3^-$, etc., may also play an important role in nonaqueous solutions as well as in solids. The association constant for $Cl^- + HCl = HCl_2^-$ in nitrobenzene at 25°C has been estimated as 500 to 1000 l/mole.* Conductance behavior of the hydrogen halides in acetonitrile has been attributed to HX_2^- as the anion.†

Water in its reactions with alkali metal hydroxides is quite similar to HF with MF. Thus solid KOH is occasionally used to remove water vapor from gas streams (especially where it is also desirable to remove CO_2 simultaneously).

$$KOH(s) + H_2O(g) \longrightarrow KOH \cdot H_2O(s) + 20.1 \text{ kcal}$$

Again there is an increase in the heat of hydration on going from LiOH to CsOH, being -14.3 kcal for the former and -22.7 kcal for the latter for the monohydrates. Since H_2O is monomeric in the gas phase, -22.7 kcal per g-ion may be taken as the minimum heat of reaction for

$$HO^- + H_2O \longrightarrow [HOHOH]^-$$

It is very probable that one or both of the terminal hydrogens in the $HOHOH^-$ unit are hydrogen bonded to another $HOHOH^-$ unit.

The hydroxide ion may interact with more than one water molecule, just as a halide ion may interact with more than one hydrogen halide molecule. Thus the compounds $KOH \cdot H_2O$, $KOH \cdot 2H_2O$, and $KOH \cdot 4H_2O$, are known.

As has been noted earlier, strong hydrogen bonds are to be expected in ion–molecule interactions where there is equal competition for the proton, a charge to delocalize, and a dipole to interact with the ion. The experimental energies of some hydrogen bonds in anion–molecule systems specifically designed to minimize lattice energy effects are given in Table 5.3. Even when competition for the proton is unequal, as in $^-Cl \cdots HCCl_3$,

* Herbrandson, H. F., and R. T. Dickerson, Jr., *J. Am. Chem. Soc.,* **81**, 4102 (1959).
† Janz, G. J., and S. S. Danyluk, *J. Am. Chem. Soc.,* **81**, 3854 (1959).

TABLE 5.3

Some Energies of Hydrogen Bonds in Anion–Molecule Systems

$-\Delta H$ in kcal/mole H-bond			
$H_2NH \cdots F^{-b}$	$HOH \cdots Cl^{-c}$	$CH_3OHOC_4H_9^{-c}$	FHF^{-b}
8.9	10.5	19.3	37
$^-Cl \cdots HCCl_3{}^a$		$HSHSH^{-a}$	$ClHCl^{-d}$
9.4		> 7	14.2
$H_2NH \cdots Cl^{-b}$			$BrHBr^{-d}$
10.2			12.8
$H_2NH \cdots Br^{-b}$			IHI^{-d}
6.2			12.4
$H_2NH \cdots I^{-b}$			
5.4			

[a] Evans, W. G., Ph.D. thesis, University of Cincinnati, 1964.
[b] Harrell, S. A., Ph.D. thesis, University of Cincinnati, 1964.
[c] Valleé, R. E., Ph.D. thesis, University of Cincinnati, 1962.
[d] McDaniel, D. H., and R. E. Valleé, *Inorg. Chem.,* **2**, 996 (1963).

the hydrogen bonds are much stronger than in molecule–molecule interactions (see Table 5.2). Among the wide variety of oxyacids that are known there are numerous possibilities of similar molecule–ion interactions. Some of the compounds whose formulas have puzzled chemists until recently are $RbNO_3 \cdot HNO_3$; $RbNO_3 \cdot 2HNO_3$; $KHCO_2 \cdot HCO_2H$; $KHCO_2 \cdot 2HCO_2H$; $KHCO_2 \cdot 3HCO_2H$; and $NaCH_3CO_2 \cdot CH_3CO_2H$. That hydrogen bonds in these compounds are strong hydrogen bonds is shown by the short O—H—O distance of 2.41_7 Å found in sodium hydrogen diacetate* as compared with the value 2.76 Å found in ice.

Equal competition for the proton in a hydrogen bond may also occur in ion–ion interactions as in sodium sesquicarbonate hydrate, $Na_2CO_3 \cdot NaHCO_3 \cdot 2H_2O$, containing the

$$
\begin{bmatrix}
\quad\quad\quad O \\
\quad\quad\quad \diagup \\
O—C \\
\quad\quad \diagdown \\
\quad\quad\quad O—H \cdots O \\
\quad\quad\quad\quad\quad\quad \diagdown \\
\quad\quad\quad\quad\quad\quad C—O \\
\quad\quad\quad\quad\quad \diagup \\
\quad\quad\quad\quad O
\end{bmatrix}^{3-}
$$

units which are further hydrogen bonded into sheets by the water molecules. The O—H···O distance in these units is 2.50 Å.† Charge delocalization is expected to make an important contribution to the hydrogen bond energy in this case.

To the extent that $CrO(OH)$, $FeO(OH)$, and $AlO(OH)$ may contain the ions O^{2-} and OH^-, charge delocalization will also contribute to the hydrogen bond energy in these cases. The hydrogen bonds in these anion–anion interactions are not expected to be as strong as those involved in molecule–anion interactions due to the anion–anion repulsion involved in the former.

Cation–Molecule Interactions‡

The nature of the hydrogen ion in water has been a subject for speculation for the last sixty years. Largely on the basis of the existence of isomorphous crystals of perchloric acid hydrate ($H_3O^+ClO_4^-$) and ammonium perchlorate ($NH_4^+ClO_4^-$) it was assumed that the hydrogen ion in water existed as H_3O^+, termed the oxonium ion. In 1936, Huggins§ suggested that in water the hydrogen ion would exist as

$$
\begin{bmatrix}
H \quad\quad\quad\quad H \\
\diagdown \quad\quad\quad \diagup \\
\quad O \cdots H \cdots O \\
\diagup \quad\quad\quad \diagdown \\
H \quad\quad\quad\quad H
\end{bmatrix}^{+}
$$

in which, unlike ice, the hydrogen in the hydrogen bond would be equidistant from

---

* Speakman, J. C., *Proc. Roy. Soc. (London)*, 316 (1959).
† Bacon, G. E., and N. A. Curry, *Acta Cryst.*, **9**, 82 (1956).
‡ See Clever under General References.
§ Huggins, M., *J. Am. Chem. Soc.*, **58**, 694 (1936).

both oxygen atoms. In 1954 Eigen et al.* proposed that the hydrogen ion in water exists as $H_9O_4^+$ with a structure as shown below.

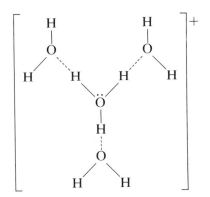

Support for a hydration number of four for the hydrogen ion comes from specific heat studies of aqueous hydrochloric acid solutions,* from extraction studies on HCl, HBr, and $HClO_4$,† from activity coefficients of aqueous acids‡ and more recently from data obtained by field emission mass spectrometry.§

The exceptionally high mobility of the hydrogen ion in water is not expected for a species as large as $H_9O_4^+$. This may be explained by the ease of realignment of hydrogen bonds to form new $H_9O_4^+$ species incorporating water previously in a secondary hydration sphere.

In solids one may find the hydrated hydrogen ion in species varying from H_3O^+ up to $H_9O_4^+$ as illustrated by the hydrates of hydrogen bromide given below with their melting points.

	m.p. (°C)	
$HBr \cdot 4H_2O$	−56.8	
$HBr \cdot 3H_2O$	−48	
$HBr \cdot 2H_2O$	−11	
$HBr \cdot H_2O$	− 4	(incongruent melting point)

The increase in melting point on going from HBr (m.p. −86°C) to $HBr \cdot H_2O$ (oxonium bromide) (m.p. −4°C) is due to a change from a covalent lattice to an ionic lattice (with hydrogen bonding). The decrease in melting points on going to higher hydrates is due to expansion of the crystal lattice to accommodate the larger hydrated species accompanied by a loss in lattice energy. Similar hydrates exist for HI while HCl forms only $HCl \cdot H_2O$, $HCl \cdot 2H_2O$, and $HCl \cdot 3H_2O$ but not a higher hydrate. A layer of the structure of oxonium chloride, $HCl \cdot H_2O$ is shown in Figure 5.9. The tetrahydrate probably does not form with HCl due to (a) the loss of lattice energy in adding an additional H_2O molecule, (b) the more effective competition of Cl^- (than Br^- or I^-) with H_2O in serving as a hydrogen acceptor in a hydrogen bond.

* Wicke, E., M. Eigen, and T. Ackerman, *Z. Physik. Chem.*, **1**, 340 (1954).
† Tuck, D. G., and R. M. Diamond, *Proc. Chem. Soc.*, **1958**, 236.
‡ Glueckauf, E., *Trans. Faraday Soc.*, **51**, 1235 (1955).
§ Beckey, H. D., *Z. Naturforsch.*, **14a**, 712 (1959).

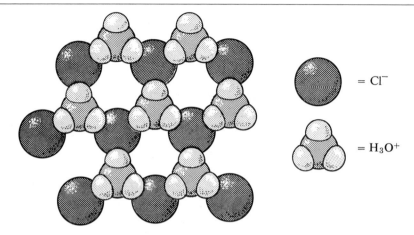

= Cl⁻

= H₃O⁺

FIGURE 5.9. *Layer structure of oxonium chloride* [*Yoon and Carpenter*, Acta Cryst., 12, *17 (1959)*].

$$
\begin{array}{c}
\text{H} \\
| \\
\text{O} \\
/ \quad \backslash \\
\text{H} \qquad \text{H} \\
\backslash \\
\overset{..}{\text{O}}{}^{+}\!\!-\!\!\text{H}\cdots\text{Cl}^{-} \\
\\
\text{H} \qquad \text{H} \\
\backslash \quad / \\
\text{O} \\
| \\
\text{H}
\end{array}
$$

Hexabromostannic(IV) acid can only be isolated as an octahydrate, $H_2SnBr_6\cdot 8H_2O$, which is readily explainable on the basis of a crystal lattice containing $SnBr_6{}^{2-}$ units and $H_9O_4{}^+$ units.

Hexachlorostannic(IV) acid can only be isolated as the hexahydrate. Here again one may assume that one of the partially negative chlorine atoms of the $SnCl_6{}^{2-}$ ion is serving to hydrogen bond with one of the acidic protons of a hydronium ion while the other two are hydrogen bonded to water.

$$
\begin{array}{c}
\text{H} \\
| \\
\text{O} \\
/ \quad \backslash \\
\text{H} \qquad \text{H} \\
\backslash \\
\text{O}\!-\!\text{H}\cdots\text{Cl}\!-\!\text{Sn} \\
\\
\text{H} \qquad \text{H} \\
/ \\
\text{O} \\
| \\
\text{H}
\end{array}
$$

Tetrachloroauric(IV) acid forms both a trihydrate and a tetrahydrate, the latter presumably having $H_9O_4^+$ ions and the former probably having units such as

$$
\begin{array}{c}
H \\
| \\
O \\
\diagup \quad \vdots \\
H \quad\quad H \\
\qquad\qquad \diagdown \\
\qquad\qquad O\text{—}H\cdots Cl\text{—}Au\text{—}Cl \\
\diagdown \qquad \diagup \\
H \qquad H \\
\qquad \diagdown \vdots \\
\qquad\quad O \\
\qquad\quad | \\
\qquad\quad H
\end{array}
$$

From the heat of the reaction

$$HAuCl_4 \cdot 3H_2O(s) + H_2O(g) \longrightarrow HAuCl_4 \cdot 4H_2O$$

the minimum heat of reaction of

$$H_7O_3^+ + H_2O(g) \longrightarrow H_9O_4^+$$

may be estimated to be -12.9 kcal. This may be taken as the minimum energy per mole for the hydrogen bond in $H_9O_4^+$. More correctly this value represents the difference in the $O\text{—}H\cdots Cl$ hydrogen bond energy in $HAuCl_4 \cdot 3H_2O$ and the energy of the last hydrogen bond formed in $H_9O_4^+$.

The composition of sulfuric acid hydrates ranges from mono- to hexahydrates. In liquid solutions these hydrates may be in equilibrium with each other, i.e., the species $H_9O_4^+$ through H_3O^+ may be in equilibrium. The H_3O^+ species itself should be a stronger acid than $H_9O_4^+$ since in transferring a proton to a base the $H_9O_4^+$ species loses the energy due to three strong hydrogen bonds in addition to the $O^+\text{—}H$ bond energy. In aqueous acid solutions as the water activity decreases the H_3O^+ activity increases, i.e., $H_9O_4^+ \leftrightarrows H_7O_3^+ + H_2O \leftrightarrows H_5O_2^+ + 2H_2O \leftrightarrows H_3O^+ + 3H_2O$ for strong acid solutions in which water is the strongest base present, the acidity of the solution (as measured by the ability of the solution to transfer a proton to an indicator base) should vary inversely as a function of the partial pressure of water above the solution. This conclusion was reached by a more rigorous approach to these equilibria by Wyatt[*] and empirically by Braun.[†]

The relationship between the acidity of strong acid solutions and the aqueous vapor pressure explains the increase in acidity that occurs on addition of neutral salts to acid solutions.[‡] The water activity is decreased, due to ion hydration, and the acidity thereby enhanced—an explanation differing only slightly from the original one. Practical application of this phenomenon has been made in titrations of weak bases (with K_b as low as 10^{-12}) with $0.5N$ HCl containing 6 to 8 molar concentrations of neutral salts.[§]

[*] Wyatt, P. A. H., *Discussions Faraday Soc.*, **24**, 162 (1957).
[†] Braun, M., M.S. thesis, University of Pittsburgh, February, 1957.
[‡] Thomas, A. W., and M. E. Baldwin, *J. Am. Chem. Soc.*, **41**, 1981 (1919).
[§] Critchfield, F. E., and J. B. Johnson, *Anal. Chem.*, **30**, 1247 (1958).

Hydrogen bonding phenomena play an important role in protonic acid–base reactions in nonaqueous solutions as well as in water. In a series of studies of the relative strength of acids and bases in benzene, Davis, Hetzer, and co-workers* formulate the reactions between acid (HA) and base (B) as

$$B + HA \rightleftharpoons BH^+ \cdots A \qquad (1)$$
$$BH^+ \cdots A + B \rightleftharpoons (BHB)^+ A^- \qquad (2)$$

The first step, termed "the primary reaction," is the formation of a hydrogen bonded ion pair. With a given indicator base, the value of the equilibrium constant of reaction (1) may be taken as a measure of the acid strength of HA. The second step, termed the "secondary reaction" shows the breakup of BHA and the formation of a new hydrogen bonded species, BHB^+.

Just as the proton in sufficient water forms $(H_3O \cdot 3H_2O)^+$, in liquid ammonia it might be expected to form $(NH_4 \cdot 4NH_3)^+$. The formula $NH_4I \cdot 4NH_3$ (m.p. $-5.1°C$) suggests that such an ion exists.

Oddly enough, the set of equilibria which Moore set out to study early in this century (p. 162) are still incompletely understood. The solubility of ammonia is much higher in solutions of ammonium salts than in water itself. This is contrary to predictions based on the equilibria represented on page 162. From recent high field conductance studies† on aqueous solutions of ammonia the species present in 1.3×10^{-3} molar ammonia are: 75% of the total ammonia as NH_3, 15% as the hydrated form and 10% as the ammonium ion. This stoichiometry suggests that the "NH_3" present exists as a hydrogen bonded species such as

These species, like the clusters of hydrogen bonded water molecules proposed by Frank,‡ would probably be breaking up and reforming continuously. Such a structure was first proposed by Gordy§ to account for the exceptionally broad, and sometimes double, —O—D stretching band of alcohols in amines.

* Davis, M. M., and H. B. Hetzer, *J. Res. Natl. Bur. Std.,* **60**, 569 (1958) and references 1a through 1h of this paper.
† Arnold, E., H. Freitag, and A. Patterson, Jr., *The Structure of Electrolytes,* edited by W. J. Hamer (New York: John Wiley and Sons, Inc.; London: Chapman and Hall, Limited, 1959).
‡ Frank, H. S., *Proc. Roy. Soc. (London),* **247A**, 481 (1958).
§ Gordy, W., *J. Chem. Phys.,* **7**, 93 (1939).

GENERAL REFERENCES

Pimentel, G. C., and A. L. McClellan, *The Hydrogen Bond* (San Francisco and London: W. H. Freeman and Company, 1960).
Hadzi, D., editor, with the co-operation of H. W. Thompson, *Hydrogen Bonding; Papers presented at the Symposium on Hydrogen Bonding held at Ljubljana, 29 July-3 August 1957* (New York: Pergamon Press, 1959).
Pauling, L., *The Nature of the Chemical Bond* (3rd Ed., Ithaca: Cornell University Press, 1960).
Clever, H. L., "The Hydrated Hydronium Ion," *J. Chem. Educ.,* **40**, 637 (1963).

Problems

1.   Indicate whether positive, negative, or no deviation from Raoult's law might be expected for the following binary systems: (*a*) $HCl-(CH_3)_2O$; (*b*) $H_2O-C_8H_{18}$; (*c*) $HCCl_3-CCl_4$; (*d*) $HCCl_3-(C_2H_5)_3N$.

2.   The heat released in the reaction $Br^-(g) + HCl(g) \rightarrow BrHCl^-(g)$ has been found to be 9.1 kcal. By devising a suitable thermochemical cycle, and using available data, evaluate the expected heat released in the reaction $Cl^-(g) + HBr(g) \rightarrow ClHBr^-(g)$.

3.   Explain why a comparison of a normal melting point and a melting point taken with the compound under water may sometimes be used to distinguish between intra- and inter-molecular hydrogen bonding. [See E. D. Amstutz, J. J. Chessick, and I. M. Hunsberger, *Science,* **111**, 305 (1950).]

4.   Why does CsCl react with HCl(g) at low temperatures while NaCl does not?

5.   It has been suggested that the higher m.p. of *p*-methylpyridine-*N*-oxide compared to the *o*- and *m*- isomer may be due to hydrogen bonding. How might this be tested experimentally? Be specific. Mention both the data to be gathered, with what it might be compared, and how this would serve to establish hydrogen bonding or its absence.

6.   The anhydrous acid $HICl_4$ cannot be isolated, but the crystalline hydrate $HICl_4 \cdot 4H_2O$ may be obtained from ICl_3 in aqueous HCl. How may this be explained?

CHAPTER VI

Acids and Bases

Historical Background

Acids as a class of compounds were well known to the alchemists, being character-ized by their sour taste (Latin *acidus*, sour), their ability to dissolve many substances which are water insoluble, and their action on various vegetable dyes. When Priestly announced his discovery of "dephlogisticated air" in 1775, Lavoisier, whose experi-ments on combustion had started the overthrow of the phlogiston theory, concluded that in combination with nonmetals the newly discovered substance was the common constituent of acids. Accordingly he named the new substance oxygen (Fr. *oxys*, sharp or acid + genesis). The German name "Sauerstoff" is a translation of the French name. Davy proved that not all acids contain oxygen and proposed that hydrogen was the common constituent of acids. Liebig firmly established the protonic concept of acids and described an acid as a substance composed of a replaceable hydrogen and an acid radical.

The theory of electrolytic dissociation of Arrhenius and Ostwald led to our present view of acid–base equilibria in water. Here the theory focuses on the self-dissociation or autoprotolysis of water.

$$HOH \leftrightharpoons H^+(aq) + OH^-(aq)$$

At 25°C about one in every half-billion water molecules is dissociated into a hydrogen ion and a hydroxide ion. An aqueous solution is said to be neutral when the concentra-tion of hydrogen ions and the concentration of hydroxide ions are equal, acidic when there are more hydrogen ions, and basic when there are more hydroxide ions. An in-crease in hydrogen ion concentration may be brought about either by adding a sub-stance that provides additional hydrogen ions for the system, such as hydrogen chloride, or by adding a substance that will remove hydroxide ion from the system, such as boric acid.

$$B(OH)_3 + OH^- \rightleftharpoons B(OH)_4^-$$

Such substances are termed acids. Similarly, hydroxide ion may be increased by direct dissociation to produce hydroxide ions as in the case of sodium hydroxide, or by com-bination with hydrogen ions in solution as in the case of ammonia. Combinations of the latter type are often referred to as hydrolysis (p. 198). Neutralization reactions in water consist of the combination of hydrogen ions and hydroxide ions to form water.

Many solvents other than water undergo autoprotolysis, and acid–base equilibria in these solvents may be treated on a conceptual basis similar to the Arrhenius–Ostwald picture.* Thus in liquid ammonia a substance producing ammonium ions would be an acid, a substance producing amide ions would be a base, and a neutralization reaction would consist of the reaction of ammonium ion and amide ion to produce ammonia. A more general solvent theory defines an acid as a substance that produces positive solvent ions and a base as a substance that produces a negatively charged solvent ion. Neutralization consists of a combination of these ions to produce solvent.

A protonic acid–base picture, which does not involve the solvent, was presented by Brønsted and Lowry in 1923. According to their views an acid is a proton donor and a base is a proton acceptor. An acid–base reaction consists of the transfer of a proton from an acid to a base to produce another acid, termed the conjugate acid of the original base, and another base, termed the conjugate base of the original acid.

$$HCl \quad + \quad NH_3 \quad \longrightarrow \quad NH_4^+ \quad + \quad Cl^-$$

acid	base	conjugate acid	conjugate base

A general theory of acids and bases that covers all of the preceding cases and extends the definition to some substances not included above was set forth by G. N. Lewis,[†] who defined an acid as an electron pair acceptor and a base as an electron pair donor. Neutralization in the Lewis theory consists of the formation of a new covalent bond between an electron *pair* donor and an electron *pair* acceptor.

$$BF_3 \quad + \quad (CH_3)_3N: \longrightarrow (CH_3)_3N:BF_3$$

acid	base

This chapter deals mainly with the factors that affect the relative strength of acids and bases. Protonic acids are treated first since there are fewer factors involved than with other Lewis acids and, in the case of protonic acids, these factors are more easily isolated. The pK_a, i.e., $-\log K_a$, will often be used here; the higher the numerical value of the pK_a, the weaker the acid under discussion. For the acid HA, the dissociation constant, K_a, is defined by the activity quotient $K_a = (H^+aq)(A^-)/(HA)$.

Protonic Acids

Proton Affinities

The simplest acid–base reaction to analyze theoretically would be a gas phase protonation reaction. The energy released in the reaction

$$A(g) + H^+(g) \longrightarrow AH^+(g)$$

* Bjerrum, N., *Chem. Rev.*, **16**, 287 (1935).
† Lewis, G. N., *J. Franklin Inst.*, **226**, 293 (1938).

Acids and Bases

is termed the proton affinity of A. Although only lower limits for the value of proton affinities can be directly determined (by the use of mass spectrometry) they can be evaluated by appropriate energy cycles or from *a priori* calculations. Thus the cycle

$$
\begin{array}{c}
H\cdot(g) \;+\; X\cdot(g) \\
\end{array}
$$

$$
+I \uparrow \qquad -E \uparrow \qquad \searrow\; +D
$$

$$
H^+(g) \;+\; X^-(g) \xrightarrow{\;PA\;} H - X(g)
$$

permits an evaluation of the proton affinity (*PA*) of the halide ions from the electron affinity of the halogen (*E*), the ionization potential of hydrogen (*I*), and the bond energy of the hydrogen halide (*D*). The values calculated for the halides and hydrogen in this manner are shown in Table 6.1. The variation of proton affinities for the halide ions is due almost entirely to the variation in the bond dissociation energy of HX (*D*). Some of the values given in Table 6.1 have been estimated using the assumption that within a group the variation in proton affinity will be controlled by the bond dissociation energy.

TABLE 6.1[a]
Estimated Proton Affinities kcal/mole

H^-	CH_3^-	NH_2^-	OH^-	F^-		CH_4	NH_3	H_2O	HF
402	405	393	375	367		161	209	182	91
		PH_2^-	SH^-	Cl^-			NH^{2-}	O^{2-}	
		392	346	331			613	554	
		AsH_2^-	SeH^-	Br^-					
		374	340	321					
			TeH^-	I^-					
			321	311					

[a] Values for halide ions from R. P. Bell (see ref. p. 221); N and O values from T. C. Waddington (see ref. p. 133, Chapter III); HF, CH_4 and CH_3^- from F. W. Lampe and J. H. Futrell, *Trans. Faraday Soc.*, **59**, 1957 (1963); S, Se, Te, P, As based on the assumption that proton affinity parallels bond energy within a group.

The proton affinity of the negative ions decreases with increasing radius. This is expected on an electrostatic basis. A similar trend is often assumed for neutral molecules (such as NH_3, PH_3, etc.), but an electrostatic argument would not support this.

The variation of proton affinity in the series H_2O (182) > OH^- (375) > O_2^{2-} (554) is that expected as proton–proton repulsion is decreased in these isoelectronic ions. Similarly, the proton affinity of F^- (367) is less than that of O^{2-} (554) due to the repulsion of an additional nuclear proton. The variation of proton affinity in the isoelectronic sequence NH_2^- (392) > OH^- (375) > F^- (367) reflects the greater proton–proton repulsion exerted by nuclear protons than by external protons, due to the smaller distance between the nuclear protons and the external protons than between external protons. The break at CH_4 in the sequence of proton affinities CH_4 < NH_3 > H_2O > HF is due to the formation of the electron deficient species CH_5^+. Even so, the proton affinity of CH_4, a molecule having no free electron pairs, is greater than that of HF!

Differentiating and Leveling Solvents

The proton affinities in Table 6.1 are all positive—in the gas phase the proton will apparently stick to anything that is not itself positive.

In order to compare experimentally the strength of a series of acids (A), a reference base (B) must be chosen and the equilibrium constant determined for the reaction

$$AH + B \rightleftharpoons A^- + BH^+$$

It is often convenient to use the solvent as a reference base. If proton transfer to the solvent is essentially complete for all of the acids in a series no distinction may be made among them. In such solutions the only species capable of transferring a proton is the BH^+ species. Such solvents in which complete proton transfer occurs are termed "leveling solvents." Thus in liquid ammonia, hydrogen fluoride and hydrogen chloride appear to be of equal strength since both give $\sim 100\% \; NH_4^+$ ions. In water HF is only partially ionized, whereas HCl and HBr are $\sim 100\%$ ionized. Thus, water is a *differentiating* solvent for HF, but not for HCl or HBr. If glacial acetic acid is used as a solvent both HCl and HBr are incompletely ionized to give H_2Ac^+ and X^-, hence glacial acetic acid is a differentiating solvent for HCl and HBr. HBr is more highly ionized, hence it may be concluded that it is the stronger acid.

Summarizing the above, it may be concluded that *in a given solvent that acid is strongest which is most highly ionized (at a given concentration)*. The ionization constant of an acid may be taken as a quantitative measure of the strength of that acid.

Hammett H_0 Scale

As stated earlier, once the proton has been transferred from the acid to the solvent, the protonated solvent is the acidic species in solution. The more basic the solvent the greater the degree of ionization of acids in it. The more basic the solvent the less willing it will be to transfer a proton to another base in solution. *Hence an acid will form the most acidic solution in the solvent in which it is least ionized.*

One quantitative measure of the acidity of a solution is the Hammett H_0 value,[*] which measures the ability of a solution to transfer a proton to a neutral base. It is operationally defined by the relationship

$$H_0 = pK_a - \log \frac{BH^+}{B}$$

where pK_a is the pK_a value of an indicator, BH^+/B the ratio of protonated to unprotonated form existing in solution. From the equation for the pK_a, one may write

$$H_0 = \frac{-\log a_H \gamma_B}{\gamma_{BH^+}}$$

For dilute aqueous solutions the H_0 and pH scale become identical.

---

[*] Hammett, L. P., see ref. p. 221).

Acidic Behavior of the Binary Hydrides

Table 6.2 indicates the pK_a values for the more acidic binary hydrides.

TABLE 6.2[a]
pK_a Values of the More Acidic Hydrides

CH_4	NH_3	H_2O	HF
(58)	(35)	$pK_1 = 15.74$	3.17
		$pK_2 = 36$	
H_2	PH_3	H_2S	HCl
(38)	(27)	$pK_1 = 6.96$	-7
		$pK_2 = 14.0$	
		H_2Se	HBr
		$pK_1 = 3.72$	-9
		$pK_2 = 15^b$	
		H_2Te	HI
		$pK_1 = 2.64$	-10
		$pK_2 = 11$	

[a] From R. P. Bell (see p. 221) or W. M. Latimer (see ref. p. 158, Chapter IV). All values refer to the dissociation of hydrogen ion from the species listed to form species such as H^-, CH_3^-, NH_2^-, PH_2^-, etc.
[b] Wood, R. H., *J. Am. Chem. Soc.*, **80**, 1559 (1958).

Within a given group or within a given period the order of acidities in Table 6.2 is that expected on the basis of the proton affinities in Table 6.1. Inversions that occur outside these groupings (as with H_2S and HF) are due to solvation effects. The following free energy cycle shows these effects more clearly.

$$HA(g) \xrightarrow{\ ii\ } H^+(g) + A^-(g)$$

with step i upward on the left, step iii downward on the right,

$$HA(soln.) \xrightarrow{\ iv\ } H^+(soln.) + A^-(soln.)$$

Step iv corresponds to the dissociation of the acid in solution and the standard free energy change may be obtained from the observed solution equilibrium in the case of aqueous acids having a pK_a value in the range of 0 to 14. The pK_a values in Table 6.2 have been determined directly only for HF and the Group VI hydrides. H_2O is included here with the assumption that its own activity in pure water is the same as its molality. It has been estimated for the other binary acids listed by a variety of methods, including the above cycle.

The free energy change for step ii is simply the proton affinity less a relatively constant entropy term.

The solvation energies for neutral molecules involved in step i will be relatively small compared to the solvation energies for ions involved in step iii. Step iii will include a large term for the solvation of the proton (presumably with the formation and solvation of $H_9O_4^+$ — see p. 179, Chapter V), which will be the same for all protonic acids, and it will include a term for the solvation of the anion. The latter will be dependent on the size of the anion and its ability to interact specifically with the solvent, i.e., its hydrogen bonding ability. Solvation effects will be relatively constant within a period (or increase slightly with increasing Z). Within a group solvation energy will increase with decreasing Z; the difference is greatest between the second and third period elements due to hydrogen bonding. Solvation thus contributes an acid strengthening effect, which increases with decreasing Z in a group. The net effect of solvation within a given group will be to decrease the difference in strength of neutral acids in solution compared to their strength in the gas phase.* Solvation effects cause a reversal of acid strengths in solution compared to the gas phase in cases such as H_2S and HF. Although the proton affinity of F^- is greater than that of SH^-, the energy released in solvating the fluoride ion is much greater than the energy released in solvating the SH^- ion, resulting in a greater acidity for hydrofluoric acid than for hydrosulfuric acid.

For cationic acids, BH^+, solvation effects will have an opposite effect on acidity as compared to neutral or anionic acids.

$$\begin{array}{ccc} BH^+(g) & \xrightarrow{\;ii\;} & B(g) + H^+(g) \\ {\scriptstyle i}\big\uparrow & & \big\downarrow{\scriptstyle\;iii} \\ BH^+(soln.) & \xrightarrow{\;iv\;} & B(soln.) + H^+(soln.) \end{array}$$

Step *iii* will differ only slightly from one cationic acid to the next. Strong solvation will stabilize the undissociated cationic acid. This solvation will be dependent on the size of the cation (being greatest for a small cation) and on the hydrogen bonding ability of the cation. Within a group, solvation effects enhance the difference in strengths of cationic acids (particularly in comparisons between 2nd and 3rd period elements). These differences in solvation effects on neutral and cationic acids may be seen in the following pK comparisons:

	pK		pK	diff.
NH_3	35	PH_3	27	8
NH_4^+	9.5	PH_4^+	−12	21.5

Cosolvating Agents

It is possible to add to a solution of an acid substances that interact more strongly with the anion, A^-, or the neutral molecule, B (or even a cationic residue), than the solvent itself. Such substances might be termed cosolvating agents, and these cosolvating agents will enhance the acidity of the solution. Thus BF_3 serves as a cosolvating agent for HF and solutions of HF and BF_3 are more acidic than solutions containing the same concentration of either HF or BF_3. In nonaqueous media the pair $HF-BF_3$ is a very strong acid. Likewise the interaction of a metal ion such as Cu^{2+} with NH_3 is much stronger than that of water with ammonia. Thus the acidity of ammonium ions is enhanced in the presence of Cu^{2+}. The effect of mannitol on the titration curve of

---

* See Table 10, p. 91 of R. P. Bell, *The Proton in Chemistry* (Ithaca: Cornell University Press, 1959) for an analysis of the thermodynamic factors involved in the dissociation of the hydrohalic acids.

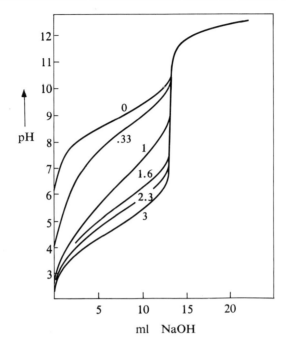

FIGURE 6.1. *Effect of mannitol on the titration of boric acid (moles of mannitol per mole of boric acid given on curve)* [*from J. H. Hildebrand, J. Am. Chem. Soc., 35, 847 (1913)*].

boric acid may be seen in Figure 6.1. The effect of polyols in stabilizing the anion of the acid is not unique with boric acid, but occurs also with germanic, arsenious, and telluric acids.* With boric acid the equilibria involved are

$$H_3BO_3 + H_2O \rightleftharpoons H^+ + [B(OH)_4]^-$$

* Roy, G. L., A. L. Laferriere, and J. O. Edwards, *J. Inorg. Nucl. Chem.*, **4**, 106 (1951); P. J. Antikainen, *Acta Chem. Scand.*, **13**, 312 (1959).

Oxy Acids

The oxy acids may be thought of as derivatives of water. Replacement of the hydrogen in water with a more electronegative group leads to an increase in acid strength.

	pK
HOH	16
HOI	11
HOBr	8.7
HOCl	7.4

An increase in the oxidation state of the group replacing hydrogen brings about a corresponding increase in the acidity. As may be noted in the following series of pK values of the oxy acids of chlorine, the acidity parallels the increase in the formal charge of the central atom.

$$\text{H—O—Cl}^0 \qquad \text{H—O—Cl}^{1+}\text{—O}^{1-} \qquad \text{H—O—}\overset{\text{O}^{1-}}{\underset{}{\text{Cl}^{2+}}}\text{—O}^{1-} \qquad \text{H—O—}\overset{\text{O}^{1-}}{\underset{\text{O}^{1-}}{\text{Cl}^{3+}}}\text{—O}^{1-}$$

pK   7.4   2.0   −1   (−10)

For the purpose of figuring the formal charge for the above generalization all oxygen atoms are represented as being bound to the central atom by single bonds. Pauling, among others, has given an empirical rule for estimating the strength of oxy acids. Pauling's rule is that for an acid of the general formula $XO_m(OH)_n$ the value of pK_1 varies in approximate steps of 5 units and is related to m, the number of nonhydroxylic oxygen atoms, in the following approximate manner:

$$\begin{aligned}
\text{For} \quad m &= 0 \qquad pK = 7 \\
m &= 1 \qquad pK = 2 \\
m &= 2 \qquad pK = -3 \\
m &= 3 \qquad pK = -8
\end{aligned}$$

(pK_2 will be approximately 5 units greater than pK_1 due to the electrostatic effect — this will be discussed more fully in a later section.)

The formal charge approach implies that the increase in acid strength is due to an inductive effect. It also implies a lack of π bonding in these compounds. The opposite extreme would be to view all nonhydroxylic oxygens as bound to the central atom by both π and σ bonds. Ionization would then give a reduction in the π character of these bonds and allow the negative charge to be delocalized over the entire anion.

$$\text{H—O—}\overset{\text{O}}{\underset{\text{O}}{\overset{\|}{\underset{\|}{\text{Cl}}}}}\text{=O} \rightleftharpoons H^+(aq) + \overset{O^{-\frac{1}{4}}}{\underset{O^{-\frac{1}{4}}}{\overset{\|}{\underset{\|}{\text{Cl}}}}}\text{—O}^{-\frac{1}{4}} \quad {}^{-\frac{1}{4}}O$$

The greater the number of oxygen atoms, the greater the charge delocalization. It is probable that neither of these extreme viewpoints is entirely correct, and the contribution to the acid strength from these factors will vary from one acid to another. As one factor decreases the other should increase, thus acids having the same number of nonhydroxylic oxygens will have comparable strength. It should be pointed out that Pauling's empirical rule is based on data for strengths of oxy acids of nonmetals. It might be expected that the predictions will not be as good for the oxy acids of the metals due to their lower electronegativity and to differences in their tendency to π bond.

Earlier it was pointed out that the difference in molecular form of HNO_3 and H_3PO_4 might be attributed to a greatly decreased tendency for p-p-π bonding beyond the second period elements and to the increased radius of P over that of N. There is some evidence that suggests the importance of p-d-π bonding for nonmetals decreases for elements beyond the third period. Thus from bond length data Nightingale estimates the per cent π bond character as 21 in IO_3^-, 37 in BrO_3^-, and 54 in ClO_3^-.* Since π bonding is not as effective in removing the positive charge of the larger atoms in the highest oxidation state more σ bonds are formed by increasing the coordination number. Thus in aqueous solution periodic acid exists as H_5IO_6 and telluric acid as H_6TeO_6. There is some question about the existence of antimonic acid, which can not be isolated in an anhydrous state but derivatives of a hypothetical $HSb(OH)_6$ are known.

In addition to the large effect of nonhydroxylic oxygens on acid strengths, one should also note the relatively small effect of hydroxyl groups (both HNO_2 and H_5IO_6 have a pK of about 3.3, etc.). One might suppose that two hydroxyl groups would have about the same effect as one "keto" oxygen. This is not found to be the case. In addition to the formal charge and resonance possibilities which the "keto" oxygen brings to the situation, solvation of the keto oxygen will be acid strengthening, but solvation of the hydroxy group will be acid weakening.

$$H—O—X\!\!=\!\!\!=\!\!O\cdots H—O\diagdown_H$$

Acid strengthening solvation drains electrons away from X.

$$H—O—X\diagup^{O—H\cdots O\diagup^{H}}_{\diagdown_{O—H}}{}_{\diagdown_H}$$

Acid weakening solvation pushes electrons toward X.

Some evidence that solvation of the hydroxy groups is acid weakening may be seen in the following pK_1 values: H_3PO_4, 2.16; $(CH_3O)PO_3H_2$, 1.52; and $(CH_3O)_2PO_2H$, 0.76.† The effect of replacing H— by CH_3— is the opposite of that normally expected on the basis of the inductive effect of a methyl group (see p. 194), but may be explained by the removal of the hydrogen bonding to the solvent.

---

* Nightingale, see reference p. 59, Chapter II.
† Bunton, C. A., et al., *J. Chem. Soc.,* **1958**, 3574; 1960, 3293.

The oxy acids of phosphorus provide some further interesting dissociation constants (see Table 6.3).

TABLE 6.3[a]

Strength of the Oxy Acids of Phosphorus

Acid	Formula	pK_1	pK_2	pK_3	pK_4	pK_5	pK_6
(ortho) phosphoric[b]	H_3PO_4	2.161	7.207	12.325			
phosphorous[b]	H_3PO_3	*2.00*	6.58				
hypophosphorous[b]	H_3PO_2	~ 1					
pyrophosphoric[b]	$H_4P_2O_7$	1.52	2.36	6.60	9.25		
triphosphoric[c]	$H_5P_3O_{10}$		*1.06*	2.30	6.50	9.24	
tetraphosphoric[c]	$H_6P_4O_{13}$			*1.36*	*2.23*	7.38	9.11
trimetaphosphoric[b]	$H_3P_3O_9$	2.05					
tetrametaphosphoric[b]	$H_4P_4O_{12}$	2.74					
hypophosphoric[b]	$H_4P_2O_6$	< 2.2	2.81	7.27	*10.03*		

[a] At 25° and zero ionic strength except for italicized values which are for other ionic strengths and/or temperatures.
[b] From J. Bjerrum, G. Schwarzenbach, and L. G. Sillén, "Stability Constants, Part II: Inorganic Ligands," *Chem. Soc. (London) Spec. Publ.,* **7** (1958).
[c] From J. I. Watters, P. E. Sturrock, and R. E. Simonaitis, *Inorg. Chem.,* **2**, 765 (1963).

The pK_1 value for phosphoric acid is consistent with the predicted value of 2. The value of *2.00* for phosphorous acid suggests that the structure of this acid is

This structure has recently been confirmed by an analysis of the NMR spectrum of phosphorous acid. (See Chapter XII.) In contrast to this, arsenious acid has a pK value of 9.2, which is consistent with the structure

Hypophosphorous acid is monoprotic and its pK value is consistent with the structure

The pK_2 and pK_3 values of H_3PO_4 show the expected decrease in acidity as the negative charge on the anion, which the proton is leaving, increases. It is somewhat surprising that the effect of increasing charge is so slight for the successive dissociation constants of the polyphosphoric acids. The phosphorus units in a polyphosphoric acid appear to behave almost independently. Thus there is one fairly acidic hydrogen for each phosphorus atom in a polyphosphoric acid. The terminal units carry an additional weakly acidic hydrogen, having a pK comparable to the pK_2 of phosphoric acid. The difference in the last two pK values for polyphosphoric acids indicates that there may be some interaction between the ends of the chain due to the flexibility of the chain.

The ratio of terminal units to total units in a polyphosphoric acid can be determined from the ratio of weakly acidic hydrogen atoms to moderately acidic hydrogen atoms (i.e., from the titration curves). Largely from this type of data, Van Wazer and Holst* have concluded that no branched polyphosphates exist in aqueous solution.

Organic Acids

Much of our knowledge of the finer details of the factors affecting the strengths of protonic acids has arisen from the study of organic acids. The possibility of systematic variation of substituents on a parent acid molecule is greater with organic compounds than with inorganic compounds. A knowledge of the probable effect of a substituent on the acid strength of a complex organic molecule is valuable to the inorganic chemist in attempting to select complexing agents for metal ions.

ACETIC ACIDS AND THE INDUCTIVE EFFECT

On substituting a halogen atom for a hydrogen atom in acetic acid, an increase in acid strength is noted. This increase in acid strength roughly parallels the electronegativity of the halogen substituent. (See Table 6.4). Since the halogens are all more electronegative than carbon, the carbon–halogen bond is expected to have an electro-

* Van Wazer, J. R., and K. A. Holst, *J. Am. Chem. Soc.*, **72**, 639 (1950).

TABLE 6.4[a]
pK_a Values of Some Substituted Acetic Acids in Water at 25°C

$(CH_3)_3CCH_2CO_2H$	5.05	$CH_3OCH_2CO_2H$	3.53	FCH_2CO_2H	2.66
$(CH_3)_3SiCH_2CO_2H$	5.22[b]	$CH_3SCH_2CO_2H$	3.72	$ClCH_2CO_2H$	2.86
HCH_2CO_2H	4.70			$BrCH_2CO_2H$	2.86

[a] Except as noted in this chapter, pK_a values of organic acids are taken from H. C. Brown, D. H. McDaniel, and O. Häfliger, in E. A. Braude and F. C. Nachod, eds., *Determination of Organic Structures by Physical Methods* (New York: Academic Press, Inc., 1955) Chapter 14.
[b] Sommer, L. H., J. R. Gold, G. M. Goldberg, and N. S. Marans, *J. Am. Chem. Soc.*, **71**, 1509 (1949).

static bond moment, the carbon atom having a $\delta+$ charge and halogen atom having a $\delta-$ charge (the $\delta+$ and $\delta-$ are used to refer to charges expected to be less than unit charges and represent a change in charge density on going from the parent compound to the substituted compound; $\delta\delta+$ is used to indicate a smaller change in charge density than that represented by $\delta+$). The $\delta+$ charge on the carbon atom, resulting from the C—X bond, increases its electronegativity and causes a change in the ionic contribution of the C—C bond resulting in a $\delta\delta+$ charge for the carboxyl carbon atom. This internal bond polarization proceeds with a damping of magnitude from one atom to the next to the O—H bond. The increase in positive charge on the oxygen atom results in a decreased attraction of the oxygen atom for the proton with a consequent increase in acidity of the haloacetic acid.

Replacing the α-hydrogen atom in acetic acid by an atom (or group) that is less electronegative than hydrogen results in a decrease in the strength of the substituted acid as in the case of trimethysilylacetic acid.

Again the δ charges refer to changes in charge compared to similar atoms in acetic acid. Groups such as the halogens are said to have an electron withdrawing inductive effect $(-I)$; those such as trimethylsilyl are said to have an electron releasing inductive effect $(+I)$.

In addition to the effect of the substituent brought about by the internal bond polarization proceeding through a chain of atoms, the dipole moment of the substituent bond will interact directly with the ionizable proton through the dielectric media of the solvent and of the acid molecule itself. This direct interaction is termed the field effect; the internal bond polarization is sometimes termed the inductive effect, although this term is also used to include both types of interactions.

From the dissociation constants of substituted acetic acids the following order of electron withdrawing inductive effects may be established:* $—NO_2 > CH_3SO_2— > NC— > \phi SO_2— > \phi SO— > F— > Cl— > Br— > —CF_3 > N_3— > I— > C_2H_5O_2C— > CH_3O— > CH_3S— > \phi— > CH_2{=}CH—$. Some generalizations may be made. The electron withdrawing inductive effect usually increases with an increase in oxidation number of the central atom as in series such as $CH_3S—$, $CH_3SO—$, $CH_3SO_2—$ or $—CH_3$, $CH_2{=}CH—$, $\phi—$, $C_2H_5O_2C—$ or $(CH_3)_2N—$, $N_3—$, $—NO$, $—NO_2$; or $—I$,

---

* This order is essentially the same, for groups included on both lists, as the inductive constants derived by Taft from data on ester hydrolysis. See Table II in R. W. Taft, Jr., and I. C. Lewis, *J. Am. Chem. Soc.*, **80**, 2436 (1958).

—IO, —IO$_2$. Also, the electron withdrawing inductive effect of a group increases as the σ bond hybridization changes from sp^3 to sp^2 to sp as in the series CH$_3$— to CH$_2$=CH— to HC≡C— or for —CONH$_2$ to —C≡N.

AROMATIC ACIDS AND RESONANCE EFFECTS

The effect of introducing a substituent in an aliphatic acid on its acid strength can usually be explained in terms of the inductive effect of the substituent. In aromatic acids the effect of a substituent may be further complicated by conjugative, or resonance, effects. Let us consider the pK$_a$ data in Table 6.5.

TABLE 6.5

Substituent	Subst. Benzoic Acid		Subst. Anilinium Ion	
	meta	*para*	*meta*	*para*
H	4.20		4.62	
Cl	3.83	3.99	3.32	3.81
NO$_2$	3.45	3.44	2.45	1.11
(CH$_3$)$_3$Si	4.24	4.27	4.64	4.36
CH$_3$O	4.09	4.47	4.20	5.29

The effect of the chloro group can be understood in terms of an electron withdrawing inductive effect that diminishes with increasing separation between the substituent and the ionizable proton, i.e., the *meta*-chloro aromatic acids are stronger acids than the *para*-chloro aromatic acids.

The nitro group also shows an acid strengthening effect in aromatic acids, but unlike the chloro group, this effect is greater from the *para* position than the *meta* position. With the nitrobenzoic acids the difference in strength between the *meta* and *para* isomers is slight, with the anilinium ions the effect is large. The increased effect of the nitro group in the *para* position of the anilinium ion is attributed to the resonance stabilization of aniline as compared to the anilinium ion.

$$H_2\ddot{N}\!-\!\!\left\langle\bigcirc\right\rangle\!\!-\!NO_2 \leftrightarrow H_2\overset{+}{N}\!=\!\!\left\langle\bigcirc\right\rangle\!\!=\!\overset{+}{N}\!\!\diagup^{O^-}_{\diagdown O^-}$$

In the case of the trimethylsilylanilines it is noted that the group exerts an, almost negligible, electron releasing inductive effect from the *meta* position, but from the *para* position the group exerts an acid strengthening influence, which may be attributed to an electron withdrawing resonance effect involving the *d*-orbitals of the silicon atom.

$$H_2\ddot{N}\!-\!\!\left\langle\bigcirc\right\rangle\!\!-\!Si(CH_3)_3 \leftrightarrow H_2\overset{+}{N}\!=\!\!\left\langle\bigcirc\right\rangle\!\!=\!\overset{-}{Si}(CH_3)_3$$

It may be noted that this resonance effect does not show up in the trimethylsilylbenzoic acids where direct conjugation is not possible.

Finally, let us consider the effects of the methoxy group. In the *meta* position this group shows the expected acid strengthening electron withdrawing inductive effect. In the *para* position, however, the group exerts an acid weakening influence, which may be interpreted as due to an electron releasing resonance effect that more than offsets the electron withdrawing inductive effect of the group.

In general, by examining the dissociation constants of the *meta* and *para* derivatives of an aromatic acid it is possible to determine the nature of inductive and resonance interactions which the group may undergo. If the *meta*-substituted compound is a stronger acid than the unsubstituted compound the group is said to have an electron withdrawing inductive effect. If the effect is in the same direction but of greater magnitude in the *para* position this may be taken to mean that the group has a resonance effect which operates in the same direction as the inductive effect (i.e., electron withdrawing or electron releasing). If a reversal of effects occurs on moving the substituent from the *meta* to the *para* position, this may be interpreted as meaning that the resonance and inductive effects of the group act in opposite directions, and that in the *para* position the resonance effect is predominate (MeO, Me$_3$Si in anilinium ions). If, on moving a group from the *meta* to the *para* position, the effect exerted by the group is diminished this may be taken as meaning that the resonance effects are small compared to the inductive effects of the group. It should be noted that a system such as the substituted anilinium ions or phenols is most suitable for observing electron withdrawing resonance effects, but systems such as benzoic acids or pyridinium ions are best for observing electron releasing resonance effects. In fact, several groups (vinyl, phenyl, etc.) show either an electron withdrawing or an electron releasing resonance effect depending on the demands of the situation.

	H	m—C$_6$H$_5$	p—C$_6$H$_5$
		pK$_a$ Values	
Phenols	9.95	9.59	9.51
Pyridinium ions*	5.17	(4.80)	(5.55)

Taft[†] has suggested that resonance effects from the *meta* position are about $\frac{1}{3}$ of their magnitude from the *para* position. Hence the apparent electron releasing inductive effect of the —NH$_2$ group in the *meta* position is probably a result of the masking of the inductive effect by a strong electron releasing resonance effect. The *meta* —OH group shows an electron withdrawing effect due to its greater electron withdrawing inductive effect and its smaller resonance effect.

Hammett[‡] has used the difference in pK$_a$ values of substituted and unsubstituted benzoic acids to establish a set of substituent constants, σ's, which may be used to correlate or predict equilibrium constants or rate constants in homologous series of *meta*- and *para*-substituted aromatic compounds. The Hammett equation has the form

$$\log \frac{k}{k^0} = \rho\sigma \qquad \text{where } \sigma \equiv pK_0 - pK_s$$

* Katritzky, A. R., and P. Simmons, *J. Chem. Soc.*, **1960**, 1511.
† Taft, R. W., Jr., and I. C. Lewis, *J. Am. Chem. Soc.*, **81**, 5343 (1959).
‡ Hammett, L. P., *Physical Organic Chemistry* (New York: McGraw-Hill Book Co., 1940) Chapter VII; H. H. Jaffé, *Chem. Rev.*, **53**, 191 (1953).

k is a rate or equilibrium constant for a *meta-* or *para-*substituted aromatic compound, k^0 is the rate or equilibrium constant for the unsubstituted aromatic, ρ is a constant for a given reaction, and σ is a constant for a given substituent. This value is different for *meta* and *para* substituents.

For strongly conjugating groups such as —NO$_2$, it is necessary to use a different σ value for a substituent in the phenol and aniline derivatives than that derived from benzoic acids. Further, it should be stated that many σ values have been established from reactions or equilibria other than the benzoic acid ionization.

The ρ value of different types of reaction may be interpreted either as a measure of the transmission of the electrical effect of the substituent to the reaction center or as a measure of the sensitivity of the reaction to changes in charge density. Log (k/k^0) *vs.* σ plots for a number of acids are shown in Figure 6.2.

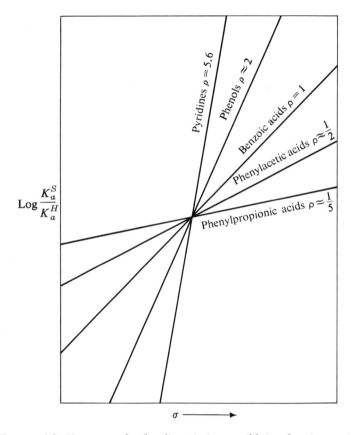

FIGURE 6.2. *Hammett plot for dissociation equilibria of various acids showing the effect of side-chain length on the reaction constant ρ.*

Hydrolysis and Aquo Acids*

A reaction in which water is written as a reactant, and which brings about a change in the hydrogen ion concentration of the solution, is termed an hydrolysis reaction. An alternative view is to consider such reactions as hydration reactions followed by dis-

* Sillén, L. G., *Quart. Rev., 13*, 146 (1959).

sociation of the aquo acid that is produced. One may then speak of the dissociation constant of the aquo acid. These equilibria are generally somewhat more complex than those we have been discussing thus far, due mainly to polymerization reactions that may take place simultaneously with the dissociation. Thus, the main species produced by the hydrolysis of Bi^{3+} in acid solution contains six bismuth atoms and has a charge of 6+.* It is not possible to deduce the nature of the species in solution from a study of the acidity alone, but when the acidity is studied in combination with emf data, or some other measure of the activity of a mononuclear species, it is often possible to describe fairly completely the species present under given conditions. Knowledge of the species present under given conditions is essential not only for calculations of acid–base equilibria but also for other equilibria.

The dissociation constants of the metal hydroxides in water may be related to the dissociation constants of the cationic aquo acids (or hydrolysis constants) through the equation $K_a K_b = K_w$, or $pK_a + pK_b = pK_w$. Accordingly, hydrolysis will be slight for cations forming strong bases and *vice versa*.

For cations having an inert gas configuration, the interaction between the metal ion and the hydroxide ion is essentially electrostatic,† i.e., the pK_b varies in a linear fashion with z^2/r, where z is the charge on the ion and r is the ionic radius, and pK_b refers to the loss of the last hydroxide group. Thus the basicity of LiOH is the lowest of the alkali metal hydroxides, and the hydrolysis of lithium salts is greater than that of the other alkali metal salts.

$$LiOH(aq) = Li^+(aq) + OH^-(aq) \qquad pK_b = 0.18$$
$$\text{or} \qquad Li(H_2O)_3OH(aq) = Li(H_2O)_4{}^+(aq) + OH^-(aq)$$
$$\text{Hence} \qquad Li^+(aq) + H_2O = LiOH(aq) + H^+(aq)$$
$$\text{or} \qquad Li(H_2O)_4{}^+ = Li(H_2O)_3OH(aq) + H^+(aq) \qquad pK_a = 13.82$$

The first equation in each pair given above makes no implications about the degree of solvation occurring. The second equation in each pair indicates speculation regarding the primary hydration of the lithium ion and the lithium hydroxide ion pair. The increase in ionic radius of Na^+ over Li^+ results in NaOH being a stronger base ($pK_b = -0.7$) than LiOH. KOH, RbOH, and CsOH are even stronger bases, which appear to approach the limiting pK_b value of -1.7, i.e., K^+, Rb^+, and Cs^+, are not measurably hydrolized in aqueous solution.

The ionic radii of Be^{2+}, Mg^{2+}, Ca^{2+}, Sr^{2+}, and Ba^{2+} are about 0.3 Å less than the corresponding isoelectronic alkali metal ions, and the ionic charge is, of course, twice as great. Accordingly, these ions are all more highly hydrolyzed in solution than the lithium ion, the pK_a values varying from about 13.35 for Ba^{2+} to 11.42 for Mg^{2+} for the reaction $M^{2+}(aq) + H_2O = MOH^+(aq) + H^+(aq)$. The Be^{2+} ion is still more extensively hydrolyzed, forming polynuclear species in solution. The unhydrolyzed Be^{2+} ion exists in appreciable concentration only in dilute solutions under fairly acid conditions. Figure 6.3 shows the distribution of Be^{2+} among some possible species as worked out by Sillén et al. for a total concentration of Be^{2+} of 0.1 molar. The fraction of Be^{2+} existing as a particular species at a given pH_c is given by the fraction of the vertical line appearing in the field of that species. Thus at a pH_c of 4, in a $0.1M$ solution of Be(II) there would be approximately 20% Be^{2+}, 5% Be_2OH^+, and 75% $Be(OH)_3{}^{3+}$. These

---

* Olin, A., *Acta Chem. Scand.*, **11**, 1445 (1957). (See also p. 327.)
† Davis, C. W., *J. Chem. Soc.*, **1951**, 1256.

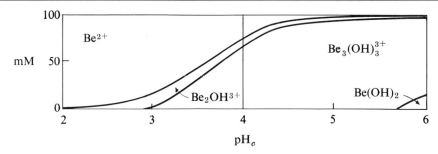

FIGURE 6.3. *Field distribution diagram of* Be^{2+} *taken from H. Kakihana and L. G. Sillén,* Acta Chem. Scand., *10, 985–1005 (1956).*

formulas do not show hydrated water and do not distinguish between $Be(OH)_2$ and BeO.

Sillén suggests that the species $Be_3(OH)_3^{3+}$ may be

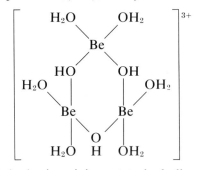

i.e., a cyclic structure with hydration giving a tetrahedrally coordinated Be.

An extension of the electrostatic approach beyond the alkaline earth metal ions gives less satisfactory results, as may be seen in Figure 6.4. Thus, although we might expect a decrease in hydrolysis of the ions in the series Mg^{2+}, Zn^{2+}, Cu^{2+}, Cd^{2+}, and Hg^{2+} due to the increasing size of the respective ions, the reverse is actually found. Mg^{2+} is the least hydrolyzed ($pK_a = 11.42$) and Hg^{2+} is the most hydrolyzed ($pK_a = 3.70$). This inversion of order may be explained on the basis of the increasing polarizability of the metal ions in the series given and also their increasing electronegativity (Mg^{2+} 1.3 to Hg^{2+} 2.0). Both factors lead to an increase in the covalence of the M—O bond. The hydrolysis of Cu^{2+} may also be slightly favored by crystal field stabilization energy (see Chapter X). A somewhat perplexing set of data is provided by Sillén et al., who conclude that the second dissociation constant of the aquo mercuric cationic acid is *greater* than the first.

$$Hg(H_2O)^{2+} \rightleftharpoons Hg(OH)(H_2O)_y^+ + H^+ \qquad pK_a = 3.70$$
$$HgOH(H_2O)_y^+ \rightleftharpoons Hg(OH)_2 + H^+ \qquad pK_a = 2.60$$

An explanation for these data probably involves a change in the coordination number of mercury during hydrolysis. The difference between pK_1 and pK_2 of other cationic aquo acids is smaller than the 5 units generally found for aquo acids (i.e., Zr^{4+} $pK_1 = 0.22$, $pK_2 = 0.62$, $pK_3 = 1.05$, $pK_4 = 1.17$). This indicates that the charge on the metal ion is not greatly affected by the loss of a proton from a coordinated water molecule. By way of contrast a change of a unit charge on the metal brings about a large change in hy-

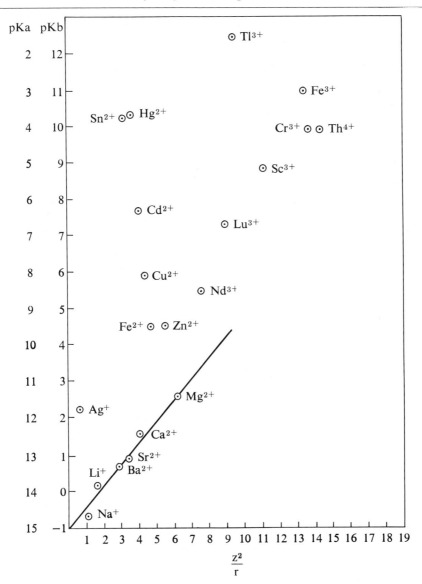

FIGURE 6.4. *Relationship between acidity of aquo ions and the ionic charge squared to radius ratio.*

drolysis (for Fe^{2+}(aq) $pK_a = 9.5$, for Fe^{3+} $pK_a = 3.05$). We may conclude that the loss of a proton by a water molecule is not transmitted, but a change in charge of M affects all M—O bonds and has a profound effect on the acidity.

Although the pK values for reported mononuclear species have been used in our discussion, it should be stated that the mononuclear species for many of these exist only at high dilution. Thus the main hydrolysis product of Fe^{3+} in solution is $Fe_2(OH)_2^{4+}$, a diamagnetic species in contrast to the paramagnetic Fe^{3+} or $FeOH^{2+}$.*

* Mulay, L. N., and P. W. Selwood, *J. Am. Chem. Soc.,* **77,** 2693 (1955).

Several types of polynuclear equilibria have been observed. Sillén concludes that if a single polynuclear species is indicated in solution, then the species probably has a closed ring structure; if a series of complexes are present, then the species probably join to form chains or sheets. Such structures are probably related to the precipitates that come out of solution.

Basic Precipitations

Thus far, we have been discussing homogeneous solution equilibria. Many of our ideas of the relative strengths of bases have been obtained from studies of hetero-geneous equilibria, i.e., solubility of hydroxides. In many cases it was assumed that the species existing in solution are simply the metal ions and hydroxide ions, with a negligible amount of neutral metal hydroxide molecules. Such assumptions are frequently unwarranted. Even if justified, one then has to assume that the equilibrium constant for $M(OH)_x(s) \rightleftharpoons M(OH)_x(aq)$ is the same (or proportional to K_{sp}) for all bases. Within a closely related series of metals of the same charge type (such as the rare earth metals) such an assumption may be acceptable, but for all hydroxides in general it would not appear likely. Accordingly, we may expect only a rough parallelism between the homogeneous solution data (on which we have been basing conclusions about acid and base strength) and the precipitation equilibria.

The lowest pH at which precipitation of various metal hydroxides or oxides occurs follows the sequence*

$Fe(III) \sim Zr(IV) \sim Sn(II) \sim Hg(NO_3)_2$ (pH $\approx$ 2) $< Ce(IV) < Hg_2^{2+}$ (pH $\approx$ 3) $< In(III) <$ $Th(IV) < Al(III)$ (pH $\approx$ 4.1) $< U(IV) < Cr(III) < Cu(II) < Fe(II) < Be(II) < Pb(II)$ (pH $\approx$ 6) $< Ni(II) \approx Ca(II) < Y(III) \approx Co(II) \approx Sm(III) < Zn(II) \approx Nd(III)$ (pH $\approx$ 7) $< Pr(III)$ $< HgCl_2 < Ce(III) < Ag(I)$ (pH $\approx$ 8) $< La(III) < Mn(II) < Mg(II)$ (pH $\approx 10\frac{1}{2}$).

Although this sequence may not give us the order of base strength in solution there is certainly some correlation. Further, it might be said that this sequence is the one useful for separation by hydroxide precipitation. We may note that Hg^{2+} has several positions in the precipitation table, i.e., precipitation of HgO requires a higher OH^- concentration in the presence of Cl^- ion than when the anion is NO_3^-. This is due to the cosolvation (or complexing) of Hg^{2+} by the chloride ion, thereby favoring the dissociation of the OH^-. This is quite analogous to the cosolvation discussed on p. 189 for the anions of acids.

$$H_2O + HgO + Cl^- \longrightarrow HgCl_x(H_2O)_{4-x} + 2OH^-$$

Advantage is taken of this "cosolvation" or complexing, and of the large atomic weight of Hg, in using HgO as a reagent for standardizing acid solutions. Excess iodide ion is added to form the iodomercurate ion.

$$HgO + 4KI + 2H^+ \longrightarrow K_2HgI_4 + H_2O + 2K^+$$

---

* See H. T. S. Britton, *Hydrogen Ions, Their Determination and Importance in Pure and Industrial Chemistry*, Vol. 2 (4th ed., Princeton: D. Van Nostrand Co., 1956) p. 102 for a more precise listing of the pH at which 0.02M solutions will give precipitates.

Amphoteric Oxides

An oxide (or hydroxide) may be classified as acidic or basic according to its behavior on dissolving—acidic oxides increase the hydrogen ion concentration of the solution on dissolving whereas basic oxides decrease the hydrogen ion concentration of the solution. An oxide displaying acidic or basic behavior depending on the pH of the solution is termed amphoteric. Figure 6.5 shows the amphoteric behavior of Al_2O_3. A reference titration curve of HCl is given. The solid curve shows the variation of pH during the titration of HCl with NaOH. The dashed curve shows a similar titration in which some aluminum hydroxide has been dissolved.

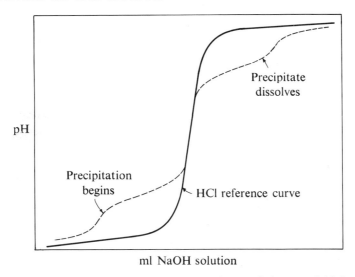

ml NaOH solution

FIGURE 6.5. *Titration curve showing amphoteric behavior of* Al_2O_3.

At high acidities the pH is raised by the basic behavior of the $Al(OH)_3$ (which yields cationic aluminum species), but in a highly basic medium the pH is lowered by the acidic behavior of $Al(OH)_3$ (which yields anionic aluminum species). Even though the behavior may not be observed in aqueous solution, the ability to form cations is taken as a characteristic of a basic oxide and the ability to form anions of an acidic oxide. Just as many cationic aquo ions are polynuclear, anionic aquo ions may be polynuclear.

Boric acid at low dilution forms $B(OH)_4^-$, but at higher concentrations a complex $B_3O_3(OH)_4^-$ has been reported.

Among the amphoteric oxides, (i.e., those forming either cations or anions depending on the solvent acidity) may be listed oxides of Zn(II), Cd(II), possibly Be(II), Ge(II), Sn(II), Pb(II), Cu(II), Fe(II), Fe(III), Al(III), Sb(III), Cr(III), Bi(III), Sn(IV), Pb(IV), Pt(IV), Th(IV), V(IV), V(V), and U(VI). The oxides of metals in the oxidation states of II are generally more readily soluble in acid than in base; the reverse is true for the higher oxidation states. Most of these oxides become practically insoluble on being fused or heated. The group in the oxidation state of IV may not properly belong here because of competing reactions. The cations formed in acid solution may involve coordination with the anion of the acid rather than formation of aquo cations. The cation formed by UO_3 is UO_2^{2+}, the uranyl ion, and probably involves the use of f orbitals in the bonding. Similar ions are formed by Np, Pu, and Am. On the other hand, the ion usually written as VO^{3+}, vanadyl, and VO_2^+ are probably mixed aquo, hydroxo complexes, i.e., $[V(OH)_2(H_2O)_2]^{3+}$ and $[V(OH)_4(H_2O)_2]^{3+}$. The zirconyl ions "ZrO^{2+}" are polynuclear ions such as

$$
\begin{bmatrix}
 & & OH & & \\
 & \diagup & & \diagdown & \\
(H_2O)_4Zr & & & & Zr(OH_2)_4 \\
 & \diagdown & OH & \diagup & \\
OH\ \ OH & & & OH\ \ OH \\
 & \diagup & OH & \diagdown & \\
(H_2O)_4Zr & & & & Zr(OH_2)_4 \\
 & \diagdown & OH & \diagup &
\end{bmatrix}^{8+}
$$

The anions show a similar tendency towards condensation, but many mononuclear species probably do exist in solution with formulas such as $M(OH)_4^{2-}$ or $M(OH)_6^{3-\,or\,4-}$.

It is likely that most oxides exhibit amphoteric character, however, under normal conditions in aqueous solution an insufficient range of acidity is covered to show both acidic and basic properties. Thus N_2O_3 forms NO_2^-, nitrite ion, in basic solution, whereas in highly acid media NO^+, the nitrosyl cation is formed. Likewise N_2O_5 forms NO_3^- in basic media, but NO_2^+, the nitryl cation, in concentrated sulfuric acid. Scholder and co-workers have isolated from basic solution a series of salts containing $Zn(OH)_4^-$, $Zn(OH)_6^{4-}$, $Cu(OH)_4^{2-}$, $Cu(OH)_6^{4-}$, $Pb(OH)_4^{2-}$, $Pb(OH)_6^{4-}$, etc.* One might suppose that in a medium where bases of greater strength than OH^- are available it might be possible to remove the remaining protons in these complexes. The oxide ion is much more basic than the hydroxide ion, but in water it is rapidly converted to the hydroxide ion. In fused alkali or alkaline earth metal oxides however, it is possible to prepare compounds such as Li_8PbO_6 or Ba_3MoO_6.†

Nonprotonic Concepts of Acid–Base Reactions

Lux Concept

In the reaction sequence

$$
\begin{aligned}
BaO + H_2O &\longrightarrow Ba(OH)_2(aq) \\
CO_2 + H_2O &\longrightarrow H_2CO_3(aq)
\end{aligned}
\Bigg\rangle \longrightarrow BaCO_3(s) + H_2O
$$

* See Table 12.12 in F. Basolo, in *The Chemistry of the Coordination Compounds*, edited by J. C. Bailar (New York: Reinhold Publishing Corp., 1956). "Acids, Bases, and Amphoteric Hydroxides," Chapter 12.
† Scholder, R., *Angew. Chem.*, **70**, 583 (1958).

the last stage is clearly an acid–base reaction. The reaction may be carried out directly with BaO and CO_2, i.e.,

$$BaO + CO_2 \longrightarrow BaCO_3$$

Many other examples are known of the direct reaction between acidic and basic anhydrides in the absence of water or of hydrogen ions.

$$3Na_2O + P_2O_5 \longrightarrow 2Na_3PO_4$$
$$CaO + SiO_2 \longrightarrow CaSiO_3$$

The Brønsted definition of an acid by the equation

$$\underset{\text{acid}}{AH} \quad \rightleftharpoons \quad \underset{\text{base}}{B^-} \quad + \quad \underset{\text{proton}}{H^+}$$

is not applicable. Lux has proposed for oxide systems the defining equation

$$\underset{\text{base}}{B} \quad \rightleftharpoons \quad \underset{\text{oxide ion}}{O^{2-}} \quad + \quad \underset{\text{acid}}{A}$$

According to this definition a base is an oxide ion donor, and an acid is an oxide ion acceptor. This view is particularly applicable to high temperature chemistry, as in the fields of ceramics and metallurgy. Thus the ores of Ti, Ta, and Nb may be brought into solution around 800° in sodium pyrosulfate ($Na_2S_2O_7$) or potassium pyrosulfate.

$$\underset{\text{base}}{TiO_2} + \underset{\text{acid}}{Na_2S_2O_7} \longrightarrow Na_2SO_4 + Ti(SO_4)_2 \text{ or } (TiO)SO_4$$

The displacement of the more volatile acid from solution is seen in the following reactions of sand or clay

$$3SiO_2 + Ca_3(PO_4)_2 \xrightarrow{\Delta} 3CaSiO_3 + P_2O_5 \uparrow$$

$$\underset{\text{acid}}{SiO_2} + \underset{\text{base}}{CaSO_4(\text{gypsum})} \xrightarrow{\Delta} \underset{\text{base}}{CaSiO_3} + \underset{\text{acid}}{SO_3} \uparrow$$

By this same scheme one may classify substances as amphoteric if they show both a tendency to take up or give up oxide ions depending on the circumstances, i.e.,

$$\underset{\text{base}}{ZnO} + S_2O_7^{2-} \longrightarrow Zn^{2+} + 2SO_4^{2-}$$

$$Na_2O + \underset{\text{acid}}{ZnO} \longrightarrow 2Na^+ + ZnO_2^{2-}$$

A parallelism between the thermodynamic stabilities of sulfates and carbonates towards evolution of SO_3 and CO_2, respectively, at high temperature, has been pointed out by Flood and Forenson. The order of increasing ease of decomposition is $Ba^{2+} > Li^+ > Ca^{2+} > Mg^{2+} > Mn^{2+} > Cd^{2+} > Pd^{2+} > Co^{2+} > Ag^+ > Fe^{2+} > Ni^{2+} > Cu^{2+} > Fe^{3+} > Be^{2+}$. This order of stability is approximately the order of base strength of the hydroxides.

The Lux oxide transfer picture of acid–base reactions can be extended to any negative ion, i.e., the halides, sulfides, or even carbanions! The following illustrate these reactions:

Negative ion donor   Negative ion acceptor

$$NaF \quad + \quad AlF_3 \xrightarrow{\text{high temp}} 3Na^+ + AlF_6{}^{3-}$$

$$Na_2S \quad + \quad CS_2 \longrightarrow 2Na^+ + CS_3{}^{2-}$$

$$EtNa \quad + \quad Et_2Zn \longrightarrow Na^+ + ZnEt_3{}^-$$

base   acid   acid   base

Solvent Ion Theory of Acids and Bases

The acid–base reactions considered in the preceding section (Lux theory and extensions) were ones in which there was no solvent other than the reactants themselves. A large number of reactions are more conveniently studied in solution, the solvent often facilitating the reaction. A useful picture of acid–base reactions in solution is obtained by considering the autoionization of the solvent, i.e.,

$$H_2O(liq) \longrightarrow H^+(aq) + OH^-(aq)$$
or $$NH_3(liq) \longrightarrow NH_4{}^+ + NH_2{}^-$$
or $$BrF_3 \longrightarrow BrF_2{}^+ + BrF_4{}^-$$
$$N_2O_4 \longrightarrow NO^+ + NO_3{}^-$$

A substance that increases the solvent cations is considered an acid, but one that increases the anions is considered a base.* Autoionization reactions for a number of solvents are given in Table 6.6. (Not all of these ionizations necessarily occur to an appreciable extent—see later sections.) Neutralization reactions have a precise meaning in this theory, neutralization being the combination of solvent cations and solvent anions to form neutral solvent. An amphoteric substance is one that can dissolve in acidic or basic solution to produce cations or anions. Discussion of some specific solvents is given below:

LIQUID AMMONIA

Since NH_3 boils at $-33°$ at one atmosphere pressure, reactions in it are usually carried out under reflux conditions using a Dry Ice cooled finger condenser.

Liquid ammonia is a solvent in many ways similar to water. Franklin pointed out the correspondence in behavior of the amide and nitride ions in the ammonia system and the hydroxide ion and the oxide ion in the water system. The imide ion, NH^{2-}, is intermediate. This correspondence extends to organic derivatives.

The dissolution of amide, imide, or nitride of a Group I or II metal in liquid ammonia produces a basic solution, since the amide ion is produced.

$$Li_3N + 2NH_3 \xrightarrow[\text{liq } NH_3]{} 3LiNH_2$$

The alkali metal hydrides produce basic solutions on dissolving.

$$NaH + NH_3 \xrightarrow[\text{liq } NH_3]{} Na^+ + NH_2{}^- + H_2 \uparrow$$
basic ion

The solubility of the alkali metal amides increases with increasing atomic number of the alkali metal.

* Cady, H. P., and H. M. Elsay, *J. Chem. Educ.*, **5**, 1425 (1928).

TABLE 6.6[a]

Autoionization of Various Solvents

	Cation	Anion
Protonic Solvents		
H_2O	H_3O^+	OH^-
NH_3	NH_4^+	NH_2^-
CH_3CO_2H	$CH_3CO_2H_2^+$	$CH_3CO_2^-$
HF	H_2F^+	FHF^-
HCl	H_2Cl^+	$ClHCl^-$
H_2SO_4	$H_3SO_4^+$	HSO_4^-
NH_2NH_2	$N_2H_5^+$	$N_2H_3^-$
HCN	H_2CN^+	CN^-
Halide–Oxyhalide Solvents		
BrF_3	BrF_2^+	BrF_4^-
IF_5	IF_4^+	IF_6^-
AsF_3	AsF_2^+	AsF_4^-
ICl	I^+	ICl_2^-
$HgBr_2$	$HgBr^+$	$HgBr_3^-$
I_2	I^+	I_3^-
$NOCl$	NO^+	Cl^-
$POCl_3$	$POCl_2^+$	Cl^-
$SeOCl_2$	$SeOCl^+$	Cl^-
$COCl_2$	$[COCl \cdot COCl_2]^+$	Cl^-
Oxide Solvents		
N_2O_4	NO^+	NO_3^-
SO_2	SO^{2+}	SO_3^{2-}

[a] Mainly from Gutmann, V., *Quart. Rev.*, **10**, 451 (1956).

Ammonia is a more basic solvent than water (in the Brønsted sense) and hence acids that are only partially dissociated in water are often completely dissociated in liquid ammonia. Thus, in liquid ammonia, hydrogen chloride and acetic acid appear to be equally strong acids since both are essentially 100% dissociated.

$$CH_3CO_2H + NH_3 \longrightarrow NH_4^+ + CH_3CO_2^-$$
$$\text{acidic ion}$$

$$HCl + NH_3 \xrightarrow[\text{liq } NH_3]{} NH_4^+ + Cl^-$$

Liquid ammonia solutions containing amide ion turn phenolphthalein indicator red; these solutions may be titrated to a colorless end point with a liquid ammonia solution containing ammonium ion.

$$NH_4CH_3CO_2 + KNH_2 \longrightarrow CH_3CO_2K + NH_3$$

One of the properties of aqueous acids is the ability to dissolve active metals with the evolution of hydrogen. Similar properties are shown by solutions containing ammonium ion in liquid ammonia. Aluminum in the form of an amalgam can also dissolve in liquid ammonia solution containing amides. Amphoteric character is also found with zinc ions as indicated by the following sequence of reactions:

$$ZnI_2 \text{ (solvated)} + 2KNH_2 \longrightarrow Zn(NH_2)_2 \downarrow + 2KI$$
$$Zn(NH_2)_2(s) + 2KNH_2 \longrightarrow K_2[Zn(NH_2)_4]$$

The tetraamidozincate ion formed corresponds to the tetrahydroxozincate ion formed in aqueous solution. Addition of ammonium ion to the amidozincate ion will reprecipitate zinc amide, but further ammonium ion will redissolve the precipitate.

ACETIC ACID AS A SOLVENT

The autodissociation of acetic acid may be written as

$$2CH_3CO_2H \leftrightharpoons CH_3CO_2H_2^+ + CH_3CO_2^-$$

Hence, metal acetates or substances producing acetate ions are basic in this medium. Due to the greater proton donating ability of acetic acid than that of water, bases such as ammonia and many amines are essentially completely ionized in acetic acid.

$$CH_3CO_2H + NH_3 \longrightarrow NH_4^+ + CH_3CO_2^-$$
$$\text{base}$$

However, acetic acid is a much poorer proton acceptor than water so acids such as HCl and HNO_3 are only partially dissociated. From conductance studies the relative order of acid strengths in acetic acid has been found to be $HClO_4 > HBr > H_2SO_4 > HCl > HNO_3$. This order provides some support for the estimates given earlier.* Titrations of amines, which are very weak bases in H_2O, may be carried out with strong acid dissolved in acetic acid using crystal violet indicator.

Zinc chloride shows amphoteric character in acetic acid, just as the zinc ion does in many other solvents. Addition of sodium acetate first precipitates zinc acetate from solution of $ZnCl_2$ in acetic acid and then dissolves the precipitate with the formation of a tetraacetatozincate ion.

BROMINE TRIFLUORIDE†

The autoionization of BrF_3 may be written as $2BrF_3 \rightleftharpoons BrF_2^+ + BrF_4^-$. Accordingly, KF forms a basic solution by the reaction

$$KF + BrF_3 \longrightarrow K^+ + BrF_4^-$$
$$\text{base}$$

and SbF_5 forms an acidic solution by the reaction

$$SbF_5 + BrF_3 \longrightarrow BrF_2^+ + SbF_6^-$$
$$\text{acid}$$

---

* Raman and NMR studies however indicate the dissociation constants may be only of the order of 100 even for $HClO_4$ in H_2O.
† Gutmann, V., *Quart. Rev.*, **10**, 451 (1956).

Mixing these two solutions would give a neutralization reaction producing the solvent and the salt $KSbF_6$. Neutralization reactions such as this provide a synthesis route to many salts that might be difficult to obtain in other fashions. The solvent BrF_3 is particularly convenient for preparing many salts because of its high fluorinating power as well as its ability to undergo self-dissociation. Thus, it is not necessary to work directly with the fluoride whose salts are desired, but only with substances which may be fluorinated to give the starting materials. Some typical reactions utilizing the fluorinating ability of BrF_3 and subsequent neutralization reactions are

$$Au \longrightarrow [BrF_2^+AuF_4^-]$$
$$Ag \longrightarrow [Ag^+BrF_4^-]$$
$$\longrightarrow AgAuF_4$$

$$GeO_2 \longrightarrow [(BrF_2^+)_2GeF_6^{2-}]$$
$$NOCl \longrightarrow [NO^+BrF_4^-]$$
$$\longrightarrow (NO)_2GeF_6$$

$$SO_3 \longrightarrow [BrF_2^+SO_3F^-]$$
$$NO_2 \longrightarrow [NO_2^+BrF_4^-]$$
$$\longrightarrow NO_2SO_3F$$

DINITROGEN TETROXIDE*

Liquid N_2O_4 may be written as undergoing autodissociation of the type

$$N_2O_4 \rightleftharpoons NO^+ + NO_3^-$$

The nitrosyl cation, accordingly, is the acidic species and the nitrate ion the basic species in this solvent. Support for this mode of dissociation has been obtained by Clusius and Vecchi who found rapid exchange of $^{15}NO_3^-$ with $^{14}N_2O_4$ when tetramethylammonium nitrate was placed in N_2O_4.

Nitrosyl chloride, NOCl, behaves like an incipient nitrosyl cation in N_2O_4 and may therefore be considered as an acid in this solvent. Nitrates behave as bases. The following reaction is accordingly a neutralization reaction

$$NOCl + AgNO_3 \longrightarrow AgCl + N_2O_4$$

The alkali metals, and Ca, Zn, and Hg dissolve in N_2O_4 with the production of metal nitrates and the evolution of nitrogen(II) oxide, NO. With a donor solvent (see next section) such as acetone present, U, Mn, Co, Cu, Cd, and In will also dissolve with the evolution of NO. $Zn(NO_3)_2$ dissolves in the solvent to produce $Zn(NO_3)_2 \cdot 2N_2O_4$ which may be formulated as $(NO^+)_2[Zn(NO_3)_4]^{2-}$, i.e., nitrosyl tetranitratozincate, showing again the amphoteric nature of zinc.

LIQUID HYDROGEN CHLORIDE†

Liquid HCl may be considered to undergo the autodissociation

$$\underset{\text{acid}}{2HCl \rightleftharpoons H_2Cl^+} + \underset{\text{base}}{HCl_2^-}$$

The acid ion, H_2Cl^+, would probably be stabilized by strong hydrogen bonding (if it does indeed exist in appreciable quantities!).

* Gray, P., and A. D. Yoffe, *Chem. Rev.*, **55**, 1069 (1955); C. C. Addison, *Angew. Chem.*, **72**, 193 (1960).
† Waddington, T. C., and F. Klanberg, *J. Chem. Soc.*, **1960**, 2332.

$$\left[\begin{array}{c} \text{Cl} \\ \text{H} \quad \text{H} \quad \text{H} \quad \text{H} \\ \text{Cl} \qquad\qquad \text{Cl} \end{array} \right]^{+}$$

The H_2Cl^+ ion could be formed either by a strong proton donor, such as chlorosulfonic acid, HSO_3Cl, or by a chloride ion acceptor such as BF_3, BCl_3, or $AlCl_3$.

$$HSO_3Cl + HCl \xrightarrow[\text{liq HCl}]{} \underset{\text{acid}}{H_2Cl^+} + SO_3Cl^-$$

$$BF_3 + 2HCl \xrightarrow[\text{liq HCl}]{} H_2Cl^+ + ClBF_3^-$$

The basic ion $[ClHCl]^-$, which is known to exist in tetraalkylamine hydrogen dichloride salts, can be readily formed in solution by even weak proton acceptors such as PH_3, C_5H_5N, or chloride ion donors, $(C_6H_5)_3CCl$, $POCl_3$, or PCl_5

$$PCl_5 + HCl \longrightarrow PCl_4^+ + \underset{\text{base}}{ClHCl^-}$$

When solutions of PCl_5 are mixed with solutions of HSO_3Cl in liquid HCl, neutralization occurs and the salt $(PCl_4^+)(SO_3Cl^-)$ is obtained. This salt is unstable at room temperature and has not been made by the direct reaction of PCl_5 with HSO_3Cl.

By appropriate neutralizations one can prepare salts such as $[POCl_2^+]$ $[BCl_4^-]$ and $PCl_4^+BCl_4^-$.

Some Comments on the Solvent Theory of Acidity

Although the solvent theory of acids often considers autoionization of the solvent of the type

$$SL_x \rightleftharpoons SL^{\pm m}_{x-1} + SL^{\pm m}_{x+1}$$

where L is a charged group, as the general criterion for solvent participation in acid base reactions, this concept would seem to be useful only for amphoteric solvents. Thus, either of the reactions

$$SL_x \longrightarrow SL^{\pm m}_{x-1} + L^{\pm m}$$

or

$$L^{\pm m} + SL_x \longrightarrow SL^{\pm m}_{x+1}$$

would be sufficient for solvent participation in acid–base reactions on a general ion (i.e., Lux) theory of acids and bases. The acceptance (or donation) of L^+ would occur only when an acceptor (or donor) for L^+ were present. Thus it seems reasonable to consider liquid HCl as a chloride ion acceptor, which may later give up the chloride ion to a better acceptor. There seems to be little evidence for the ionization of SO_2 as

$$SO_2 \rightleftharpoons SO^{2+} + SO_3^{2-}$$

On the other hand, it would seem natural to consider SO_2 as an oxide ion acceptor. Reaction of thionyl chloride with sulfite ion in liquid sulfur dioxide might then be considered as a nucleophilic displacement of Cl^- by SO_3^{2-} followed by decomposition of the product, i.e.,

$$2SO_2 + 2Cl^-$$

Lewis Acids and Bases*

Emphasis thus far has been placed on ion transfer reactions in our discussions of acids and bases — either proton transfers or anion transfers. We have previously recognized the basic properties of ammonia (as a proton acceptor) and the acidic properties of boron trifluoride (as a fluoride or chloride ion acceptor) and it seems reasonable to think of the reaction between NH_3 and BF_3

as an acid–base reaction, even though no ions are transferred, or even formed, by this reaction. G. N. Lewis considered the fundamental characteristic of bases to be an unshared pair of electrons, and the fundamental characteristic of acids to be an ability to accept an electron pair in covalent bond formation. The Lewis acid picture covers (with occasional stretching) the ion transfer process as special cases, and extends the generality of the concept of acids and bases to nonionic compounds. It focuses attention on the strength of the new covalent bond formed.

STRENGTH OF LEWIS BASES

Comparisons of the strength of Lewis acids and bases is somewhat difficult due to the many different methods various workers have used to establish orders. Some of the various methods include gas phase dissociation data, calorimetric heats of reaction, competition experiments between several competing acids (or bases) for an insufficient amount of base (or acid), displacement methods, or studies of the volatility of addition compounds that are formed (the more volatile, the less stable the adduct within a series). Nevertheless, within a given series conclusions can be drawn, and overlap of several series permits some generalizations, although some caution should be exercised.

Position in the Periodic Table. With regard to the position in the periodic table the strength of Lewis bases towards Lewis acids parallels their basicity towards a proton, provided that only σ bonds are formed and steric factors are not great. The following examples illustrate this.

* Data largely from H. C. Brown, *J. Chem. Soc.*, **1956**, 1248.

	Molar heat of reaction with BMe$_3$	The product of reaction with HCl
Me$_3$N	−17.6 kcal	Sublimes at 250°
Me$_3$P	−16.1	Sublimes at 125°
Me$_3$As	exists only at −80°	Unstable at room temperature
Me$_3$Sb	No compound formed	Unstable at −80°C

Likewise the base strength decreases as one goes from Me$_3$N to Me$_2$O to MeF. Trimethylamine readily displaces dimethyl ether from boron trifluoride methyl etherate. The variation of strength of Lewis acids with the position in the periodic table is somewhat more complex, but for oxygen and nitrogen bases the trends parallel the tendency towards hydrolysis discussed earlier (i.e., B > Be > Li; Be > Mg > Ca, etc.). The variations within the transition metals will be discussed more fully in the chapters dealing with coordination compounds.

Effect of Substituents. The effect of substituents on the strength of Lewis acids and bases may often be predicted from a consideration of the inductive, resonance, and steric effects of the substituents. Thus an electron withdrawing inductive effect will make an acid stronger (more willing to accept an electron pair) and a base weaker (less willing to donate an electron pair). Thus the base strength decreases in the series Me$_3$N > NH$_3$ > NF$_3$, whereas the acid strength increases in the series Me$_3$B < BH$_3$* < BF$_3$. This order is precisely the order expected based on the inductive effect of these groups. The order of acid strength BF$_3$ < BCl$_3$ < BBr$_3$ is not the order expected from the inductive effects, but may be explained as due to the greater resonance stabilization of BF$_3$ as compared to BCl$_3$ (see p. 58, Chapter II).

The weakness as an acid of methylborate, (MeO)$_3$B as compared to trimethylboron may be attributed to resonance.

Steric Effects. Steric effects generally have only slight influence on ion transfer equilibria, especially when the ions differ by only a proton. In Lewis acid–base reactions steric effects may be quite large. Thus while 2-methylpyridine is a stronger base towards a proton than pyridine (as would be expected from the inductive effect) it is a much weaker base towards Lewis acids than pyridine.

ΔH Reaction with B(CH$_3$)$_3$	−17 kcal stable	−17.6 kcal stable	−10 kcal unstable

* After correction for bridge breaking.

With an acid such as trimethylboron the 2-*tert*-butylpyridine does not form a compound, although pyridine forms a stable compound. This may be attributed to the strain between nonbonded groups attached to different atoms which have conflicting steric requirements. Such strain is termed "F-strain."* The inductive effects would be expected to be the same in triethylamine and quinuclidine, but the heat of reaction of quinuclidine is much greater than that of Et_3N with BMe_3 due to the greater "F" strain in the triethylamine complex.

Triethylamine ΔH with $B(CH_3)_3 \approx -10$ kcal

[Sterically similar to]

Quinuclidine ΔH with $B(CH_3)_3 \approx -20$ kcal

A change in hybridization during the formation of a molecular addition compound may also bring about a change in steric requirement. Thus boron changes from sp^2 to sp^3 hybridization during acid–base reactions of trialkylboron compounds. Branching of the alkyl groups greatly reduces the acid strength of trialkylboron. Trimesitylboron is inert even to such strong bases as methoxide ion, since there would be too much crowding if the mesityl groups were forced from a planar to a tetrahedral configuration.

inert due to B-strain in sp^3 configuration

Some Inverted Orders. Although BF_3 is "normally" a stronger acid than diborane, B_2H_6, the latter forms a compound with CO, i.e., H_3BCO, but the former does not. Likewise the compound dimethylsulfide is a stronger base than dimethylether towards BH_3 although the reverse is true with BF_3. Both of these may be explained on the basis

* Brown, H. C., *Rec. Chem. Prog.*, **14**, 83 (1953).

of hyperconjugation of the BH_3 group, stabilizing the addition compound, i.e.,

$$H-\underset{\underset{H}{|}}{\overset{\overset{H}{|}}{B^-}}-C\equiv O|^+ \quad \longleftrightarrow \quad H-\underset{\underset{H}{|}}{\overset{\overset{H^+}{|}}{B^-}}=C=\bar{O}| \qquad \text{3 eq structures}$$

$$H-\underset{\underset{H}{|}}{\overset{\overset{H}{|}}{B^-}}-\underset{\underset{Me}{|}}{\bar{S}^+}-Me \quad \longleftrightarrow \quad H-\underset{\underset{H}{|}}{\overset{\overset{H^+}{|}}{B^-}}=\underset{\underset{Me}{|}}{\bar{S}}-Me \qquad \text{3 eq structures}$$

The latter involves the $3d$ orbitals of S and hence would not be important for oxygen derivatives. These inversions due to multiple bond character are much more common in the later transition metal compounds and will be discussed more fully later.

Solvolytic Reactions

Hydrolysis

The behavior of binary, and pseudo binary,* compounds toward water and other "water-like" solvents serves as a convenient starting point for a systematic study of the reactions of these compounds in solution.

Practically all metal alkyls and metal hydrides undergo rapid hydrolysis whereas, by contrast, alkyl and hydrogen derivatives of the nonmetals are generally stable with respect to hydrolysis. On the other hand, the halides of most of the nonmetals undergo hydrolysis readily, whereas only the halides of metals in the higher oxidation states show much tendency toward hydrolysis. Hydrolysis of metal alkyls and metal hydrides is facilitated by an increase in acidity of the solution. Hydrolysis of the covalent halides is facilitated by an increase in basicity of the media.

In a hydrolysis reaction the hydrogen goes to the more electronegative atom, the hydroxyl group to the more electropositive atom. Hydrolysis of the appropriate binary compounds is often used as a means of preparing the volatile hydrogen compounds of the nonmetals.

$$
\begin{array}{llll}
 & N_2 & & \\
M^{II}+Si & P & Mg_3N_2 & NH_3 \\
\quad\quad Ge & As & Ca_2Si \xrightarrow{H_2O} SiH_4 & PH_3 \\
 & Sb & Ca_2Ge \quad\quad GeH_4 & AsH_3 \\
 & Bi & etc. & SbH_3
\end{array}
$$

Hydrolysis behavior of ionic compounds may be approached from the viewpoint of acid–base equilibria.

$$MY_n + nHOH \rightleftharpoons M(OH)_n + nHY$$

* Pseudo-binary compounds are those like $LiNH_2$ in which the amide group behaves as a single entity.

Hydrolysis is favored if Y is the anion of a weak acid and/or if M is the cation of a weak base. The effect of the anion is illustrated by the behavior shown below.

$$Li_2C_2 \xrightarrow{\text{HOH}} LiOH + C_2H_2$$

$$\left.\begin{array}{l} Li_3N \\ Li_3P \\ Li_3As \\ Li_3Sb \end{array}\right\} \xrightarrow{\text{HOH}} Li^+ + OH^- + YH_3$$

$$\left.\begin{array}{l} Li_2O \\ Li_2S \\ Li_2Se \\ Li_2Te \end{array}\right\} \xrightarrow{\text{HOH}} 2Li^+ + OH^- + YH^-$$

$$\left.\begin{array}{l} LiF \\ LiCl \\ LiBr \\ LiCl \end{array}\right\} \xrightarrow{\text{HOH}} Li^+(aq)Y^-(aq)$$

If the cation combines with the hydroxide ion then hydrolysis is facilitated, as in the case of Al salts.

$$Al_2Te_3 + 6H_2O \longrightarrow 2Al(OH)_3 + 3H_2Te$$

If the acidity of the solution is increased even cations of very weak bases may be made to take up a proton as in the laboratory preparation of HCl by the reaction of NaCl and concentrated sulfuric acid.

$$NaCl + H_2SO_4 \longrightarrow NaHSO_4 + HCl$$

The trends in hydrolysis of halides with variation in the central atom are those expected on the acid–base approach, i.e., the extent of hydrolysis reactions generally decreases on descending in a given group of the periodic table. This is illustrated in the following examples:

$$
\begin{array}{llllll}
PCl_3 & + & H_2O & \longrightarrow & H_3PO_3 & + & HCl \\
BiCl_3 & + & H_2O & \longrightarrow & BiOCl & + & HCl \\
TiCl_4 & + & H_2O & \longrightarrow & TiO_2 & + & HCl \\
ZrCl_4 & + & H_2O & \longrightarrow & ZrOCl_2 & + & HCl
\end{array}
$$

Hydrolysis of the metal halides may often be completely repressed by addition of the hydrohalic acid, or the hydrolysis may be furthered by the addition of base.

With many covalent compounds the acid–base approach to hydrolysis is not satisfactory. Thus boron trifluoride is not appreciably hydrolyzed, but boron trichloride is rapidly and completely hydrolyzed, in contrast to what might have been expected on the basis of the relative basicity of a fluoride and a chloride ion. In place of the acid–base approach, a consideration of the bond energies for the bonds being made and broken serves better for predictive purposes in solvolysis reactions of covalent compounds. An estimate of the heat of reaction may be made from electronegativity values, but, as in the present example π bonding may make an undetermined contribution. It should further be pointed out that many reactions, which are thermodynamically favorable, do not occur at appreciable rates because of a high activation energy for the reaction. Accordingly a knowledge of mechanisms of reaction is desirable. The probable mechanism for the hydrolysis of boron trichloride involves formation of an addition compound between H_2O and BCl_3 which rearranges via a proton shift and the subsequent leaving of HCl, i.e.,

$$H_2O + BCl_3 \xrightarrow[\text{slow}]{} \left[\begin{array}{c} \overset{H}{\underset{\oplus}{|}} \quad \overset{Cl}{\underset{|}{|}} \\ H-O-B\overset{}{-}Cl \\ \underset{Cl}{\overset{\ominus}{|}} \end{array}\right] \longrightarrow \left[\begin{array}{c} H-Cl^{\oplus} \\ | \\ HO-B^{\ominus}-Cl \\ | \\ Cl \end{array}\right]$$

$$\Big\downarrow \text{fast}$$

$$\xleftarrow[\text{fast}]{\text{etc.}} \left[\begin{array}{c} H \\ | \\ {}^{\oplus}O-H \\ | \\ HO^{\ominus}-B-Cl \\ | \\ Cl \end{array}\right] \xleftarrow[\text{slow}]{H_2O} \left[\begin{array}{c} HO-B-Cl \\ | \\ Cl \end{array}\right] + HCl$$

With BF_3 the addition compound with water forms, but the compound does not evolve HF. It may be noted in the postulated mechanism that in the coordination complex the coordinated protonic solvent (H_2O in this case) becomes more acidic and the leaving group (the chloro group) becomes more basic. The enhanced acidity of the solvent on coordination is dependent on the nature of the central atom and the groups originally attached to it. When the central atom is in a high oxidation state, the enhancement of acidity is great.

The importance of a low energy path for reaction is illustrated by the inertness of SF_6 to hydrolysis even though such a reaction is highly favored thermodynamically. A maximum coordination number of six is observed for the third period elements, hence, a reaction proceeding by a seven coordinated transition state would involve a high activation energy. On the other hand, TeF_6 is known to form addition compounds such as $(R_3N)_2TeF_6$. It is accordingly not surprising that TeF_6 undergoes complete hydrolysis to H_2TeO_6 and HF although the reaction is slow. Uranium(VI) is also known in complexes with coordination numbers greater than six. UF_6 undergoes violent hydrolysis.

The mechanism postulated for the hydrolysis of boron trichloride has a nucleophilic attack on BCl_3 by water as the rate determining step (i.e., the slowest step in the reaction sequence). At the other extreme of the mechanistic scale are hydrolysis reactions in which the rate determining step is an electrophilic attack by a hydronium ion. The phenylboronic acids* and the group IV organometals† appear to hydrolyze by such a mechanism

$$RC_6H_4Sn(C_6H_{11})_3 + H_3O^+ \xrightarrow[\text{slow}]{} (RC_6H_4 \cdot H)SnC_6H_{11}{}^+$$

$$\Big\downarrow \text{fast}$$

$$RC_6H_5 + Sn(C_6H_{11})_3{}^+$$

* Kuivila, H. G., and K. V. Nahabedian, *J. Am. Chem. Soc.*, **83**, 2159 (1961).
† Eaborn, C., and J. A. Waters, *J. Chem. Soc.*, **1961**, 542.

Correlations of the rates of hydrolysis with the Hammett σ values are helpful in deciding whether a reaction such as the one above is initiated by an electrophilic or nucleophilic attack. Electron releasing substituents would increase the rate of an electrophilic attack, but would retard a nucleophilic attack.

Synthesis of Deuterated Compounds

The availability of D_2O makes it a common starting material for the synthesis of many deuterated compounds. Many of the reactions are simple hydrolysis reactions,

$$Mg_3N_2 + D_2O \longrightarrow 3Mg(OD)_2 + 2ND_3$$
$$CaC_2 + D_2O \longrightarrow Ca(OD)_2 + C_2D_2$$
$$CaH_2 + D_2O \longrightarrow Ca(OD)_2 + DH$$
$$CH_3COCl + D_2O \longrightarrow (CH_3CO)_2O + 2DCl$$

In the presence of excess D_2O the last reaction gives CH_3CO_2D as a product. Since the D_2O is the more expensive reagent, the reaction is carried out by dropping D_2O into acetyl chloride, thus assuring that the acetyl chloride will be present in excess. The reaction with CaH_2 has been used as a means of analyzing heavy water, the DH being detected in a stream of H_2 carrier gas by thermal conductance measurements.[*]

Hydrolysis may be coupled with reductions with $LiAlD_4$ or $LiAlH_4$ to produce compounds of the desired degree of deuteration. Thus CD_3OH may conveniently be made from ethylene carbonate by the following sequence of reactions.[†]

$$\begin{matrix} CH_2-O \\ | \quad\quad C=O + LiAlH_4 \longrightarrow Li \left(\begin{matrix} CH_2-O \\ | \quad\quad \\ CH_2-O \end{matrix}\right)_2 Al + Li[(CD_3O)_4Al] \\ CH_2-O \end{matrix}$$

$$\downarrow H_2O$$

$$CD_3OH + LiOH + Al(OH)_3$$

Alcoholysis[‡]

Alcohols resemble water in their solvolysis reactions, except that the tendency to go all the way to oxides is less due to the greater stability of the C—O bond compared to the H—O bond. Thus a number of alkoxides have been obtained by the direct reaction of a metal halide and an alcohol with the equilibrium displaced by the addition of anhydrous ammonia or an alkali metal alkoxide.

$$TiCl_4 + 4ROH + 4NH_3 \longrightarrow Ti(OR)_4 + 4NH_4Cl$$
$$TiCl_4 + ROH + NaOR \longrightarrow Ti(OR)_4 + NaCl$$

With varying experimental conditions these reactions have been used to make alkoxides of Ti, Zr, Ce, Nb, Ta, Fe, V, Pu, and Th.

[*] Arnett, E. M., M. Strem, N. Hepfinger, J. Lipowitz, and D. McGuire, *Science*, **131**, 1680 (1960).
[†] Edgell, W., and L. Parts, *J. Am. Chem. Soc.*, **77**, 5515 (1955).
[‡] Bradley, D. C., "Metal Alkoxides," in *Progress in Inorganic Chemistry*, Vol. II, F. A. Cotton, ed. (New York: Interscience, 1960).

Phosphorous acid may be conveniently prepared in the laboratory by the hydrolysis of PCl_3. Solvolysis with alcohols plus a Lewis base produces a trialkylphosphite.

$$PCl_3 + 3ROH \longrightarrow P(OR)_3 + 3HCl$$

On heating, the phosphite esters undergo rearrangement to give esters of the corresponding alkylphosphonic acid.

$$P(OR)_3 \xrightarrow[\Delta]{} RPO(OR)_2$$

The latter are the alkyl analogs of phosphorous acid. Interestingly, the reaction of PBr_3 with alcohols yields alkyl bromides and phosphorous acid.

$$PBr_3 + 3ROH \longrightarrow 3RBr + P(OH)_3$$

Hydrolysis of PCl_5 with a deficiency of water produces $POCl_3$ and complete hydrolysis produces phosphoric acid, H_3PO_4. Alcoholololysis of PCl_5 produces esters of phosphoric acid, but a more convenient preparative method is the reaction of $POCl_3$ with alcohol.

$$POCl_3 + 3ROH \longrightarrow PO(OR)_3 + 3HCl$$

Methyl borate, $B(OMe)_3$, and aluminum methoxide may be made through the reaction of the chloride with methyl alcohol, however, more convenient routes to these compounds are

$$B(OH)_3 + 3MeOH \rightleftharpoons B(OMe)_3 + 3HOH$$

and

$$Al + 3MeOH \longrightarrow Al(OMe)_3 + \frac{3}{2}H_2$$

Although methyl borate is a weak Lewis acid, it will still combine with a very strong Lewis base such as the hydride ion.

$$LiH + B(OMe)_3 \xrightarrow{Et_2O} LiBH(OMe)_3$$

The product is a very mild reducing agent used for selective organic reductions. The aluminum alkoxides also find application in organic chemistry, as catalysts in the Meerwein–Ponndorf–Verley reaction.

$$R_2CO + R_2{}'CHOH \longrightarrow R_2CHOH + R_2{}'CO$$

With hydrides, alcohols react to give the alkoxide, i.e.,

$$KH + BuOH \longrightarrow KOBu + H_2$$
$$LiAlH_4 + 4MeOH \longrightarrow LiAl(OMe)_4 + 4H_2$$
$$LiBH_4 + 4MeOH \longrightarrow LiB(OMe)_4 + 4H_2$$

Further Solvolysis Reactions

Alcohols are not the only class of compounds that resemble water in solvolysis reactions. Other molecules possessing an unshared electron pair, and a hydrogen atom which may become slightly acidic in coordination compounds, may also behave in a fashion like water. Such substances include H_2O_2, NH_3, H_2NNH_2, RNH_2, R_2NH, HF, H_2S, and RSH, where R is an alkyl or aryl group. The reactions

$$2H_3SiCl + H_2O \longrightarrow H_3Si-O-SiH_3 + 2HCl$$

and

$$3H_3SiCl + 4NH_3 \longrightarrow (H_3Si)_3N + 3NH_4Cl$$

provide synthetic routes to the interesting silyl ether and trisilylamine. The latter is planar, due presumably to p-d-π bonding. Further analogies with hydrolysis may be seen in the following examples of solvolysis of chlorosulfonic acid:

$$
\begin{aligned}
HOSO_2Cl + H_2O &\longrightarrow HOSO_2OH &&+ HCl \\
HOSO_2Cl + ROH &\longrightarrow HOSO_2OR &&+ HCl \\
HOSO_2Cl + H_2O_2 &\longrightarrow HOSO_2(OOH) &&+ HCl \\
HOSO_2Cl + NH_3 &\longrightarrow HOSO_2NH_2 &&+ HCl \\
HOSO_2Cl + H_2NNH_2 &\longrightarrow HOSO_2NHNH_2 &&+ HCl
\end{aligned}
$$

Many fluorides can be prepared by treating the corresponding chloride with HF, a reaction often carried out at room temperature (i.e., with $TiCl_4$, VCl_4, etc.).

Some solvolysis products have no oxygen analogs, i.e.,

$$PCl_5 + 4C_6H_5NH_2 \longrightarrow (C_6H_5NH)_4PCl + 4HCl$$

The above compound is a low melting phosphonium salt derivative.

Deficit Solvolysis

The products of a solvolysis reaction may often be altered by a change in the relative amounts of reagent involved in the reaction. Thus sulfuryl chloride, SO_2Cl_2, reacts with an excess of ammonia in petroleum ether to give sulfamide $SO_2(NH_2)_2$. If the sulfuryl chloride is in excess then a sulfimide $(SO_2NH)_n$ is produced. The trisulfimide may be presumed to have a ring structure such as

The dative bonds indicated would be p-d-π bonds and are suggested, in part, by the slightly acidic character of the remaining hydrogens.

Ammonium chloride dissociates into NH_3 and HCl on heating. Accordingly, heating a substance with NH_4Cl may be used to bring about a deficit amonolysis reaction. When PCl_5 and NH_4Cl are heated together around 150°C, the trimer and tetramer of

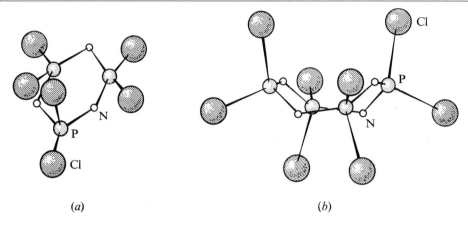

FIGURE 6.6. *Structure of (a)* (PNCl$_2$)$_3$ *and (b)* (PNCl$_2$)$_4$. *[*(PNCl$_2$)$_4$ *from R. Hazelkamp, T. Migchelsen, and A. Vos, Acta Cryst., 15, 539 (1962).]*

phosphonitrilic chloride are produced

$$PCl_5 + NH_4Cl \longrightarrow (PNCl_2)_n + 4HCl$$

These are cyclic compounds as shown in Figure 6.6.

At temperatures around 250°C rubber-like linear polymers are produced.

At still higher temperatures (above 350°C) depolymerization takes place. Phosphonitrilic chloride is solvolyzed in liquid ammonia to give eventually $[PN(NH_2)_2]_n$. Hydrolysis of the phosphonitrilic halides to give metaphosphimic acids $[PO(OH)NH]_n$ is slow unless a mutual solvent such as diethyl ether is added to the mixture. Other active hydrogen compounds such as alcohols and primary and secondary amines will also solvolyze phosphonitrilic chloride. Typical trimers produced by these reactions are shown below:

The reaction of NH$_4$Cl and BCl$_3$ in chlorobenzene also yields a deficit amonolysis product.

$$3NH_4Cl + 3BCl_3 \xrightarrow{150^\circ} (BClNH)_3 + 9HCl$$

The trimer produced has possibilities for benzene-like resonance involving p-p-π double bonds. The remaining chlorine, unlike that in phosphonitrilic chloride, reacts readily with Grignard reagents to give tri-B-alkylborazines.

Solvolytic Reactions Accompanied by Disproportionation

Occasionally the normally expected solvolysis product is not itself stable, but undergoes an auto-oxidation–reduction reaction to produce several new species. Thus the product normally expected for the hydrolysis of ICl_3 might be HIO_2 and HCl, but since HIO_2 is not stable, the products actually found in addition to HCl are HIO_3 and HI. Some other examples of disproportionation following solvolysis are given below.

$$2TeX_2 + 3H_2O \longrightarrow Te + H_2TeO_3 + 4HX$$
$$Hg_2^{2+} + H_2S \longrightarrow Hg + HgS + 2H^+$$
$$Hg_2^{2+} + 2(OH^-) \longrightarrow Hg + HgO + H_2O$$

Basic solvolysis accompanied by disproportionation is typical of the elemental forms of the nonmetals.

$$Cl_2 + 2(OH^-) \xrightarrow[\text{cold soln}]{} Cl^- + OCl^- + H_2O$$

$$3Cl_2 + 6(OH^-) \xrightarrow[\text{hot soln}]{} 5Cl^- + ClO_3^- + 3H_2O$$

$$P_4 + 12(OH^-) + 12H_2O \longrightarrow 4PH_3 + 12H_2PO_2^-$$

When hypophosphorous acid is the desired product of the disproportionation reaction of phosphorus, barium hydroxide is used as the base. The barium ion is then precipitated with a stoichiometric amount of sulfuric acid.

$$Ba(H_2PO_2)_2 + H_2SO_4 \longrightarrow BaSO_4 + 2H_3PO_2$$

In these base hydrolysis reactions, the mechanism may be assumed to be of the S_N2 type, i.e.,

$$HO^- + Cl{-}Cl \longrightarrow [H{-}O{\cdots}Cl{\cdots}Cl]^- \longrightarrow HOCl + Cl^-$$
$$H_2S + Hg{-}Hg^{2+} \longrightarrow [H_2S{\cdots}Hg{\cdots}Hg]^{2+} \longrightarrow HgS + Hg + 2H^+$$

GENERAL REFERENCES

Bell, R. P., *The Proton in Chemistry* (Ithaca: Cornell University Press, 1959).

Hammett, L. P., *Physical Organic Chemistry* (New York: McGraw-Hill Book Company, Inc., 1940) Chapter IX.

Audrieth, L. F., and J. Kleinberg, *Non-Aqueous Solvents* (New York: John Wiley and Sons, Inc., 1953).

Jolly, W. L., *Synthetic Inorganic Chemistry* (Englewood Cliffs: Prentice-Hall, Inc., 1960) Chapter 3.

Problems

1. Which of the following would be expected to have the stronger electron withdrawing inductive effect?

$H_2CCH—$ or $HCC—$

$CH_3SO_2—$ or $CH_3SO—$

$CH_3O—$ or $CH_3S—$

$HO_2C—$ or $^-O_2C—$

2. The pK_a of benzoic acid is 4.20. Substitution of Y in the meta position shifts the pK_a to 5.0 and the para substituted compound has a pK_a of 5.3. What conclusions may be drawn about the inductive and resonance effects of Y?

3. Estimate a ρ value for the dissociation of phenylphosphonium ions and combine this with the σ value of $+0.37$ for m—Cl to predict the difference in pK_a values of p—$ClC_6H_4PH_3^+$ and $C_6H_5PH_3^+$ in water.

4. Give the approximate pK_a values for the following acids.

    (a) H_3PO_3 $pK_1 =$ $pK_2 =$

    (b) HNO_3 $pK_1 =$

    (c) $HClO_4$ $pK_1 =$

    (d) H_5IO_6 $pK_1 =$ $pK_2 =$

5. Select the best answer and give the basis for your selection.

    (a) Thermally most stable: PH_4Cl PH_4Br PH_4I

    (b) Strongest acid: H_2O H_2S H_2Se H_2Te

    (c) Acidic oxide: Ag_2O V_2O_5 CO Ce_2O_3

    (d) Strongest acid: MgF_2 $MgCl_2$ $MgBr_2$

    (e) Stronger base (towards a proton): PH_2^- NH_2^-

6. Give equations to explain why the addition of ammonium acetate to either zinc amide(s) in liquid ammonia or zinc acetate(s) in acetic acid causes the solid to dissolve.

7. Would the following *increase, decrease*, or have *no effect* on the acidity of the solution?

    (a) Addition of Li_3N to liquid NH_3

    (b) Addition of HgO to an aqueous KI solution

    (c) Addition of SiO_2 to molten $Fe + FeO$

    (d) Addition of $CuSO_4$ to aqueous $(NH_4)_2SO_4$

    (e) Addition of $Al(OH)_3$ to aqueous $NaOH$

    (f) Addition of $KHSO_4$ to H_2SO_4

    (g) Addition of CH_3CO_2K to liquid NH_3

8. Select the best response within each horizontal group and indicate the major factor governing your choice.

    Strongest protonic acid:

SnH_4	SbH_3	H_2Te
NH_3	PH_3	SbH_3
H_5IO_6	H_6TeO_6	HIO
$Fe(H_2O)_6^{3+}$	$Fe(H_2O)_6^{2+}$	H_2O
$Na(H_2O)_x^+$	$K(H_2O)_x^+$	

Strongest Lewis acid:

BF$_3$	BCl$_3$	BI$_3$
BeCl$_2$	BCl$_3$	
B(nBu)$_3$	B(tBu)$_3$	

Most basic toward protonic acids:

o-xylene	m-xylene	p-xylene	
NH$_3$	MeNH$_2$	Me$_2$NH	Me$_3$N
Be(OH)$_2$	Mg(OH)$_2$	Zn(OH)$_2$	

More basic toward BMe$_3$:

Me$_3$N	Et$_3$N		
2-MePy	4-MePy	Py	(Py = pyridine)
2-MeC$_6$H$_4$CN	C$_6$H$_5$CN		

9. Explain briefly the observation that *ortho*-alkyl groups increase the acidity of benzoic acids but decrease the acidity of phenylboric acids.

CHAPTER VII

The Halogens

General Trends

Some properties of the halogens are listed in Table 7.1.

TABLE 7.1
Fundamental Properties of the Halogens

	F	Cl	Br	I	At
Crystal Radius	1.36	1.81	1.95	2.16	
Covalent Radius (Å)	0.72	1.00	1.14	1.35	
Pauling Electro-negativity	4.0	3.0	2.8	2.5	2.2
1st Ionization Potential (eV)	17.418	13.01	11.84	10.454	9.5
Outer Electron Configuration	$2s^2 2p^5$	$3s^2 3p^5$	$3d^{10}4s^2 4p^5$	$4d^{10}5s^2 5p^5$	$4f^{14}5d^{10}6s^2 6p^5$
E^0 $X^- \longrightarrow \frac{1}{2}X_2 + e$ (V)	−2.87	−1.36	−1.07	−0.535	−0.3
E^0_B $X \longrightarrow XO^- + e$ (V)	–	−0.40	−0.45	−0.45	0.0
Dissociation Energy (kcal)	37.8	58.0	53.4	51.0	27.7
Electron Affinity (kcal)	79.52	83.33	77.56	70.64	68
Polarizability (cc/atom)	1.04×10^{-24}	3.66×10^{-24}	4.77×10^{-24}	7.10×10^{-24}	

It may be noted that the difference between fluorine and chlorine is generally greater than the differences between the succeeding heavier halogens. Chlorine and bromine are the most similar in chemical properties of the halogens. The crystal radius of the bromide ion is only slightly greater than that of the chloride ion. This may be attributed to the incomplete nuclear shielding that occurs as the $3d$ electrons are added. The small difference in electronegativity of bromine and chlorine indicates there should be little difference in the degree of covalency of the bonds formed by these halogens with any particular element. The large differences between the effect of fluorine and chlorine and the similarity between that of chlorine and bromine are illustrated in the pK_a values of HX (Table 6.2) and of XCH_2CO_2H (Table 6.4), oxidizing ability of X_2 (Table 7.1), the solubilities of the silver halides (Chapter IX, p. 312) and the alkali metal halides (Chapter IX, p. 302), oxidation states of known binary compounds (Chapter IX, p. 322), structures of compounds (Chapter III, p. 120), hydrogen bond strength of XHX^- (Table 5.3), etc.

The high oxidizing ability of fluorine together with its small size permits it to form many compounds in which the elements exhibit their highest oxidation state. Thus there are sixteen known binary hexafluorides (see Tables 7.5 and 9.14), but no known hexaiodides. On the other hand, the lack of low lying empty d orbitals prevents fluorine from forming more than one normal covalent bond. It forms no oxy acids or oxy anions as do the heavier halogens.

The crystal structures of the halides depend not only on the radius ratio of cation to anion, but also on the electronegativity difference of the metal and the halogen and on the polarizabilities of each. For compounds of the types MX, MX_2, or MX_3, the fluorides have structures anticipated from the radius ratio, since fluorine is sufficiently electronegative to form essentially ionic bonds with metals in low oxidation states and the fluoride ion is not very polarizable. The chlorides, bromides, and iodides of the compounds of the MX_2 and MX_3 types show the effect of lower electronegativities and greater polarizabilities by the formation of layer structures except with the largest metal ions, (see Chapter III, p. 120). Covalent bond formation or strong polarization of the halide ion is necessary to account for these layer structures since the environments of the halide ions have low local symmetry in the charge distribution.

The colors of many of the halides and halide complexes may also be related to the polarizability of the anions. Thus the colors of the $TiX_6{}^{2-}$ ions vary from colorless for the fluoro complex to yellow for the chloro complex, red for the bromo complex, and deep red for the iodo complex. These spectra are due to the excitation of an electron essentially in a halogen orbital to an orbital belonging to the metal. The energy of this transition is least for the iodo complex, which has the longest wavelength absorption band (see also Chapter II, p. 91).

Occurrence

The halogens occur in combined form in the earth's crust in the approximate amounts of F 0.08%, Cl 0.05%, Br 0.001%, and I 0.001%. Chlorides and bromides are concentrated in the oceans by the leaching processes of natural waters, (see Table 7.2). Large deposits of sodium chloride and, to a lesser extent, calcium, potassium, and magnesium chlorides are found in the dried up beds of landlocked lakes. Calcium and magnesium sulfates and mixed salts of potassium and magnesium bromide are also found in the lake beds. Due to differences in concentrations and temperature during deposition the different salts are often well separated. The fluoride content of sea water is limited by the large concentration of calcium ion present and the very low solubility of calcium fluoride. The low solubility of calcium fluoride compared to the other calcium halides is due to the high lattice energy of the fluoride, which in turn is due to the small radius of the fluoride ion. Natural deposits of calcium fluoride, called fluorspar or fluorite, serve as the primary source of fluorine. Cryolyte, Na_3AlF_6, is also a commercially important fluoride mineral, being used as the electrolyte in the production of aluminum.

TABLE 7.2

Abundances of the More Prevalent Elements in Sea Water^a (in moles/liter)

Cl	0.535	Si	0.0001
Na	0.457	Sr	0.00009
Mg	0.0555	F	0.00007
S	0.0276	N	0.00006
Ca	0.0100	Li	0.00003
K	0.00974	P	0.000002
C	0.00233	Rb	0.000001
Br	0.000815	I	0.0000005
B	0.00043	Ba	0.0000002

^{a} These and other abundances given by E. D. Goldberg, *Ann. Rev. Phys. Chem.,* **12**, 32 (1961); M. N. Hill, Ed., *The Sea,* Vol. II, "The Composition of Sea Water and a Comparative and Descriptive Oceanography" (London: Interscience Publishers, 1963); "Chemistry and the Oceans," *Chem. Eng. News,* June 1, 1A-48A (1964).

Although the concentration of iodine in the ocean is small, it is selectively absorbed by seaweed and may be obtained from this source. A more important source is sodium iodate and sodium periodate which occur in deposits in Chile. The natural occurrence of these oxy anions for iodine contrasts sharply with the lack of natural deposits of oxy salts of chlorine and bromine and illustrates the greater ease with which iodine attains the higher oxidation states compared to the lighter halogens.

Astatine occurs naturally in very small amounts as the beta decay product of ^{215}Po, ^{216}Po, and ^{218}Po. As polonium itself is rather rare, and α decay is the usual decay route, astatine has not been isolated from natural sources. It has been prepared by α bombardment of bismuth, $^{209}Bi(\alpha,2n)^{211}At$. Astatine itself is radioactive, its longest lived isotope having a half-life of 8.3 hr.

Preparation of the Elements

Since fluorine, chlorine, and bromine are found in nature as halides, the preparation of the elements involves suitable oxidation reactions. Electrolytic oxidation of fused KF–HF adducts (Chapter V, p. 176) is used to produce fluorine. HF is removed from the F_2 by reaction with NaF. The cells are constructed of copper, monel, or steel with amorphous carbon anodes. Graphite electrodes cannot be used due to the formation of graphite compounds. Chlorine is produced by electrolysis of either fused sodium chloride or by the electrolysis of concentrated aqueous solutions of sodium chloride. The latter is the more commonly used method.

$$Na^+ + Cl^- + H_2O \xrightarrow[\text{elect.}]{} Na^+ + OH^- + \frac{1}{2}Cl_2 + \frac{1}{2}H_2$$

In the laboratory Cl_2 may be made by the action of oxidizing agents such as MnO_2 on HCl, (see Chapter IV, p. 149).

Bromine is produced commercially from bromides in sea water by the oxidizing action of chlorine. The pH of the sea water is adjusted to a value between 1 and 4 with sulfuric acid and then treated with chlorine. The liberated bromine is blown out by an air stream and the bromine concentrated by a sequence of reactions, such as absorption in a carbonate solution and subsequent acidification.

$$Cl_2 + 2Br^- \longrightarrow Br_2 + 2Cl^-$$
$$3Br_2 + 3CO_3{}^{2-} \longrightarrow 5Br^- + BrO_3{}^- + 3CO_2$$
$$5Br^- + BrO_3{}^- + 6H^+ \longrightarrow 3Br_2 + 3H_2O$$

Chlorine is removed from the bromine produced by reaction with a bromide such as iron(III) bromide.

Iodine is produced by the sulfite reduction of iodates. The iodine is purified by sublimation.

$$2NaIO_3 + 5NaHSO_3 \xrightarrow{\text{aq. soln.}} 3NaHSO_4 + 2Na_2SO_4 + H_2O + I_2$$

Some physical properties of the halogens are listed in Table 7.3.

TABLE 7.3
Properties of the Halogens

	Fluorine	Chlorine	Bromine	Iodine
Isotopes	19	35,37	79,81	127
Melting Point (°C)	−223	−102.4	− 7.3	+113.7
Boiling Point (°C)	−187.9	− 34.0	+58.8	+184.5
Density g/cc	1.108^a	1.57^a	3.14	4.94
Color of Gas	light yellow	greenish yellow	reddish brown	violet

^{a} For the liquid at the boiling point.

The Hydrogen Halides

The hydrogen halides may be prepared by the action of a nonvolatile, nonoxidizing acid on a halide salt. Sulfuric acid serves well for the preparation of hydrogen fluoride and hydrogen chloride, but is too strong an oxidizing agent to be used with bromides and iodides.

$$CaF_2 + H_2SO_4 \longrightarrow CaSO_4 + 2HF$$
$$NaCl + H_2SO_4 \longrightarrow NaHSO_4 + HCl$$

Phosphoric acid serves for the similar preparation of hydrogen bromide and hydrogen iodide. Commercially much hydrogen chloride is prepared from the direct reaction of chlorine with hydrogen. With water vapor present the reaction between chlorine and hydrogen is violent. Although all of the hydrogen halides may be obtained commercially, these usually contain appreciable amounts of impurities. Hydrogen fluoride, hydrogen chloride, and hydrogen bromide usually have hydrogen present from reaction with the metal cylinder. Hydrogen iodide usually contains I_2 in addition to H_2

from thermal decomposition. For laboratory use the best source of hydrogen fluoride is the thermal decomposition of dry KHF_2. Hydrogen iodide is usually prepared by dropping the aqueous solution on phosphorus pentoxide.

Some of the properties of the hydrogen halides and their aqueous solutions are given in Table 7.4.

TABLE 7.4
Properties of the Hydrogen Halides

	HF	HCl	HBr	HI
Melting point (°C)	−83.07	−114.19	−86.86	−50.79
Boiling point (°C)	19.9	−85.03	−66.72	−35.35
Density at b.p. (g/cc)	0.991	1.187	2.160	2.799
Dielectric constant of liquid	66	9	6	3
Per cent dissociation at 1000°C	–	3×10^{-7}	0.003	19
Composition of azeotrope with water at 1 atm (wt-%)	35.37	20.24	47	57.0

The following topics relating to the hydrogen halides have already been discussed: the effect of hydrogen bonding on the boiling point of hydrogen fluoride (Chapter V, p. 163), the ability to form hydrogen bonds with halide ions (Chapter V, p. 175), the acid strength of the hydrohalic acids (Chapter VI, p. 188), and liquid hydrogen chloride as a solvent system (Chapter VI, p. 209). Further specific discussion will be limited to hydrogen fluoride as a solvent system.

Hydrogen fluoride is highly toxic and should be handled only in a good fume hood. Due to its reaction with glass, it is handled in metal systems, especially copper and monel. It is characterized by its dehydrating ability and its strong acidity. Due to its high dielectric constant and low viscosity, most of its solutions show a high conductivity although the pure liquid itself has a conductivity comparable to distilled water. Many of the reaction products formed on dissolving substances in HF have been inferred from conductivities. The following are some typical reactions.

$$HNO_3 + HF \rightleftharpoons H_2NO_3^+ + F^-$$
$$H_2SO_4 + HF \rightarrow HSO_3F + H_3O^+ + F^-$$
$$NaCl + HF \rightarrow NaF + HCl$$
$$ZnO + HF \rightarrow ZnF_2 + H_3O^+ + F^-$$

Anhydrous HF has a Hammett H_0 value of −10.2 and is thus comparable in strength to anhydrous H_2SO_4, which has an H_0 value of −11.0.[*] The only known acids in anhydrous HF are fluoride acceptors such as NbF_5, SbF_5, AsF_5, and BF_3. The strongest of these acids is SbF_5; a $3M$ solution of SbF_5 in HF has an H_0 estimated to be −15.2.[†]

$$2HF + SbF_5 \rightleftharpoons H_2F^+ + SbF_6^-$$

[*] Hyman, H. H., M. Kilpatrick, and J. J. Katz, *J. Am. Chem. Soc.*, **79**, 3668 (1957).
[†] Hyman, H. H., et al., *J. Am. Chem. Soc.*, **65**, 123 (1961).

Addition of metal fluorides to such solutions would precipitate the metal hexafluoro-antimonate(v).

Reactions of the Halogens

The reactions of the halogens with other elements often give products dependent on the temperature and pressure at which the reaction is carried out. The effect of these variables may be grasped most readily by means of idealized phase diagrams.

Generalized pressure–composition isotherms expected for a halogen–metal system are shown in Figure 7.1. In this system the MX_y compounds are assumed to be non-volatile and no solid solutions are formed.

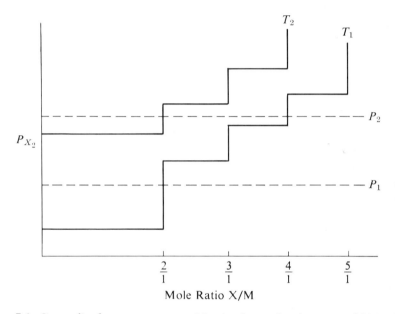

FIGURE 7.1. *Generalized pressure–composition isotherms for the system* $M(s) - X_2(g)$.

The vertical sections of the isotherms indicate the existence of a single solid compound (with the stoichiometry indicated on the abscissa) in equilibrium with gaseous X_2. The horizontal sections or plateaus indicate the coexistence of two solid phases in equilibrium with gaseous X_2. As the pressure of X_2 is increased, for a given equilibrium temperature, a higher halide will be produced. As the equilibrium temperature is increased, for a given pressure of X_2, a lower halide will be produced. From the phase diagram in Figure 7.1, heating X_2 and M together at a pressure of P_2 produces MX_2 at the higher temperature T_2 and MX_4 at the lower temperature T_1. MX_2 may also be formed at the lower temperature T_1 by reducing the pressure of X_2 to P_1. The metal can coexist in equilibrium with only the lowest halide. Accordingly, heating the metal with an excess of a particular metal halide with no additional halogen will produce some of the next lower halides at equilibrium. If equilibrium is rapidly obtained, it may be necessary to quench the products to keep other phases from forming on cooling.

The temperature range within which the various platinum chlorides may exist at 1 atmosphere pressure of chlorine is as follows: $PtCl_4$, below 370°; $PtCl_3$, 370–435°; $PtCl_2$, 435–481°; $PtCl$, 481–482°; Pt, above 482°.*

Although the discussion here has used the systems $M–X_2$ as an example, similar considerations apply to other gas–solid systems in which the products are nonvolatile, $O_2(g)–M(s)$, $NH_3(g)–MX_y(s)$, $H_2O(g)–MO_y(s)$, etc. When manganese oxides are ignited in a Bunsen flame in air, Mn_3O_4 is produced. If the partial pressure of oxygen is increased from 0.2 to 1 atm by using pure oxygen, Mn_2O_3 is formed, and, at still higher pressures, MnO_2 is formed.†

Less is known about the equilibria in $M(s)–X_2(g)$ systems where one of the products itself is volatile. It is known that in the reactions of fluorine with many metals, higher temperatures are necessary to achieve higher fluorides! The explanation appears to lie in the volatility of the fluorides of the metals in their highest oxidation states. The factors involved may be illustrated in the following somewhat speculative discussion of the mechanism of production of uranium hexafluoride.‡

Uranium hexafluoride is the most volatile compound of uranium known, subliming at 56.54°C and melting under pressure at 64°C. The existence of a single naturally occurring isotope of fluorine makes uranium hexafluoride a choice compound for the separation of uranium-235 from uranium ores. Although fluorine reacts directly with UO_3, U_3O_8, or UO_2 to produce uranium hexafluoride and oxygen, the preferred route is to use hydrogen fluoride, as a less expensive source of fluorine, to produce uranium tetrafluoride and to use elementary fluorine to bring about the oxidation to uranium hexafluoride.

$$UO_2(s) + 4HF(g) \xrightarrow[400°C]{} UF_4(s) + 2H_2O(g)$$

$$UF_4(s) + F_2(g) \longrightarrow UF_6(g)$$

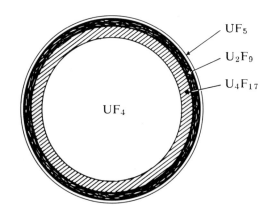

FIGURE 7.2. *Idealized* UF_4 *pellet undergoing fluorination.*

* Wöhler, L., and S. Streicher, *Ber.*, **46**, 1591 (1913).

† Ephraim, F., *Inorganic Chemistry*, 6th English edition by P. C. L. Thorne and E. R. Roberts (New York: Interscience Publishers Inc., 1954) p. 468.

‡ This discussion is based on a free interpretation of a paper by V. Y. Labaton and K. D. B. Johnson, *J. Inorg. Nucl. Chem.*, **10**, 74 (1959).

In the fluorination process no reaction is observed at 220°C, but reaction does take place above 230°. The uranium tetrafluoride pellets develop a fluoride-rich coating from which uranium hexafluoride evolves as the pellets shrink. These pellets may be visualized as in Figure 7.2. The layers from the center out correspond to known fluorides of uranium. The fluorine activity decreases from the surface inward in accord with the stepwise pressure–composition isotherm. Additionally, a pressure–composition isotherm may be drawn for the volatile uranium hexafluoride and the nonvolatile

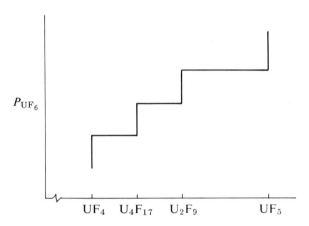

FIGURE 7.3. *Pressure–composition isotherm for $UF_6(g)$–$UF_x(s)$ (speculative).*

solids, as shown in Figure 7.3. The plateaus in Figure 7.3 correspond to the decomposition pressures of UF_6 in the disproportionation reactions

$$3UF_5(s) \rightleftharpoons U_2F_9(s) + UF_6(g)$$
$$7U_2F_9(s) \rightleftharpoons 3U_4F_{17}(s) + 2UF_6(g)$$
$$2U_4F_{17}(s) \rightleftharpoons 7UF_4(s) + UF_6(g)$$

These reactions will occur if the external partial pressure of UF_6 is less than the decomposition pressure of the uranium fluoride on the surface film. An increase in reaction temperature serves to increase the decomposition pressure of UF_6, as well as to increase the rate of the disproportionation reactions. These reactions apparently have an activation energy of about 19 kcal. It may be noted from Figure 7.3 the UF_6 itself should be capable of fluorinating uranium and the lower fluorides. This is, in fact, observed.

The volatile fluoride produced in the disproportionation reactions may have too high a fluorine decomposition pressure to exist for an appreciable time at the reaction temperature. In such cases, as with NpF_6, PuF_6, RhF_6, and PtF_6, the hexafluorides must be collected by trapping on a cold surface.*

When the reaction is homogeneous, as for gas phase reactions, the situation is more complex and a number of species may coexist under a given set of conditions. A description of the species might then be made in terms of field distribution diagrams

---

* See J. J. Katz and I. Sheft under general references.

similar to those used in describing complexation phenomena (see Chapter VI, p. 199). A high activity of halogen should favor the formation of a high halide.

Some predictions as to whether a compound might be stable with respect to disproportionation may be made from known and/or estimated (as in Chapter III, p. 119) heats of formation of the halides.*

The heat of the reaction

$$2MX \longrightarrow M + MX_2$$

may be found from

$$\Delta H = \Delta H_f MX_2 - 2\Delta H_f MX$$

If ΔH is negative, then ΔF will probably also be negative and MX will be unstable with respect to disproportionation. More generally, if a plot of ΔH_f is made against the number of halogen atoms in MX_y as in Figure 7.4, only the highest halide is stable if the curve has an increasing rate of ascent (A), all halides are stable if the curve has a decreasing rate of ascent but no maximum (B), and if a maximum does occur only those halides at and preceding the maximum are stable (C). These situations are often approximated by the transition metal fluorides (A), the chlorides (B), and the bromides and iodides (C) (see Table 9.14, Chapter IX, p. 322).

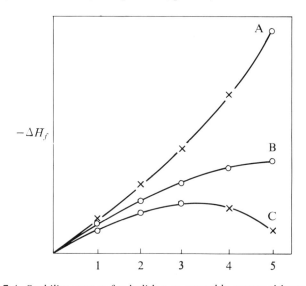

FIGURE 7.4. *Stability curves for halides, x, unstable compositions; °, stable compositions* [*L. H. Long,* Quart. Rev., *7, 134–174 (1953)*].

Preparation of the Binary Metal Halides

The binary metal halides of the transition elements are listed in Table 9.14. The metal halides formed in the solid state for the Group IA, IIA, and IIIA elements are those expected, i.e., MX, MX_2, and MX_3, respectively.

* L. H. Long, *Quart. Rev.*, 7, 134 (1953).

The preparation of MX or MX_2 may usually be carried out by treating an oxide or carbonate of M with aqueous HX, evaporating the solution to obtain the metal halide hydrate and then removing the water by means of a suitable desiccant, or if necessary to prevent hydrolysis, in a stream of HX. The dehydration step is often troublesome and many specific procedures for individual preparations have been developed which do not involve aqueous solutions. Several preparations use the metal hydride as starting material.*

$$2LiH(xs.) + I_2 \xrightarrow[\text{Ether}]{} 2LiI + H_2$$

$$BaH_2(xs.) + 2NH_4I \xrightarrow[\text{Pyridine}]{} BaI_2 + 2NH_3 + H_2$$

The excess hydride is insoluble in the solvent and may be removed by filtering.

The uranium(III) halides are conveniently made through the reaction of the hydrogen halide with uranium hydride.

$$2U + 3H_2 \xrightarrow[250°]{} 2UH_3$$

$$UH_3 + 3HX \xrightarrow[250-300°]{} UX_3 + 3H_2 \quad X = F, Cl$$

Anhydrous $FeCl_2$ has been obtained by the reaction

$$C_6H_5Cl + FeCl_3 \longrightarrow C_6H_4Cl_2 + FeCl_2 + HCl$$

Compounds of the type MX_3, MX_4, and MX_5 are usually obtained by one of the following reactions

$$M + X_2 \longrightarrow MX_n$$
$$M + HX \longrightarrow MX_n + H_2$$
$$MO + C + X_2 \longrightarrow MX_n + CO$$
$$MO + CCl_4 \longrightarrow MX_n + CO + COCl_2$$
$$MO + S_2Cl_2 \longrightarrow MX_n + SO_2$$

Since the direct reaction of the metal with the halogen is usually vigorous, an inert solvent medium is often used with Br_2 or I_2, the solvent serving as a diluent. The vapor of the halogen is often used, and for further safety an inert gas is sometimes used as a diluent. In the van Arkel process for purifying metals (Ti, Hf, Zr, V, W, etc.) advantage is taken of (*1*) the formation of a volatile halide by direct reaction of the halogen with the metal; (*2*) the decomposition of the metal halide to the metal and halogen at a higher temperature.

The reaction of the metal directly with anhydrous HX is useful for metals above hydrogen in the activity series. $AlCl_3$ and $CrCl_2$ may be made in this way. In the reactions involving C, S_2Cl_2, or CCl_4 it may be presumed that reduction to metal occurs followed by halogenation.

Where a series of halides exists with the metal in different oxidation states, a lower halide may be produced by hydrogen reduction of the higher halide.

Direct reaction of the elements with fluorine is generally used to prepare metal fluorides only when other methods cannot be used successfully. Thus reaction with

* Taylor, M. D., and L. R. Grant, *J. Am. Chem. Soc.*, **77**, 1507 (1955).

elemental fluorine is the preferred, and frequently the only, method of producing the metal fluorides listed in Table 7.5. All of these compounds are themselves strong oxidizing and fluorinating agents.

TABLE 7.5
Metal Fluorides Made Using Fluorine[a]

CrF_4							
CrF_5	MnF_3		CoF_3				
		RuF_5					
	TcF_6	RuF_6		PdF_3	AgF_2		
		OsF_4	IrF_4	PtF_4		PbF_4	BiF_5
	ReF_6	OsF_6	IrF_6	PtF_6			
UF_6	NpF_6	PuF_6					

[a] Data taken in part from H. J. Emeleus, in *Fluorine Chemistry*, Vol. I, edited by J. H. Simons (New York: Academic Press Inc., 1950) Chapter I.

PROPERTIES OF THE METAL HEXAFLUORIDES*

The transition metal hexafluorides display a pronounced effect of d orbital occupancy on volatility and reactivity. The hexafluorides formed by W, Re, Os, Ir, and Pt have, respectively, $5d^0$, $5d^1$, $5d^2$, $5d^3$, and $5d^4$ electronic configurations. In this series the boiling point increases regularly from 17.1°C for WF_6 to 69.1°C for PtF_6. This is understandable in terms of the increase in polarizability with increasing d orbital occupancy. An increase in polarizability would result in an increase in the van der Waals attraction. Contrary to expectations based on simple crystal field theory (Chapter X) the stability of the hexafluorides decreases with increasing d orbital occupancy. The d^4PtF_6 is the least stable, the $d^0 WF_6$ is the most stable. The stability of the metal hexafluorides of a given d orbital configuration increases as the principal quantum number of the d orbital increases. Thus CrF_6 is very unstable while WF_6 is stable. The other hexafluorides of the first transition series are unknown and unexpected. The actinide hexafluorides (U, Np, Pu) show a decrease in stability with increasing f orbital occupancy, however, their volatilities are all about the same.

Binary Compounds of the Halogens and the Nonmetals

The known binary compounds formed by the halogens and the nonmetals of Groups V, VI, VII, and VIII are listed in Tables 7.6 and 7.7. (The compounds with the metals Sb, Bi, and Po are also included in these tables.) In Groups V, VI, and VII, binary compounds are lacking only for iodine with sulfur. In Group VIII only some of the fluorides are known.

* Weinstock, B., *Chem. and Eng. News*, **Sept. 21**, 86 (1964).

TABLE 7.6
Regular Halides of the Nonmetals

	F	Cl	Br	I
N	NF_3	NCl_3	NBr_3[a]	NI_3
P	PF_3, PF_5	PCl_3, PCl_5	PBr_3, PBr_5	PI_3
As	AsF_3, AsF_5	$AsCl_3$	$AsBr_3$	AsI_3
Sb	SbF_3, SbF_5	$SbCl_3$, $SbCl_5$	$SbBr_3$	SbI_3
Bi	BiF_3, BiF_5	$BiCl_3$	$BiBr_3$	BiI_3
O	OF_2	OCl_2	OBr_2	—
S	SF_2, SF_4, SF_6	SCl_2, SCl_4	—	—
Se	— SeF_4, SeF_6	$(SeCl_2)$ $SeCl_4$	— $SeBr_4$	SeI_2
Te	— TeF_4, TeF_6	$TeCl_2$, $TeCl_4$	$TeBr_2$, $TeBr_4$	TeI_4
Po	(PoF_2) (PoF_4) PoF_6	$PoCl_2$, $PoCl_4$	$PoBr_2$, $PoBr_4$	PoI_4
Cl	ClF, ClF_3			
Br	BrF, BrF_3, BrF_5	$BrCl$		
I	$(IF)IF_3$, IF_5, IF_7	ICl, ICl_3	IBr	
At			$AtBr$	AtI
Kr	KrF_2, KrF_4			
Xe	XeF_2, XeF_4, $XeF_6(XeF_8)$			

[a] Known only as an amminate.

COVALENT STATES OF THE HALIDES OF THE NONMETALS

As Table 7.6 indicates, the covalent states that are found are mainly those expected on the basis of available unpaired electrons including states involving promotion of electrons to low lying empty d orbitals. The heavier halogens are unable to bring out the highest possible covalent state except for PCl_5, $SbCl_5$, and PBr_5. The geometries for the covalent compounds are generally those expected on the basis of including lone pairs in the σ bond hybridization (Chapter II, p. 60). Exceptions occur due to polymerization $(ICl_3)_2$ or the formation of ionic solids, $PCl_4^+PCl_6^-$ and $PBr_4^+Br^-$, BiF_5.

The similarities in the Raman spectra of $TeCl_4$ and $SbCl_3$ and between $SeCl_4$ and $AsCl_3$ have led to the conclusion that $TeCl_3^+$ and $SeCl_3^+$ ions may exist in the tetra-halides.*

The "irregular" binary halogen compounds shown in Table 7.7 fall into two categories. The oxides of Cl, Br, and I are "irregular" due to the positive oxidation states brought out by oxygen. The remaining "irregular" compounds contain catenated

* Gerding, H., *Rec. Trav. Chim.*, **75**, 589 (1956).

TABLE 7.7
"Irregular" Binary Halogen Compounds of the Nonmetals

	O_nF_2	$n = 2, 3, 4$
N_2F_2 *cis* and *trans*		
N_2F_4		
FN_3	ClO_2	
BrN_3	Cl_2O_6	
	Cl_2O_7	
	Br_3O_8	
	BrO_2	
	BrO_3	
	I_2O_5	
	I_4O_9	
	I_2O_4	
	S_2F_2	
	S_2F_{10}	
P_2Cl_4	S_nCl_2	$n = 2 \ldots 8$
P_2I_4	S_nBr_2	
	Te_2F_{10}	

nonmetal atoms, i.e., similar atoms linked together. The chlorosulfanes have terminal chlorine atoms on a sulfur chain.

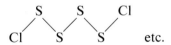

S_2F_2, on the other hand, has a pyramidal structure with both fluorine atoms on the same sulfur atom.*

At low temperatures Raman spectra indicate a similar form of S_2Cl_2 may exist. The O_nF_2 structures presumably resemble the chlorosulfanes. The irregular nitrogen halides not only contain N—N single bonds, but may contain NN multiple bonds as in

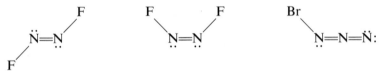

* Kuczkowski, R. L., and E. Bright Wilson, *J. Am. Chem. Soc.*, **85**, 2028 (1963).

PREPARATION OF THE HALIDES OF THE NONMETALS

Most of the "regular" halides shown in Table 7.6 may be prepared by the combination of the elements—the particular stoichiometry of the product is determined by the relative amounts of the reactants and by the reaction conditions employed. The halides of C, N, and O generally require specific reactions.

Carbon tetrachloride cannot be prepared by the direct chlorination of carbon. It is prepared commercially by the chlorination of carbon disulfide, which may be made directly from carbon and sulfur,

$$C + 2S \longrightarrow CS_2$$
$$CS_2 + 3Cl_2 \longrightarrow CCl_4 + S_2Cl_2$$

The S_2Cl_2 produced in this reaction is used in the vulcanization of rubber.

The nitrogen trihalides cannot be directly prepared from nitrogen, but may be made by the action of the halogen on ammonia. $NBr_3 \cdot 6NH_3$ results from the reaction of Br_2 with NH_3 in a glow discharge. With the exception of NF_3 all of the nitrogen halides are explosive compounds.

Oxygen difluoride is produced by the action of F_2 on NaOH.

$$2F_2 + 2NaOH \longrightarrow OF_2 + 2NaF + H_2O$$

Most of the "irregular" halides shown in Table 7.7 require special methods of preparation. The azides of iodine or bromine may be made from AgN_3 and the halogen in ether. The O_nF_2 compounds are prepared by direct reaction of the elements at low temperature and with an electric discharge. The S_nCl_2 compounds are prepared from S_2Cl_2 and H_2S_x or from S_2Cl_2 and H_2 on chilling the hot vapor.

An extensive chemistry of fluorocarbons* now exists as a result of research initiated during World War II to develop materials that could withstand contact with uranium hexafluoride. The direct reaction of fluorine with hydrocarbons is highly exothermic and leads to extensive fragmentation in the resulting fluorocarbon. The reaction of cobalt(III) fluoride with hydrocarbons is much less exothermic and gives high yields of fluorocarbons with little fragmentation.

$$-CH_2- + CoF_3 \xrightarrow[150-400°]{} -CF_2- + 2HF + 4CoF_2$$

The cobalt(III) fluoride may be regenerated using elemental fluorine.

$$2CoF_2 + F_2 \xrightarrow[250°]{} 2CoF_3$$

Some other reactions involving halogen compounds as halogenating agents are discussed on pages 241–242.

VOLATILITY AND PHYSICAL STATE

There is a fairly sharp break in the volatility and usual physical state of the fluorides on crossing a given period of the periodic table. This break occurs approximately in the region separating the metals from the nonmetals.

* See Chapter II, p. 92 concerning the boiling points of these compounds.

BeF$_2$(s)	BF$_3$(g)			
	−99			
	AlF$_3$(s)	SiF$_4$(g)		
	1257(s)	−95.5(s)		
	GaF$_3$(s)	GeF$_4$(g)		
	950	−36.8		
		SnF$_4$(s)	SbF$_5$(1)	TeF$_6$(g)
		705(s)	149	−38.6

Although data such as these were at one time interpreted as being due to a sharp change from ionic compounds to covalent compounds, this explanation is no longer accepted. The slight difference in electronegativity of neighboring elements indicates that there should be little change in the ionic character of the bonds in the examples given. The explanation appears rather to be in the coordination number of the central atom, which is, in turn, determined by the cation to anion radius ratio. If this coordination number may be satisfied without the sharing of one or more halides, then the halide is fairly volatile. The coordination numbers in the fluorides of the previous examples are

Be	4	B	3				
		Al	6	Si	4		
		Ga	6	Ge	4		
				Sn	6	Sb	6	Te	6

The sharp decrease in volatility occurs where the coordination number exceeds the fluoride stoichiometry. The heat of vaporization must include the energy necessary to break these excess bonds—although in some cases not all excess bonds are broken and the vapor contains polymeric units (the average molecular weight of SbF$_5$ in the vapor at its boiling point corresponds approximately to a pentamer).

It may be noted that an unshared electron pair may effectively occupy a coordination position. Thus, OF$_2$ with two unshared pairs of electrons on O is a gas at room temperature and BeF$_2$ with no unshared pairs on Be is a solid.

The generalization has been made that the volatility of metal halides increases on going from F to I, but the volatility of nonmetal halides shows the reverse trend. This may be explained as due to the decreased coordination number expected for the heavier halides of the same metal, and exceptions to the generalization occur in cases where the coordination number of the metal is satisfied without sharing fluorides. The decrease in volatility of the nonmetal halides on going from F to I is accounted for by the usual increase in van der Waals forces with increasing molecular weight.

It has been pointed out by Peacock* that transition metal oxyfluorides have physical properties similar to the binary fluorides of similar empirical formulas. Thus, the volatile MoOF$_4$ and MoF$_5$ have similar melting and boiling points. TiOF$_2$ and TiF$_3$ are both high melting solids.

It is interesting to note that the fluoride of an element in its highest valence state is more volatile than the next lower fluoride. (See Table 7.8.) It is tempting to attribute this to the fact that the fluoride of the highest valence state should be a symmetrical

---

* Peacock, R. D., "Fluorine Compounds of the Transition Metals," in *Progress in Inorganic Chemistry*, F. A. Cotton, ed. (New York: Interscience, 1960) Vol. 2.

TABLE 7.8
*Comparison of Boiling Points of Some Mononuclear
Fluorides Involving Several Valence States*

PF_3	-75	SF_4	-40	ClF	-101	
PF_5	-101.15	SF_6 subl	-65	ClF_3	11.8	
AsF_3	63	SeF_4	106	BrF	20	
AsF_5	-53	SeF_6	-47	BrF_3	125.8	
				BrF_5	40.9	
SbF_3	319	TeF_4 melts	130			
SbF_5	150	TeF_6 subl	-39	IF	$-$	XeF_2
				IF_3	$-$	XeF_4 Increasing
BiF_3	$-$			IF_5	100.6	XeF_6 volatility
BiF_5	230			IF_7 subl	40	

molecule with no dipole moment, although the next lower fluoride is generally unsymmetrical with a consequent *nonzero* dipole moment.

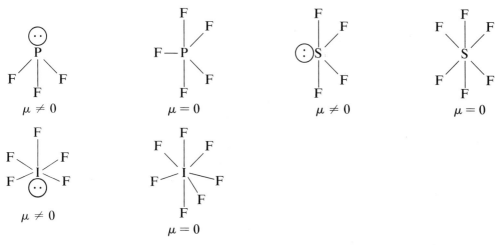

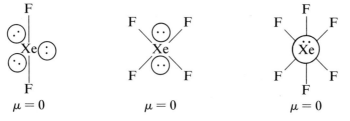

Although numerical data are not currently available for comparison the volatilities of the recently prepared xenon fluorides increase with increasing fluoride content. In this case all of the molecules should have a zero dipole moment.

However, the polarizability of XeF_2 and XeF_4 should be much higher than that of XeF_6 since the polarizability should decrease with increasing oxidation number. Xenon hexafluoride has a vapor pressure of $\sim$ 7mm at 0°C and $\sim$ 30mm at 25°C, and is thus the least volatile of the known hexafluorides. (UF_6 has a vapor pressure of $\sim$ 120mm at 25°C.) Solid XeF_6 is yellow above 42°C and the vapor is a pale yellow. The high symmetry of the hexafluorides must also be a factor in their volatility since ReF_7 is less volatile than ReF_6.

Although fluorides of the nonmetals exist largely as gases, the chlorides and bromides exist largely as liquids and the iodides as solids under standard conditions. The relative volatility of the higher halides depends on whether the compound is molecular or ionic. Thus $SbCl_5$ (b.p. 150°C) is molecular and is more volatile than the trichloride (b.p. 223°C). On the other hand, PCl_5 forms a solid containing PCl_4^+ and PCl_6^- ions. It melts at 148°C as compared with a boiling point of PCl_3 of 76°C. Solid PBr_5 contains PBr_4^+ and Br^- ions. It decomposes before reaching its boiling point.

MIXED HALIDES OF THE NONMETALS

An interesting series of mixed pentahalides of phosphorus have been prepared in the covalent and ionic forms.* The melting and boiling points of these different modifications are compared in Table 7.9. The molecular forms are converted to the ionic forms on standing for several days.

TABLE 7.9
*Mixed Halides of Group V Elements Having Covalent
and Ionic Isomers (from Holmes)*

Molecular	m.p.	b.p.	Ionic	m.p.
$PFCl_4$	-63	67	$PCl_4^+PCl_4F_2^-$	177
PF_2Cl_3	-63			
PF_3Cl_2	-124	8	$PCl_4^+PF_6^-$	subl., 135 (dec.)
PBr_4F			$PBr_4^+PBr_4F_2^-$	87
PBr_2F_3	-20		$PBr_4^+PF_6^-$	subl., 135
			$AsCl_4^+AsF_6^-$	160
			$SbCl_4^+SbCl_4F_2^-$	
SbF_3Cl_2			$SbCl_4^+SbF_6^-$	68

Mixed fluorochlorides of antimony and of arsenic are known and are assumed to have the ionic structures $AsCl_4^+AsF_6^-$ (m.p. 160) and $SbCl_4^+SbF_6^-$ (m.p. 68). Group V compounds such as PBr_7, PCl_3Br_8, and $ISbF_{10}$ in which the halogen content exceeds the stoichiometry of the pentahalides may be assumed to be ionic with a complex halogen ion, i.e., $PBr_4^+Br_3^-$, $PBrCl_3^+Br_7^-$, $IF_4^+SbF_6^-$.

REACTIONS OF THE HALIDES OF THE NONMETALS

The halides of the nonmetals undergo a variety of reactions, which may be roughly categorized into three types: solvolysis reactions, halogenation reactions, and acid–base reactions. These reaction types are not all inclusive, nor are they always mutually exclusive. Thus complexation may be a necessary prelude to solvolysis, or may pro-

* Holmes, R., *J. Chem. Educ.*, **40**, 125 (1963).

vide the driving force for a halogenation reaction. Solvolysis reactions are discussed in a general fashion in Chapter VI, pp. 214–221.

Halogenating Agents. A halogenating agent may operate in one of several different ways. An oxidation reaction may occur—as in the reaction of IF_5 with S.*

$$IF_5 + S \xrightarrow[100-300°]{12 \text{ hr.}} SF_4 + I_2$$

or of ICl with benzene†

$$ICl + C_6H_6 \longrightarrow C_6H_5I + HCl$$

When an interhalogen compound is used as the source of the halogen, the oxidizing ability will be (thermodynamically) less than that of the more electronegative halogen and greater than that of the more electropositive halogen. (Thus F_2 reacts with S to give predominately SF_6.)

The oxidizing power increases with oxidation number in a series such as $BrF < BrF_3 < BrF_5$. Among the commercially available fluorinating agents the oxidizing power may be rated roughly as

$$F_2 > ClF_3 > BrF_3 > IF_5 > SF_4 > AsF_5 > SbF_5 > AsF_3 > SbF_3$$

The above order is the thermodynamic order of oxidizing power, not the order of the rate of reaction. Thus SF_6 would probably be better as an oxidizing agent than IF_5 based on thermodynamic considerations, but SF_6 is inert due to the lack of a low energy path for reaction to take place. In similar fashion ClF_3 is more reactive (greater *rate* of reaction) than F_2 with most substances despite its lower oxidizing power. This may be attributed to the lower energy needed to break the F_2Cl---F bond compared to the F----F bond. ClF_3 reacts explosively with substances such as cotton, paper, picien wax, and stopcock grease! ClF_3 is currently being produced for use as a fuel for short range rockets. Used with hydrazine, N_2H_4, the fuels may be stored without refrigeration. This mixture is a hypergolic fuel, that is, it ignites spontaneously on being mixed.

Exchange Reactions. Halogenating agents may operate by exchange of atoms without change in oxidation number of the atoms in the reactants and products. The driving force for exchange may be the production of a very volatile product (which is distilled out of the reaction mixture), the stability of the lattice of an ionic product, the greater stability of the covalent bonds in the products, or a combination of these. Some examples of halogenation by exchange reactions are

$$3SOCl_2 + 2AsF_3 \xrightarrow[\text{Reflux}]{} 3SOF_2(g) \uparrow + 2AsCl_3$$
$$BF_3 + AlCl_3 \longrightarrow BCl_3 + AlF_3(s) \downarrow$$
$$I_2O_5 + 5SF_4 \xrightarrow[250-300°]{\text{Autoclave}} 2IF_5 + 5SOF_2$$

In the second reaction methylborate, $B(OCH_3)_3$, may be used instead of boron trifluoride; aluminum bromide or aluminum iodide may be used to prepare the corresponding boron halides. The third reaction above illustrates the difference between oxidative halogenation and exchange halogenation. IF_5 *oxidizes* S to SF_4; SF_4 ex-

---

* Tullock, C. W., F. S. Fawcett, W. C. Smith, and D. D. Coffman, *J. Am. Chem. Soc.*, **82**, 539 (1960).
† Andrews, L. J., and R. M. Keefer, *J. Am. Chem. Soc.*, **79**, 1412 (1957).

changes with I_2O_5 to produce IF_5. SF_4 is particularly promising both as an exchange halogenator with oxides or sulfides and as a mild oxidizing agent. Exchange with sulfides is complete, whereas exchange with oxides may be only partial.* Some typical reactions are

$$P_4O_{10} + 6SF_4 \longrightarrow 4POF_3 + 6SOF_2$$
$$P_4S_{10} + 5SF_4 \longrightarrow 4PF_5 + 15S$$
$$SeO_2 + SF_4 \longrightarrow SeF_4 + SOF_2$$
$$UO_3 + 3SF_4 \longrightarrow UF_6 + 3SOF_2$$
$$4FeS_2 + 3SF_4 \longrightarrow 4FeF_3 + 11S$$

The last reaction involves both exchange and oxidation. SF_4 undergoes exchange with the oxygen of carbonyl groups and hydroxyl groups and thus provides a selective fluorinating agent for organic reactions.†

$$\begin{array}{c}\diagdown \\ \diagup\end{array}C{=}O + SF_4 \longrightarrow \begin{array}{c}\diagdown \\ \diagup\end{array}CF_2 + SOF_2$$

$$-CO_2H \xrightarrow{\ SF_4\ } -CF_3$$

Sulfur tetrafluoride itself is most conveniently prepared by the reaction of SCl_2 with NaF suspended in acetonitrile.‡

$$3SCl_2 + 4NaF \xrightarrow[70-80°]{CH_3CN} SF_4 + S_2Cl_2 + 4NaCl$$

This reaction involves both exchange and auto-oxidation–reduction. PCl_5, PCl_3, and PBr_3 are widely used in organic chemistry as halogenating agents. These reactions occur mainly by exchange.

$$ROH + PCl_5 \longrightarrow RCl + POCl_3 + HCl$$

$$\begin{array}{c}\diagdown \\ \diagup\end{array}C{=}O + PCl_5 \longrightarrow \begin{array}{c}\diagdown \\ \diagup\end{array}CCl_2 + POCl_3$$

Generalized Acid–Base Reactions of the Nonmetal Halides. The halides of the nonmetals may participate in generalized acid–base reactions by serving as halide ion donors or halide ion acceptors with the formation of ionic compounds or as Lewis acids or bases with the formation of neutral molecular complexes. NX_3 and OX_2 do not participate in any of these acid–base reactions.

Halide Ion Donors. Except for IF_7 none of the fluorides of the nonmetals in their highest oxidation states are known to behave as fluoride ion donors. Halides in which the central atom has an octet structure generally do not serve as halide ion donors. Onium ions for which reasonable evidence exists are listed in Table 7.10 along with some of the anions with which compounds are formed.

The relative strength as ion donors increases in a group with increasing atomic number, i.e., with increasing metallic character of the central atom. Thus TeF_4 will displace SeF_4 from $SeF_3^+SbF_6^-$. SeF_4, in turn, will displace SF_4 from $SF_3^+SbF_6^-$, $SF_3^+AsF_6^-$,

* Oppegard, A. L., W. C. Smith, E. L. Muetterties, and V. A. Engelhardt, *J. Am. Chem. Soc.*, **82**, 3835 (1960).
† Hasek, W. R., W. C. Smith, and V. A. Engelhardt, *J. Am. Chem. Soc.*, **82**, 543 (1960).
‡ Tullock, C. W., F. S. Fawcett, W. C. Smith, and D. D. Coffman, *J. Am. Chem. Soc.*, **82**, 539 (1960).

TABLE 7.10
Halide Donor Complexes of the Nonmetals

	SbF_6^-	AsF_6^-	BF_4^-	
SF_3^+	x	x	x	
SeF_3^+	x	x	x	
TeF_3^+	x			
BrF_2^+	x			SnF_6^{2-}
IF_4^+	x		x	

	$SbCl_6^-$	$AlCl_4^-$	BCl_4^-	
PCl_4^+	x	x	x	
$AsCl_4^+$	x	x		
$SbCl_4^+$				SbF_6^-
SCl_3^+	x		x	
$SeCl_3^+$	x	x		
$TeCl_3^+$	x	x		
ICl_2^+	x	x		

PBr_4^+	Br^-	F^-	PF_6^-	

or $SF_3^+BF_4^-$. The latter has been used as a means of purifying SF_4. After forming solid $SF_4 \cdot BF_3$ at low temperature the volatile impurities are pumped off and the SF_4 displaced at room temperature with SeF_4.*

Evidence for ion transfer is weakest for $ICl_3 \cdot AlCl_3$. X-ray studies give a distorted square planar structure for the Cl atoms about I in $ICl_3 \cdot AlCl_3$ with two long and two short I—Cl bonds. This indicates that this compound probably involves bridging chlorine rather than chloride ion transfer.

A complex is also known involving AsF_3 and SbF_5. On the basis of a single fluorine NMR signal (see Chapter XI) a bridge structure has been proposed.†

* Bartlett, N., and P. L. Robinson, *J. Chem. Soc.*, **1961**, 3417.
† Muetterties, E. L., and W. D. Phillips, *J. Am. Chem. Soc.*, **79**, 3686 (1957).

Halide Ion Acceptors. Ion acceptor properties of the nonmetal halides are illustrated in Table 7.11 below:

TABLE 7.11
Halide Acceptor Complexes of the Nonmetals

Trivalent[a]

BF_4^-	$AsF_4^-BrF_4^-$		
BCl_4^-	$AsCl_4^-ClF_4^-$		
BBr_4^-	$AsBr_4^-$	$AsBr_5^{2-}$	
BI_4^-			
	SbF_4^-	SbF_5^{2-}	
	$SbCl_4^-$	$SbCl_5^{2-}$	$SbCl_6^{3-}$
	BiF_4^-	BiF_5^{2-}	BiF_6^{3-}
	$BiCl_4^-$	$BiCl_5^{2-}$	$BiCl_6^{3-}$
	$BiBr_4^-$	$BiBr_5^{2-}$	$BiBr_6^{3-}$

Tetravalent[a]

SiF_6^{2-}	SF_5^-	
	SeF_5^-	$SeCl_6^{2-}$
		$SeBr_6^{2-}$
	$TeCl_5^-$	$TeCl_6^{2-}$
		$TeBr_6^{2-}$
		TeI_6^{2-}
	PoI_5^-	$PoI_6^{2-}, PoBr_6^{2-}, PoCl_6^{2-}$

Pentavalent[a]　　　　　　　　　　　　　　　　　　　　Hexavalent[a]

PF_6^-		
PCl_6^-		
AsF_6^-		$(TeF_7^-$ or $TeF_8^{2-})$
SbF_6^-		
$SbCl_6^-$	BrF_6^-	
BiF_6^-	IF_6^-	

[a] Used in the sense of oxidation state.

In acceptor properties the halides of the nonmetals behave very much like the halides of the metals in comparable oxidation states (AlF_6^{3-}, TiF_6^{2-}, VF_6^-, UF_8^{2-}). The strength as acceptors increases with increasing oxidation number and (apparently) within a group with increasing atomic number. Thus, SbF_5 will displace AsF_5 from complexes such as $SF_3^+AsF_6^-$. The lack of known PX_4^- and the scarcity of SX_5^- or SX_6^{2-} complexes may indicate the poor ion acceptor ability of these substances.

Lewis Acid–Base Behavior of the Nonmetal Halides. Lewis Bases: The electron withdrawing inductive effect of the halogens may be expected to decrease the basicity of the nonmetal halides compared to the corresponding hydrides or alkyl derivatives. Only the phosphorus trihalides are known to serve as simple Lewis bases—the adducts found being $F_3P \rightarrow BH_3$, $Cl_3P \rightarrow GaCl_3$, $Cl_3P \rightarrow BBr_3$, $Br_3P \rightarrow BBr_3$ and $Cl_3P \rightarrow BCl_2BCl_2 \leftarrow PCl_3$.* The basic properties of the PX_3 and the lack of such properties for NX_3 may be interpreted as due to stabilization of the PX_3 adduct by π bonding involving the halogen attached to phosphorus.

$$Br_3\overset{-}{B}\text{—}\overset{+}{P}Cl_3 \longleftrightarrow Br_3\overset{-}{B}\text{—}P\overset{Cl^+}{\diagup}\diagdown_{Cl}\text{—}Cl$$

3 equivalent contributing structures

Lewis Acids: The behavior of the nonmetal halides as Lewis acids has been studied most systematically in Group V elements. The acid strength increases on going (a) from the trihalides to the pentahalides, (b) from phosphorus to antimony, and (c) from chlorine to fluorine in the pentahalides. The following sequence has been found for the heat of reaction of pyridine with the respective halides:[†]

$$BBr_3 > BCl_3 \sim SbCl_3 > PCl_3F_2 > BF_3 \geq PCl_4F > PCl_5$$

It is interesting to note that in the boron trihalides the acidity order is that expected if resonance effects are predominant, while for the phosphorus pentahalides the acidity order is that expected if inductive effects are predominant. Trimethylamine forms 1 : 1 adducts with PF_3, PCl_3, and PBr_3. PCl_3 has been shown to be a better acceptor than PBr_3, but quantitative data for PF_3 are currently lacking.

Use has been made of the 2,6-lutidine adduct with PF_5 as a means of purifying PF_5.[‡] The adduct is formed and the volatile impurities (mainly POF_3) are pumped off at $-80°C$. The PF_5 is then displaced with a slight deficiency of HCl.

$$\underset{CH_3}{\overset{CH_3}{\diagdown}}N\text{—}PF_5 + HCl(g) \longrightarrow \underset{CH_3}{\overset{CH_3}{\diagdown}}\overset{+}{N}HCl^- + PF_5(g)$$

Sulfur tetrafluoride behaves as a weak Lewis acid forming 1 : 1 adducts with pyridine and triethylamine.[§] Tellurium tetrafluoride is presumably a stronger Lewis acid than SF_4, but side reactions have thus far prevented the isolation of simple TeF_4 adducts. Tributylphosphate apparently forms a 2 : 1 complex with $PoCl_4$.

Pyridine forms a 1 : 1 adduct with SiF_4 and 2 : 1 adducts with GeF_4 and SnF_4. In this series SnF_4 is the most acidic, while within a period SiF_4 is more acidic than SF_4.

"Back-bonded" Complexes. The trihalides of the Group V nonmetals form a number of compounds in which the trihalide may serve as a replacement for carbon monoxide or for ethylene, i.e., $Ni(PX_3)_4$, $Ni(CO)_3SbCl_3$, etc. In these complexes the trihalide is

* Holmes, R. R., *J. Chem. Educ.*, **40**, 125 (1963).
† Holmes, R. R., W. P. Gallagher, and R. P. Carter, Jr., *Inorg. Chem.*, **2**, 437 (1963).
‡ Johnson, Sidney, Ph.D. thesis, Purdue University, 1953.
§ Muetterties, E. L., *J. Am. Chem. Soc.*, **82**, 1082 (1960).

assumed to be acting both as an electron pair donor (forming the usual σ bond) and as an electron pair acceptor by "back bonding," i.e., bonding between a filled d orbital on the transition metal and an empty d orbital on the phosphorus atom (or As or Sb).

Geometry of the Complex Ions and Adducts. The geometry of MX_6^- ions is the expected octahedral arrangement of halogen atoms. Less expected, perhaps, is the regular octahedral geometry found for the hexacoordinated ions with a remaining electron pair, such as $TeCl_6^{2-}$.* A similar structure has been found for $:XeF_6$, $:SbCl_6^-$, and $:IF_6^-$. Unexpected, perhaps, is a cubic structure for $(R_3N)_2TeF_6$. This structure is inferred from the fluorine NMR spectrum, which may be interpreted as showing at low temperatures an equilibrium mixture of three isomers.†

No simple $:MX_4^-$ ions have been found. The solid $KSbF_4$ has been shown to consist of tetrameric units. The $KSbF_4$ structure is shown in Figure 7.5.

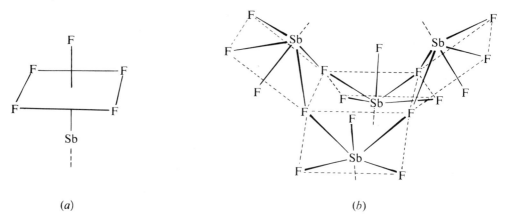

(a)	(b)

FIGURE 7.5. (a) *Pseudo octahedral unit of* SbF_5^{2-} *ion in* K_2SbF_5. (b) *Tetrameric* $Sb_4F_{16}^{4-}$ *unit in* $KSbF_4$. *Note that Sb lies below the basal plane in* SbF_5^{2-}, *and that the* $Sb_4F_{16}^{4-}$ *consists essentially of four such units joined through their common fluorides. Structures determined by A. Bystrom, S. Backlund, and K. A. Wilhemi,* Arkiv. Kemi, *4, 175 (1951). Figures from R. R. Holmes,* J. Chem. Educ., *40, 125–130 (1963).*

COMPOUNDS OF THE RARE GASES‡

Until very recently only clathrate compounds of the rare gases were known (Chapter II). The breakthrough in this area of chemistry came when Bartlett and Lohman oxidized xenon with platinum hexafluoride. They were led to this experiment by having previously prepared the unusual $O_2^+PtF_6^-$. Since the ionization potential of molecular oxygen and xenon are both 12.2 eV, only lattice energy effects would prevent formation of the xenon derivative. Bartlett describes the experiment as follows:

> The predicted interaction of xenon and platinum hexafluoride was confirmed in a simple and visually dramatic experiment. The deep red platinum hexafluoride vapor, of known

* Aynsley, E. E., and A. C. Hazell, *Chem. Ind. (London),* **1963**, 611.
† Muetterties, E. L., and W. D. Phillips, *J. Am. Chem. Soc.,* **79**, 2975 (1957).
‡ Bartlett, N., *Am. Sci.,* **51**, 114 (1963). C. L. Chernick, *Rec. of Chem. Prog.,* **24**, 139 (1963).

pressure, was mixed, by breaking a glass diaphragm, with the same volume of xenon, the pressure of which was greater than that of the hexafluoride. Combination, to produce a yellow solid, was immediate at room temperature, and the quantity of xenon which remained was commensurate with a combining ratio of 1 : 1.

Since the initial breakthrough a number of compounds of the heavier rare gases, particularly compounds of xenon, have been prepared. A number of these are listed in Table 7.12.

TABLE 7.12
Rare Gas Compounds

$XePtF_6$	XeF_2	$XeOF_4$
$Xe(PtF_6)_2$	XeF_4	$XeOF_3$
$XeRuF_6$	XeF_6	$XeOF_2$
$XeRhF_6$	XeF_8	
Xe_2SiF_6		
$XePF_6$		XeO_3
$XeSbF_6$	$XeF_2 \cdot SbF_5$	
		$Na_4XeO_4 \cdot 6H_2O$
		$Na_4XeO_4 \cdot 8H_2O$
	KrF_2	$Ba_2XeO_6 \cdot xH_2O$
	KrF_4	$K_4XeO_6 \cdot 2XeO_3$

The compounds of ruthenium and rhodium are produced in a manner similar to $XePtF_6$, and the silicon, phosphorus, and antimony compounds are made by the reaction of xenon with fluorine in the presence of the nonmetal fluoride.*

$$2Xe(g) + F_2(g) + SiF_4(g) \longrightarrow XeSiF_6(s)$$

The above reaction is accompanied by an enormous decrease in entropy due to the large number of gas molecules involved. The silicon and phosphorus compounds decompose around room temperature, but $XeSbF_6$ decomposes considerably above room temperature. These compounds may be assumed to contain the Xe^+ ion.

Disproportionation of $XePtF_6$ takes place on heating and the new compound $Xe(PtF_6)_2$, which contains the X^{2+} ion, is formed.

The binary fluorides of xenon may be formed from the elements at temperatures ranging from 300° to 700°C and pressures from 2 to 200 atm, the higher temperatures and pressures giving the higher fluorides. The difluoride is obtained using quenching techniques. KrF_4 is prepared by electric discharge through a mixture of the elements at liquid air temperature.

The xenon fluorides hydrolyze† as follows:

$$XeF_2 + H_2O \longrightarrow Xe + \frac{1}{2}O_2 + 2HF$$

$$3XeF_4 + 6H_2O \longrightarrow 2Xe + \frac{3}{2}O_2 + 12HF + XeO_3$$

$$XeF_6 + 3H_2O \longrightarrow XeO_3 + 6HF$$

* Clifford, A. F., and G. R. Zeilenga, *Science,* **141**, 1431 (1964).
† Appleman, E. H., and J. G. Malm, *J. Am. Chem. Soc.,* **86**, 2141, 2297 (1964).

The xenon trioxide is stable in dilute aqueous acid but very explosive when anhydrous. It behaves as a weak acid in aqueous solution with a pK_a of ~10.5. The manner of dissociation is possibly

$$H_2O + XeO_3 \longrightarrow H^+(aq) + HXeO_4^-$$

or

$$3H_2O + XeO_3 \longrightarrow H^+(aq) + H_5XeO_6^-$$

In basic solution XeF_6 disproportionates

$$2XeF_6 + 4Na^+ + 16OH^- \longrightarrow Na_4XeO_6 + Xe + O_2 + 12F^- + 8H_2O$$

The standard half-cell emf values have been estimated* as

$$E_A^O \quad Xe(g) \xrightarrow{-2.45} Xe^+ \xrightarrow{-1.67} XeO_3 \xrightarrow{-3.0} H_4XeO_6$$

with a -1.8 bridge over $Xe^+ \to XeO_3$, and

$$Xe(g) \xrightarrow{-2.2} XeF_2$$

and $\quad E_B^O \quad Xe(g) \xrightarrow{-0.9} HXeO_4^- \xrightarrow{-0.9} HXeO_6^{3-}$

Estimates of the acid strength of perxenic acid are p$K_1 \approx 2$, p$K_2 \approx 6$, p$K_3 \approx 10.5$, the last value being an experimental one. Perxenic acid is an extremely powerful oxidizing agent.

The xenon fluorides are soluble in liquid hydrogen fluoride. The low conductivity of XeF_2 and XeF_4 indicates poor ion donor and ion acceptor properties. The xenon hexafluoride solutions show a high conductivity and the ions XeF_5^+ and FHF^- are presumably formed to the extent of about 30% of the XeF_6 present.

A number of ion–molecule species involving the inert gases have been observed by means of the mass spectrometer.† This instrument combines an isolated environment with an energetic situation favorable to the production of such ions. Observed species include Ar_2^+, ArI^+, XeH^+, $XeCH_4^+$, $XeOH^+$, XeO^+, XeO_2^+.

PSEUDOHALOGENS‡

Analogy plays an important role in descriptive chemistry. The ionic groups given in Table 7.13 behave chemically very much like halide ions and are often called "pseudo-halides."

The approximate order of electronegativities of the pseudohalogens and the halogens is $F^- > N_3^- > NC^- > Cl^- > NCS^- > Br^- > N_3SCS^- > I^-$.§

The order of strength as oxidizing agents is approximately $F_2 > Cl_2 > Br_2 > (SCN)_2 > (CN)_2 > I_2 > (SCSN_3)_2 > (SeCN)_2$.

---

* Appleman, E. H., and J. G. Malm, *J. Am. Chem. Soc.*, **86**, 2141, 2297 (1964).
† Field, F. H., and J. L. Franklin, *J. Am. Chem. Soc.*, **83**, 4509 (1961).
‡ See T. Moeller, *Inorganic Chemistry* (New York: John Wiley and Sons, Inc., 1952).
§ See McDaniel and Yingst, ref. Chapter IV, p. 156.

TABLE 7.13
The Pseudohalogens

Ion	Dimeric molecule	m.p. of X_2, °C	pK$_a$ of HX
N$_3^-$ azide	—	—	4.55
CN$^-$ cyanide	(CN)$_2$ cyanogen	m.p. -27.9 b.p. -21.17	9.21
OCN$^-$ cyanate	(OCN)$_2$ oxycyanogen	—	3.92
SCN$^-$ thiocyanate	(SCN)$_2$ thiocyanogen	-2 to $-3°$	(-0.74)
SeCN$^-$ selenocyanate	(SeCN)$_2$ selenocyanogen	Yellow powder	—
SCSN$_3^-$ azidocarbondisulfide ion	(SCSN$_3$)$_2$ azidocarbondisulfide	White, unstable cryst. solid	1.67

Electrolysis or chemical oxidation may be used to prepare many of the pseudo-halogens from their ions.

$$HSCN + MnO_2 \longrightarrow (SCN)_2 + Mn(SCN)_2 + 2H_2O$$

Similarities to the halogens may be seen in reactions such as hydrolysis, addition to carbon–carbon double bonds, formation of complex ions and pseudo-interhalogen compounds, and insolubility of silver, lead and mercurous salts.

$$(CN)_2 + 2OH^- \longrightarrow OCN^- + CN^- + H_2O$$
$$CH_2CH_2 + (SCN)_2 \ {}^- \rightarrow NCSCH_2CH_2SCN$$
$$Ag^+ + CN^- \longrightarrow AgCN \downarrow$$
$$AgCN(s) + CN^- \longrightarrow Ag(CN)_2^-$$

The pseudohalides, like the halides themselves, have more than one pair of electrons with which coordinate bonding can take place and may thus serve as bridging groups. However, the bridging may result in a different degree of polymerization of the parent compound due to the different geometric orientation of the available electron pairs. Thus, although dialkylgold chloride and bromide are dimeric the cyanide is tetrameric.

$$
\begin{array}{ccc}
\text{R} & & \text{R} \\
| & & | \\
\text{R—Au—N} & \equiv \text{C—Au—R} \\
| & & | \\
\text{C} & & \text{N} \\
\| & & \| \\
\text{N} & & \text{C} \\
| & & | \\
\text{R—Au—C} & \equiv \text{N—Au—R} \\
| & & | \\
\text{R} & & \text{R}
\end{array}
$$

In each case the geometry about the gold atom is square planar.

Other differences between the halogens and the pseudohalogens occur in the polymerization of many of the pseudohalogens under heating

$$x(CN)_2 \xrightarrow[400°]{} \frac{1}{2}(CN)_x$$

$$x(SCN)_2 \xrightarrow[\text{room temp.}]{} \frac{1}{2}(SCN)_x$$

The Oxy Acids and Oxy Anions of the Halogens

The preparation of the oxy anions of chlorine was discussed in Chapter IV, p. 149–151. Intercomparisons among the halogen oxy ions and some further descriptive material follow.

The Hypohalites

The relative increase in ease of oxidation of the halide ion with increasing atomic number may be seen in the following emf diagrams for basic solution.

$$
E_B^0 \quad Cl^- \xrightarrow[-1.36]{} \overset{\displaystyle \overset{-0.89}{\overbrace{\hphantom{Cl_2 \longrightarrow}}}}{Cl_2} \xrightarrow[-0.40]{} ClO^-
$$

$$
Br^- \xrightarrow[-1.07]{} \overset{\displaystyle \overset{-0.71}{\overbrace{\hphantom{Br_2 \longrightarrow}}}}{Br_2} \xrightarrow[-0.45]{} BrO^-
$$

$$
I^- \xrightarrow[-0.535]{} \overset{\displaystyle \overset{-0.49}{\overbrace{\hphantom{I_2 \longrightarrow}}}}{I_2} \xrightarrow[-0.45]{} IO^-
$$

All of the above hypohalite ions may be formed from the disproportionation of the corresponding halogen in base. The stability of the hypohalite ions with regard to further disproportionation to halite ions and halide ions decreases with increasing atomic number. Thus although hypoiodite solutions decompose within a few hours, hypochlorite solutions decompose only slightly over a period of weeks, relative rates being ClO⁻ 1, BrO⁻ 100, and IO⁻ 3 × 10⁶. Accordingly, hypobromite is generated for analytical use from hypochlorite solutions at a pH of around 10.

$$ClO^- + Br^- \longrightarrow BrO^- + Cl^-$$

Hypobromite is often a faster oxidizing agent than hypochlorite despite its lower emf. This phenomenon is discussed at greater length under the section dealing with halate ions, where it also occurs.

Hypoiodite ion is an oxidant used to determine β-keto functions through the "iodoform" reaction, the name coming from one of the reaction products.

$$\underset{\underset{O}{\parallel}}{RCCH_3} + 3I_2 + 4OH^- \longrightarrow HCI_3 + RCO_2^- + 3I^- + 3H_2O$$

The anhydrous hypohalite acids cannot be isolated. Their pK_a values are discussed in Chapter VI, p. 191. Hypoiodous acid also undergoes dissociation to produce hydroxide ion in solution, its pK_b being 10.

The Halites

Only chlorine forms a halite ion and a halous acid. The acid cannot be obtained in anhydrous form, see Chapter IV, p. 151.

The Halates

The oxidizing strengths of chlorate and bromate solutions are similar but the iodate is much weaker.

$$E_B^0 \quad Cl^- \xrightarrow{\ -0.63\ } ClO_3^-$$
$$Br^- \xrightarrow{\ -0.61\ } BrO_3^-$$
$$I^- \xrightarrow{\ -0.29\ } IO_3^-$$

The standard emf values are all more negative by 0.83 V in acid solution.

The rates of reaction of these ions as oxidizing reagents are in the order $IO_3^- > BrO_3^- > ClO_3^-$. This order has been explained as due to the decreasing multiple bond character* in the oxygen halogen bond as the atomic number increases. The iodate thus has more negative charge at the oxygen surface than the bromate, which in turn has more surface charge than the chlorate. The increase in surface charge would allow oxygen to coordinate more readily with other ions and the low multiple bond character would also allow the iodine to expand its coordination sphere more readily through dative bonding to empty *d* orbitals.

The low double bond character and consequent higher negative charge on oxygen would also account for the generally lower solubility of transition metal iodates compared to chlorates or bromates and also for the greater viscosity of comparable solu-

* See Nightingale, ref. Chapter II, p. 59.

tions of iodates compared to chlorates. It might also help explain why acid salts containing the hydrogen bonded units $(IO_3 \cdot HIO_3)^-$ and $(IO_3 \cdot 2HIO_3)^-$ are formed with iodic acid, but not with bromic or chloric acids. The high molecular weight of $KH(IO_3)_2$ and ease of purification through recrystallization make it suitable for standardizing base solutions for analytical work.* Iodic acid can also be isolated in anhydrous form in contrast to chloric and bromic acids.

Both iodic and bromic acids can be made in the laboratory by oxidizing the halogen or halide ion with chlorine, the chloride ion being removed with silver oxide.

$$X_2 + 5Cl_2 + H_2O \longrightarrow 2HXO_3 + 10HCl$$
$$2HCl + Ag_2O \longrightarrow 2AgCl + H_2O$$

Commercially, iodates and bromates are produced by electrolytic oxidation. As with chlorine, reaction with hot basic solution will produce the halate

$$3X_2 + 6OH^- \longrightarrow XO_3^- + 5X^- + 3H_2O$$
$$X = Cl, Br, I$$

In acidic solution, the above reaction is reversed for $X = Br$ and I, and this serves as a convenient method of preparing Br_2 and I_2 in solution, usually using an excess of the halide ion.

$$6H^+ + 5Br^- + BrO_3^- \longrightarrow 3Br_2 + 3H_2O$$

The extent of unsaturation in olefins may be determined by the addition of the bromine produced to the double bond.

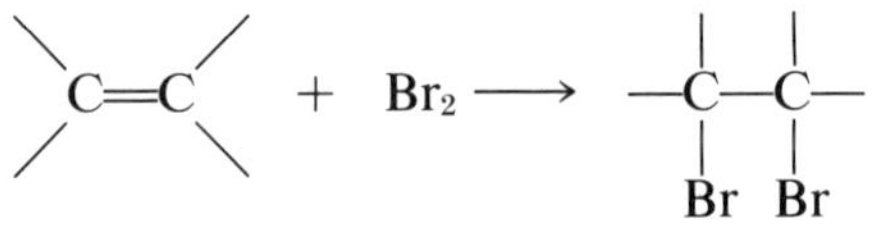

The excess bromine may be determined by adding potassium iodide and titrating with thiosulfate solution:

$$2I^- + Br_2 \longrightarrow 2Br^- + I_2$$
$$I_2 + S_2O_3^{2-} \longrightarrow 2I^- + S_4O_6^{2-}$$

Unlike the reactions of iodates and bromates with their halide ions, chlorates react with chloride ion in the presence of acid to produce chlorine dioxide as well as chlorine.

$$2HClO_3 + 2HCl \longrightarrow 2ClO_2 + Cl_2 + H_2O$$

Perhalates

The differences between the oxyhalogen acids are greatest with the perhalic acids and perhalate salts. Only chlorine and iodine form perhalic acids and these differ widely in their molecular formulas and properties. Greater regularity in trends within the periodic table may be found within a given period than within the group. This is illustrated by an examination of the properties of the acids shown.

* Smith, G. F., see general references.

H₃PO₄	H₂SO₄	HClO₄

$$H_3PO_4 \qquad H_2SO_4 \qquad HClO_4$$
$$H_3AsO_4 \qquad H_2SeO_4 \qquad -$$
$$HSb(OH)_6{}^a \qquad H_6TeO_6 \qquad H_5IO_6$$

^{a}(in solution only)

The acid strength and oxidizing ability increase regularly on going from phosphoric acid to sulfuric acid to perchloric acid,* the melting points decrease and the tendency toward formation of polyacid units decreases from phosphoric acid to perchloric acid, which forms no polyacids. Likewise the ability to form metal ion complexes decreases from phosphate through perchlorate. Arsenic and selenic acid resemble phosphoric and sulfuric acids more than they do the antimonic and telluric acids. This resemblance appears in acid strength, solubility of salts, and structure of the salts. Presumably, perbromic acid, if it could be made, would resemble perchloric acid more than periodic acid. Arsenic and selenic acid are much stronger oxidizing agents than phosphoric and sulfuric acids. Unlike sulfuric acid, selenic acid is unstable toward decomposition to O_2, H_2O, and Se on heating. Extrapolating these properties, the hypothetical perbromic acid would probably be an extremely powerful oxidizing agent, but also should decompose at moderate temperatures to give oxygen and a lower oxidation state of bromine.

An increase in coordination number of oxygen about the central atom occurs for antimonates and tellurates, which show only six coordination. The smaller size of I^{7+} compared to Te^{6+} and Sb^{5+} permits iodine to show a coordination number of four as well as six in periodates.† Typical salts formed by these acids are $NaSb(OH)_6$, $LiSb(OH)_6$, $Na_3H_2TeO_6$, Ag_6TeO_6, Ag_5IO_6, $Na_3H_2IO_6$, and KIO_4.

PERIODATES

Periodates may be made in the laboratory by the oxidation of an iodate in basic solution using chlorine. Commercially, periodates are prepared by electrolytic oxidation of iodates.

The equilibria involved in the dissocation of periodic acid in water have recently been reinvestigated with the following results.‡

$$H_5IO_6 \rightleftharpoons H^+(aq) + H_4IO_6^- \qquad K_1 = (10 \pm 4) \times 10^{-4}$$
$$H_4IO_6^- \rightleftharpoons H^+(aq) + H_3IO_6^{2-} \qquad K_2 = (3 \pm 1) \times 10^{-7}$$
$$H_4IO_6^- \rightleftharpoons 2H_2O + IO_4^- \qquad K = 43 \pm 17$$

Periodic acid is thus a much weaker acid than perchloric acid. The H_5IO_6 form is called "paraperiodic acid" and is the form of the acid that is stable as a solid in contact with water. At 100°C this form loses water and is converted into *meta*-periodic acid, HIO_4. The preparation of some of the various silver periodates is shown in the following reaction scheme taken from Wells.§

* Although the rate of oxidation by perchloric acid is not appreciable except in hot concentrated solutions— see section under perchloric acid.

† This approach does not infer the existence of isolated ions of charges as high as these—see Chapter III, p. 108.

‡ Laurie, S. H., J. M. Williams, and C. J. Nyman, *J. Chem. Phys.*, **68**, 1311 (1964).

§ From A. F. Wells, *Structural Inorganic Chemistry*, second edition. (Oxford: Clarendon Press, 1950.)

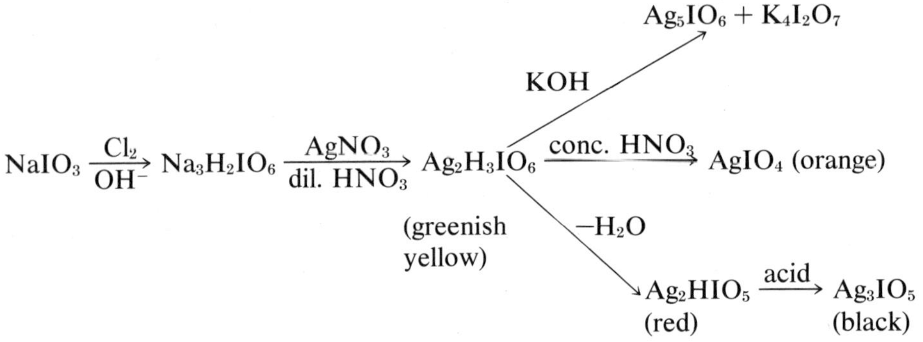

$$Ag_5IO_6 + K_4I_2O_7$$

$$NaIO_3 \xrightarrow[OH^-]{Cl_2} Na_3H_2IO_6 \xrightarrow[\text{dil. HNO}_3]{AgNO_3} Ag_2H_3IO_6 \xrightarrow{\text{conc. HNO}_3} AgIO_4 \text{ (orange)}$$

(greenish
yellow)

$-H_2O$

$$Ag_2HIO_5 \xrightarrow{acid} Ag_3IO_5$$
(red)   (black)

Periodic acid is especially useful as an analytical reagent for the quantitative determination of α,β-dihydroxyorganic compounds.

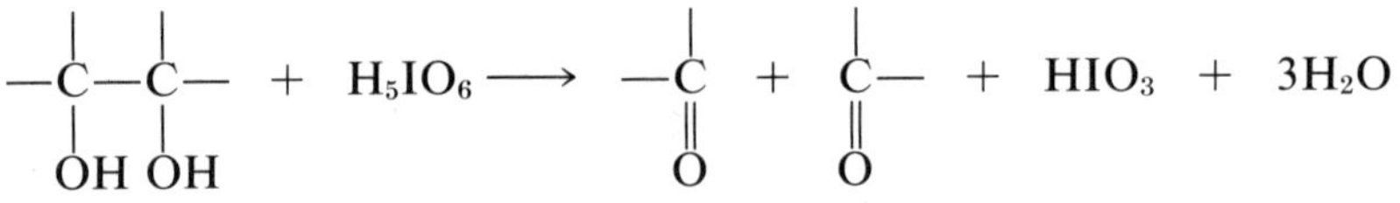

$$-\overset{|}{\underset{OH}{C}}-\overset{|}{\underset{OH}{C}}- + H_5IO_6 \longrightarrow -\overset{|}{\underset{O}{\overset{\|}{C}}} + \overset{|}{\underset{O}{\overset{\|}{C}}}- + HIO_3 + 3H_2O$$

An intermediate in this highly selective reaction is the complex

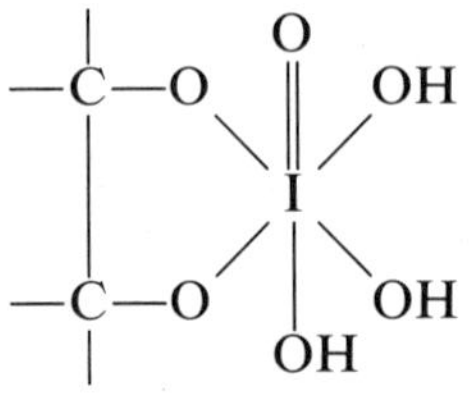

similar to complexes formed by boric acid, germanic acid, etc. (Chapter VI, p. 190). Mercuric ion may be determined by precipitating it as $Hg_5(IO_6)_2$.

PERCHLORIC ACID*

Perchloric acid is the only oxy acid of chlorine that may be isolated in an anhydrous state. It is most readily prepared through the dehydration of the dihydrate by fuming sulfuric acid and removal of the anhydrous perchloric acid by vacuum distillation in a grease free system.

$$HClO_4 \cdot 2H_2O + 2H_2S_2O_7 \xrightarrow{25-80°} HClO_4 + 2H_2SO_4$$

The anhydrous acid melts at $-102°C$. The $HClO_4$ molecular units exist in the gas, liquid, and solid.† Contact with organic materials such as wood, paper, and rubber produces violent explosions. It may be stored without explosive decomposition for 30 to 60 days at liquid air temperature ($-190°$) or for 10 to 30 days at room temperature. It is normally colorless, but develops an amber color prior to detonation. A number of

* Smith, G. F., *Anal. Chim. Acta*, **8**, 397 (1953); *Analyst*, **80**, 946 (1955).
† Dahl, A. J., J. C. Towbridge, and R. C. Taylor, *Inorg. Chem.*, **2**, 654 (1963).

hydrates of perchloric acid are known and these are all stable at room temperature. The melting points of these and the weight per cent perchloric acid are

	m.p.	% $HClO_4$
$HClO_4 \cdot H_2O$	49.905	84.79
$HClO_4 \cdot 2H_2O$	-17.8α	73.60
$HClO_4 \cdot 2H_2O$	-19.5β	
$HClO_4 \cdot 2.5H_2O$	-29.8	69.05
$HClO_4 \cdot 3H_2O$	$-37\ \alpha$	65.02
$HClO_4 \cdot 3H_2O$	$-43\ \beta$	
$HClO_4 \cdot 3.5H_2O$	41.4	61.44

Perchloric acid and water form an azeotrope boiling at approximately 203°C at one atmosphere pressure and having a composition of 72.5% perchloric acid. Under these conditions appreciable decomposition of the acid occurs. Under reduced pressure the azeotropic composition approaches 73.60% perchloric acid. The commercially available concentrated acid is 70% perchloric acid.

Cold concentrated perchloric acid (70%) is a weak oxidizing agent. Hot concentrated perchloric acid has been used as a rapid "wet ashing" procedure for organic materials. This reaction has been named "the liquid fire reaction." Hydroxyl groups should not be present as the perchlorate esters formed may explode, particularly ethyl perchlorate. This hazard can be eliminated by using a mixture of concentrated nitric and perchloric acids. The nitric acid oxidizes the alcohols and other readily oxidizable groups, and is itself displaced on heating. The temperature of the reaction mixture slowly increases as the perchloric acid is concentrated, approaching the azeotropic conditions. As the temperature and perchloric acid concentration increase, the oxidizing ability of the solution increases.

The end point of the reaction may often be determined by adding a small amount of $K_2Cr_2O_7$ to the reaction mixture. This reacts more rapidly with the organic material than the perchlorate, giving colorless or green solutions containing Cr(III) ion. At the end of the reaction the Cr(III) ion is oxidized to orange CrO_3. Wet ashing in this fashion may be carried out in as little time as ten to fifteen minutes. It has been used for analysis of samples of organic origin such as leather, wood, grain, and coal.

Due to the very great acid strength of perchloric acid it has been used as a titrant for very weak bases in acetic acid as a solvent.

PERCHLORATES

Ammonium perchlorate was used a half century ago as a nonfreezing blasting compound in mining operations. Today it is being used as an oxidant in solid fueled missiles.

The perchlorate ion is less extensively hydrated than the other oxyhalogen anions and also shows very little tendency to form complexes with metal ions. It is accordingly often used as an inert anion in studies of metal ion complexes. The inertness of the perchlorate ion has been attributed to a high degree of double bond character in the

Cl—O bonds, which drains the negative charge from the surface of the ion and localizes it on the chlorine atom.

Magnesium perchlorate is a very efficient desiccant. In this case the magnesium ions behave as if they were isolated in an inert matrix and accordingly form a very stable hexahydrate when in contact with water. Ammonium perchlorate will absorb sufficient ammonia to liquify at room temperatures giving solutions resembling Diver's solution, (NH_4NO_3, NH_3).

Perchlorate salts are often isomorphous with permanganate, perrhenate and tetra-fluoroborate salts. One of the few salts in which perchlorate occupies a coordination site on a metal is in the trimethyltin perchlorate in which tin has the unusual coordination number of five.* The three methyl groups lie in the trigonal plane about a tin atom with the perchlorate ions bridging the tin atoms to form a chain. The trimethyltin tetra-fluoroborate apparently has a similar structure.

GENERAL REFERENCES

Brasted, R. C., *Comprehensive Inorganic Chemistry, Vol. III, The Halogens* (New York: D. Van Nostrand Company, Inc., 1954).

Simons, J. H., ed., *Fluorine Chemistry*, Vols. I and II (New York: Academic Press Inc., 1950, 1954).

Hyman, H. H., ed., *Noble-Gas Compounds* (Chicago: University of Chicago Press, 1963).

Katz, J. J., and I. Sheft, "Halides of the Actinide Elements," in *Advances in Inorganic and Radiochemistry*, Vol. 2, edited by H. J. Emeléus and A. G. Sharpe (New York: Academic Press Inc., 1960).

Smith, G. F., *Analytical Applications of Periodic Acid and Iodic Acid and Their Salts* (Columbus: G. F. Smith Chemical Co., 1950).

Wiebenga, E. H., E. E. Havinga, and K. H. Boswijk, "Interhalogen Compounds and Poly-halides," in *Advances in Inorganic and Radiochemistry*, Vol. 3, edited by H. J. Emeléus and A. G. Sharpe (New York: Academic Press Inc., 1961).

George, J. W., "Halides and Oxyhalides of the Elements of Groups VI and VII," in *Progress in Inorganic Chemistry*, edited by F. A. Cotton (New York: Interscience Publishers, Inc., 1960). See also references given under Remy, Sidgwick, Wells, and Peacock, Chapter IX, p. 330.

Problems

1. Use the Pauling electronegativities to estimate the ΔH for reactions $\frac{1}{2}X_2(g) + \frac{1}{2}Y_2(g) \rightarrow XY(g)$ where XY are the diatomic interhalogen compounds. Experimental values are given by Wiebenga et al. (as ΔH^+) (see general ref. above). Can the heat of reaction for the formation of XY_3 be estimated from Pauling electronegativities?

2. The ΔH^0_f of BrF(g), $BrF_3(l)$, and $BrF_5(l)$ are -14.7, -75, and -127.5 kcal/mole, respectively. Which of these species should be predominate on reacting Br_2 and F_2 under standard conditions?

3. Indicate reactions which might be suitable for the preparation of:

(*a*) Anhydrous tetramethylammonium fluoride; (*b*) aluminum bromide; (*c*) barium iodide.

* Clark, H. C., and R. J. O'Brien, *Inorg. Chem.*, **2**, 740 (1963).

4. Use the emf data in the appendix to predict the results of mixing the following:
    (*a*) Cl^- and BrO_3^- in $1N$ acid;   (*b*) Cl_2 and IO_3^- in $1N$ base;   (*c*) At_2 and Cl_2 in $1N$ base.

5. Compare the expected *rate* of reaction of AtO_3^- and IO_3^- as oxidizing agents. What formula is expected for perastatinate? Why?

6. Give any evidence you can find in the literature to indicate whether the following might usefully be classed as pseudohalogens:
    (*a*) $(NO_2)_2$; (*b*) $(NF_2)_2$; (*c*) $(OH)_2$.

7. XeF_6 gives solutions in HF which conduct electricity. How might one distinguish between the following possible modes of dissociation:

$$XeF_6 + HF \rightleftharpoons XeF_5^+ + HF_2^-$$
$$\text{and}\quad XeF_6 + 2HF \rightleftharpoons XeF_7^- + H_2^+F$$

8. How might one distinguish between Xe^+ ions and Xe_2^{2+} ions in the compound $XePtF_6$?

CHAPTER VIII

Electron Deficient Compounds

Most of the molecules we have considered have had a number of electrons equal to, or greater than, the number of atomic orbitals of low energy present in the molecule. Accordingly, satisfactory valence bond structures could be written in which a valence bond indicated occupancy of the atomic orbitals of *two* atoms by an electron pair; or, the electron pair could be said to be occupying a localized two-center molecular orbital. The concept of resonance allows a description of multicenter orbitals (as in CO_3^{2-} or benzene) by the valence bond structures, but up to this point it has been invoked only when more electrons than low energy orbitals were available.

Boron Hydrides

Structure and Properties

Compounds in which the number of low energy atomic orbitals exceeds the number of valence electrons are called electron deficient compounds. One of the simplest electron deficient compounds is diborane, B_2H_6. The monomer BH_3, which might have been expected to be the stable species, does not exist in appreciable quantities at ordinary temperatures. Such a monomer would necessarily have left vacant one of the low energy orbitals of boron.

Diborane was first prepared by the pyrolysis of tetraborane obtained from the acidic hydrolysis of magnesium boride, MgB_2. It is now more conveniently prepared by either of the following reactions

$$3LiAlH_4 + 4(C_2H_5)_2O:BF_3 \xrightarrow{(C_2H_5)_2O} 3LiF + 3AlF_3 + 2B_2H_6 + 4(C_2H_5)_2O$$

$$2NaBH_4 + (HPO_3)_x \longrightarrow B_2H_6 + 2H_2 + 2NaPO_3$$

As prepared, it is spontaneously flammable in air (due to the presence of higher boron hydrides), readily hydrolyzed to boric acid and hydrogen, and highly toxic. Consequently, it is usually handled in the laboratory by vacuum line techniques. Polyphosphoric acid is preferred in the above reaction to concentrated sulfuric acid, which has often been used, since the latter undergoes some reduction to produce sulfur dioxide.

One of the most revealing reactions of diborane is a redistribution reaction that occurs with trimethylboron

$$B_2H_6 + B(CH_3)_3 \rightleftharpoons B_2H_5(CH_3) + B_2H_4(CH_3)_2 + B_2H_3(CH_3)_3 + B_2H_2(CH_3)_4$$

Only the boron–hydrogen bonds are subject to hydrolysis in these diborane derivatives and hence the location of the methyl groups may be determined from the hydrolysis products. Hydrolysis of $B_2H_2(CH_3)_4$ yields only $(CH_3)_2BOH$, showing that a maximum of two methyl groups may be joined to a given boron atom in the dimer. Hydrolysis of trimethyldiborane gives $(CH_3)_2BOH$ and $CH_3B(OH)_2$, i.e., the 1,1,1-trimethyldiborane does not exist. This suggests that the hydrogens are not all equivalent in diborane, a suggestion which is completely supported by structural studies. The following atomic positions for diborane are based on recent diffraction and spectral studies.

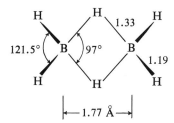

The two "bridge" hydrogens are in a plane perpendicular to the plane of the boron and the other four hydrogens.

"No bond" resonance structures can be written to give a valence bond representation of diborane.

This representation is somewhat awkward, and becomes even more awkward with the heavier boron hydrides. The currently accepted practice is to introduce a new symbol, , to represent a three-center orbital involving a bridging hydrogen atom. Thus the modified valence bond representation of diborane is

In this representation the terminal B—H bonds are the usual two-center bonds, and a single pair of electrons is used in each of the BHB bridge bonds represented by the curved lines.

In terms of molecular orbitals, the three-center BHB orbital may be considered to result from the combination of one sp^3 orbital from each boron and the s orbital of the hydrogen.

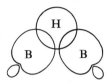

The nonbonding and antibonding orbitals, which would also arise, would be unfilled. The observed bond angles in B_2H_6 are far from tetrahedral angles so that the molecular orbitals probably have some of the character of sp^2 hybrids also. A more complete description of the bonding in diborane is given in Appendix D.

A number of higher boron hydrides are known. Decaborane and the lower members through hexaborane-10 were prepared by Stock and co-workers, who pioneered in this field.* The currently available physical properties of these along with those of diborane are given in Table 8.1. In addition to these, the compounds B_8H_{12}, B_8H_{18}, $B_{10}H_{16}$, and two isomers of $B_{18}H_{22}$ have been prepared.†

The structures of the boron hydrides, which have been isolated, have been determined and, for those originally prepared by Stock, the boron atoms are located at the vertices of incomplete octahedra or icosahedra. Some of these structures are shown in Figure 8.1.

The connecting lines in the figure do not necessarily represent bonds, but are used to indicate geometric shape.

Figure 8.2 indicates the structure of some boron hydrides which may be thought of as derived by the fusion of simpler units.

* Stock, A., *Hydrides of Boron and Silicon* (Ithaca: Cornell University Press, 1933).
† See R. E. Enrione, F. P. Boer, and W. N. Lipscomb, *J. Am. Chem. Soc.*, **86**, 1451 (1964); R. Schaeffer, *Chem. Eng. News*, April 12, 46 (1965).

TABLE 8.1[a]

Physical Properties of the Boron Hydrides

Formula	Name	Melting Point(°C)	Boiling Point(°C)
B_2H_6	Diborane-6	−165.5	−92.5
B_4H_{10}	Tetraborane-10	−121.6	18
B_5H_9	Pentaborane-9	−46.6	48
B_5H_{11}	Pentaborane-11	−123	63
B_6H_{10}[b]	Hexaborane-10	−62.3	108
B_6H_{12}[c]	Hexaborane-12	−83	80–90
B_9H_{15}[b]	Enneaborane-15	2.6	−
$B_{10}H_{14}$	Decaborane-14	99.7	213
$B_{20}H_{16}$[d]	Icosaborane-16	196–199	−

[a] Except as noted values from F. G. A. Stone, 1960, see references p. 283.
[b] Burg, A. B., and R. Kratzer, *Inorg. Chem.*, **1**, 725 (1962).
[c] Gaines, D. F., and R. Schaeffer, *Inorg. Chem.*, **3**, 438 (1964).
[d] Miller, N. E., and E. L. Muetterties, *J. Am. Chem. Soc.*, **85**, 3506 (1963).

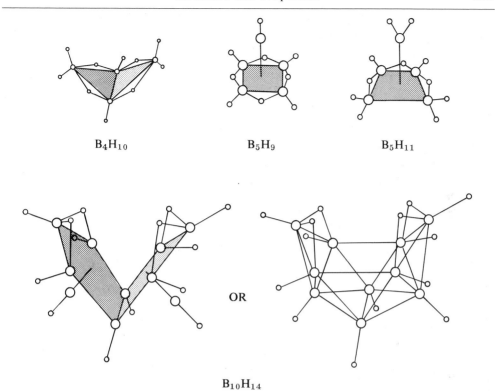

FIGURE 8.1. *Structures of some boron hydrides. Planes containing the greatest number of boron atoms are shaded* [*after W. N. Lipscomb*, J. Chem. Phys., **22**, *985 (1954)*].

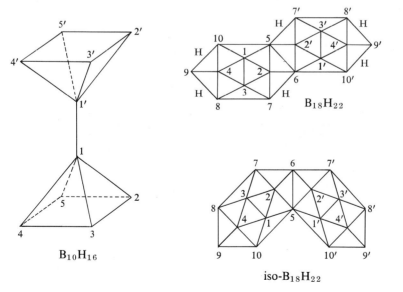

FIGURE 8.2. *Structures of some more complex boron hydrides (boron skeleton only shown).* [*from Dr. W. N. Lipscomb*, Boron Hydrides *(New York: W. A. Benjamin, Inc., 1963*].

The structure of $B_{10}H_{16}$ is related to that of B_5H_9 by the removal of the apical hydrogens of two B_5H_9 units with the formation of a B—B bond. The structures of the $B_{18}H_{22}$ isomers resemble two fused $B_{10}H_{14}$ units sharing an edge of the two icosahedra with the removal of two boron atoms.

Equations of Balance*

In addition to BHB three-center bonds and the B—H bonds found in diborane, the higher hydrides may also contain two-center B—B bonds and three-center BBB bonds. Two types of BBB bonds can arise from the available orbitals of B giving rise to the symbols B̲   B̲   and   as shown in Figure 8.3.

If all the low energy orbitals of boron are to be used, then the possible number and types of bonds present in a given boron hydride may be calculated from the simultaneous solution of three equations, known as the equations of balance. For a neutral molecule of the general formula B_pH_{p+q} the following equations of balance may be written:

$$s + x = q \tag{8.1}$$
$$s + t = p \tag{8.2}$$
$$p = t + y + q/2 \tag{8.3}$$

where s is the number of bridge hydrogen atoms; x is the number of extra hydrogen, i.e., BH_2 units; t is the number of three-center BBB bonds; y is the number of two-center BB bonds.

Equation 8.1 arises from a consideration of the boron hydrides as made up of BH units; the number of hydrogen atoms in excess of the number of boron atoms will either form extra B—H bonds or go into three-center bonds. Equation 8.2 simply states that the number of three-center bonds will be equal to the number of boron atoms; this is

* Lipscomb, W. N., see under general references.

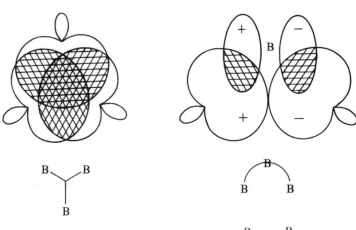

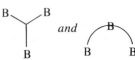

FIGURE 8.3. *Atomic orbital overlap represented by*

due to each boron atom having four low energy orbitals but only three electrons available for bonding. Equation 8.3 states that the two electrons of each :BH unit make up the total of framework bonds, except for BHB bonds in which the hydrogen brings in one electron.

The application of these equations to B_4H_{10} is as follows:

$$\text{For } B_4H_{10} \ p = 4 \text{ and } q = 6$$

Equation 8.3 thus gives $4 = t + y + 3$.

One solution is $t = 1$, $y = 0$. Substitution of $t = 1$ in Equation 8.2 gives $s + 1 = 4$ or $s = 3$. Substitution of this value in Equation 8.1 gives $3 + x = 6$ or $x = 3$. Thus one possible solution is $t = 1$, $y = 0$, $s = 3$, and $x = 3$. The other possible solution would be for $y = 1$, $t = 0$ and hence $s = 4$ and $x = 2$. Generally, the structure found is that with the highest degree of symmetry. The equations of balance do not always give unequivocal answers but aid in limiting the structures to be considered. For B_4H_{10} structural data favor the second solution and the bonding may be represented as

Additional criteria, such as reasonable direction for the hybridized orbitals and necessity of bonding of adjacent boron atoms leads to topological formulas given in Figure

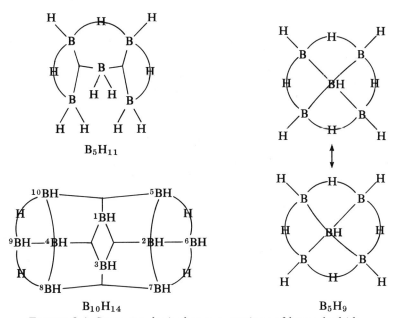

FIGURE 8.4. *Some topological representations of boron hydrides.*

8.4, which are consistent with the structures found by diffraction and spectral methods and shown in Figure 8.1.

Molecular Orbital Treatment of the Boron Hydrides*

The use of resonance in describing the structure of B_5H_9 may be noted in Figure 8.4. This indicates that the electrons are more highly delocalized than even a three-center bond suggests. In general, where resonance is used to describe bonding, a better bonding picture may be obtained from a molecular orbital approach.

For B_5H_9, consider the apical boron as having sp hybridization and the borons in the basal plane as having sp^3 hybridization. After the hydrogen atoms have been taken care of, by two- and three-center bonds, each basal boron has one sp^3 orbital left and the

* Eberhardt, W. H., B. Crawford, Jr., and W. N. Lipscomb, *J. Chem. Phys.*, **22**, 989 (1954).

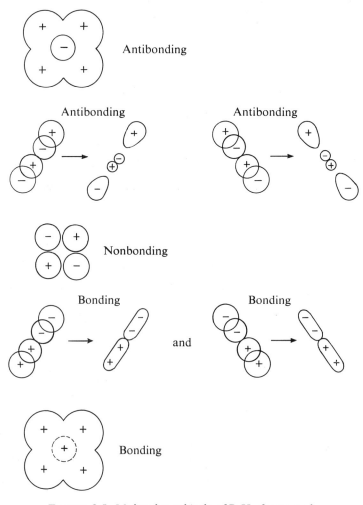

FIGURE 8.5. *Molecular orbitals of B_5H_9 framework.*

apical boron has one *sp* orbital and two *p* orbitals (perpendicular to the *sp*) left. Six electrons are left to fill these seven orbitals. These six electrons will fill the three lowest of the seven molecular orbitals resulting from the combination of the seven atomic orbitals. The lowest energy molecular orbital will result from the combination of the *sp* orbital of the apical boron with the four sp^3 orbitals of the remaining boron atoms, all orbitals taken with the same sign for the ψ function.

The next lowest orbitals occur as a degenerate pair resulting from the combination of the *p* orbitals from the apical boron with the sp^3 orbitals of the two diagonally opposite boron atoms. These bonding molecular orbitals, which take up the six electrons are sketched in Figure 8.5 along with the one nonbonding and three antibonding orbitals.

Equations of Balance for Electron Deficient Ions

The equations of balance for ions of general formula $[B_pH_{p+q+c}]^c$, where c is an ionic charge, differ from Equations 8.1, 8.2, and 8.3 only in that "c" is added as a term to the right-hand side of each of the equations. Thus Equation 8.1 becomes $s+x=q+c$. Some ions of the boron hydrides will be discussed in the section covering reactions of these compounds.

The equations of balance for ions may be applied to other electron deficient systems of second period elements if these are considered as pseudoboron hydrides. Thus a carbon atom has four valence electrons, and a charge of -1 would appear in the pseudoboron hydride for each carbon atom. Consider the carbonium ion $C_4H_7^+$, which would be equivalent to a hypothetical boron hydride ion $[B_4H_7]^{3-}$. Here $p=4$, $c=-3$, and $q=6$. Two solutions are possible for the equations of balance.

$$y=4,\ t=0,\ s=1,\ x=2$$

and

$$y=3,\ t=1,\ s=0,\ x=3$$

The second solution suggests a tetrahedral structure

which has greater symmetry than any of the other possibilities. The carbonium ion $C_4H_7^+$ appears as an intermediate in the nitrous acid deamination reaction of

CH—CH$_2$—NH$_2$. The nonclassical carbonium ion structure involving a three-center bond has received strong experimental support from tracer studies.* Further interesting nonclassical carbonium ions have been proposed by Winstein but will not be given here (see problem 5).

Hyperconjugation

Despite the success of the equations of balance in correlating and predicting possible structures, it is apparent that nothing will come out that has not been put in! If a type of bonding occurs which does not fall into the types considered in writing the equations it will be overlooked. Thus trimethylboron, $(CH_3)_3B$, might be expected to be either a dimer or possibly it might be considered as a pseudo $B_4H_9^{3-}$ ion which, from the equations of balance, would lead to a prediction of a three-center bond. However, the structural data point to a monomeric molecule with three equivalent methyl groups. This monomer provides a good argument for *hyperconjugation*, a type of no bond resonance frequently cited in organic chemistry. Hyperconjugation provides an additional pair of electrons for the boron, making bridging unnecessary.

The extent and importance of hyperconjugation is a matter of some controversy, and the failure of $B(CH_3)_3$ to dimerize may also be explained as due to steric effects.

Hyperconjugation should be of little importance in an addition compound such as $(CH_3)_3B—N(CH_3)_3$ compared to $B(CH_3)_3$ because the B atom in the addition compound has a complete octet. The reaction of $B(CH_3)_3$ with $N(CH_3)_3$ to form the addition compound has been studied and compared to the analogous reaction of the deuterated

$$B(CH_3)_3(g) + N(CH_3)_3(g) \rightleftharpoons (CH_3)_3B—N(CH_3)_3(g)$$

compound $B(CD_3)_3$.† The ratio of the equilibrium constant (for the reaction shown) for $B(CD_3)_3$ to that for $B(CH_3)_3$ is 1.25 ± 0.03, a value at least 36% higher than expected on the basis of the mass effect. The greater tendency for $B(CD_3)_3$ to form the addition compound compared to $B(CH_3)_3$ is to be expected if $B(CH_3)_3$ is really stabilized to a much greater extent by hyperconjugation compared to $B(CD_3)_3$. Hyperconjugation should be generally less important for deuterium compounds than for those of hydrogen.

The hyperconjugative structures for neutral molecules require charge separation. This is not necessary for positively charged species and it provides a means for delocalizing the positive charge. Hyperconjugation would be expected to be quite important for charged species such as carbonium ions bearing a number of methyl groups.

* Roberts, J. D., and R. H. Mazur, *J. Am. Chem. Soc.,* **73**, 3542 (1952).
† Love, P., R. Taft, and T. Wartik, *Tetrahedron,* **5**, 116 (1959).

Anionic hyperconjugation, involving

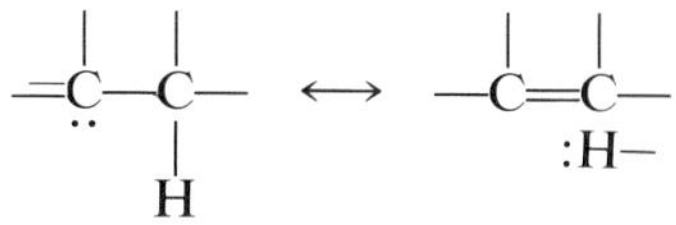

$$=\overset{|}{\underset{\underset{\overset{|}{H}}{\cdot\cdot}}{C}}-\overset{|}{\underset{|}{C}}- \quad \longleftrightarrow \quad -\overset{|}{C}=\overset{|}{\underset{:H-}{C}}-$$

might be important for negative ions such as carbanions, as a means for delocalizing the charge.

Some Other Electron Deficient Molecules

Aluminum trimethyl is a dimer, $[Al(CH_3)_3]_2$, as one would expect if hyperconjugation is the reason for the failure of $B(CH_3)_3$ to dimerize. Double bonds of the *p-p* type are much less important for third period elements such as Al. The structure is presumed to be very similar to B_2H_6 with two bridge bonds involving methyl groups. Each three-center bridge bond in $[Al(CH_3)_3]_2$ is interpreted as the result of the overlap of sp^3 orbitals from the two aluminum atoms and one of the bridge methyl groups.

Another interesting example of an electron deficient compound is $[Be(CH_3)_2]_n$, a long chain polymer. One orbital of each methyl group and all of the beryllium sp^3 orbitals are presumably involved in bridge bonds.

Some structures involving methyl bridges are shown in Figure 8.6. The tetrameric structure of platinum tetramethyl is particularly interesting as it indicates that the bridging methyl group is involved in a four-center orbital and has C.N. 6.

Reactions of Boron Hydrides and the Relationship to Their Structure

Formation of Hydrides

Most of the higher hydrides of boron can be formed by the controlled pyrolysis of diborane. One mechanism postulated for the growth of higher hydrides from diborane involves successive addition of BH_3 or B_2H_6 followed by loss of hydrogen. The following sequence illustrates this; the currently known hydrides are italicized.

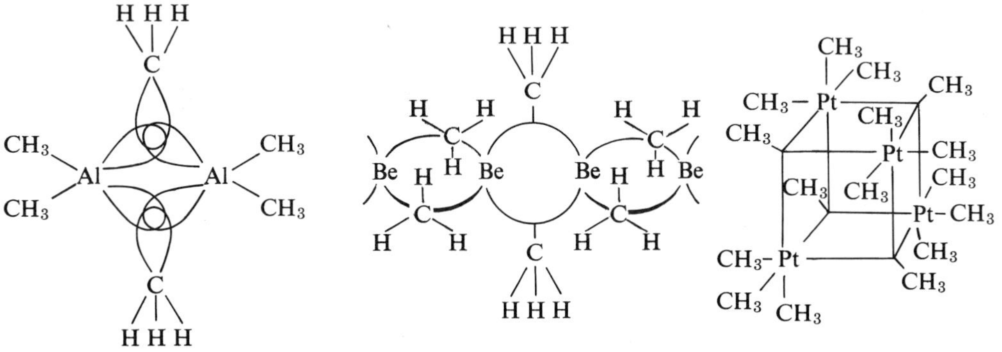

FIGURE 8.6. *Some electron deficient compounds showing polycentered orbitals.*

$$B_2H_6 \xrightarrow{BH_3} B_3H_9 \xrightarrow{-H_2} B_3H_7 \xrightarrow{B_2H_6} B_5H_{13} \xrightarrow{-H_2} B_5H_{11} \xrightarrow{-H_2} B_5H_9 \xrightarrow{BH_3}$$

$$\xrightarrow[\;\;-BH_3\;\;]{} B_4H_{10} \quad \text{etc.} \qquad B_6H_{12}$$

All of the boron hydrides have greater (up to 1.5 ×) heats of combustion per unit weight than the most nearly comparable hydrocarbons. Accordingly, it is not surprising that they are of interest as potential rocket fuels.

Reactions of Diborane

Reactions might be expected between electron deficient compounds and compounds having unshared pairs of electrons (Lewis Bases) and indeed are common. The reactions of diborane have been studied more extensively than those of the other boron hydrides. Some of these reactions are

$$\frac{1}{2}B_2H_6 + (CH_3)_2O \longrightarrow (CH_3)_2\ddot{O}{:}BH_3 \tag{8.4}$$

$$\frac{1}{2}B_2H_6 + CO \longrightarrow H_3B{:}CO \tag{8.5}$$

$$\frac{1}{2}B_2H_6 + C_5H_5N \longrightarrow C_5H_5N{:}BH_3 \tag{8.6}$$

$$\frac{1}{2}B_2H_6 + (CH_3)_3N \longrightarrow (CH_3)_3N{:}BH_3 \tag{8.7}$$

$$\frac{1}{2}B_2H_6 + MH \longrightarrow MBH_4 \tag{8.8}$$

In all of the above reactions the diborane is split into BH_3 units, each of which accepts an electron pair from the attacking reagent, thereby completing its octet of electrons. The order of thermal stability of the products is generally that expected on the basis of strength of the Lewis base (see Chapter VI), dimethyl ether–borane being the least stable of the above and the borohydride being the most stable. (See p. 213, Chapter VI, for a discussion of H_3BCO.)

Reactions 8.4 and 8.6 have both been used in the purification of diborane. When dimethyl ether is used the unstable addition compound with diborane is formed at $-78.5°C$. Other volatile compounds that may be present are removed by pumping on the addition compound at $-100°$. On warming to -78.5 the addition compound is sufficiently dissociated to allow vacuum line fractionation of the methyl ether and the regenerated diborane. The technique of purifying a volatile compound through the formation of an adduct, which is stable at one temperature but which dissociates at a higher temperature, is a fairly general one. Other examples include the purification of HF through the KHF_2 adduct (p. 175, Chapter V), of BF_3 through the anisole adduct, of low molecular weight ethers through the $LiBH_4$ adducts, etc.

Thermal dissociation of the pyridine–borane adduct cannot be used for the recovery of diborane due to an irreversible decomposition to give hydrogen and other products. In this case the diborane is regenerated by displacing it from solution by the addition of boron trifluoride etherate.

The last reaction (8.8) proceeds only in the presence of a solvent, diethyl ether being satisfactory for the formation of $LiBH_4$ and diglyme (i.e., diethylene glycol dimethyl ether) for $NaBH_4$. These compounds are thermally quite stable; $LiBH_4$ loses hydrogen at 275° and $NaBH_4$ loses hydrogen above 400°. The borohydride ion, BH_4^-, is reasonably stable in water at high pH values. Lithium borohydride slowly reacts with water, apparently due to the hydrolysis of the Li^+ ion, which increases the hydrogen ion concentration (see Chapter VI). Lithium borohydride is slightly soluble in diethyl ether (2.5 g/100g) and in isopropyl amine (3–4 g/100). Sodium borohydride is very soluble in liquid NH_3 (104 g/100) and moderately soluble in primary alkylamines, the solubility decreasing with increasing molecular weight. Other borohydrides may be prepared by metathetical reactions with $LiBH_4$ and $NaBH_4$.

In the reaction of a Lewis base with an excess of diborane a species containing a single three-center bond may be obtained

This type of reaction (given above for pyridine) has been reported for reactions 8.6, 8.7, and 8.8. The second BH_3 group is not held as firmly as the first and is lost to reform diborane on warming the pyridine or amine complex to room temperature, or on pumping on the borohydride complex. The borohydride–borane complexes may be made directly from borohydride and diborane in an appropriate solvent. A number of interesting complexes may be made from diborane and other hydrides, i.e.,*

$$LiAlH_4 + B_2H_6 \longrightarrow Li(BH_4 \cdot AlH_3)$$
$$NaAlH_4 + B_2H_6 \longrightarrow Na[AlH(BH_4)_2AlH_4]$$
$$Na[Al(AlH_4)(BH_4)_3] \text{ etc.}$$

In addition to those containing boron, there are complexes such as $Li[GaH_3AlH_4]$, which may also be assumed to have a single hydrogen bridge bond. It may appear that little is to be gained from the addition of diborane to a borohydride ion, since the number of BH bonds and of BHB bonds

remains the same. However, the bridge bond in the product exists in a *charged* species, and charge delocalization stabilizes the ion.

* Noth, H., *Angew. Chem.*, **73**, 371 (1961).

The situation is similar to that previously discussed in comparing the strengths of hydrogen bonds in neutral molecules (such as water) with ion–molecule interactions such as HO---H---OH$^-$ (see p. 175, Chapter V). The ion Al(BH$_4$)$_4^-$ is analogous to F(HF)$_4^-$, the structure of these probably being

$$
\left[
\begin{array}{c}
BH_3 \\
\vdots \\
H \\
\vdots \\
H_3B\text{---}H\text{---}Al\text{---}H\text{---}BH_3 \\
\vdots \\
H \\
\vdots \\
BH_3
\end{array}
\right]^-
\quad \text{and} \quad
\left[
\begin{array}{c}
F \\
| \\
H \\
\vdots \\
F\text{---}H\text{---}F\text{---}H\text{---}F \\
\vdots \\
H \\
| \\
F
\end{array}
\right]^-
$$

The major difference between these would be in the occupancy of nonbonding orbitals in the F(HF)$_4^-$ species. Aluminum may have a higher coordination number than 4 with hydrogen by forming two-bridge bonds with some boron atoms.

It should be pointed out that the single bridge bonds for electron deficient compounds have not yet been established by structural investigations, but only inferred from their stoichiometry.

The reaction of diborane with excess ammonia at low temperatures also appears to give a species with a single bridge hydrogen

$$H_3N + B_2H_6 \longrightarrow H_3N\text{---}BH_2\text{---}H\text{---}BH_3$$
$$(I)$$

On removing ammonia at $-78°$ a white solid is formed, which has been shown to be

$$
\left[
\begin{array}{c}
H \qquad NH_3 \\
\diagdown \diagup \\
B \\
\diagup \diagdown \\
H \qquad NH_3
\end{array}
\right]^+
\left[
\begin{array}{c}
H \qquad H \\
\diagdown \diagup \\
B \\
\diagup \diagdown \\
H \qquad H
\end{array}
\right]^-
$$

The compound [H$_2$B(NH$_3$)$_2$]$^+$[BH$_4$]$^-$ is known as the "diammoniate of diborane," and its formation represents the only proven case of nonsymmetrical cleavage of diborane by consecutive substitution.* Nonsymmetrical cleavage here is defined as the splitting out of a BH$_2$ unit from diborane in contrast to symmetrical cleavage, which splits out a BH$_3$ unit. Nonsymmetrical attack of I is favored by electrical factors (see Chapter VI) and it is believed that steric factors are responsible for the symmetrical cleavage observed with amines and ethers. Compounds containing the species H$_2$B(base)$_2^+$ may be obtained in low yield by the treatment of the base in a polyether with excess diborane at temperatures around 175°C. The following reactions are better methods† (the base is represented by D)

$$D:BH_3 + DH^+X^- \longrightarrow H_2BD_2^+X^- + H_2$$

* Parry, R. W., and S. G. Shore, *J. Am. Chem. Soc.*, **80**, 15 (1958). The reaction LiNH$_2$ + B$_2$H$_6$ → LiBH$_4$ + H$_2$BNH$_2$ does not have a second incoming group.
† Miller, N. E., and E. L. Muetterties, *J. Am. Chem. Soc.*, **86**, 1033 (1964).

X must not compete favorably with D for the Lewis acid, i.e., X = I$^-$ works well, but X = Cl$^-$ gives DBH$_2$X as the product. With very weak bases such as thioethers or arsines, the base and an equivalent amount of HX is used. Alternatively, salts of H$_2$BD$_2{}^+$X$^-$ may be prepared by displacing a weaker base with a stronger base. The observed order of displacing ability is diamine > amine > phosphines > arsine > thioethers. The compound H$_3$N:BH$_3$ may be prepared by displacing (CH$_3$)$_2$O from (CH$_3$)$_2$O:BH$_3$ with NH$_3$. Heating the diammoniate of diborane to 200° produces B$_3$N$_3$H$_6$, borazine, which is sometimes referred to as "inorganic benzene" due to their very similar physical properties, isoelectronic structures and consequent possibilities of "aromaticity," and a slight chemical resemblance with regard to type reactions.

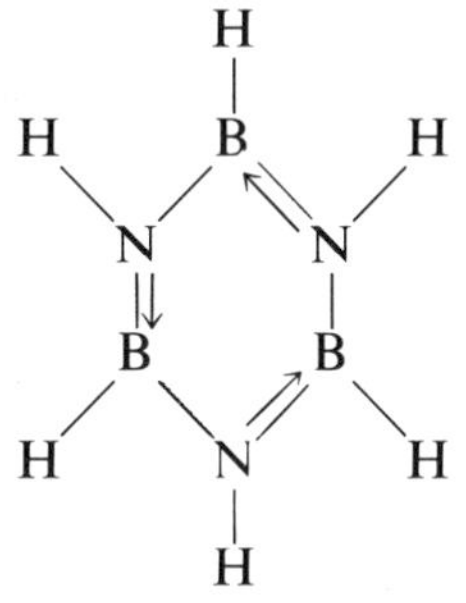

Borazine

This compound has been discussed elsewhere in detail.* Complete pyrolysis of this compound, or of any compound containing a 1:1 ratio of B to N, yields boron nitride, sometimes referred to as "inorganic graphite."

As might be expected, the electron deficient diborane will react with reducing agents such as sodium or potassium amalgam. The reaction is facilitated by the use of diethyl ether as a solvent. The reaction may be written as†

$$2Na(Hg)_x + 2B_2H_6 \longrightarrow NaBH_4 + NaB_3H_8$$

From the equations of balance the bonding in the B$_3$H$_8{}^-$ ion could be either

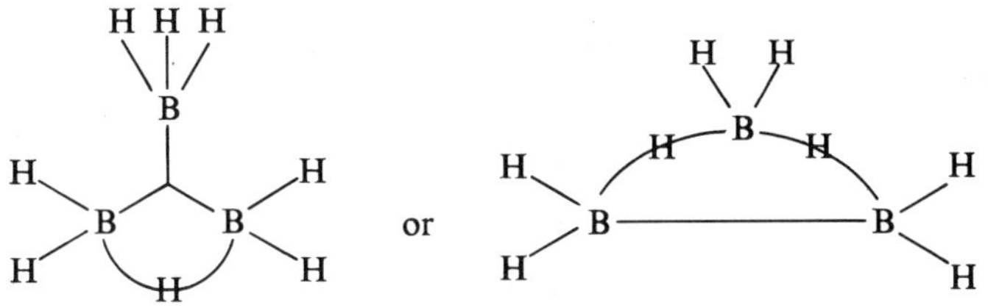

---

* Sheldon, J. C., and B. C. Smith, *Chem. Rev.,* **14,** 200 (1960).
† Hough, W. V., L. J. Edwards, and A. D. McElroy, *J. Am. Chem. Soc.,* **78,** 689 (1956).

These species have the same symmetry elements so a clear choice cannot be made arbitrarily.

Diborane attacks the double bonds in olefins and has the further unique property of undergoing reversible addition and dissociation during which time the double bond "walks" to the end of the chain!* Alkaline peroxide oxidation then produces predominately terminal alcohols from mixed olefins.

$$-\overset{|}{\underset{|}{C}}-\overset{|}{\underset{|}{C}}-\overset{|}{C}=\overset{|}{C}-\overset{|}{\underset{|}{C}}- \;+\; B_2H_6 \longrightarrow -\overset{|}{\underset{|}{C}}-\overset{|}{\underset{|}{C}}-\overset{|}{\underset{|}{C}}-\overset{|}{\underset{|}{C}}-\overset{|}{\underset{|}{C}}-BH_2$$

$$\Big\downarrow [O]$$

$$-\overset{|}{\underset{|}{C}}-\overset{|}{\underset{|}{C}}-\overset{|}{\underset{|}{C}}-\overset{|}{\underset{|}{C}}-\overset{|}{\underset{|}{C}}-OH$$

The diborane is prepared *in situ* from the reaction of $LiBH_4$ or $NaBH_4$ with acids such as boron trifluoride etherate, hydrogen chloride, or sulfuric acid. An ether solvent such as ethyl ether, tetrahydrofuran, or polyethers, must be used. The oxidation is also usually carried out *in situ*.

Reactions of the Higher Boron Hydrides

The reactions the higher boron hydrides undergo are often similar to those of diborane. Thus tetraborane reacts with Lewis bases to give borane and triborane adducts. Representing the Lewis base by S: [where S: may be $(CH_3)_3N:$, $R_2\ddot{O}:$, $(CH_3)_3P:$ or $:H^-$] the reactions may be pictured as

---

* Brown, H. C., "Organoboranes," Chapter 4 in *Organometallic Chemistry,* edited by H. Zeiss (New York: Reinhold Publishing Corp., 1960); H. C. Brown, *Hydroboration* (New York: W. A. Benjamin, Inc., 1962).

i.e., $S: + B_4H_{10} \rightarrow S:BH_3 + S:B_3H_7$. When excess trimethylamine is used, the $(CH_3)_3NB_3H_7$ undergoes further attack giving more $(CH_3)_3N:BH_3$ and $[HB:N(CH_3)_3]_x$.

The reaction of tetraborane with ammonia proceeds by nonsymmetrical cleavage as in the case of diborane.

$$2NH_3 + B_4H_{10} \longrightarrow [H_2B(NH_3)_2]^+ \; [B_3H_8]^-$$

It is possible to obtain an ammonia–triborane adduct in the same fashion as the ammonia–borane adduct, i.e., displacing the ether from an etherate with ammonia.

$$H_3N + R_2O:B_3H_7 \longrightarrow H_3N:B_3H_7 + R_2O.$$

The reaction of ethylene with tetraborane differs from that with diborane in that hydrogen is evolved.[*]

$$C_2H_4 + B_4H_{10} \longrightarrow B_4H_8C_2H_4 + H_2$$

The product apparently has a structure as indicated below.

Decaborane undergoes some unique reactions not yet found in the lower hydrides. One such reaction is the slow loss of a proton in base, allowing titration of this

$$B_{10}H_{14} + NaOH \rightleftharpoons NaB_{10}H_{13} + H_2O$$

substance using phenolphthalein indicator. The reaction is believed to involve removal of one of the bridge hydrogens with a conversion of this bond to a two-center bond.

Rapid exhange of *four* of the hydrogen atoms in $B_{10}H_{14}$ for deuterium atoms in a D_2O–dioxane mixture supports the view that the bridge hydrogen atoms are acidic.

The acidic hydrogens of decaborane will react with methyl magnesium iodide in ethyl ether to release methane and form the inorganic Grignard reagents $B_{10}H_{13}MgI$ and $B_{10}H_{12}(MgI)_2$.[†] These appear to undergo the expected Grignard reactions. Thus, reaction of $B_{10}H_{13}MgI$ with benzyl chloride produces benzyldecaborane, $B_{10}H_{13}CH_2C_6H_5$. The benzyl group is *not* on boron atoms 6 or 9 (see Figure 8.4).

[*] Harrison, B. C., I. J. Solomon, R. D. Hites, and M. J. Klein, *J. Inorg. Nucl. Chem.*, **14**, 195 (1960).
[†] Siegel, B., J. L. Mack, J. V. Lowe, Jr., and J. Gallaghan, *J. Am. Chem. Soc.*, **80**, 4523 (1958).

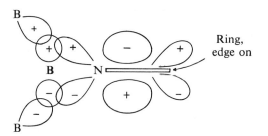

FIGURE 8.7. *Interaction of π-orbitals of pyridine with p-orbitals of boron framework (framework fragment only shown).*

Lewis bases such as CH_3CN, C_5H_5N, and Me_2S react with decaborane to liberate hydrogen

$$2CH_3CN + B_{10}H_{14} \longrightarrow B_{10}H_{12} \cdot 2CH_3CN + H_2$$

Structural data support the following representation

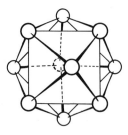

With the pyridine adduct, spectral data indicate an interaction between the π orbitals of pyridine and the p orbital of the boron framework,[*] as depicted in Figure 8.7

Triethylamine reacts with the bis-acetonitrile decaborane to give two compounds of the formula $B_{10}H_{12} \cdot 2(C_2H_5)_3N$. One is assumed to be a covalent compound similar to those discussed above since it is soluble in benzene and the amine may be readily dis-

FIGURE 8.8. *The $B_{10}H_{10}^{2-}$ framework.*

* Graybill, B. M., and M. F. Hawthorne, *J. Am. Chem. Soc.,* **83,** 2673 (1961).

placed by triphenylphosphine. The other compound is ionic, containing the triethyl-ammonium ions and an ion $B_{10}H_{10}^{2-}$ which has the structure shown in Figure 8.8.[*]

The ionic compound may also be obtained by the direct reaction of triethylamine with decaborane. Oxidative coupling produces an interesting series of ions retaining the B_{10} unit structure.[†]

$$2B_{10}H_{10}^{2-} + Fe^{3+} \longrightarrow B_{20}H_{18}^{2-} + 2H^+ + 2Fe^{2+}$$
$$B_{10}H_{10}^{2-} + Ce(\text{IV}) \longrightarrow B_{20}H_{18}^{2-} + B_{20}H_{19}^{3-} + Ce(\text{III}) + H^+$$

The B_{10} units are joined by hydrogen bridge bonds to give centrosymmetric ions shown below

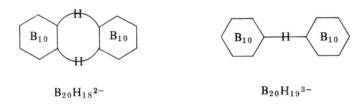

$$B_{20}H_{18}{}^{2-} \qquad\qquad B_{20}H_{19}{}^{3-}$$

The $B_{20}H_{19}^{3-}$ ion has a pK_a of 6.3, presumably ionizing by the bridge hydrogen to give $B_{20}H_{18}^{4-}$.

When triethylamine is allowed to react with iododecaborane a new ion $B_{12}H_{12}^{2-}$ is produced in small amounts.[‡] The $B_{12}H_{12}^{2-}$ ion may be prepared in high yield by the reaction of sodium borohydride with diborane in triethylamine. This ion has an icosahedral shape as shown in Figure 8.9.

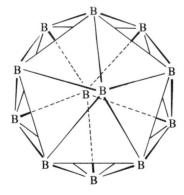

FIGURE 8.9. *Framework of the $B_{12}H_{12}^{2-}$ ion.*

[*] Lipscomb, W. N., A. R. Pitochelli, and M. F. Hawthorne, *J. Am. Chem. Soc.*, **81**, 5834 (1959).
[†] See W. N. Lipscomb, *Boron Hydrides* under general ref.; M. F. Hawthorne et al., *J. Am. Chem. Soc.*, **85**, 3705 (1963).
[‡] Pitochelli, A. R., and M. F. Hawthorne, *J. Am. Chem. Soc.*, **82**, 3228 (1960).

The $B_{10}H_{10}^{2-}$ and $B_{12}H_{12}^{2-}$ ions are remarkably stable to strong acid or base.* They can be converted to stable aqueous acids $(H_3O)_2B_{10}H_{10} \cdot xH_2O$ and $(H_3O)_2B_{12}H_{12}$, which are comparable in strength to sulfuric acid. They do react with the halogens to give partial or complete substitution of the hydrogen, i.e., $B_{12}F_{12}^{2-}$, $B_{10}I_{10}^{2-}$, $B_{10}H_6I_4^{2-}$, etc. With hydrogen halides they yield the partially halogenated ions, $B_{12}H_{11}Cl^{2-}$, etc. With dimethyl sulfoxide under acidic conditions the $B_{10}H_{10}^{2-}$ ion gives $(CH_3)_2S_2B_{10}H_8$ and $(CH_3)_2SB_{10}H_9^-$. Many other derivatives have been prepared.

In addition to the $B_{10}H_{10}^{2-}$ and $B_{12}H_{12}^{2-}$ polyhedral ions, molecular orbital theory predicts the ion $B_6H_6^{2-}$. This ion has recently been found, and the isoelectronic $B_4C_2H_6$ is known. The B_6^{2-} unit is found in a number of borides.

The neutral B_4Cl_4 and B_8Cl_8 molecules have boron frameworks of tetrahedra and square antiprisms, respectively. As in BCl_3, the BCl bonds in these molecules may be expected to have some double bond character. The corresponding hydrides are not known, nor are they expected.

Cage Boron Nomenclature† and the Carboranes

The prefix "clovo" from the Greek word for cage is used to designate a closed polyhedron lacking bridge hydrogens. Thus B_4Cl_4 may be named tetrachloroclovotetraborane and the $B_{12}H_{12}^{2-}$ anion may be named dodecahydroclovododecaborate(-2). Substituents may be located in clovo compounds by the numbering system in which an apex atom is given the number "one," the belt or girdle atoms are numbered consecutively, and finally the opposite apex given the highest number. This numbering system is illustrated below.‡

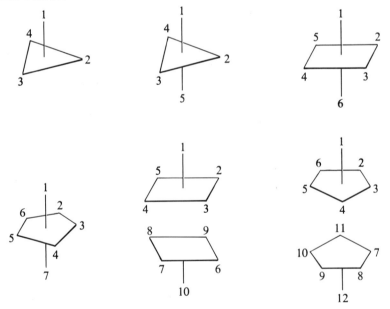

* W. H. Knoth et al., *J. Am. Chem. Soc.*, **84**, 1056 (1962); see also W. R. Hertler, W. H. Knoth, and E. L. Muetterties, *Inorg. Chem.*, **4**, 288 (1965) and references cited therein.
† Adams, R., *Inorg. Chem.*, **2**, 1087 (1963).
‡ *Inorganic Chemistry* is the original source of these figures and the American Chemical Society is the publisher and copyright owner of that journal.

When carbon replaces boron *in the polyhedron* the compound is named as a *"carba-clovoborane"* with the numbering to designate the position of the carbon atoms selected to be as low as possible. Thus 1,2-dicarbaclovohexaborane(6) indicates the compound

$$
\begin{array}{ccc}
& \text{CH} & \\
& | & \\
\text{HB}\!\!\!-\!\!\!\!\!\!-\!\!\!\!\!\!-\!\!\!\!\!\!-\!\!\!\!\!\!-\!\!\!\!\!\!& & \text{CH} \\
\text{HB}\!\!\!-\!\!\!\!\!\!-\!\!\!\!\!\!-\!\!\!\!\!\!-\!\!\!\!\!\!-\!\!\!\!\!\!& & \text{BH} \\
& | & \\
& \text{BH} &
\end{array}
$$

while 1,6-dicarbaclovohexaborane(6)* would indicate

$$
\begin{array}{ccc}
& \text{CH} & \\
& | & \\
\text{HB}\!\!\!-\!\!\!\!\!\!-\!\!\!\!\!\!-\!\!\!\!\!\!-\!\!\!\!\!\!-\!\!\!\!\!\!& & \text{BH} \\
\text{HB}\!\!\!-\!\!\!\!\!\!-\!\!\!\!\!\!-\!\!\!\!\!\!-\!\!\!\!\!\!-\!\!\!\!\!\!& & \text{BH} \\
& | & \\
& \text{CH} &
\end{array}
$$

The "hexaborane" in these names indicates that the total number of cage atoms is six, the number of boron atoms is thus six minus the two carbon atoms, or four. The "(6)" is used to indicate the number of hydrogen atoms.

The generic term "carborane" is used for clovo compounds with both boron and carbon atoms in the polyhedral framework. An extensive series of derivatives of dicarbaclovododecaboranes has been prepared.† The parent compounds are isoelectronic with the $B_{12}H_{12}^{2-}$ ion. The 1,2-dicarbo derivative is itself sometimes called carborane. It may readily be prepared from the reaction of acetylene with $B_{10}H_{12}(base)_2$ compounds where the base is acetonitrile (see p. 274), diethylsulfide, etc., or with decaborane in the presence of a suitable base.

$$B_{10}H_{12}(CH_3CN)_2 + C_2H_2 \longrightarrow B_{10}H_{10}C_2H_2 + H_2 + 2CH_3CN$$

or

$$B_{10}H_{14} + C_2H_2 \xrightarrow{base} B_{10}H_{10}C_2H_2 + H_2$$

It is very stable to oxidation or reduction, being unaffected by chromic acid, hypochlorous acid, or lithium aluminum hydride. If substituted acetylenes are used in the synthesis, then 1,2-disubstituted-1,2-dicarbaclovododecaboranes are produced. Prolonged heating of the 1,2-carborane in an inert atmosphere results in isomerization to a compound, neocarborane, believed to be 1,7-dicarbaclovododecaborane

$$B_{10}H_{10}C_2H_2 \xrightarrow[24\text{-}48\ hr.]{465\text{-}500°} HCB_{10}H_{10}CH$$

The neocarborane is even more stable than the 1,2-carborane. Thus refluxing meth-

---

* See T. P. Onak, F. J. Gerhart, and R. E. Williams, *J. Am. Chem. Soc.*, **85**, 3378 (1963) for the synthesis of this and other carboranes.
† Heying, T. L., et al., *Inorg. Chem.*, **2**, 1089–1107 (1963); R. P. Alexander and H. Schroeder, *ibid.*, **2**, 1107 (1963); M. M. Fein, et al., *ibid.*, **2**, 1111–1128 (1963); D. Grafstein and J. Dvorak, *ibid.*, **2**, 1128 (1963).

anolic potassium hydroxide does not attack the neo-isomer but does degrade the 1,2-dicarbo isomer. In both of these compounds the hydrogens attached to the carbon atoms are more acidic than the others. This allows many derivatives to be prepared via the lithium compounds.

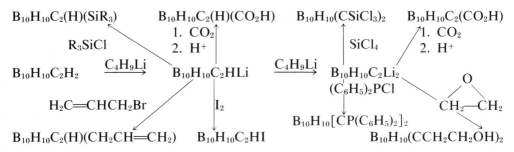

The Borohydrides and Lithium Aluminum Hydride

Synthesis

The synthesis of lithium borohydride was brought about as a direct result of the application of the Lewis acid–base concept to the metal hydrides and boron compounds.[*] The hydride ion is a very strong Lewis base, and will react even with the weak Lewis acid methyl borate.

$$NaH(s) + B(OCH_3)_3(l) \xrightarrow[68°]{} NaBH(OCH_3)_3$$

The relative strengths of Lewis acids in the sequence $BF_3 > (BH_3)_2 > (CH_3)_3B > B(OCH_3)_3$ suggested that diborane might displace methyl borate from the trimethoxyborohydride ion.

$$2NaHB(OCH_3)_3 + B_2H_6 \longrightarrow 2NaBH_4 + 2B(OCH_3)_3$$

This reaction does take place — so rapidly that it may be used to absorb diborane from a gas stream. The commercial synthesis of sodium borohydride is carried out without the necessity of using diborane. The reaction used is

$$4NaH + B(OCH_3)_3 \xrightarrow[225-275°]{} NaBH_4 + 3NaOCH_3$$

The reaction of lithium hydride with aluminum chloride in dry ether yields lithium aluminum hydride

$$4LiH + AlCl_3 \xrightarrow[(C_2H_5)_2O]{} LiAlH_4 + 3LiCl$$

It has recently been found possible to prepare the alkali metal aluminum hydrides directly from the elements in a tetrahydrofuran solvent.[†]

$$Na + Al + H_2(5000 \text{ psi}) \xrightarrow[THF]{140°} NaAlH_4$$

[*] Schlesinger, H. I., and H. C. Brown et al., *J. Am. Chem. Soc.*, **75**, 186 (1953).
[†] Ashby, E. C., G. J. Brendel, and H. E. Redman, *Inorg. Chem.*, **2**, 499 (1963).

Reactions of the Borohydrides

The borohydride ion serves as a starting material for most of the boron hydrides and the hydroborate ions. The reactions between diborane and the borohydride ion provide an excellent example of product control by variations in pressure, temperature, solvent, or "inert cation."*

$$MBH_4 + B_2H_6 \xrightarrow[\text{no solvent}]{} \text{no reaction} \quad M = Li, Na, K \tag{8.9}$$

$$(C_2H_5)_4NBH_4 + \frac{1}{2}B_2H_6 \xrightarrow[-80]{1 \text{ atm.}} (C_2H_5)_4NB_2H_7 \tag{8.10}$$

$$NaBH_4 + \frac{1}{2}B_2H_6 \xrightarrow[\text{polyethers}]{0°} NaB_2H_7 \tag{8.11}$$

$$NaBH_4 + B_2H_6 \xrightarrow[\substack{3 \text{ atm.} \\ \text{polyethers}}]{25 \text{ to } 50°} NaB_3H_8 \quad (90\% \text{ yield}) + H_2 \tag{8.12}$$

$$NaBH_4 + B_2H_6 \xrightarrow[\text{polyethers}]{120°} NaB_{11}H_{14}(50\%) + Na_2B_{12}H_{12}(40\%) + H_2 \tag{8.13}$$

$$NaBH_4 + 5B_2H_6 \xrightarrow[\text{dioxane}]{120°} NaB_{11}H_{14} + 10H_2 \tag{8.14}$$

$$2NaBH_4 + 5B_2H_6 \xrightarrow[(C_2H_5)_3N]{100 \text{ to } 180°} Na_2B_{12}H_{12} + 13H_2 \tag{8.15}$$

$$NaBH_4 + B_2H_6 \xrightarrow[\text{polyethers}]{162°} Na_2B_6H_6 \; (5\text{--}10\% \text{ yield}) + H_2 \tag{8.16}$$

The following, somewhat speculative, explanations may be offered for the differences in behavior displayed above. Reactions 8.9 and 8.10 are analogous to those discussed on pp. 176 and 177, Chapter V. The energy released in forming the $B_2H_7^-$ ion must be greater than that needed to expand the MBH_4 lattice. Thus reaction occurs with tetraethylammonium borohydride where the tetraethylammonium ion dominates the lattice and only slight expansion is needed to accommodate the new ion formed.† With the smaller cations Li^+, Na^+, and K^+ no reaction occurs in the absence of solvent. Polyethers form relatively stable complexes with sodium ion, and this large solvated cation loses relatively little ion–pair energy in solution (or lattice energy in the solid) when the $B_2H_7^-$ species is formed from BH_4^- (Reaction 8.11). Potassium ion due to its larger size does not solvate as readily and hence KBH_4 does not react at low temperatures with B_2H_6 in polyethers.

At the higher pressures of reaction 8.12 it is probable that a $B_3H_{10}^-$ species forms, which splits out hydrogen to form the $B_3H_8^-$ ion.‡

---

* See H. C. Miller, N. E. Miller, and E. L. Muetterties, *J. Am. Chem. Soc.*, **85**, 3886 (1963) for reactions (8.12) through (8.15). For reaction (8.11) see H. C. Brown and P. A. Tierney, *J. Am. Chem. Soc.*, **80**, 1552 (1958). For reaction (8.16) see J. L. Boone, *J. Am. Chem. Soc.*, **86**, 5036 (1964).
† Evans, W. G., Ph.D. Thesis, University of Cincinnati, 1964.
‡ Gaines, D. F., R. Schaeffer, and F. Tebbe, *Inorg. Chem.*, **2**, 526 (1963).

$$\left[\begin{array}{c} H \quad\quad\quad H \\ | \quad\quad\quad\quad | \\ H-B \quad\quad\quad B-H \\ H \; H \quad\quad H \; H \\ B \\ / \quad \backslash \\ H \quad H \end{array}\right]^{-} \longrightarrow \left[\begin{array}{c} H \quad\quad\quad H \\ | \quad\quad\quad\quad | \\ H-B \overline{\quad\quad\quad} B-H \\ H \quad\quad\quad H \\ B \\ / \quad \backslash \\ H \quad H \end{array}\right]^{-} + H_2$$

Reactions 8.13, 8.14, and 8.15 appear to occur as a result of the formation of decaborane and subsequent reaction of the decaborane. Thus reaction 8.14 may be carried out by reacting sodium borohydride with decaborane at 90°.* At 25° the BH_4^- abstracts

$$MBH_4 + B_{10}H_{14} \xrightarrow[R_2O]{90°} MB_{11}H_{14} + 2H_2$$

a proton from $B_{10}H_{14}$ to give $B_{10}H_{13}^-$, H_2, and B_2H_6. This is thought to be a step in reaction 8.14, followed by the addition of BH_3, i.e.,

$$R_2O:BH_3 + MB_{10}H_{13} \longrightarrow MB_{11}H_{14} + H_2 + R_2O$$

The last reaction has been shown to occur at 90°.

The $B_{11}H_{14}^-$ ion is postulated to resemble $B_{12}H_{12}^{2-}$, but with a triangular H_3^+ group replacing a BH group.

In reaction 8.15 the triethylamine solvent would form a relatively stable borane adduct thereby stopping the reaction producing $B_{11}H_{14}^-$. The route to $B_{12}H_{12}^{2-}$ has not been established, but may involve solvent coordination to the $B_{10}H_{14}^-$ species. The solvent used in reaction 8.13 is probably intermediate in base strength between dioxane and triethylamine.

The emf values for boron half-reactions are†

$$\begin{array}{cccccc} & & & & 0.48 & \\ & & & \overbrace{\quad\quad\quad\quad\quad\quad\quad\quad\quad\quad\quad\quad} & & \downarrow \\ E_A^0 & BH_4^- & \xrightarrow{0.36} B_2H_6 & \xrightarrow{0.14} B & \xrightarrow{0.90} & H_3BO_3 \\ \\ E_N & BH_4^- & \xrightarrow{0.57} B_2H_6 & \xrightarrow{0.56} B & \xrightarrow{1.31} & H_3BO_3 \\ \\ E_B^0 & BH_4^- & \xrightarrow{0.78} B_2H_6 & \xrightarrow{0.98} B & \xrightarrow{1.82} & B(OH)_4^- \end{array}$$

The BH_4^- species is stable in water above a pH of 9. It is a mild reducing reagent, useful for selective organic reductions in water or alcohol solvents. It reduces aqueous solutions of arsenites, antimonites, germanates, or stannates to the corresponding hydrides.

$$3BH_4^- + 4H_3AsO_3 + 3H^+ \longrightarrow 3H_3BO_3 + 4AsH_3 + 3H_2O$$

---

* Aftandilian, V. D., et al., *Inorg. Chem.*, **1**, 734 (1963).
† Sister Mary Concetta Waller, *Inorganic Chemistry of Borohydrides* (Beverly, Massachusetts: Metal Hydrides Incorporated, Congress Street, 1961).

Many transition metal ions are quantitatively reduced to lower oxidation states in aqueous solution—the products being dependent on their half-cell emf values.

As indicated earlier, strong acids, protonic or Lewis, displace B_2H_6 from borohydrides. If the solutions are dilute aqueous solutions, complete hydrolysis of the borohydride takes place to give boric acid and hydrogen.

*Reactions of Lithium Aluminum Hydride**

Lithium aluminum hydride is a much stronger reducing agent than the borohydrides. It reacts violently with water. Its solutions in ethyl ether or tetrahydrofuran are widely used for organic reductions. Its reaction with binary halides provides a general method for the preparation of the volatile hydrides.

$$SiCl_4 + LiAlH_4 \xrightarrow{(C_2H_5)_2O} SiH_4 + LiCl + AlCl_3$$
$$PCl_3 + LiAlH_4 \xrightarrow{(C_2H_5)_2O} PH_3 + LiCl + AlCl_3$$

The solvent plays an essential role in the above reactions—thus the reduction of phosphorus trichloride does not take place in the absence of ether.

Lithium aluminum hydride reacts with diborane to produce a liquid aluminum borohydride.

$$LiAlH_4 + 2B_2H_6 \longrightarrow LiBH_4 + Al(BH_4)_3$$

This borohydride is believed to have six bridge bonds about each aluminum.

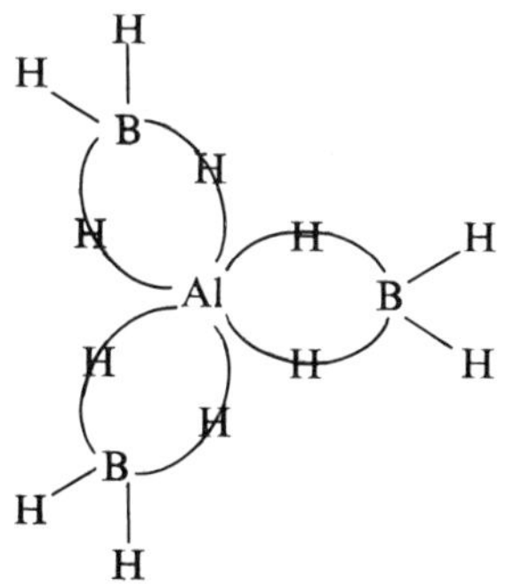

It is extremely hazardous, detonating violently on contact with air containing trace amounts of moisture. It slowly evolves hydrogen on standing at room temperature. It is the most volatile aluminum compound known. It has been used to prepare heavy metal borohydrides such as those of uranium, thorium, hafnium, zirconium and titanium.

$$UF_4 + 2Al(BH_4)_3 \longrightarrow U(BH_4)_4 + 2AlF_2BH_4$$

Uranium(IV) borohydrides is also quite volatile and probably has a structure containing hydrogen bridge bonds.

* Gaylord, N. G., *Reduction with Complex Metal Hydrides* (New York: Interscience Publishers, Inc., 1956).

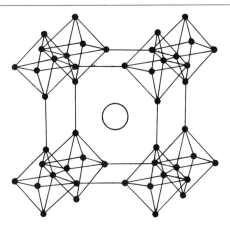

FIGURE 8.10. *The* MB_6 *structure (from L. Pauling,* The Nature of the Chemical Bond, *Third edition, © 1960 by Cornell University, p. 366. Used by permission of Cornell University Press).*

The Borides*

Metal borides are known which have a variety of different formulas, i.e., M_2B, MB, M_3B_4, MB_2, MB_4, MB_6, and MB_{12}. The compounds MB_4 through MB_{12}, and elemental boron itself, may be considered to be made up of boron polyhedra having internal electron requirements similar to the $B_nH_n^{2-}$ ions discussed above and connected together through B—B bonds, with occasional additional boron atoms providing bridges. Thus the MB_6 compounds, which include CaB_6, SrB_6, BaB_6, YB_6, LaB_6, CeB_6, PrB_6, NbB_6, SmB_6, GdB_6, ErB_6, YbB_6, and ThB_6, contain B_6 octahedral units in a CsCl type crystal (p. 103). Each boron atom has five nearest neighbor boron atoms, four in the same octahedron and one in the adjacent B_6 octahedron (see Figure 8.10).

According to Lipscomb and Britton these MB_6 compounds may be thought of as containing M^{2+} and B_6^{2-} groups. Seven pairs of electrons are needed for internal bonding in the B_6 group and the remaining 6 electrons are used to bond to other octahedra. The metals forming MB_6 other than Ca, Sr, and Ba, have some electrons left over after providing the two to form B_6^{2-} and hence these have more metallic character as revealed by their increased conductance, luster, etc. The MB_4† compounds, such as ThB_4, CeB_4, and UB_4, have ethylene-like B_2^{2-} units bridging the B_6^{2-} units. Uranium, zirconium, and several of the rare earths give MB_{12} compounds containing B_{12} polyhedra in a NaCl type lattice.‡ The B_{12}^{2-} units are cubooctahedra (see Figure 8.11) and are crosslinked. Each B_{12}^{2-} unit requires 26 electrons for its internal bonding. The compound B_4C has a NaCl type lattice containing B_{12} icosahedral (see Figure 8.11) units and C_3 units. The boron atoms are linked either to boron atoms in other icosahedra, or to the terminal

---

* See W. N. Lipscomb and D. Britton, "Valence Structures of the Higher Borides," *J. Chem. Phys.,* **33**, 275 (1960).
† See B. Post, D. Moskowitz, and F. W. Goser, *J. Am. Chem. Soc.,* **78**, 1800 (1956).
‡ LaPlaca, S., I. Binder, and B. Post, *J. Inorg. Nucl. Chem.,* **18**, 113 (1961).

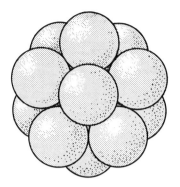

Icosahedral Unit
(one atom not shown).

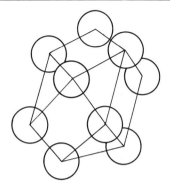

Cubo-octahedron
(Cube with corners sliced off—
three atoms not shown).

FIGURE 8.11. *Icosahedral and cubo-octahedral units.*

carbons in the C_3 units. The icosahedral unit also occurs in the tetragonal forms of elemental boron.

GENERAL REFERENCES

Lipscomb, W. N., *Boron Hydrides* (New York: Benjamin, 1963).
Lipscomb, W. N., "Recent Studies of the Boron Hydrides," in *Advances in Inorganic and Radiochemistry*, Vol. 1, edited by H. J. Emeléus and A. G. Sharpe (New York: Academic Press, Inc., 1959).
Lipscomb, W. N., *J. Inorg. Nucl. Chem.*, **11**, 1 (1959).
Parry, R. W., and L. J. Edwards, *J. Am. Chem. Soc.*, **81**, 3554 (1959).
Stone, F. G. A., *Quart. Rev.*, **8**, 190 (1955).
Stone, F. G. A., "Chemical Reactivity of the Boron Hydrides and Related Compounds," in *Advances in Inorganic and Radiochemistry*, Vol. 2, edited by H. J. Emeléus and A. G. Sharpe (New York: Academic Press, Inc., New York, 1960).
Noth, H., *Angew. Chem.*, **73**, 371 (1961).

Problems

1. How may $(CH_3)_2B_2H_4$ be prepared? Draw structural formulas for all isomers expected for $(CH_3)_2B_2H_4$. How might one identify these isomers if they are separated?
2. Give a reasonable method for preparing and purifying B_2H_6. How might the purity of the sample be determined? How could one dispose of the diborane?
3. Solve the equations of balance for B_3H_6 (not known) and write a "reasonable" structure for such a hydride.

4.   What is the maximum number of three-center BBB bonds compatible with the formula B_9H_{15}?

5.   Solvolysis of OTS   is presumed to involve an intermediate $C_6H_9^+$. Use the equations of balance to help arrive at a structure for this ion. See S. Winstein, J. Sonnenberg, and L. DeVries, *J. Am. Chem. Soc.,* **81**, 6523 (1959).

6.   Indicate the most probable site for protonation of B_4H_{10}. (This reaction is not yet known to occur.)

7.   Explain the acidic behavior of $B_{10}H_{14}$.

8.   Use the equations of balance to obtain a reasonable bonding picture of 1,5-dicarba-clovopentaborane(5).

CHAPTER IX

Metals

Valence Bond Approach

The large coordination numbers of metal atoms in the solid state as compared to the number of valence electrons of the metal atoms indicates that the two-center valence bond is not likely to be of importance here. Nevertheless, the valence bond approach, using the resonance concept to bring in electron delocalization, provides a good qualitative explanation of many of the properties of metals and interstitial compounds.*

The variation in cohesive energies of the elements of the three long periods is shown in Figure 9.1. The related properties, such as boiling points, melting points, heats of fusion, and hardness, show similar variation. The third long period (the rare earth elements have been omitted) shows the greatest regularity in cohesive energies, and may

* Pauling, L., *The Nature of the Chemical Bond* (3rd Ed.; Ithaca: Cornell University Press, 1960). J. S. Griffith, *J. Inorg. Nucl. Chem.*, **3**, 15 (1956).

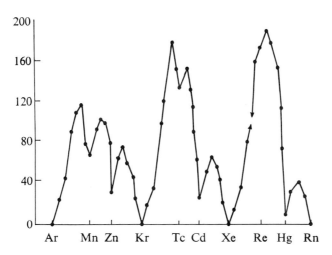

FIGURE 9.1. *Cohesive energies in the three long periods* [*from J. S. Griffith,* J. Inorg. Nucl. Chem., *3, 15 (1952)*]. *The energies are those required to produce a gaseous atom from the elements in their standard states.*

be interpreted as showing an increase in the number of metallic bonds per atom from one in cesium to six in tungsten. Further increase in atomic number and corresponding number of electrons does not increase the bonding but indeed decreases it, until a minimum is reached at mercury. Griffith has rationalized the cohesive energies of Figure 9.1 on the basis of the use of *d* and *s* orbitals for bonding until the *d* and *s* orbitals are completely filled in the isolated atom, with the *s* and *p* orbitals used in subsequent bonding. In order to form a bond there must be a half-filled orbital, which then pairs its electron through bond formation. According to this picture, the number of covalent bonds should reach a maximum with six electrons occupying the *d* and *s* orbitals. Further occupancy of these orbitals decreases the number of bonds that may be formed.

	6 Bonding Orbitals	2.28 N.B.	0.72 "Metallic"	Metal Bonds
K				1
Ca				2
Sc				3
Ti				4
V				5
Cr				6
Mn				6
Fe				6
Co				6
Ni				6
Cu				5.56
Zn				4.56
Ga				3.56
Ge				2.56
As				1.56
Se				0.56
Br				0

× or > indicates partial filling of the orbital.

When the *d* orbitals are completely filled, *s* and *p* orbitals are used, and the number of covalent bonds reaches a maximum with four electrons in the *s* and *p* orbitals.

Some of the trends within the groups of the periodic table may also be explained on this picture. Thus the *d* and *s* orbitals have more closely matched energies in the later periods and the reverse is true of the *s* and *p* orbitals. Accordingly, the $d^n s$ hybridization gives stronger bonds in the later periods, but the sp^n hybridization gives weaker bonds in the later periods.

The above view does not account for the magnetic properties of the metals. A picture presented by Pauling accounts for the magnetic properties by assuming that of the nine orbitals in the valence level (the $(n-1)d^5$, ns, and np^3), 6 may be used for bonding, 0.72 kept empty for metallic conduction, and the remaining 2.28 are nonbonding. The empirical value 0.72 is for orbitals per atom and merely indicates that at a given instant not all atoms have equivalent electronic configurations. The orbital filling and number of metallic bonds per atom are shown on page 286 for K through Br. The number of metal bonds per atom is determined from the number of electrons represented as singly occupying the bonding orbitals. These become paired in the metal. The electrons represented as singly occupying the nonbonding orbitals do not pair up in the solid and hence determine the magnetic properties of the solid. The magnetic properties of Mn, Fe, Co, and Ni are clearly indicated by the above arrangement (as indeed they should be, since the magnetic properties were the main factor in deciding the number of "metallic" orbitals present). Magnetic properties of alloys may be predicted from the above. Nevertheless, the Pauling picture does not predict the cohesive energies as satisfactorily as the simpler picture, i.e., it does not account for the binodal shape of the cohesive energy curve in a period.

Crystal Structure of Metals, Bond Orders, Hybridization

There are three common arrangements for metal atoms in the solid state, face-centered cubic (also called cubic close-packed), hexagonal close-packed, and body-centered cubic. The first two correspond to the closest possible packing of similar spheres, just as their names imply. These are related to the close-packed layers as shown in the drawings in Figure 9.2. In both of these close-packed structures each metal atom has twelve nearest neighbors. In the body-centered cubic structure (see Figure 9.3) each metal atom has eight nearest neighbors and 6 next nearest neighbors only slightly ($\sim 10\%$) further away. The degree of single bond formation with a neighboring metal atom may be taken as the number of metal bonds per atom divided by the number of nearest neighbors per atom. The distance between metal atoms, *D*, is related to their Pauling bond order, *n*, by an empirical equation of the form

$$D_{(n)} = D_{(1)} - 0.600 \log n$$

The single bond interatomic distance $D_{(1)}$ may be expected to decrease on crossing a given period and the bond order goes through a maximum with Groups VI, VII, and VIII of the transition metals. When the above two factors are coupled with increasing atomic weight with increasing atomic number, the variation of density of the metals with atomic number is understandable. The density is also affected by the crystal lattice type, although this is not an overriding factor for the three types discussed.

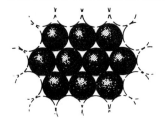

1st Close-Packed Layer

2nd Close-Packed Layer.   Repetition of the 1st and 2nd layers gives the hexagonal close packed structure.

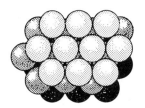

3rd Close-Packed Layer in the cubic closest packed structure (or face centered cubic structure).

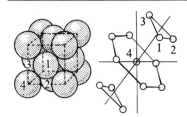

Face-Centered Cubic Structure.   Relation of position of atoms to close packed layers indicated by atom marked 1,2,3, and 4 in the two sketches.

FIGURE 9.2. *Close-packed layers stacked to give hexagonal or cubic closest packed structures.*

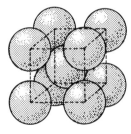

FIGURE 9.3. *Body-centered cubic structure.*

The variation in lattice type for the metals shows some regularity in group behavior, but it is difficult to see any pattern in the variation between groups (see Table 9.1). An attempt to relate the lattice type to the hybrid orbitals used in bonding has been made by Altman, Coulson, and Hume-Rothery.*

TABLE 9.1
Crystal Structures of Some Transition Metals

K	Ca	Sc	Ti	V	Cr	Mn	Fe	Co	Ni
bcc	cph	fcc	bcc	bcc	bcc	bcc	bcc	fcc	fcc
	fcc	cph	cph			fcc	fcc	cph	
						complex	bcc		

Rb	Sr	Y	Zr	Nb	Mo	Tc	Ru	Rh	Pd
bcc	bcc	cph	bcc	bcc	bcc	cph	cph	fcc	fcc
	cph		cph						
	fcc								

It will be discussed briefly here primarily because it provides further details of a "chemical" approach to bonding in metals. Since, in general, a metal has more nearest neighbors than bonding orbitals, for metallic bonding, a particular atomic orbital should have favorable directional properties for overlapping with more than one neighboring atom's orbital.† The hybrids of the *s* and *d* orbitals are generally more suitable for this than the hybrids of *s* and *p* as shown in Figures 9.4 and 9.5.

The resulting *sd* hybrid orbital has lobes which may give strong bonding with two neighboring atoms, whereas the *sp* hybrid orbital will give strong bonding with only one neighbor. The spatial distribution of some hybrid orbitals that might be used in metallic bonding are shown in Figure 9.5.

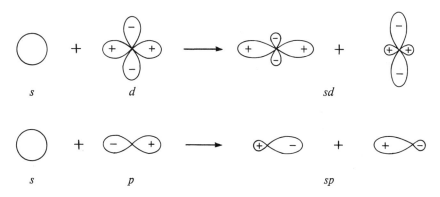

FIGURE 9.4. *Shapes of sd and sp hybrid orbitals.*

---

* Altman, S. L., C. A. Coulson, and W. Hume-Rothery, *Proc. Roy. Soc., (London)*, **A240**, 145 (1957).
† This idea was developed for interstitial compounds in the late forties by Rundle and will be discussed more fully at the end of this section.

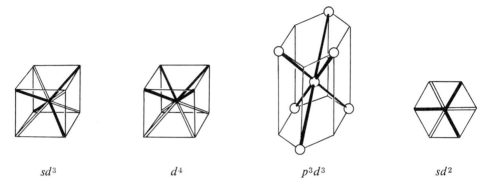

sd^3 $\qquad\qquad$ d^4 $\qquad\qquad$ p^3d^3 $\qquad\qquad$ sd^2

FIGURE 9.5. *Geometry associated with various hybridized orbitals. Light and dark lines indicate the use of one orbital for bonding two atoms to the central atom, i.e., half bonds* [*S. L. Altman, C. A. Coulson, and W. Hume-Rothery,* Proc. Roy. Soc. (London), **A240**, *145 (1957)*].

Due to the difference in symmetry of the three common metal lattices, the hybrid orbitals that may be used for bonding will be different. More particularly the importance of *d*-orbital hybrids will vary. Table 9.2 shows some hybrid orbitals suitable for metal bonding and the relative amount of *d*-orbital character in the resulting bonds. The extent of hybridization of *d* and *s* orbitals is expected to be greatest when the *d* and *s* orbitals are of nearly equal energy. For the isolated atoms we know that the order of energies for Rb is $5p > 4d > 5s$ and for Ag the order is $5p > 5s > 4d$. Accordingly, somewhere in the middle of this series of elements we might expect $5s \approx 4d$ and accordingly *d* orbital hybridization to be most important. Examination of Table 9.1 shows that Groups VA and VIA form bcc structures. As the *d*-orbital contribution to the hybrid decreases on either side of these groups one finds a change successively to hcp and fcc structures. The alkali metals provide an exception to this and indicate that the hybridization aspects are not the sole factor governing the lattice type.

TABLE 9.2
(After Altman, Coulson, and Hume-Rothery)

Crystal Structure	Hybrids	Atoms Bound	Relative d-orbital character
fcc	p^3d^3		0.5
	spd^4	Neighbors in planes above and below	
hcp	pd^5	Neighbors in basal plane	0.7
	sd^2		
bcc	sd^3	Nearest neighbors	0.9
	d^4		
	d^3	Second nearest neighbors	

Band Theory of Metals*

The covalent bond approach used so far has given us some understanding of the strength of bonding in metals and also to a lesser extent the lattice types found for different metals. However, it has not, thus far, accounted for the properties that allow us to distinguish metals from nonmetals, i.e., electrical conductivity, metallic luster, etc. These properties may be accounted for by the band theory of metals, which shall now be considered.

The combination of atomic orbitals to form molecular orbitals results in the splitting of the energy levels of the original atomic orbitals. The magnitude of this splitting depends upon the extent of overlap of the original atomic orbitals and, accordingly, is strongly dependent upon the internuclear separations involved and the orientation of the atomic orbitals with which we are concerned. In a metal, the combination of the n atomic orbitals of a given type will give rise to a series of molecular orbitals of closely spaced energies called an energy band. Due to the low degree of orbital overlap the band width for inner shell electrons is very small and the energy of the electrons in these bands is virtually the same as in the isolated atoms. For the outer or valence electrons, however, the energy range of electrons in a given band may be relatively large.

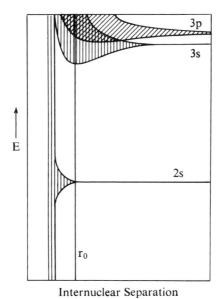

Internuclear Separation

FIGURE 9.6. *Energy bands of sodium [from J. C. Slater,* Introduction to Chemical Physics *(New York: McGraw-Hill Book Co., 1939) p. 494. Used by permission.].*

* It should be pointed out that although the approach used here is one that starts with the individual atomic orbitals from which the molecular orbitals of the metal may be constructed, the more useful approach is to start with the electrons in the force field of an array of nuclei. Energy bands appear naturally, then, from particle in a box type calculations, with the inclusion of multiple barrier potentials. We do not deal with this theory here, but state that the qualitative conclusions that may be drawn from a band picture are independent of the starting point from which the bands may be derived. For further details see Hume-Rothery and also Azaroff, general references.

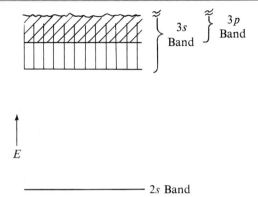

FIGURE 9.7. *Energy bands of sodium at equilibrium distance of atoms.*

The width of different bands may cause different bands to overlap. These features are illustrated in Figure 9.6.

An energy level diagram for a particular internuclear separation may be constructed from Figure 9.6 by taking the band width and position corresponding to the internuclear separation. Such a diagram is shown in Figure 9.7. The energy level diagram fails to give us information regarding the number of electrons of given energy which the system may contain. Figure 9.8 shows the distribution function of electrons with energy in a given band. As electrons are added to a given metal lattice, the lowest energy levels will be filled first. The spacing of the bands and the filling of the bands determines whether a substance is a conductor, insulator, or semiconductor (metal, nonmetal, or metalloid). If the bands are completely filled or completely empty and the energy spacing between bands is large, Figure 9.8c, the substance will be an insulator. Only a substance having a partially filled band will serve as a conductor.

Thus in Figure 9.8, *a* and *b* would show metallic conduction, *c* would be an insulator, and *d* would be a semiconductor. *a* is typical of 1 electron metals which would have exactly half the number of electrons the band would hold. The two electron metals such as Mg and Zn would have enough electrons to completely fill the *s* band were it not for overlap with the *p* band, which causes the *p* band to begin to fill before the *s* band is completely filled. For a semiconductor with an electron distribution similar to that

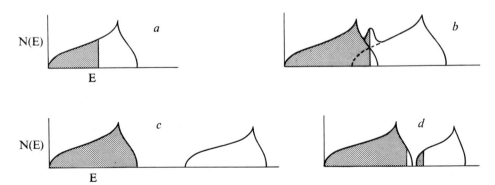

FIGURE 9.8. *Distribution of energy states. The shading indicates occupied states.*

shown in Figure 9.8*d* some electrons may be thermally excited from the nearly filled band to the nearly empty band. The number of electrons so excited will increase with temperature and hence the conductivity of a semiconductor, unlike that of a metal, will increase with increasing temperature. If the energy gap between the filled band and the empty band corresponds to the energy of the optical spectrum, electrons may be promoted from the filled band to the empty band by the absorption of light. This phenomenon is called photoconductivity. Conductivity of a semiconductor may be controlled by the introduction of atoms from a neighboring group. Thus germanium, which has been "doped" with a small amount of arsenic, will have a partial filling of the next higher band giving rise to conductance roughly proportional to the amount of arsenic present. Since the conductance is proportional to the number of electrons, or negative charge carriers in this band the semiconductor is called an *n*-type semiconductor (*n* for negative charge carrier). If germanium is doped with gallium the conductivity will be proportional to the vacancies created in the previously filled (or nearly filled) band. These vacancies may be thought of as having motion in an opposite direction to that of electron flow and hence this type of semiconductor is referred to as a *p*-type (*p* for positive charge carrier) (see p. 124).

Intermetallic Compounds

On the addition of Zn to Cu to form brass, different lattice types, or phases, are encountered at different compositions. A temperature–composition phase diagram giving the boundaries of existence of the phases is shown in Figure 9.9, the new phases being designated as they appear from left to right by letters of the Greek alphabet.

The α phase of brass, being essentially a solid solution of Zn in Cu, has a face-centered cubic lattice. This goes over into a body-centered cubic lattice for the β phase and

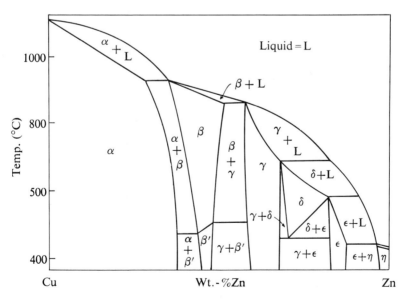

FIGURE 9.9. *Phase diagram for Cu–Zn system* [*from J. C. Slater,* Introduction to Chemical Physics *(New York: McGraw-Hill Book Co., 1939) p. 287. Used by permission.*]

a more complex cubic lattice or structure for the γ phase and goes over finally to a hexagonal closest packed structure for the ϵ phase. Although a range of composition is noted for these various phases, the formulas CuZn, Cu_5Zn_8, and $CuZn_3$ may be taken as the approximate composition of the β, γ, and ϵ phases, respectively. It has been pointed out by Hume-Rothery that many intermetallic compounds have similar structures to β, γ, and ϵ brass at the same electron to atom ratio as the corresponding brass compounds. Some examples of these compounds, which are often referred to as *electron* compounds, are given in Table 9.3.

TABLE 9.3
Hume-Rothery Phases

β-Brass $\left(\dfrac{electron}{atom} = \dfrac{3}{2} \; or \; \dfrac{21}{14}\right)$	$\gamma \left(\dfrac{21}{13}\right)$	$\epsilon \left(\dfrac{21}{12} \; or \; \dfrac{7}{4}\right)$
CuZn	Cu_5Zn_8	$CuZn_3$
AgZn	Ag_5Zn_8	$AgZn_3$
AuZn	Cu_9Al_4	Ag_5Al_3
AgCd	$Cu_{31}Sn_8$	Cu_3Sn
Cu_3Al	$Na_{31}Pb_8$	Cu_3Si
Cu_5Sn	Rh_5Zn_{21}	
CoAl	Pt_5Zn_{21}	
FeAl	etc.	
NiAl		

In counting the electron-to-atom ratio the valence electrons of the metals are considered to be the same in number as the group number in the periodic table with the exception of the Group VIII metals, which are considered to have no valence electrons available for metallic bonding.

Thus NiAl is considered to have an electron-to-atom ratio of 3:2, similar to β brass, CuZn. The existence of these similar binary metallic phases at similar electron to atom ratios is best understood on the basis of the filling of electronic bands in such a fashion

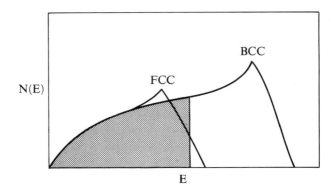

FIGURE 9.10. *Distribution of energy states for an electron/atom ratio of 3/2 showing favoring of bcc structure.*

as to give the lowest possible energy. The electron energy distributions corresponding to face-centered cubic and body-centered cubic lattices are shown in Figure 9.10.

Although these electron compounds still have incompletely filled electron bands, a number of other intermetallic compounds which have an electron-to-atom ratio of 8:3 have completely filled bands. Depending on the energy separation of the next higher empty band, the properties of these vary from insulators to conductors. Thus Mg_2Si is almost an insulator, whereas Mg_2Pb is a good metallic conductor. These compounds have the CaF_2 structure (see p. 103).

The radius ratio of the metal atoms in many cases determines the stoichiometry of the compound. Numerous examples have been investigated by Laves and consequently these compounds are often referred to as Laves phases. Thus the compounds Cu_2Mg, W_2Zr, KBi_2, and Au_2Bi have in common a relatively constant radius ratio of 1.25. Likewise the series of compounds $CeFe_5$, $SmFe_5$, $DyFe_5$, $HoFe_5$, $CeCo_5$, $CeNi_5 - HoNi_5$ have in common a constant radius ratio.

With metals differing greatly in their electronegativity, electron transfer to the more electronegative species may occur permitting the more electronegative species to fill, or nearly fill, the bonding orbitals of a particular framework. Such compounds are called Zintl phases. The electropositive metal involved is usually an alkali metal or an alkaline earth metal with the electronegative metal usually being a metal with an underlying d^{10} structure. In NaTl, LiCd, and LiZn the atoms of the more electronegative metal have an arrangement similar to a diamond lattice. In NaTl there are sufficient electrons to fill completely the electron bands for a diamond lattice (i.e., four per Tl) and the compound is colorless. With LiCd and LiZn there are insufficient electrons to fill completely the diamond lattice and the compounds in these cases are colored. The compound $CaZn_2$ has a structure, which places Zn atoms in a graphite-like lattice with Ca atoms lying in the planes between sheets of the Zn network. Here it appears that Ca has transferred its electrons to Zn. Some more complex Zintl phases are found with the formula AB_{13} where A may be Na, K, Ca, Sr, Ba with Zn or K, Rb, Cs with Cd.

The distinction between metals and nonmetals in compounds is often not a clear one. The description of MB_2 borides where M = Al, Ti, Zr, V, Nb, or Ta, is similar to that of $CaZn_2$ discussed above. The graphite-like layer may be considered as made up of B_2^{2-} units. It is interesting that the electrical conductance of TiB_2 and ZrB_2 is greater than that of the metals themselves. The borides MB_4 (where M = Ce, Th, or U) are intermediate between the MB_2 structure and the MB_6 structure discussed earlier (p. 282). In the MB_4 compounds B_6^{2-} octahedra are joined through B_2^{2-} ethylenic type units. The metal in MB_4 may thus be assumed to be M^{2+}.

Interstitial Compounds of the Metals

An examination of models of either the cubic closest packed or hexagonal closest packed structures shows the presence of voids or interstices of several different types. Considering only two adjacent close-packed layers these voids may be classified as either tetrahedral voids with a coordination number of four or octahedral voids with a coordination number of six. For N atoms in a close-packed structure there are $2N$ tetrahedral voids and N octahedral voids. Filling of the octahedral voids of a metal having a cubic close-packed structure with nonmetallic atoms leads to a NaCl type lattice. A body-centered cubic lattice also has octahedral and tetrahedral voids, however, in con-

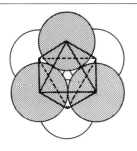

white = plane 1
gray = plane 2

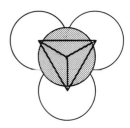

Octahedral Void   Tetrahedral Void

FIGURE 9.11. *Voids in closest packed structures.*

trast to the closest packed structures the polyhedra describing these voids are not regular polyhedra but are slightly distorted. This distortion causes the tetrahedral voids to be slightly larger than the octahedral voids, again in contrast to the closest packed structures. These voids for the closest packed structures are illustrated in Figure 9.11.

The geometry and number of the voids are particularly important in determining the stoichiometry and nature of many of the compounds of the transition metals with the second period elements B, C, N, and O. A number of compounds of the transition metals in Groups III through VI have the stoichiometry MX and a sodium chloride type structure (see Table 9.4).

TABLE 9.4
Some Binary Transition Metal Compounds Having the NaCl Structure

ScN	TiC	TiN	TiO	VC	VN	VO	CrC[a]		CrN[a]
	ZrC	ZrN	ZrO	NbC	NbN	NbO	MoC[a]		MoN[a]
LaN	HfC	—	—	TaC	—	—	WC[a]		WN[a]
	ThC	ThN	ThO				UC	UN	UO

[a] Hexagonal structures for metal atoms in compound.

These compounds retain a number of the properties of metals, such as electrical conductivity, which decreases with increasing temperature, high thermal conductivity, and metallic luster, but unlike metals they have a brittle character. Many of these compounds have extremely high melting points and are extremely hard. To account for the unusual properties of these compounds, Rundle* developed a theory of "half bonds" to which we have already been partially exposed with regard to bonding in metals (see p. 289). Rundle considered the points the theory would have to explain with regard to these compounds to be: (*1*) the preference for the NaCl structure; (*2*) the increased melting point and hardness despite a slight increase in atom–atom distance on going from the metal to the compound; (*3*) the brittle character; and (*4*) the conductivity. The preference for the sodium chloride structure and the brittleness were interpreted in terms of metal–nonmetal covalent bonding, such covalent bonding having a directional nature. Metal–nonmetal covalent bonding would also increase the over-all bonding in the solid despite the loss of some metal–metal bonding. Since each nonmetal atom has six nearest neighbor metal atoms to which it is bonded and only four low energy or-

* Rundle, R. E., *Acta Cryst.,* **1**, 180 (1948).

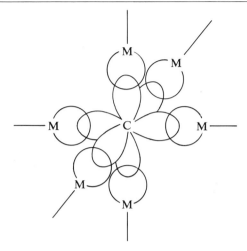

FIGURE 9.12. *Bonding of carbon atoms to metal atoms showing use of both lobes of the p-orbitals.*

bitals, the usual two-center valence bond concept cannot be used. Instead, Rundle proposed that the bonding might be p^3 bonding in which each lobe of the nonmetal p orbital overlaps with an orbital of the metal (Figure 9.12).

Since a single p orbital can accommodate only two electrons and a single nonmetal orbital is being used to bond with two metal atoms, these bonds are spoken of as "half bonds." The p_x, p_y, and p_z orbitals are at right angles to each other and thus have the directional properties necessary to bond with the six nearest metal atoms in the NaCl type structure. If one of the p orbitals is hybridized with the s orbital, the two resulting linear sp orbitals will be perpendicular to the remaining unhybridized p orbitals. The sp hybrid orbitals could then form normal covalent bonds to two of the metal atoms and the other four metal atoms would be held by "half bonds." Resonance, however, would remove any preferred direction and make all bonds equivalent. The net result of sp hybridization would then be to allow four orbitals to participate in the formation of the six bonds to the metal atoms. With this hybridization there would be $\frac{2}{3}$ of an electron pair per "bond" or the bond order would be $\frac{2}{3}$. Bond distance data indicate a bond order of $\frac{2}{3}$ (corresponding to sp-p^2) in most of the carbides of Table 9.4, but for the oxides a bond order of $\frac{1}{2}$ (corresponding to p^3 bonding) is more common. The nitrides show bond orders of $\frac{1}{2}$ for the lanthanides, but of $\frac{2}{3}$ for many of the other compounds.

It may be noticed that not all of the parent metals in Table 9.1 have a closest packed structure, but presumably go over to such a structure in their interstitial compounds at some slight expense to the metal–metal bonding, which is more than compensated for by the metal–nonmetal bonding. Some of the metals have a hexagonal closest packed structure in the interstitial compounds. With these substances the metal orbitals are being used efficiently in the metal itself for bonding and there is less net gain in forming an interstitial compound. Beginning with the Cr group a number of interstitial compounds are formed in which a lower number of possible sites are occupied as in Mo_2C and W_2C. The series of compounds Fe_3C, Co_3C, Ni_3C, Mn_3C, and Fe_2MnC represent an occupancy of trigonal prismatic voids with a low occupancy of the voids. These compounds react with water to produce methane, hydrogen, and trace amounts of other hydrocarbons. Still lower occupancy is shown in Fe_4C, Cr_4C, Fe_4N, Mn_4N in which $\frac{1}{4}$ of the octahedral sites of a cubic closest packed structure are occupied.

The hydrides of the transition metals tend to have the limiting formulas LaH_3, HfH_2, and TaH; experimental values such as $LaH_{2.76}$ and $TaH_{0.76}$ are typical. The limiting stoichiometry here suggests that the electron from hydrogen is going, at least in part, to the metal bonds—thus providing the particular metal with a net of six electrons for bonding. Accordingly, the hydrides of the Groups VI, VII, and VIII transition metals are either of lower stability or completely unknown. With compounds such as HfH_2 or Zr_4H the hydrogen apparently occupies tetrahedral voids. These transition metal hydrides decompose at high temperatures and use has been made of this fact in using the hydrides for powder metallurgical fabrications. Palladium forms the compound Pd_2H. Hydrogen will readily diffuse through a hot Pd plug. The rate of diffusion is proportional to the square root of the hydrogen pressure indicating the diffusing species is atomic hydrogen. This is used in obtaining extremely pure H_2.

Periodic Relationships among the Metals

Group IA — The Alkali Metals

The alkali metals are soft and low melting because of the weak bonding in the solid state. There is only one electron beyond the inert gas core available for bonding (see p. 286). The melting points, boiling points, and hardnesses decrease with increasing

TABLE 9.5
The Alkali Metals

ns^1	$_3$Li	$_{11}$Na	$_{19}$K	$_{37}$Rb	$_{55}$Cs
Abundance					
(% of earth's crust)	0.0065	2.74	2.47	0.028	3.2×10^{-4}
Density (g/cm³)	0.534	0.97	0.87	1.53	1.873
Melting point (°C)	179	97.9	63.7	38.5	28.5
Boiling point (°C)	1317	883	760	668	705
Sublimation energy					
(kcal/mole 25°C)	37.07	25.98	21.51	20.51	18.83
Ionization potential (eV)					
1st	5.390	5.138	4.339	4.176	3.893
2nd	75.619	47.29	31.81	27.5	25.1
3rd	122.419	71.65	46	40	35
Atomic radius (Å)	1.52	1.85	2.31	2.46	2.63
Ionic radius (Å)	0.60	0.95	1.33	1.48	1.69
Heat of hydration of					
M^+(g) (kcal/mole)	123	97	77	70	63
E^0 for					
$M(s) \rightleftharpoons M(aq)^+ + e$	+3.045	+2.714	+2.925	+2.925	+3.08

atomic number, indicating a weakening in the bonding between the atoms. The atoms are partly associated as diatomic molecules at temperatures just above the boiling points; the dissociation energies of the molecules decrease from 26.3 kcal/mole for Li_2 to 10.4 kcal/mole for Cs_2. The densities of the metals are low because of the large radii. The densities increase with increasing atomic number except for K, which has a lower density than Na. This irregularity is the result of differences in the rate of change in atomic weights as compared to the changes in the atomic radii. See Table 9.5 for a summary of some properties of the alkali metals.

The low ionization potentials make the alkali metals the most active family of metals. The metals have a bright luster, but they tarnish rapidly in air. The metals are commonly stored under oil to protect them from atmospheric oxidation.

Since the alkali metals give only 1+ ions with inert gas configurations, the properties of their compounds vary in a more systematic way than in any other family in the periodic table. It can be seen from the very high second ionization potentials that oxidation states higher than +1 are ruled out for the alkali metals. Most of the compounds are predominantly ionic in character and since the ionic radii increase regularly down through the family, the Born treatment (p. 115) is particularly successful. The cations have low charge and large radii, i.e., each of these cations has the largest radius of any cation from the same period, so that the lattice energies of their salts are relatively low. Consequently, most of the simple salts of the alkali metals are water soluble. The low interionic attraction also results in high conductance of the salts in solution or in the molten state. Most of the salts are completely dissociated in aqueous solution and the hydroxides are among the strongest bases available.

Occurrence. The only members of the alkali metal family which are abundant in the earth's crust are sodium and potassium. The abundance of light elements is generally high, but the abundance of lithium, like that of beryllium and boron, is quite low. Not only is the terrestrial abundance of these elements low, but also the cosmic abundance. According to any of the current theories of the origin of the elements these elements with low nuclear charge would be expected to undergo thermonuclear reactions to produce heavier elements and/or helium. The low nuclear charge gives a low potential barrier for proton or alpha capture reactions. Presumably these elements could not accumulate during the formation of the elements because they were used up in such reactions.

Geochemically, the most important occurrence of the alkali metals is in the alumino-silicate minerals, which make up the bulk of the earth's crust. Since the abundances of Rb and Cs are low, these elements rarely form independent minerals, but are often found in potassium minerals. In spite of its low abundance, lithium does form independent minerals because the lithium ion is too small to replace sodium or potassium ions in their minerals. Lithium occurs in minerals along with magnesium in alumino-silicates, which would be expected to separate in the very late stages of crystallization of a magma.* In addition to the lithium ores obtained from pegmatite minerals,† Searles Lake in California is an important source which furnishes about half of the world's supply of lithium. Searles Lake is an almost dry lake in the Mohave Desert. It is strongly alkaline (pH of 9.48).

---

* A *magma* is the parent molten mass from which igneous rocks can be considered to separate.
† Pegmatites are formed during the last stages of cooling and solidification of a deep-seated plutonic igneous rock. Pegmatites are characterized by large and irregular grain size. Since they represent the end product of the crystallization of a magma, rare elements become concentrated and the conditions are right for further differentiation and the growth of large crystals. The overall composition of pegmatites is not greatly different from granites, but they are coarser grained and are important sources of many rare elements.

Although the bulk of the sodium and potassium present in the earth's crust is in the alumino-silicate minerals, the important ores are found in the sedimentary rocks.* Sodium and potassium are leached from the parent rocks by weathering. The sodium tends to concentrate in the seas, but potassium ion is strongly adsorbed by clays. Some sodium chloride is recovered from sea water, but the most important sources are the extensive deposits of rock salt which have resulted from the evaporation of isolated bodies of water. Deposits of potassium salts of marine origin are also important as sources of potassium.

PREPARATION OF METALS

The most important general process for the preparation of the alkali metals is the electrolysis of fused salts or hydroxides. Sodium is the metal of this family produced in the greatest quantity and most of it is obtained by the electrolysis of fused sodium chloride. Lithium is also obtained by electrolysis of the fused chloride, although KCl is usually added to lower the melting point of the mixture and permit the electrolysis to be carried out at a lower temperature (about 450°C). The heavier alkali metals are also obtained by electrolysis, but thermal reduction processes are also important. Potassium is obtained by reduction of KF with CaC_2. Reduction of KCl with Na produces a K–Na alloy suitable for use as a heat exchanger. The heavier alkali metals are also obtained by reduction of the oxides with Al, Mg, Ca, Zr, or Fe.

$$2KF + CaC_2 \longrightarrow CaF_2 + 2K + 2C$$
$$3Cs_2O + 2Al \longrightarrow Al_2O_3 + 6Cs \uparrow$$

In this process advantage is taken of the high lattice energy of the oxides of the metals used as reducing agents and of the volatility of the alkali metals, which are vaporized in the process. Cesium can be obtained by the reduction of Cs_2CO_3 with carbon or by the thermal decomposition of cesium tartrate. All of the alkali metals except Li can be obtained in a high state of purity by the thermal decomposition of the azides. Lithium forms the very stable nitride, Li_3N, and cannot be prepared in this way.

$$Cs_2CO_3 + 2C \longrightarrow 2Cs + 3CO$$
$$2NaN_3 \longrightarrow 2Na + 3N_2$$

The strong reducing power of the alkali metals accounts for their major use. Sodium is the metal usually used for this purpose because it is easily available and inexpensive. Lithium is used to impart toughness to certain alloys and acts as a scavenger in steel. It is the only alkali metal that reacts readily with N_2 to form the nitride. Cesium is used in photoelectric cells since the absorption of radiant energy in the visible region of the spectrum can remove an electron because of its low ionization potential. Rubidium and cesium serve as "getters" in vacuum tubes to remove the last traces of corrosive gases in the tube when it is first put into use.

SOLUTIONS OF THE ALKALI METALS IN AMMONIA

In the presence of catalysts, such as Fe, the alkali metals react with ammonia to form the metal amide and hydrogen. If no impurities are present, the metals dissolve without the liberation of hydrogen and can be recovered by evaporating the ammonia. All of the

---

* The sedimentary rocks are secondary in origin, such as those formed by weathering of other rocks. In the geological sense, a rock is any bed, layer or mass of the material of the earth's crust. Natural waters are rocks composed mainly of the mineral water.

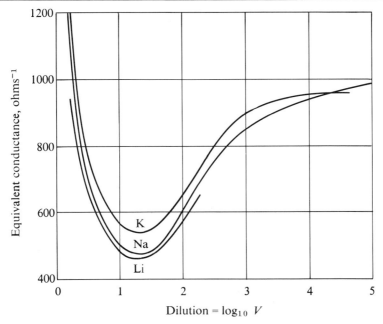

FIGURE 9.13. *The equivalent conductance of solutions of potassium, sodium, and lithium in liquid ammonia at* $-33.5°C.$ $V =$ *liters of ammonia per gram-atom of metal.* [*from Dr. W. L. Jolly,* The Inorganic Chemistry of Nitrogen *(New York: W. A. Benjamin, Inc., 1964) p. 32.*]

alkali metals dissolve to give solutions, which are bronze if concentrated and blue if dilute. The bronze solutions conduct electricity about as well as many metals and the blue solutions conduct electricity somewhat better than solutions of strong electrolytes (see Figure 9.13).

The characteristics of the solutions are essentially the same for all of the alkali metals, for the more active alkaline earth metals, and for europium and ytterbium. Thus the metals that dissolve in liquid ammonia are those with high positive oxidation emf's, or, in different words, metals with low ionization potentials, low sublimation energies, and high solvation energies. The solubilities of the alkaline earth metals are much lower than those of the alkali metals. The solubilities of the alkaline earth metals are limited, in part, by the tendency to form ammoniates. A saturated solution of cesium contains 25.1 moles of metal per 1000 g of ammonia at $-50°C$.

The very dilute blue solutions are regarded as solutions of electrolytes with the metal atoms dissociated to give ammoniated cations and ammoniated electrons. Since there is a very marked increase in volume when the metals dissolve in ammonia, the electrons are considered to occupy cavities with the surrounding NH_3 molecules oriented such that the hydrogens are directed inward. The unusually high conductivity for an electrolyte results from the high mobility of the solvated electron.

In the polarographic reduction of the alkali metals in liquid ammonia amalgams are formed. In effect, the alkali metal ions are captured by the electron-rich mercury electrode. A cathodic wave is observed polarographically for a solution of tetrabutylammonium iodide in ammonia, but this corresponds to the dissolution of electrons.[*] Instead of the tetraalkylammonium ions dissolving in the mercury, the electrons are re-

[*] Laitinen, H. A., and C. J. Nyman, *J. Am. Chem. Soc.,* **70**, 2241, 3002 (1948).

leased as ammoniated electrons. The process is described by

$$e + x\text{NH}_3 = e(\text{NH}_3)_x \qquad E^0 = -1.89 \text{ V at } -34°\text{C}$$

When the electrolysis is carried out on a large scale a blue solution results.

The decrease in conductance with increasing concentration is considered to result from the metal ions becoming bound together in clusters by the electrons. At high concentrations the clusters become large enough to resemble liquid metals with the cationic sites occupied by ammoniated metal ions.

DIAGONAL RELATIONSHIPS — THE ANOMALOUS BEHAVIOR OF LITHIUM

In many of its properties lithium is quite different from the other alkali metals. This behavior is not unusual in that the first member of each main group of the periodic table shows marked deviations from the regular trends for the group as a whole. The deviations shown by lithium can be explained on the basis of the small radius of Li^+ and its high charge density. The nuclear charge of the Li^+ ion is screened only by a shell of two electrons. The ionic radius of Li^+ (0.60 Å) is closer to that of Mg^{2+} (0.65 Å) than to that of Na^+ (0.95 Å). Consequently, lithium is more similar to Mg than to Na in a number of respects. Such *diagonal relationships* are of great importance among the active metals, e.g., Na^+ and Ca^{2+}, K^+ and Sr^{2+}, Be^{2+} and Al^{3+}, etc.

The diagonal relationship is well illustrated by noting that the solubilities of lithium compounds in water resemble those of magnesium compounds to a greater extent than those of the other alkali metal compounds. Thus the fluoride, carbonate, and phosphate of lithium or magnesium are relatively insoluble and those of the other alkali metals are reasonably soluble. Addition of acid increases the solubility of the lithium or magnesium salts mentioned through the formation of acid salts (FHF^-, HCO_3^-, H_2PO_4^-). However, addition of acid to a solution of sodium carbonate precipitates NaHCO_3. Similar, though less pronounced, behavior is observed with potassium carbonate.

The low solubility of NaHCO_3 in water serves as the basis for the production of Na_2CO_3 by the Solvay process. In this remarkably efficient process CO_2 (from limestone, CaCO_3) is passed through a water solution of ammonia and salt,

$$\text{NaCl} + \text{NH}_4\text{HCO}_3 \rightleftharpoons \text{NaHCO}_3 + \text{NH}_4\text{Cl}$$

The sodium hydrogen carbonate that precipitates is converted to sodium carbonate by heating,

$$2\,\text{NaHCO}_3 \longrightarrow \text{Na}_2\text{CO}_3 + \text{H}_2\text{O} + \text{CO}_2$$

The CO_2 is recycled. After decomposing the NH_4HCO_3 in the mother liquor by warming, the NH_3 (from NH_4Cl) is displaced by adding Ca(OH)_2 (from the CaO produced on heating limestone). A solution of sodium carbonate is strongly basic because of hydrolysis. For many large scale uses calling for a strong base, sodium carbonate can be substituted for more expensive bases such as NaOH. Because of the efficiency of the Solvay process and the low cost raw materials, sodium carbonate is the least expensive strong base. Consequently, it is produced in very large quantities.

Lithium is the only alkali metal that reacts with N_2 gas. Presumably the expected high lattice energy of Li_3N is responsible for the much greater stability of Li_3N as compared to Na_3N. On burning Mg in air, some Mg_3N_2 is formed along with MgO. Lithium carbide is the only alkali metal carbide that forms readily by direct reaction. It is considerably more stable than the other alkali metal carbides.

Lithium salts of small anions, like those of magnesium, have exceptionally high lattice energies, accounting for their high stability and low solubility. The anomalous behavior of lithium salts formed by large anions was discussed in the treatment of radius ratio effects (p. 110). For these salts the lattice energies are smaller than expected because of anion–anion repulsion.

The hydration energy of lithium ion is greater than that of any other alkali metal ion because of the smaller radius of Li^+. Even though the lithium ion is the smallest of the alkali metal ions, its ionic mobility is the lowest of the group because of the extensive hydration of the small ion. Lithium is the only one of the alkali metals for which hydrolysis of salts is of any importance. In this respect also it resembles magnesium.

Several lithium compounds find uses because of properties, appreciably different from those of sodium compounds. Lithium alkyls are used in organic syntheses where they undergo reactions similar to Grignard reagents (RMgX). $LiAlH_4$ and $LiBH_4$ are used extensively as reducing agents in organic reactions. The lithium salts are used because of their solubility in organic solvents.

The ionization potentials and sublimation energies decrease regularly down through the alkali metal family. However, although the IP and S are greatest for Li, the oxidation emf of Li is as positive as that of cesium. The reason for the great activity of lithium as a reducing agent is its very high hydration energy. The energy released in the hydration of the small Li^+ ion more than compensates for its higher IP and S. On the basis of heat effects alone, one would conclude that Li should be much more active than Cs. We have neglected the unfavorable entropy change for the formation of a well-ordered sheath of water molecules in a highly hydrated ion such as $Li(aq)^+$. Although there are no outstanding anomalies among the oxidation emf's of the remaining alkali metals, the order is not perfectly regular. The heat and entropy effects are rather delicately balanced so that the differences between the emf's are small and somewhat irregular.

COMPOUNDS OF THE OTHER ALKALI METALS

The trends in the properties of the compounds of the alkali metals do not become really regular until one gets to K, Rb, and Cs. Sodium does not deviate from the regular trends nearly as much as lithium does, but it does differ from the heavier alkali metals in properties such as the solubilities and the extent of hydration of salts. Except for a few lithium salts, which were mentioned, and $NaHCO_3$, the slightly soluble salts of the alkali metals are those of K, Rb, and Cs, e.g., the perchlorates and hexachloroplatinates. Since the ammonium ion is comparable in size (ionic radius 1.48 Å) to the potassium ion (1.33 Å), the solubility of ammonium salts frequently parallel those of potassium. Actually the radius of the ammonium ion is the same as that of Rb^+, but the comparison is usually made to potassium salts because they are more common. Some differences between ammonium and alkali metal salts are to be expected because of specific interactions between NH_4^+ ion and a solvent such as water through hydrogen bonding.

Because of the similarity among the alkali metal salts, there is often no reason to prefer the salt of one alkali metal over another. Consequently when one wants a soluble salt with a cation not likely to cause interference, the sodium salt is selected because of its lower cost and availability. Potassium salts are sometimes preferred, especially for analytical purposes, because they are less often hydrated and are not usually hygroscopic. The more expensive rubidium and cesium salts rarely offer advantages over those of sodium or potassium.

The products formed on burning the alkali metals in air (Li_2O, Na_2O_2, KO_2, RbO_2, and CsO_2) were discussed earlier from the standpoint of the thermochemical quantities involved (see p. 117).

FRANCIUM

Element 87 was found in nature as a product of the decay of ^{227}Ac by Mlle. Perey in 1939. The major product is ^{227}Th by β decay, but about 1% of the ^{227}Ac undergoes α decay to produce ^{223}Fr. This nuclide undergoes β decay with a half-life of 21 min.

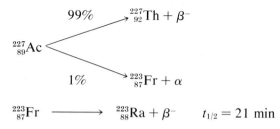

$$^{223}_{87}Fr \longrightarrow \quad ^{223}_{88}Ra + \beta^- \qquad t_{1/2} = 21 \text{ min}$$

Enough tracer work has been done to confirm that the chemistry of Fr is similar to that of cesium. Considering the great similarity between Rb and Cs, the properties of Fr should be easily predictable.

Group IIA – The Alkaline Earth Metals

The alkaline earth metals originally included only calcium, strontium, and barium, but it is convenient to extend the definition to include Be, Mg, and Ra. The metals of this family are harder, more dense, and higher melting than the corresponding members of the group of alkali metals. Each of the metal atoms has two valence electrons beyond the inert gas configuration. Hence the alkaline earth metal atoms are more strongly bonded in the solid state than the alkali metals. The trends in the properties dependent on the bonding between the atoms indicate a decrease in the strength of the bonding with increasing atomic radius, as is true for the alkali metals.

The first ionization potentials of the alkaline earth metals are higher than those of the corresponding alkali metals because of the smaller radii and higher nuclear charge (compare Tables 9.5 and 9.6). Since the second ionization potentials are considerably greater than the first, compounds of the metals in the +1 oxidation state might be expected. Indeed, the formation of a compound such as MgF is an exothermic process ($\Delta H = -20$ kcal/mole) for MgF(g) and such molecules exist at high temperatures in the gaseous state. Although the heat of formation of MgF(s) would be considerably larger than -20 kcal/mole, the much greater lattice energy of MgF_2 favors the disproportionation to give Mg and MgF_2 in the solid state (see p. 119). MgCl(g), CaCl(g), and CaF(g) have also been reported. In solution the monohalides are unstable because of the much higher hydration energy of the divalent cations. The removal of a third electron would break up an inert gas configuration and the energy required is prohibitively high, so oxidation states higher than +2 are not encountered.

TABLE 9.6
The Alkaline Earth Metals

ns^2	$_4Be$	$_{12}Mg$	$_{20}Ca$	$_{38}Sr$	$_{56}Ba$	$_{88}Ra$
Abundance (% of earth's crust)	6×10^{-4}	2.00	3.45	0.015	0.040	1.3×10^{-10}
Density (g/cm³)	1.845	1.74	1.54	2.6	3.5	~5
Melting point (°C)	1284	651	851	770	710	(960)
Boiling point (°C)	2507	1103	1440	1380	1500	(1140)
Sublimation energy (kcal/mole, 25°C)	76.63	35.9	46.04	39.2	41.96	31
Ionization potential (eV)						
1st	9.320	7.644	6.111	5.692	5.210	5.277
2nd	18.206	15.031	11.868	11.027	10.001	10.144
3rd	153.850	80.12	51.21	43.6	35.5	—
Atomic radius (Å)	1.11	1.60	1.97	2.15	2.17	—
Ionic radius (Å)	0.31	0.65	0.99	0.81	0.68	
Heat of hydration of $M^{2+}(g)$, kcal/mole	570	464	382	350	316	—
E^0 for $M(s) = M^{2+}(aq) + 2e$	+1.85	+2.37	+2.87	+2.89	+2.90	+2.92

The large amount of energy necessary to sublime the metals and remove two electrons is compensated for by the high hydration energy of the divalent cations (or high lattice energy of the solids) so that the more active alkaline earth metals are comparable in activity to the alkali metals. Beryllium and magnesium are reasonably stable in air in spite of their high oxidation emf's presumably because oxidation is inhibited by the formation of a thin, adherent layer of metal oxide on the surface. The oxidation emf's increase in magnitude with increasing atomic radius following the order of decreasing ionization potentials. The high hydration energy of beryllium is not great enough to offset the trend established by the ionization potentials and sublimation energies because of the very large amount of energy required for these two processes.

The salts of the larger alkaline earth cations are typically ionic and conduct electricity well in aqueous solution and in the molten state. The conductances of fused salts of beryllium are low. Magnesium salts containing large, polarizable anions are also poor conductors of electricity in the fused state.

Occurrence. Magnesium and calcium are the only abundant alkaline earth metals in the earth's crust. The cosmic, as well as the terrestrial, abundance of beryllium is low, as is true for lithium and for the same reasons (p. 299). Most of the beryllium in the earth's crust is found in silicate minerals replacing Si in tetrahedral SiO_4 units. Additional cations must be incorporated in the crystal lattice to prevent an imbalance of charge brought about by the replacement of Si(IV) by Be(II). The most important beryllium mineral is beryl, Be_3Al_2-

$[Si_6O_{18}]$. Emerald is crystalline beryl colored by a small amount of Cr^{3+}; aquamarine is also beryl of gem quality. Magnesium is enriched in minerals, which might be considered to separate in the early stages of the crystallization of a magma. The mantle is believed to consist largely of forsterite, Mg_2SiO_4, and olivine, $(Mg,Fe)_2SiO_4$. The important magnesium ores are magnesite, $MgCO_3$; dolomite, $(Mg,Ca)CO_3$; and brucite, $Mg(OH)_2$. These ores are found primarily in the sedimentary rocks. Sea water is also an important source of Mg.

Calcium is concentrated in minerals expected to separate during the main stage of crystallization of a magma. The bulk of the calcium in the earth's crust is found in the feldspars, which make up about $\frac{2}{3}$ of the crust. The calcium leached from rocks as a result of weathering does not concentrate in the sea because of the low solubility of $CaCO_3$. The $Ca^{2+} + CO_2 + H_2O \rightleftharpoons CaCO_3 + 2H^+$ equilibrium is important in regulating the acidity of the sea and the CO_2 in the atmosphere. The most important calcium ore is $CaCO_3$ as limestone, marble, or sea shells. There are also extensive deposits of gypsum, $CaSO_4 \cdot 2H_2O$.

Strontium and barium form few independent minerals. Strontium is frequently found accompanying calcium and sometimes accompanies potassium. Barium often replaces potassium in minerals such as the potash feldspars. Heavy spar, $BaSO_4$, is an important barium ore. Radium is found only as one of the daughters in the radioactive decay of heavier elements. It occurs in all uranium minerals.

PREPARATION OF THE METALS

Beryllium metal can be obtained by the electrolysis of a fused BeF_2–NaF mixture. The NaF is added to permit the bath to operate at a lower temperature and to improve the conductivity of the melt. Beryllium is used in alloys with copper for nonsparking tools. It is also added to alloys to improve the resilience and fatigue-resisting properties of springs.

Magnesium is the most important metal of the alkaline earth family. It is obtained by the electrolysis of fused KCl–$MgCl_2$ mixture. The $MgCl_2$ can be obtained from magnesium ores or from sea water. The magnesium is precipitated from sea water as the hydroxide by the addition of $Ca(OH)_2$. The $Mg(OH)_2$ is then converted to the chloride for use in the electrolytic cell. Magnesium is also obtained by reduction of MgO with CaC_2, C, or Si. The reduction must be carried out at high temperature followed by quenching of the products to prevent reversal of the reaction. Magnesium is used as a structural metal because of its low density. Oxidation of the metal is slowed down by an adherent layer of the oxide. Magnesium reacts rapidly with water at elevated temperatures, but slowly at ordinary temperatures. Some of its low density alloys (Mg–Al and Mg–Mn) are much more resistant to air oxidation than the pure metal, presumably because the alloys form protective oxide layers to a greater extent.

The remaining alkaline earth metals can also be obtained by the electrolysis of fused salts or by reduction of the alkaline earth metal oxide or chloride with aluminum. Calcium, strontium, and barium are rapidly oxidized in air. They are produced in small amounts compared to magnesium.

ANOMALOUS BEHAVIOR OF BERYLLIUM

Like lithium, beryllium stands apart from the remainder of the family in many respects. The hardness of beryllium (6–7 on Mohs' scale) is much greater than that of Mg(2.6) or Ca(2.2–2.5). The melting points of all of the alkaline earth metals are within a narrow range except for Be (Table 9.6).

The ionic potential (charge to size ratio) of Be^{2+} (6.4) is closer to that of Al^{3+} (6.0) than it is to that of Mg^{2+} (3.1). Consequently there is some validity to the statement that beryllium is more similar to aluminum (diagonal relationship) than it is to magnesium, at least with respect to those properties dependent on size-charge effects. Beryllium compounds are largely covalent, even the halides. Thus, fused $BeCl_2$ is a rather poor electrolyte. Beryllium oxide is hard and refractory, like Al_2O_3; when fired it is practically insoluble in acids. Beryllium nitrate, sulfate, and the halides are all soluble, but the hydroxide, oxide, and phosphate are all insoluble. The normal beryllium carbonate, like that of Al, is unstable except in the presence of CO_2. Basic beryllium carbonate of variable composition is precipitated by the addition of sodium carbonate to a solution of a soluble beryllium salt. Be_2C and Al_4C seem to be the only common salt-like metal carbides that yield methane on hydrolysis.

The extent of hydrolysis of beryllium salts in solution is much more nearly comparable to that of aluminum salts than to the salts of the rest of the alkaline earth family. Beryllium has a great tendency to form stable complexes with F^- or oxy anions. Tetrahedral complexes are usually formed. Salts of the type $[NaBeF_3]_n$ contain long chains of repeating BeF_3^- units. These are analogous to the metasilicates $(SiO_3{}^{2-})_n$ and metaphosphates $(PO_3^-)_n$. Fluorides can be considered as weakened models of oxides of the same structural type, e.g., BeF_2 for SiO_2, MgF_2 for TiO_2, and NaF for CaO. The fluorides have lower lattice energies than the corresponding oxides because of the lower charges. Because of the charge effects, salts of $(BeF_3^-)_n$ are more similar to those of $(PO_3^-)_n$ in solubilities and melting points than to the salts of $(SiO_3{}^{2-})_n$.

The remaining members of the family show little tendency to form complexes except with rather exceptional ligands such as EDTA (ethylenediaminetetraacetic acid). The complexes of the alkaline earth metals other than Be are usually octahedral.

Beryllium forms an unusual compound by combination with acetic acid (also with other carboxylic acids). The compound is basic beryllium acetate, $Be_4O(O_2CCH_3)_6$, in which the four beryllium ions are arranged tetrahedrally around a central oxide ion with a carboxylate ion spanning each of the six edges of the tetrahedron (Figure 9.14). The molecule contains interlocking 6-membered rings, satisfying the tetrahedral bond-

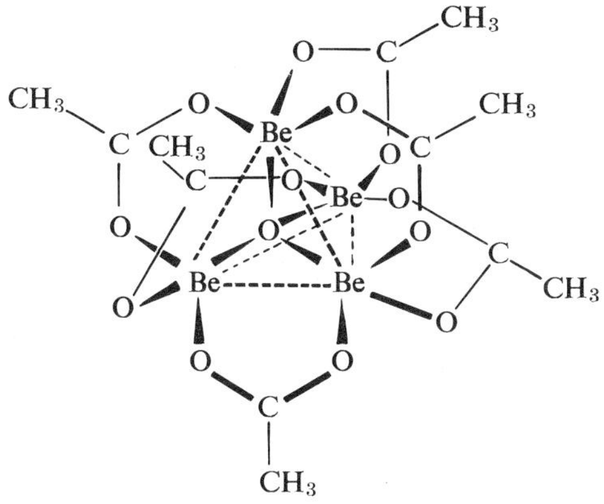

FIGURE 9.14. *Basic beryllium acetate.*

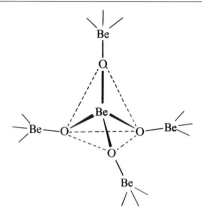

FIGURE 9.15. *The* $Be^{2+}(BeO)_4$ *complex ion.*

ing requirements of Be^{2+}. Basic beryllium acetate is insoluble in water, but soluble in organic solvents such as chloroform. It can be distilled under reduced pressure. Similar, though less stable, compounds of Zn^{2+} and ZrO^{2+} are known.

Beryllium also shows its great tendency to form complexes involving oxide bridges in that the solubilities of both BeO and $BeSO_4$ are increased when both are present in the same solution. Individually $BeSO_4$ is moderately soluble and BeO is virtually insoluble. Together they form a complex in which the Be^{2+} is "solvated" with four BeO molecules (Figure 9.15). The coordination requirements of these BeO molecules can be satisfied by hydration.

The analytical separation of beryllium from the remaining alkaline earth metals is easily accomplished, but the separation from aluminum is difficult. One can take advantage of the formation of basic beryllium acetate, which can be extracted into chloroform, leaving Al^{3+} in the aqueous phase. Also, aluminum is precipitated as the hydroxide by the addition of an excess of ammonium carbonate, but beryllium is soluble, probably because of the formation of a carbonato complex. Aluminum is precipitated as $AlCl_3 \cdot 6H_2O$ by the addition of ether to a solution saturated with HCl gas. Beryllium chloride remains in solution.

Beryllium compounds are highly toxic. It is not recommended that anyone try to verify the sweet taste of beryllium compounds, which led to the old name glucinium used for beryllium.

COMPOUNDS OF THE REMAINING ALKALINE EARTH METALS

Most of the compounds of the remaining members of Group IIA are rather typical ionic compounds for which the trends are quite regular. The hydroxides are not very soluble except for $Ba(OH)_2$ (a saturated solution is about $0.1N$). Barium hydroxide is a strong base and although slaked lime, $Ca(OH)_2$, is quite caustic, milk of magnesia, $Mg(OH)_2$, is mild enough to be swallowed as a laxative.

Magnesium bridges the gap between beryllium and the heavier members of the family in its slight tendency to hydrolyze and slight tendency to form complex ions. The compounds of Ca, Sr, and Ba are quite similar to one another in many respects. In an analytical separation scheme these three metals are usually precipitated as the carbonates and then separated from one another utilizing differences in the solubilities of salts such as $MCrO_4$ at different acidities.

MAGNESIUM ALKYLS

The Grignard reagents, usually given the general formula RMgX, have been widely used in organic reactions. The reagents are prepared by the reaction of magnesium metal with the alkyl or aryl halide, e.g., C_2H_5Br yields C_2H_5MgBr in anhydrous ether. It was supposed that C_2H_5MgBr was in equilibrium with $MgBr_2$ and $(C_2H_5)_2Mg$. However, it has been shown that there is no exchange between Mg^*Br_2 and $(C_2H_5)_2Mg$ so that no C_2H_5MgBr is obtained in this way. Similar studies have shown that no exchange occurs between Be^*Br_2 and $(C_2H_5)_2Be$. Evidence for a complex between $(C_2H_5)_2Mg$ and $MgBr_2$ in ether has been obtained. The current evidence supports the following structure for the ethyl Grignard reagent in ethyl ether at concentrations of $1M$ or greater.

$$
\begin{array}{ccc}
\text{Et} & \text{X} & \text{OEt}_2 \\
\diagdown\diagup\diagdown\diagup\diagdown\diagup \\
\text{Mg} \quad \text{Mg} \\
\diagup\diagdown\diagup\diagdown \\
\text{Et} & \text{X} & \text{OEt}_2
\end{array}
$$

Group IB – The Coinage Metals

Although potassium and copper each contain a single electron in the fourth shell, the differences in properties are very great. The copper atom has a smaller radius as a result of contraction through the transition series and it has a higher nuclear charge. Both factors favor an increase in the ionization potential and sublimation energy of Cu, resulting in a decrease in electropositive character or reactivity as a metal (see Table 9.7). The increases in sublimation energies and ionization potentials are both quite large and each contributes significantly to the nobility of the coinage metals. However, the differences in the activities of the alkali and coinage metals are even greater than would be expected on the basis of the decrease in size and increase in nuclear charge through the transition series. The additional factor is the difference in the electronic configuration. Beneath the outer shell each of the alkali metals has an inert gas core, but each of the coinage metals has an 18 electron shell, a pseudo-inert gas configuration. The 18 electron shell does not screen the positive nuclear charge as effectively as an 8 electron shell. The contrast in reactivity is obvious from the fact that the alkali metals include the most active metals and the coinage metals include gold, the most noble metal.

The coinage metals are in striking contrast to the alkali metals in another respect, that is, the coinage metals decrease in reactivity with increasing atomic number. Because of the less effective shielding of the nuclear charge by the eighteen electron shell, the increase in nuclear charge is more important than the increase in atomic radius in determining the attraction for electrons. The formation of Ag^+ requires more energy than for Cu^+, as indicated by the emf values, even though the first ionization potential of Ag is slightly *lower* than that of Cu and the sublimation energy is appreciably lower. Only the higher hydration energy of the smaller Cu^+ ion makes the oxidation process more favorable for Cu (see Table 9.7). The fact that the lanthanide series comes between Ag and Au causes the atomic radii to be the same. The resulting increase in the first ioniza-

TABLE 9.7
The Coinage Metals

$(n-1)d^{10}ns^1$	$_{29}Cu$	$_{47}Ag$	$_{79}Au$
Abundance			
(% of earth's crust)	7×10^{-3}	1×10^{-5}	5×10^{-7}
Density (g/cm³)	8.94	10.49	19.32
Melting point (°C)	1083	960.5	1063
Boiling point (°C)	2595	2212	2966
Sublimation energy			
(kcal/mole, 25°C)	81.52	69.12	82.29
Ionization potential (eV)			
1st	7.724	7.574	9.22
2nd	20.29	21.48	20.5
3rd	36.83	34.82	—
Atomic radius (Å)	1.28	1.44	1.44
Ionic radius (Å)	Cu^+ 0.96	Ag^+ 1.26	Au^+ 1.37
	Cu^{2+} 0.72	Ag^{2+} 0.89	Au^{3+} 0.85
Heat of hydration of M^{n+}	Cu^+, 139	Ag^+, 116	Au^+, 154
(kcal/mole)	Cu^{2+}, 507		
E^0 for $M(s) \rightarrow M^+(aq) + e$	−0.521	−0.799	*ca.* −1.68
$M(s) \rightarrow M^{2+}(aq) + 2e$	−0.337	−1.39	—

tion potential and the much higher sublimation energy account for the much greater nobility of gold.

The coinage metals are among the most dense metals (Table 9.7). Their melting points are very close together. There is a surprisingly large minimum in the sublimation energy for silver. These metals have the highest electrical conductivities of any elements. They are the most malleable and ductile metals. Gold can be rolled into sheets as thin as 10^{-5} cm.

> *Occurrence.* In spite of their low abundances the coinage metals are among those which have been known to man longest. All three metals occur in the native state. Native gold is usually found in placer deposits, such as in the bed of a stream, as a result of the weathering of the original rocks. The gold is dense and resistant to oxidation so that it remains after most of the other minerals present have been removed by chemical attack or by the mechanical forces of weathering. The coinage metals also commonly occur as sulfide minerals from which early man could have obtained the metals in his campfire because of their ease of reduction.

PREPARATION OF THE METALS

The copper sulfide ores are converted to the oxide by roasting in air. The oxide is reduced to the metal by carbon. If the supply of air is cut off before the conversion to the oxide is complete, the copper can be obtained directly by the following reactions:

$$2Cu_2S + 3O_2 \rightleftharpoons 2Cu_2O + 2SO_2$$
$$2Cu_2O + Cu_2S \rightleftharpoons SO_2 + 6Cu$$

The copper obtained directly from the ores is generally of low purity. Purification can be accomplished by heating the crude copper in a furnace to form some Cu_2O, which serves to oxidize the more reactive metals present. The remaining Cu_2O is reduced to the metal by wood charcoal or by stirring with wooden poles. The copper obtained is more than 99% pure.

Electrolytic refining is the more important process for obtaining pure copper. The crude blister copper cast as a large anode is suspended in an acidified copper sulfate solution containing a small amount of chloride ion. Electrolysis oxidizes copper and the more active metals to their ions and deposits pure copper at the cathode. Noble metals present in the blister copper are not oxidized and fall to the bottom of the cell along with other impurities as the anode *mud*. Any lead that is oxidized precipitates as lead sulfate; any silver that might be oxidized would precipitate as AgCl. The recovery of precious metals from the anode mud is profitable enough to pay for a large share of the cost of refining copper. Metals more active than copper remain in solution since the cell is operated at a very low voltage. Because of the low operating voltage (a few tenths of a volt), many cells are normally operated in series.

Silver is obtained as a by-product in the recovery of lead, zinc, and copper from their ores. Silver ores (Ag_2S, AgCl, or Ag) are commonly treated by the cyanide process. In the presence of oxygen, silver dissolves in aqueous sodium cyanide solution as the complex ion $[Ag(CN)_2]^-$. Sulfide ion is oxidized to SO_4^{2-} or SCN^-. The silver is oxidized by oxygen because of the great stability of $Ag(CN)_2^-$. The emf for the oxidation is shifted by over a volt:

$$Ag + 2CN^- = Ag(CN)_2^- + e \qquad E^0 = +0.31 \text{ V}$$

Silver is recovered from the solution by the addition of zinc dust, or in some applications, by electrolysis.

Gold-containing ore can be enriched by a washing process. The ore is broken up and suspended in water in order to separate the less dense impurities, which remain suspended from the gold, which settles rapidly because of its great density. The recovery of gold is more complete if the concentrated ore is treated by an amalgamation process. The gold dissolves in the mercury to form an amalgam. It is recovered by distilling the mercury.

The cyanide process is more important for the extraction of gold. It is applicable even to very low grade ores. The ore is finely ground and treated with a dilute cyanide solution (0.1–0.2% KCN or NaCN). Oxygen in the air oxidizes the gold to a soluble cyanide complex. The gold is obtained by the addition of zinc to the cyanide solution. Gold(I) is stabilized even more than silver(I) by coordination with CN^- so that gold becomes a strong reducing agent. The emf is shifted by over two volts:

$$Au + 2CN^- = Au(CN)_2^- + e \qquad E^0 = +0.60 \text{ V}$$

From this shift in emf, the formation constant for the complex is 2×10^{38}.

COMPOUNDS OF THE COINAGE METALS

Only one oxidation state is encountered for the alkali metals because the first ionization potentials are very low and the energy for the removal of additional electrons from the underlying inert gas shell is prohibitively high (see Tables 9.5 and 9.7). The differences among the first three ionization potentials are not so great for the coinage metals and the formation of compounds in the higher oxidation states is more favorable because of complex formation.

A number of subhalides of the type M_2X have been reported for the coinage metals, but most of them are probably mixtures. The only verified subhalide of the group is Ag_2F. This is a bronze-colored solid obtained by the cathodic reduction of AgF in aqueous solution. The solid has double layers of Ag "atoms" separated by layers of F^- ions. The silver "atoms" are held together by metal–metal bonds so that no discrete Ag^+ or Ag_2^+ ions can be identified.

+1 Oxidation State. The +1 oxidation state is common to all three of the coinage metals. Copper(I) is stable only in solid compounds or in a few complexes formed by ligands such as CN^-, SCN^-, $S_2O_3^{2-}$, thiourea, etc. Copper(II) ion is reduced by I^- or CN^- with the formation of insoluble CuI or CuCN. In the presence of an excess of CN^- soluble complexes are formed. The hydrated copper(I) ion is unstable with respect

$$2Cu^{2+} + 4I^- = 2\underline{CuI} + I_2$$
$$2Cu^{2+} + 4CN^- = 2\overline{\underline{CuCN}} + (CN)_2$$
$$\underline{CuCN} + CN^- = \overline{Cu(CN)_2^-}$$
$$2Cu^+ = Cu + Cu^{2+} \qquad E^0 = +0.37 \text{ V}$$

to disproportionation. Solutions of copper(I) complexes absorb olefins by the formation of copper(I) olefin complexes. This has been used for the separation of olefins from other hydrocarbons or for the separation of monoolefins from polyolefins. As is fairly generally true, lower oxidation states are more stable at high temperatures. CuO is converted to Cu_2O at elevated temperatures.

$$4CuO \xrightarrow{\text{heat}} 2Cu_2O + O_2$$

Silver(I) is the most stable oxidation state of silver. Silver nitrate, silver fluoride, and silver perchlorate are very soluble in water. The acetate, sulfate, chlorate, and bromate range from slightly soluble to moderately soluble. Most of the rest of the common salts are quite insoluble. The solubilities of the silver halides decrease in the order AgCl ($K_{sp} = 1.8 \times 10^{-10}$), AgBr($K_{sp} = 3.3 \times 10^{-13}$), and AgI($K_{sp} = 8.5 \times 10^{-17}$). Many silver compounds containing colorless anions are themselves colored, e.g., Ag_3PO_4, Ag_2CO_3, and AgI are yellow, and Ag_2S is black. Salts containing polarizable anions and highly polarizing cations, e.g., those with 18 or 18 + 2 electronic configurations, are often colored (see p. 91). Silver(I) forms many stable complexes, particularly with nitrogen and sulfur donors. In the stable complexes silver generally shows a coordination number of two. In solution, solvation probably increases the effective coordination number of silver(I) to four.

Gold(I) chloride and bromide are obtained by the gentle heating of the corresponding gold(III) halides. These gold(I) halides disproportionate in aqueous solution to give the metal and the corresponding gold(III) halide.

$$AuCl_3 \xrightarrow{\text{heat}} AuCl + Cl_2$$
$$3AuCl + H_2O \longrightarrow AuCl + 2Au$$
$$AuCl_3 + 3I^- \longrightarrow \underline{AuI} + I_2 + 3Cl^-$$

Gold(I) iodide is precipitated from solutions containing gold(III) compounds and iodide ion. Because of its low solubility, gold(I) iodide is decomposed more slowly by water.

Gold(I) cyanide is so insoluble that it is stable in the presence of water. It dissolves in the presence of a cyanide salt to give a soluble complex, e.g., $K[Au(CN)_2]$. Gold(I) also gives soluble complexes with $S_2O_3^{2-}$ and SO_3^{2-}. The insoluble Au_2S is precipitated from an aqueous solution of any soluble gold(I) complex by saturating the solution with H_2S.

+2 Oxidation State. The $+2$ oxidation state of copper is encountered in most of the stable copper salts and complexes in the solid state and in solution. The copper(II) complexes are usually square planar, although there are often two additional ligands or solvent molecules at slightly greater distances, one above and one below the plane of the four closer ligands. Copper(II) fluoride has the fluorite structure typical of ionic salts. Copper(II) chloride and bromide have chain structures commonly encountered among salts which have an appreciable amount of covalent character.

Silver(II) compounds are uncommon. Silver(II) fluoride is obtained by the action of F_2 on AgF. It is used as a fluorinating agent for organic compounds. An oxide, AgO, is obtained by the anodic oxidation of aqueous solutions of silver salts. It cannot be a silver(II) compound since it is diamagnetic and it is probably a silver(I)–silver(III) compound, $Ag^I[Ag^{III}O_2]$. The $+2$ oxidation state is stabilized by coordination with pyridine, $[Ag(py)_4](NO_3)_2$, pyridine derivatives such as picolinic acid, 1,10-phenanthroline, dipyridyl, and a few other heterocyclic nitrogen ligands. The complexes are presumably planar, like those of copper(II).

Several gold(II) compounds have been reported, but in most cases these have been shown to be mixed Au(I)–Au(III) compounds. The simple salts $AuSO_4$, AuO, and AuS have been reported, but are questionable as authentic gold(II) compounds. No gold(II) complexes have been verified.

+3 Oxidation State. Copper(III) and silver(III) complexes with periodate and tellurate ions have been reported, e.g., $K_7[Cu(IO_6)_2] \cdot nH_2O$ and $K_9[Cu(TeO_6)_2] \cdot nH_2O$. The fluorocomplex $K[AgF_4]$ has also been prepared. Gold(III) compounds are the ones most commonly encountered. Gold is usually dissolved in *aqua regia* to obtain chloroauric acid, $H[AuCl_4] \cdot 4H_2O$. Neither hydrochloric nor nitric acid alone will dissolve gold. Gold(III) is sufficiently stabilized by coordination with chloride ion to lower the emf required so that the oxidation can be accomplished by HNO_3.

All gold compounds are easily decomposed by heating. $AuCl_3$ and $AuBr_3$ give the monohalides on gentle heating, but the metal is formed when the halides are heated more strongly. AuI_3 is unstable with respect to the loss of I_2, even without heating. Except for a few stable solids, the gold(III) compounds encountered are planar complexes.

Group IIB — The Zinc Subgroup

The zinc subgroup elements are more dense and less active than their counterparts in the alkaline earth family, as would be expected from their smaller radii and higher nuclear charge. Sublimation energies of the Group IIB metals are lower than for any Group of metals other than the alkali metals (Table 9.8). Correspondingly, the metals have low melting points and boiling points and may be distilled. The $18 + 2$ configuration characteristic of this family practically constitutes a closed configuration from the standpoint of metal–metal bonding in the free state. The increased activity of the IIB family compared to the IB family is partly the result of the low sublimation energies of

TABLE 9.8
The Zinc Family

$(n-1)d^{10}ns^2$	$_{30}Zn$	$_{48}Cd$	$_{80}Hg$
Abundance			
(% of earth's crust)	8×10^{-3}	1.8×10^{-5}	5×10^{-5}
Density (g/cm³)	7.133	8.65	13.55
Melting point (°C)	419.5	320.9	−38.87
Boiling point (°C)	906	767	357
Vaporization energy			
(kcal/mole 25°C)	31.19	26.97	14.54
Ionization potential (eV)			
1st	9.391	8.991	10.43
2nd	17.96	16.904	18.751
3rd	39.70	37.47	34.2
Atomic radius (Å)	1.33	1.49	1.50
Ionic radius (Å)			
Heat of hydration			
of M^{2+}, (kcal/mole)	492	437	441
E^0 for			
$M \rightarrow M^{2+}(aq) + 2e$	+0.763	+0.403	−0.849

the metals and partly the result of the high hydration energy of the divalent ions. Obviously it is not caused by a decrease in the ionization potentials. The radii of the IIB metals are slightly larger than those of the corresponding IB metals.

The IIB metals decrease in activity with increasing atomic number as is true of the IB metals. The increase in nuclear charge is more important than the increase in atomic radius. Zinc and cadmium are very active metals and mercury is a distinctly noble metal. In fact, mercury has the highest first ionization potential of any metal.

The lanthanide contraction causes the radius of Hf to be about the same as that of Zr. The chemical properties of Zr and Hf are almost identical. The properties of the members of the second and third transition series diverge increasingly for each successive group. However, Group IIB is the first group after Group IVA in which the members of the first and second transition series (Zn and Cd) are more similar than the members of the second and third transition series (Cd and Hg).

Occurrence. The most important zinc ores are smithsonite, $ZnCO_3$, and zinc blende, ZnS. Cadmium occurs along with zinc in the same minerals. Independent cadmium minerals are rare. The principal mercury ore is cinnabar, HgS. Some native mercury is often associated with the cinnabar.

PREPARATION OF THE METALS

Zinc ores (ZnS or $ZnCO_3$) are roasted to give the oxide, which is then reduced with carbon. The zinc is distilled from the furnace. The electrolytic process is becoming increasingly more important than the carbon reduction. The ore is leached with sulfuric acid to give a solution of zinc sulfate. Electrolysis of the zinc sulfate solution produces zinc at a zinc cathode. Zinc is deposited even from the acidic solution because of the high hydrogen overvoltage at the zinc cathode.

Cadmium can be recovered from the zinc produced by carbon reduction because of the greater volatility of cadmium. The cadmium is obtained by repeated fractional distillation. The cadmium can also be separated from zinc in the electrolytic preparation because of the lower deposition potential of cadmium.

Mercury can be recovered by heating the sulfide in air. The mercury vapor distills. Metals more active than mercury can be removed by leaching with dilute nitric acid.

COMPOUNDS OF THE GROUP IIB METALS

The characteristic oxidation state of the Group IIB metals is +2. Many of the solid salts have typical layer type lattices. The salts are extensively associated in solution. The Group IIB metals are similar to Be and Mg in the tendency to form stable complexes. Zinc forms complexes with NH_3, OH^-, CN^-, Cl^-, SCN^-, etc. Both tetrahedral and octahedral complexes are encountered, the lower coordination number being favored for charged ligands (see Table 9.9). Most of the cadmium complexes are similar to those of zinc except for the OH^- complex. $Cd(OH)_2$ is not amphoteric.

TABLE 9.9

Formation Constants of Some Complexes of the Group IIB Metals

Ligand	Zn				Cd				Hg			
	$\log K_1$	$\log K_2$	$\log K_3$	$\log K_4$	$\log K_1$	$\log K_2$	$\log K_3$	$\log K_4$	$\log K_1$	$\log K_2$	$\log K_3$	$\log K_4$
NH_3	2.18	2.25	2.31	1.96	2.51	1.96	1.30	0.79	8.8	8.7	1.00	0.78
$NH_2C_2H_4NH_2$	5.56	4.87	(1.8)	—	5.47	4.55	2.07	—	$\log K_1 \times K_2 = 23.42$			
F^-	0.73	—	—	—	0.46	0.07	—	—	1.03	—	—	—
Cl^-	−0.32	0.27	−0.25	0.15	1.39	0.79	0.21	—	6.74	6.48	0.85	1.00
Br^-	−0.60	−0.37	−0.73	0.44	1.76	0.68	0.76	0.53	9.05	8.28	2.41	1.26
I^-	−2.93	1.25	−0.07	−0.59	2.42	0.98	1.60	1.15	12.87	10.95	3.78	2.23
$S_2O_3^{2-}$	2.29	(2.3)	—	—	3.92	2.52	—	—	$\log K_1 \times K_2 = 29.86$		2.40	1.35

The mercury(II) halides show interesting variations in lattice type (see p. 121). The fluoride has the fluorite structure common for ionic salts. Mercury(II) chloride has a molecular lattice consisting of discrete linear $HgCl_2$ molecules. The low force constants of linear molecules of the type HgX_2 are discussed elsewhere (p. 375). $HgBr_2$ and HgI_2 have layer lattices, although $HgBr_2$ represents a transition between the molecular and layer lattice since each Hg^{2+} has two nearest-neighbor Br atoms and two Br atoms at a greater distance.

Mercury(II) usually gives tetrahedral complexes. The formation constants for the addition of the first two ligands is usually considerably greater than for the last two, suggesting a definite tendency to form linear complexes with a coordination number of two (see Table 9.9). Mercury(II) shows a very marked preference for large, polarizable ligands. Although complexes containing nitrogen ligands are very stable, there is a great preference for ligands containing sulfur over those containing oxygen. The order of increasing stability of the halide complexes is $Cl^- < Br^- < I^-$, with little or no tendency to form fluoride complexes (Table 9.9). Mercury(II) oxide is basic and shows no tendency to form hydroxide complexes.

Organozinc compounds, such as $(C_2H_5)_2Zn$, were used in organic reactions before the discovery of the Grignard reagents, which can be prepared and handled more conveniently. The organometallic compounds of Li, Mg, Zn, and Cd are all rapidly decomposed in contact with oxygen or moisture. The organomercury compounds are easily formed by the reaction of Grignard reagents (organomagnesium compounds) with $HgBr_2$. The organomercury compounds are resistant to attack by oxygen or moisture and can be handled in contact with air. Unlike the beryllium and magnesium organometallics, the discrete species RHgX is stable.

+1 Oxidation State. Compounds of zinc and cadmium in the +1 oxidation state have been reported. The existence of cadmium(I) compounds has been clearly demonstrated recently, but the compounds are not stable in contact with oxygen or in water. Several mercury(I) compounds are stable. The compounds are unusual in that they contain the only common diatomic metal cation, Hg_2^{2+}. The compounds are diamagnetic and hence cannot contain the monomeric Hg^+ ion. Solid mercury(I) compounds have been shown by x-ray structure analysis to contain Hg—Hg bonds. Mercury(I) compounds can be prepared generally by the reaction of Hg with the corresponding Hg(II) compound. The equilibrium constant for the reaction

$$Hg + Hg^{2+} \rightleftharpoons Hg_2^{2+}$$

is 166. Mercury(I) gives no stable complexes in aqueous solution so the addition of a complexing agent to a mercury(I) salt usually results in disproportionation to give Hg and the Hg(II) complex. The cadmium(I) ion has been shown to be Cd_2^{2+} from Raman spectra of melts prepared from mixtures of $CdCl_2$, $AlCl_3$, and excess Cd.* The $AlCl_3$ was added in proper proportions to tie up all of the Cl^- as $AlCl_4^-$. Unusual low oxidation states of metals are often obtained in a system where the anion is $AlCl_4^-$ or some other large anion, which has little tendency to form stable complexes with the metal ion in the usual oxidation state. The bonding in the Cd_2^{2+} ion is very weak compared to Hg_2^{2+}.

Group IIIA

The trends in the family Sc, Y, La, and Ac are quite regular and follow the pattern to be expected from the properties of the Group IA and IIA metals. The metals are very active in spite of the large amount of energy required to remove three electrons and the fact that the sublimation energies are also appreciably higher than those of the alkaline earth metals. The lattice energies of the compounds containing triply charged cations or the hydration energies of the ions are sufficiently high to account for the great activity of the metals as shown by the high heats of formation of their solid compounds and the high oxidation emf's of the metals (see Table 9.10). Only the +3 oxidation state is important for these metals.

Scandium shows a much greater tendency to form complexes than do the other members of the family. Its salts hydrolyze extensively in solution. The tendency to hydrolyze decreases with increasing ionic radius of the metal ion through the family.

The Rare Earth Metals. The minerals gadolinite and cerite were discovered in Sweden in the latter part of the 18th century. The minerals were found to contain new "earths' or metal oxides, later shown to be mixtures and separated into other metal oxides. The mineral

* Corbett, J. D., *Inorg. Chem.*, **1**, 700 (1962).

TABLE 9.10

Group IIIA Metals and the Rare Earths

	Abundance (% of earth's crust)	Density (g/cm^3)	Melting point (°C)	Atomic radius (Å)	Ionic radius M^{3+} (Å)	E^0 M, M^{3+}	E^0 M^{2+}, M^{3+}	E^0 M^{3+}, M^{4+}
$_{21}$Sc	5×10^{-4}	2.992	1539	1.641	0.68	+2.08		
$_{39}$Y	2.8×10^{-3}	4.472	1509	1.801	0.88	+2.37		
$_{57}$La	1.8×10^{-3}	6.174	920	1.877	1.061	2.52		
$_{58}$Ce	4×10^{-3}	6.66	795	1.82	1.034	2.335		−1.74
$_{59}$Pr	5.5×10^{-4}	6.782	935	1.828	1.013	2.47		−2.86
$_{60}$Nd	2.4×10^{-3}	7.004	1024	1.821	0.995	2.246		
$_{61}$Pm	−	−	1035	−	(0.98)	2.42		
$_{62}$Sm	6.5×10^{-4}	7.536	1072	1.802	0.964	2.41	+1.55	
$_{63}$Eu	1×10^{-4}	5.259	826	2.042	0.950	2.41	+0.43	
$_{64}$Gd	6.5×10^{-4}	7.895	1312	1.802	0.938	2.40		
$_{65}$Tb	9×10^{-5}	8.272	1356	1.782	0.923	2.39		
$_{66}$Dy	4.5×10^{-4}	8.536	1407	1.773	0.908	2.35		
$_{67}$Ho	1.1×10^{-4}	8.803	1461	1.766	0.894	2.32		
$_{68}$Er	2.5×10^{-4}	9.051	1497	1.757	0.881	2.30		
$_{69}$Tm	2×10^{-5}	9.332	1545	1.746	0.869	2.28		
$_{70}$Yb	2.7×10^{-4}	6.977	824	1.940	0.858	2.27	+1.15	
$_{71}$Lu	7.5×10^{-5}	9.843	1652	1.734	0.848	2.25		

cerite was characterized by Berzelius as containing the new earth ceria. Ceria was later resolved into lanthanum, cerium, and didymium oxides. The name didymium, "twin," refers to the supposed new element as a twin of lanthanum. Didymium oxide was later resolved into the oxides of praseodymium, *green twin*, and neodymium, *new twin*. More careful separation and characterization of the earths obtained from these minerals ultimately yielded Sc, Y, La, and the 14 lanthanide metals.

The rare earth metals are always found together in nature because they occur as compounds of the 3+ ions, which have very similar radii. The chemical similarities are so great that their separation is very difficult. The classical separation method involves the fractional crystallization of salts from aqueous solution. Such separations are slow, tedious, and are not suitable for the production of appreciable amounts of the rare earths of high purity. Since the rare earths are among the fission products of uranium, their separation became a practical problem in the study of uranium fission. The rare earths can now be separated using ion exchange procedures or a combination of solvent extraction and ion exchange procedures. Few of the rare earth metals were available in a high state of purity until recently and these were very expensive. They are now available in a high state of purity at costs only a small fraction of those of a few years ago.

Although the decrease in radius from one element to the next is very small within the rare earth series, the cumulative decrease is quite significant. The atomic radii decrease fairly regularly through the series except for significant increases at Eu and Yb. These are the elements for which there are only two electrons beyond the respective half-filled and completely filled *f* orbitals. Apparently these metals have only two electrons available for metallic bonding rather than three as for the other rare earth metals. These irregularities disappear for the ionic radii (M^{3+}) where the three outer electrons have been removed. Although the ionic radius of La^{3+} is appreciably larger than that of Y^{3+}, the decrease in size through the rare earth series proceeds steadily until Ho^{3+} is only slightly larger than Y^{3+}, but the difference in size is compensated for by the higher nuclear charge of Ho. In the separation of the rare earths by fractional crystallization or ion exchange of the salts, Y concentrates with Dy and Ho.

The rare earth metals are very strong reducing agents because of the high lattice energies of their compounds or their high hydration energies. Consequently they are useful for thermite type reactions, taking advantage of the high ΔH_f of M_2O_3. A mixture containing mostly Ce and La, with smaller amounts of other rare earths and iron, known as mischmetall, is produced for technical uses. It is pyrophoric when finely divided. When alloyed with more Fe to increase the hardness, it is used for flints in lighters.

The rare earth metals are obtained by reduction of the anhydrous fluorides by calcium at 800–1000°C. The reduction process proceeds only to the difluorides for Sm, Eu, and Yb. These metals can be obtained by reduction of their oxides by lanthanum metal *in vacuo*, since they are more volatile than lanthanum. The anhydrous chlorides can be reduced to the metals with Ca, Mg, Li, or Na, but the chlorides are hygroscopic and those of the heavier rare earth metals are too volatile.

$$2LaF_3 + 3Ca = 3CaF_2 + 2La$$
$$2EuF_3 + \;\;Ca = 2EuF_2 + CaF_2$$
$$Eu_2O_3 + 2La = 2Eu \uparrow + La_2O_3$$

Oxidation States. The $+3$ oxidation state is characteristic of the rare earths. The oxidation states other than $+3$ for the rare earth metals occur just about as expected on the basis of the stability of a group of orbitals which is empty, half-filled, or completely filled (Table 9.11). Thus Ce^{4+} achieves an inert gas configuration. Tb^{4+} and Eu^{2+} have the same configuration as Gd^{3+}, seven electrons in the $4f$ orbitals. Yb^{2+} has completely filled $4f$ orbitals as is true of Lu^{3+}. A few other examples of oxidation states other than $+3$ are encountered for metals which do not quite achieve one of the stable configurations of the f orbitals. $Pr(IV)$ is encountered in the mixed oxide Pr_6O_{11} or in PrO_2, which can be obtained by heating Pr_2O_3 in the presence of O_2 at high pressure. The compounds PrF_4 and TbF_4 have been prepared. Terbium(IV) has been reported to form the oxide Tb_4O_7, but the composition does not agree with this formulation. TbO_2

TABLE 9.11

Electronic Configurations of Some Rare Earth Metals and Ions

Metal	Electronic Configuration	Configuration of M^{3+}	Configuration of M^{4+}	Configuration of M^{2+}
$_{57}$La	[Xe] $5d^16s^2$	[Xe]	–	–
$_{58}$Ce	[Xe] $4f^26s^2$	[Xe] $4f^1$	[Xe]	–
	|add $4f$ electrons			
$_{63}$Eu	[Xe] $4f^76s^2$	[Xe] $4f^6$	–	[Xe] $4f^7$
$_{64}$Gd	[Xe] $4f^75d^16s^2$	[Xe] $4f^7$	–	–
$_{65}$Tb	[Xe] $4f^96s^2$	[Xe] $4f^8$	[Xe] $4f^7$	–
	|add $4f$ electrons			
$_{70}$Yb	[Xe] $4f^{14}6s^2$	[Xe] $4f^{13}$	–	[Xe] $4f^{14}$
$_{71}$Lu	[Xe] $4f^{14}5d^16s^2$	[Xe] $4f^{14}$	–	–

TABLE 9.12
Oxidation States of the Actinide Elements
(The very stable states are in bold face type; the unstable states are
enclosed in parentheses)

Ac	Th	Pa	U	Np	Pu	Am	Cm	Bk	Cf	Es	Fm	Md	No	Lw
	(2)			(2)										
3	(3)		(3)	3	**3**	**3**	**3**	**3**	3	3	3	3		
	4	4	**4**	4	**4**	4	4	4						
		5	5	5	5	5								
			6	**6**	**6**	6								

has been prepared recently. Samarium(II) salts can be obtained, but the blood red Sm(II) ion is unstable in aqueous solution because it reduces water. Thulium(II) can be obtained in the solid TmI_2, but the ion is very unstable in water.

All of the rare earths have been obtained as M^{2+} ions in CaF_2 as the host lattice.* When a rare earth fluoride, MF_3, is incorporated in solid CaF_2, the M^{3+} ions would be expected to occupy the cation sites with the "extra" F^- ions in interstitial sites. If electrolysis is carried out with graphite electrodes at each end of a crystal, electrons enter from the cathode to reduce M^{3+} to M^{2+} and the "extra" F^- ions migrate into the anode.

THE ACTINIDE METALS

The metals Ac, Th, Pa, and U appeared to be members of the III, IV, V, and VI transition element families, respectively, until the discovery of the trans-uranium metals. Each additional element which was discovered made it more obvious that these metals were not members of a transition series, but rather an inner-transition series. The wide variation of the oxidation states of these metals made it difficult to determine which element was the first member of the series. Greater variation in oxidation states (compared to the rare earths) is to be expected among the actinide metals because the atomic radii are larger and the energy levels of the valence electrons are closer together. Several stable oxidation states are encountered for most of the actinide metals.

It has been suggested that the second inner-transition series begins with thorium. Most of the metals which follow thorium give dioxides which are isomorphous with ThO_2 and there are other similarities to thorium. However, on proceeding through the series the +3 oxidation state becomes increasingly more important (Table 9.12). It is one of the important oxidation states of plutonium and it is the most stable state for americium, curium, and berkelium. There now seems to be little room to doubt that the second inner-transition series begins with actinium to give a series similar to the rare earths. Because americium is the actinide counterpart of europium in the lanthanide series, it was expected to exhibit the +2 oxidation state. This has not been verified. The $5f$ electrons are more easily removed than the $4f$ electrons and consequently, for the actinide metals, the lower oxidation states are less important and the higher oxidation

* McClure, D. S. and Z. J. Kiss, *J. Chem. Phys.,* **39,** 3251 (1963); Z. J. Kiss and P. N. Yocom, *ibid.,* **41,** 1511 (1964).

states are more important compared to the lanthanide metals. Even curium gives the Cm(IV) oxidation state in solid CmO_2 and CmF_4, whereas only Gd(III) compounds are known. The Cm^{4+} ion is not stable in solution.

The last few members of this series have very short half-lives and have been produced in very small quantities (a few atoms in some cases). It is difficult to study elements which have a very high level of activity because of the drastic chemical changes which result in the sample. Even the water in which a compound of the element is dissolved is decomposed to give H_2 and O_2 by the radioactive decay. Consequently, the chemical properties of the last few actinides have not been investigated in great detail. Element 103 (Lawrencium) should be the last member of the actinide series. It would be expected to have only +3 as an important oxidation state. Element 104 should be a member of the transition metal family IVA.

Trends Among the Transition Metals

According to the Bohr classification (p. 25) the metals in the Cu and Zn families are representative elements, not transition elements. However, the chemical similarities throughout a series of metal ions such as Fe^{2+}, Co^{2+}, Ni^{2+}, Cu^{2+}, and Zn^{2+} make the exclusion of Cu and Zn from the transition series seem artificial. Hence, these metals and the others in their families are commonly included with the transition metals.

The metals of Groups IB and IIB have been discussed along with Groups IA and IIA in order to emphasize the periodic relationships among these groups. Group IIIA has been discussed separately because these metals, unlike most of the transition metals, show little variation in oxidation states and the presence of the lanthanide and actinide metals makes this group unique. Only some of the overall trends will be discussed for Groups IVA–VIIA. Group VIII will be treated separately because of its unique character.

Groups IVA-VIIA

Size Effects. The cumulative effect of the contraction in the lanthanide series causes the radii of the members of the third transition series to be very similar to those of the corresponding members of the second transition series. The effect is great enough so that Hf, which follows immediately after the rare earths, has a slightly smaller atomic radius than Zr (see Table 9.13). The almost identical ionic radii of Zr^{4+} and Hf^{4+} account for the fact that these metals always occur together in nature and are difficult to separate. Early separation methods involved fractional crystallization or precipitation procedures. Ion exchange or solvent extraction procedures have been found to be more effective.

The atomic radius of Ta is the same as that of Nb, but the two elements are not as similar to one another as are Zr and Hf. They occur together in nature, but not always in the same proportions. The mineral $Fe(MO_3)_2$ is called columbite if niobium (formerly called columbium in America) predominates and tantalite if tantalum predominates. The two metals can be separated by crystallizing the less soluble K_2TaF_7 from a concentrated HF solution. In hot water the Nb complex dissolves as $K_2[NbOF_5]$, and the

TABLE 9.13

Properties of Some Transition Metals

	$_{22}$Ti	$_{23}$V	$_{24}$Cr	$_{25}$Mn
Atomic radius (Å)	1.32	1.22	1.18	1.17
Ionic radius (Å)	M^{3+} 0.76	M^{2+} 0.88	M^{2+} 0.84	M^{2+} 0.80
	M^{4+} 0.68	M^{3+} 0.74	M^{3+} 0.69	M^{3+} 0.66
Ionization 1st	6.82	6.74	6.764	7.432
Potential(eV) 2nd	13.57	14.65	16.49	15.636
3rd	27.47	29.31	30.95	33.69
4th	43.24	48	50	52

	$_{40}$Zr	$_{41}$Nb	$_{42}$Mo	$_{43}$Tc
Atomic radius (Å)	1.45	1.34	1.30	1.27
Ionic radius (Å)	M^{4+} 0.79	M^{4+} 0.74	M^{4+} 0.70	
		M^{5+} 0.69	M^{6+} 0.62	
Ionization 1st	6.84	6.88	7.10	7.28
Potential(eV) 2nd	13.13	14.32	16.15	15.26
3rd	22.98	25.04	27.13	29.54
4th	34.33	38.3	46.4	

	$_{72}$Hf	$_{73}$Ta	$_{74}$W	$_{75}$Re
Atomic radius (Å)	1.44	1.34	1.30	1.28
Ionic radius (Å)	M^{4+} 0.78	M^{5+} 0.68	M^{4+} 0.70	M^{4+} ~0.7
			M^{6+} 0.62	
Ionization 1st	~7	7.88	7.98	7.87
Potential(eV) 2nd	14.9	16.2	17.7	16.6

tantalum complex is converted to a basic salt of low solubility. The chemical similarity between Mo and W is somewhat less—they form independent minerals and their chemical separations are accomplished much more easily. The effect of the lanthanide contraction diminishes for elements beyond W, but for each of the families of transition metals beyond Group IIIA the second and third members are much more similar in their properties than are the first and second members.

Oxidation States. The variability of oxidation states is characteristic of most of the group of transition metals. The constancy of the +3 oxidation state for the members of Group IIIA arises because the energy required for the removal of all three outer electrons is not so much greater than that needed for the removal of two electrons. The energy for the removal of three electrons is supplied by the high hydration energies of the 3^+ ions or the high lattice energies of their compounds.

The energy required for the removal of 4 or more electrons is prohibitively high for the formation of simple ions except in the case of very large atoms with low ionization potentials. An appreciable amount of covalent character is to be expected in the higher oxidation states. Except for Group VIII, each of the transition metals shows an oxidation state corresponding to the group number as the highest state. The lowest state usually encountered in simple salts is +2, corresponding to the removal of the two s electrons in the outermost shell (Table 9.14).

TABLE 9.14

Oxidation States of Some Binary Compounds of Transition and Post-transition Metals

	IVA	VA	VIA	VIIA	VIII			IB	IIB	IIIB	IVB
	Ti	V	Cr	Mn	Fe	Co	Ni	Cu	Zn	Ga[a]	Ge
F	3,4	3,4,5	2,3,4,5	2,3	2,3	2,3	2	2	2	3	4
Cl	2,3,4	2,3,4	2,3	2	2,3	2	2	1,2	2	1,3	2,4
Br	2,3,4	2,3,4	2,3	2	2,3	2	2	1,2	2	3	2,4
I	2,3,4	2,3	2,3	2	2	2	2	1	2	3	2,4
O	2,3,4	2,3,4,5	2,3, 6	2,3,4, 7	2,3	2,3	2,3,4	1,2	2	1,3	2,4
	Zr	Nb	Mo	Tc	Ru	Rh	Pd	Ag	Cd	In[a]	Sn
F	4	5	3,4,5,6	6	3, 5,6	3,6	2,3	1,2	2	3	2,4
Cl	2,3,4	3,4,5	2,3,4,5	4, 6	3,4	3	2	1	1,2	1,3	2,4
Br	4	2, 5	2,3,4	—	—	—	2	1	2	1,3	2,4
I	4	3,4,5	2,3,4	—	3	3	2	1	2	1,3	2,4
O	4	2, 4,5	3,4,5,6	4, 6,7	4, 8	3,4	2,3,4	1, 3	2	1,3	2,4
	Hf	Ta	W	Re	Os	Ir	Pt	Au	Hg	Tl	Pb
F	4	5	4, 6	4,5,6,7	4,5,6	4,6	4,6	3	1,2	1,3	2,4
Cl	3,4	2,3,4,5	2, 4,5,6	3, 5,6	2,3,4	1,2,3,4	1,2,3,4	1, 3	1,2	1,3	2,4
Br	4	3, 5	2, 4,5,6	3,4,5,6	3	1,2,3	2,3,4	1, 3	1,2	1,3	2,4
I	4	4,5	2, 4	3,4	4	1,2,3	2,3,4	1, 3	1,2	1,3	2
O	4	4,5	4,5,6	3,4, 6,7	4, 8	2,3,4,6	3,4,6	1, 3	1,2	1,3	2,4

[a] Gallium and indium dihalides are diamagnetic compounds, which can be formulated as $M^I M^{III} X_4$.

Although the first ionization potentials do not differ greatly within most families of the transition metals, the third and higher ionization potentials are generally highest for the first member of each family. The differences between successive ionization potentials are also greatest for the first member of each family. Consequently, the highest oxidation state is most stable, and the corresponding compounds are poor oxidizing agents, for the second or third member of each group (e.g., Zr^{4+} and Hf^{4+}). The lower oxidation states are relatively more stable for the first member of each group (e.g., Ti^{2+} and Ti^{3+}) as compared to the second and third members. Solid $ZrCl_2$, $ZrCl_3$, and $HfCl_3$ can be obtained by reducing MCl_4 with the free metal, but the lower oxidation states are not stable in solution. A variety of Ti(II) and Ti(III) compounds are known (see Table 9.14). Titanium(III) compounds are readily obtained in solution by reduction of Ti(IV) salts with zinc and acid, or electrolytically. Titanium(III) chloride can be obtained by dissolving titanium metal in hydrochloric acid. It finds some application as a reducing agent in analytical work.

Vanadium(II) compounds are strongly reducing, but vanadium(III) salts are stable in solution. Niobium and tantalum are most commonly encountered in the +5 oxidation state. Chromium(II) compounds are also strongly reducing and most of the common salts are those of chromium(III). The +6 oxidation state is encountered in CrO_3, K_2CrO_4, $K_2Cr_2O_7$, etc. These compounds are strong oxidizing agents, being reduced to compounds of chromium(III) in solution. As is generally true, the oxidation to higher oxidation states encountered as oxyanions is much more easily accomplished in basic solution (see emf diagram in Table 9.15) and the oxyanions are poorer oxidizing agents in basic solution. The only important compound of molybdenum in an oxidation state lower than +6 is the mineral MoS_2, molybdenite. Molybdenum disulfide has lubricant properties similar to those of graphite and it finds some use because of this property. Molybdenum or its compounds are oxidized to MoO_3 by heating in air or by reaction with HNO_3. Molybdenum trioxide dissolves in alkali hydroxides or ammonium hydroxide to form molybdates, $M_2^I[MoO_4]$. Molybdenum also forms a variety of iso- and hetero-poly acids. The formation of ammonium molybdophosphate, $(NH_4)_3[P(Mo_3O_{10})_4]\cdot 6H_2O$, with $(NH_4)_2MoO_4$ is used for the detection of phosphate ion.

Tungsten has an even greater tendency than molybdenum to form compounds in the +6 oxidation state. It forms a hexachloride, WCl_6, by heating freshly reduced W with Cl_2. The corresponding fluoride and even the bromide can be obtained. The hexahalides are completely hydrolyzed in water to give tungstic acid, H_2WO_4.

Manganese(I) is encountered in salts of the cyano complex, e.g., $K_5[Mn(CN)_6]$. The characteristic oxidation state of manganese in solution is +2 although the +3 state is stabilized in complexes such as $K_3[Mn(CN)_6]$, $K_3[Mn(C_2O_4)_3]$, and $K_3[MnF_6]$. Manganese occurs in the igneous rocks as the Mn^{2+} ion, replacing Fe^{2+} and Mg^{2+}. During the weathering process the manganese is oxidized and finally deposited as MnO_2, the important manganese ore. Potassium permanganate, $KMnO_4$, is the most important compound of Mn(VII). It can be obtained by electrolytic oxidation or Cl_2 oxidation of K_2MnO_4, which is produced by strong oxidation of $Mn(OH)_2$ or $Mn(OH)_3$ in a basic medium. Potassium permanganate is a strong oxidizing agent, which finds wide analytical applications because of the sharp color change on reduction. It is usually used in acidic solution where it is reduced to the nearly colorless Mn^{2+} ion. In the absence of an excess of strong acid or strong base MnO_2 is formed. The manganate(VI) ion is formed by reduction of MnO_4^- in concentrated sodium or potassium hydroxide solution.

The oxide, Mn_2O_7, can be obtained by the reaction of $KMnO_4$ and concentrated H_2SO_4. It is a dark oily liquid, which decomposes explosively when heated. It is an acid anhydride since it reacts with an excess of water to produce $HMnO_4$, a very strong acid.

The characteristic oxidation state of technetium and rhenium is +7. The compounds such as $KTcO_4$ and $KReO_4$ are not strong oxidizing agents. The volatile oxides, Tc_2O_7 and Re_2O_7, and sulfides, Tc_2S_7 and Re_2S_7, are stable. Technetium is much closer to rhenium in its properties than it is to manganese.

The oxidation state of rhenium of second greatest importance is +4. ReO_2 can be obtained by reducing Re_2O_7 in H_2 at about 300°C. It combines with alkali hydroxides on fusion to produce the alkali metal rhenites, $M_2^I ReO_3$. The intermediate oxidation states $+5$ and $+6$, and the lower oxidation state $+3$ are much less stable. The rhenium -1 oxidation state, which has been reported, has turned out to be a hydride compound $(ReH_9{}^{2-})$ rather than a simple solvated $1-$ ion.

The very high oxidation states of the transition metals are usually brought out in combination with fluorine or oxygen. The size of the anion is rarely the limiting factor. More important is the strength of the oxidizing power of the cation in higher oxidation states and the increasing ease of oxidation of the anions with increasing size within a group (e.g., F^-, Cl^-, Br^-, I^-). The greatest number of oxidation states of a given metal is usually encountered in the oxides although this is probably true only because the oxides have been investigated most extensively (see Table 9.14). The emf diagrams given in Table 9.15 show the relative stabilities of the various oxidation states of the metals as hydrated cations or oxy anions. The relative stabilities of the various oxidation states can be altered greatly by complex formation, e.g., the stabilization of high oxidation states in oxy anions, or by lattice forces in the solid state.

The basicity of the metal ions in various oxidation states can be treated on the basis of charge/size relationships. For the same oxidation state, e.g., $+4$ for Group IVA, there is a marked increase in basicity with increasing ionic radius and a corresponding de-

TABLE 9.15
Oxidation emf Diagrams

Group IVA

Acid Solution

$$Ti \xrightarrow{(0.83)} Ti^{2+} \xrightarrow{(2)} Ti^{3+} \xrightarrow{-(0.1)} TiO^{2+}$$

$$Ti \xrightarrow{\hspace{2cm}(0.89)\hspace{2cm}} TiO^{2+}$$

$$Zr \xrightarrow{1.53} Zr^{4+}$$

$$Hf \xrightarrow{1.70} Hf^{4+}$$

Basic Solution

$$Ti \xrightarrow{1.69} TiO_2 \text{ (hydrated)}$$

Group VA

Acid Solution

$$V \xrightarrow{(1.2)} V^{2+} \xrightarrow{0.255} V^{3+} \xrightarrow{-0.337} VO^{2+} \xrightarrow{-1.00} V(OH)_4{}^+$$

$$V \xrightarrow{\hspace{3cm}0.253\hspace{3cm}} $$

$$Nb \xrightarrow{(1.1)} Nb^{3+} \xrightarrow{(0.1)} Nb_2O_5$$

$$Nb \xrightarrow{\hspace{2cm}0.65\hspace{2cm}} $$

$$Ta \xrightarrow{\hspace{1.5cm}0.81\hspace{1.5cm}} Ta_2O_5$$

TABLE 9.15—*Continued*
Oxidation emf Diagrams

Group VIA

Acid Solution

$$Cr \xrightarrow{\;0.91\;} Cr^{2+} \xrightarrow{\;0.41\;} Cr^{3+} \xrightarrow{\;-1.33\;} Cr_2O_7{}^{2-}$$

$$Mo \xrightarrow{\;0.2\;} Mo^{3+} \xrightarrow{\;(0.0)\;} MoO_2{}^{+} \xrightarrow{\;-0.48\;} H_2MoO_4$$

$$W \xrightarrow{\;0.11\;} W^{3+} \xrightarrow{\;0.15\;} WO_2 \xrightarrow{\;0.04\;} W_2O_5 \xrightarrow{\;0.03\;} WO_3$$

Basic Solution

$$Cr \xrightarrow{\;1.4\;} Cr(OH)_2 \xrightarrow{\;1.1\;} Cr(OH)_3 \xrightarrow{\;0.13\;} CrO_4{}^{2-}$$

$$Mo \xrightarrow{\;0.87\;} MoO_2 \xrightarrow{\;1.4\;} MoO_4{}^{2-}$$
$$\underset{1.05}{\underline{\qquad\qquad\qquad\qquad}}$$

$$W \xrightarrow{\;(1.25)\;} WO_4{}^{2-}$$

Group VIIA

Acid Solution

$$Mn \xrightarrow{1.190} Mn^{2+} \xrightarrow{-1.5} Mn^{3+} \xrightarrow{-0.95} MnO_2 \xrightarrow{-(2.5)} MnO_3{}^{-} \xrightarrow{-(2.0)} MnO_4{}^{2-} \xrightarrow{-0.564} MnO_4{}^{-}$$
$$\underset{-1.23}{\underline{\qquad\qquad}} \qquad \underset{-1.695}{\underline{\qquad\qquad\qquad}}$$

$$TcH_9{}^{2-} \xrightarrow{(1)} Tc \xrightarrow{0.5} Tc^{2+} \xrightarrow{-0.281} TcO_2 \xrightarrow{-0.83} TcO_3 \xrightarrow{-0.65} TcO_4{}^{-}$$

$$ReH_9{}^{2-} \xrightarrow{(0.4)} Re \xrightarrow{-0.26} ReO_2 \xrightarrow{-0.385} ReO_3 \xrightarrow{-0.768} ReO_4{}^{-}$$

Basic Solution

$$Mn \xrightarrow{1.55} Mn(OH)_2 \xrightarrow{-0.1} Mn(OH)_3 \xrightarrow{0.2} MnO_2 \xrightarrow{-0.84} MnO_3{}^{-} \xrightarrow{-0.34} MnO_4{}^{2-} \xrightarrow{-0.564} MnO_4{}^{-}$$
$$\underset{0.05}{\underline{\qquad\qquad}} \qquad \underset{-0.588}{\underline{\qquad\qquad\qquad}}$$

$$Re \xrightarrow{(0.6)} Re(OH)_3 \xrightarrow{(0.53)} ReO_2 \xrightarrow{(0.5)} ReO_4{}^{2-} \xrightarrow{(0.7)} ReO_4{}^{-}$$
$$\underset{0.576}{\underline{\qquad\qquad}} \qquad \underset{0.595}{\underline{\qquad\qquad}}$$

crease in the covalent character of the resulting compounds. The Ti(IV) compounds are much more covalent than those of Zr(IV) or Hf(IV) and are much more extensively hydrolyzed. Thus TiCl$_4$ is a liquid while ZrCl$_4$ is a solid, although it sublimes at about 300°C. In Group VIA Cr(III) is amphoteric and can be obtained as Cr^{3+} salts or salts of the chromite ion, Cr(OH)$_4{}^{-}$. Mo(III) and W(III) are basic in character. The Cr^{2+} ion is basic because of the lower charge and larger radius (compared to Cr^{3+}). In general, the members of the first transition series give ions which are predominately basic only in

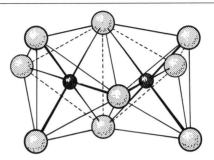

FIGURE 9.16. *Structure of* $W_2Cl_9^{3-}$.

the lower oxidation states. The oxidation states greater than $+3$ for the first members of Groups V–VIII are generally encountered in oxides or oxy anions. The second and third members of these families give ions which are much more basic, showing a much greater tendency than the first members to form cationic species in higher oxidation states. Chromium trioxide is quite acidic and is very soluble in water to give H_2CrO_4. Molybdenum trioxide is less acidic and is only slightly soluble in water, and WO_3 is very insoluble. All three oxides readily dissolve in bases. Because the difference between the radii of Mo and W is small, the basicities of the compounds of Mo and W are very similar.

Compounds Containing Metal–Metal Bonds. The dimeric cation Hg_2^{2+} was long considered to be unique. Copper(I) compounds have sometimes been formulated as Cu_2X_2 by analogy, but without experimental support. The existence of Cd_2^{2+} has been shown (p. 316), although the bonding is much weaker than in Hg_2^{2+}. The compound $K_3W_2Cl_9$ has long been known to contain discrete $W_2Cl_9^{3-}$ ions consisting of two octahedra of Cl^- ions with one face in common (Figure 9.16). The W—W distance is even less than in the metal, indicating a very strong W—W bond through the shared face.

Metal–metal bonding is encountered in several metal carbonyls. The structure of $Fe_2(CO)_9$ is similar to that of $W_2Cl_9^{3-}$ with three bridging carbonyls and an Fe—Fe bond. There are two bridging carbonyls and a Co—Co bond in $Co_2(CO)_8$. The dimeric carbonyls $Mn_2(CO)_{10}$ and $Re_2(CO)_{10}$ contain metal–metal bonds without the aid of

bridging carbonyls. Clusters of three metal atoms in an equilateral triangle are encountered in $Ru_3(CO)_{12}$, $Os_3(CO)_{12}$, $Fe_3(CO)_{12}$, and $Ni_3(C_5H_5)_3(CO)_2$. There is a tetra-

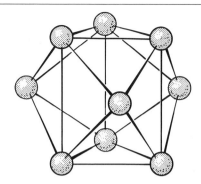

FIGURE 9.17. *Structure of* Bi_9^{5+} [*J. D. Corbett and R. E. Rundle,* Inorg. Chem., *3, 1409 (1964)*].

hedral cluster of four metal atoms in $Co_4(CO)_{12}$ and an octahedral cluster of six metal atoms in $Rh_6(CO)_{16}$.

The high selectivity of dimethylglyoxime for the precipitation of nickel(II) is not the result of unusually great stability of the discrete complex, but is caused by the unusual structure which leads to low solubility. The planar units are stacked above one another so that the nickel "atoms" are bonded. The presence of copper–copper bonds in $Cu_2(C_2H_3O_2)_4 \cdot 2H_2O$ is discussed later (p. 439).

Although it is apparent that a number of examples of compounds containing metal–metal bonds have been known for some time, they have been considered as oddities. Recent structural investigations indicate that this type of interaction is much more common than has been supposed.

It has been known for several years that bismuth formed a polymeric cation, but the structure and nature of interaction were unknown. The structure of Bi_9^{5+} has been shown to be that represented in Figure 9.17.* Lead and tin have been reported to form the anions Pb_9^{4-}, Pb_7^{4-}, and Sn_9^{4-} in liquid ammonia.

The complex cations $[Mo_6Cl_8]^{4+}$ and $[Ta_6Cl_{12}]^{2+}$ have the structures shown in Figure 9.18. In each case there is an octahedral arrangement of six metal atoms and each is surrounded by a planar group of four bridging Cl^- ions. The structures of $[Ta_6Br_{12}]^{2+}$ and $[Nb_6Cl_{12}]^{2+}$ are similar to those of $[Ta_6Cl_{12}]^{2+}$. The compounds such as $CsReCl_4$ have been presumed to contain tetrahedral $ReCl_4^-$ ions. However, the anion has been shown to be a trimer,† $[Re_3Cl_{12}]^{3-}$, with the structure shown in Figure 9.19. There is a triangular arrangement of Re "atoms" with four Cl^- in an approximately planar arrangement about each Re atom and one additional Cl^- ion attached to each Re atom in the same plane and directed away from the center of the Re_3 triangle. Cotton and co-workers have found that the Cl^- ion directed away from the center of the triangle can be replaced by other ligands or omitted altogether in $[Re_3Cl_9]$. They have also found a dimer of $ReCl_4^-$ in which there are two *eclipsed* planar $ReCl_4^-$ units joined by a Re—Re bond. The eclipsed configuration is explained as the result of δ bonding between the metal atoms. An unusually short Re—Re bond distance indicates a bond order of about 3 (σ, π, and δ bond).

* Herschaft, A., and J. D. Corbett, *Inorg. Chem.*, **2**, 979 (1963); J. D. Corbett and R. E. Rundle, *ibid.*, **3**, 1408 (1964).
† Bertrand, J. A., F. A. Cotton, and W. A. Dollase, *Inorg. Chem.*, **2**, 1166 (1963).

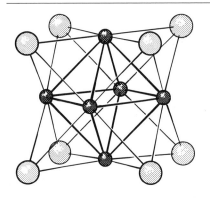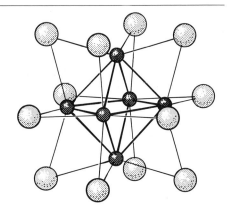

FIGURE 9.18. *Structures of* $Mo_6Cl_8^{4+}$ *and* $Ta_6Cl_{12}^{2+}$. *(From L. Pauling,* The Nature of the Chemical Bond, *Third edition,* © *1960 by Cornell University, p. 440. Used by permission of Cornell University Press.)*

One can anticipate that many more examples of compounds containing metal atom clusters will be found. Although no clear pattern has emerged, several trends are suggested by the results available:

(*1*) Low oxidation states favor the formation of metal atom clusters—the metal carbonyls give several examples. This is to be expected since the metal atom clusters might be regarded as fragments of metals where bonding would be strongest with the maximum number of valence electrons available.

(*2*) The tendency to form metal–metal bonds increases with increasing atomic number within a family—the Hg_2^{2+} ion is much more stable than Cd_2^{2+} and there are many examples of such compounds of heavier elements, e.g., Pb, Bi, W, Mo, Ta, and Re. At least within the transition series the cohesive energies for the metals increase with increasing atomic number within a group.

(*3*) The tendency to form metal–metal bonds is perhaps greatest in the vicinity of the Group VIA elements—many examples cited are from Groups VA–VIIA. Again the cohesive energies for the metals are particularly strong near the middle of each transition series.

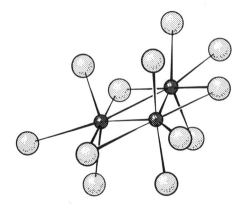

FIGURE 9.19. *Structure of* $Re_3Cl_{12}^{3-}$.

Group VIII

The group eight metals exhibit close similarities in the horizontal triads as well as in the vertical groups. Many of the properties of the complexes are most closely related to the number of d electrons, which is similar for the ions of the metals in each of the vertical columns. The radii are very similar in each horizontal triad, but the radii of the metals of the second and third transition series in each vertical column are also very similar because of the lanthanide contraction. Hence, the most useful classification places Fe, Co, and Ni in one group known as the iron group. Instead of classifying the platinum metals into light platinum metals (Ru, Rh, and Pd) and the heavy platinum metals, the chemical similarities are more apparent in the groups of two: Ru and Os, Rh and Ir, and Pd and Pt. In each of these pairs the metals have similar radii and similar electronic configurations.

The iron group metals often occur together in nature and the simple salts of the metals in the common $+2$ oxidation state are very similar. Only iron, as Fe(III), gives stable simple salts in an oxidation state other than $+2$. Iron(II) salts are easily oxidized to those of iron(III), while the hydrated Co^{3+} ion oxidizes water and nickel does not give simple salts of higher oxidation states. Strong oxidation of $Fe(OH)_3$ in strongly alkaline solution produces the ferrate(VI) ion as in K_2FeO_4. The FeO_4^{2-} ion is a very strong oxidizing agent.

The Fe^{2+} ion is a d^6 ion, which gives very stable low-spin octahedral complexes of the type $[Fe(CN)_6]^{4-}$ and $[Fe(phen)_3]^{2+}$. Most ligands other than 1,10-phenanthroline (phen) and dipyridyl give more stable complexes with Fe^{3+}, a d^5 ion, presumably because of the higher charge on the cation. The $[Fe(CN)_6]^{3-}$ ion is a low-spin complex, but most others such as FeF_6^{3-}, $[Fe(C_2O_4)_3]^{3-}$, and Fe(acetylacetonate)$_3$ are high-spin complexes. The carbonyl compounds $Fe(CO)_5$ and $K_2Fe(CO)_4$ represent oxidation states of 0 and -2, respectively.

The cobalt(II) ion forms octahedral complexes, e.g., $[Co(NH_3)_6]^{2+}$, planar complexes,

e.g.,

and tetrahedral complexes, e.g.,

$[CoCl_4]^{2-}$. However, in the presence of coordinating agents cobalt(II) is easily oxidized to cobalt(III) to give low-spin octahedral complexes such as $[Co(NH_3)_6]Cl_3$ and $K_3[Co(CN)_6]$. The cobalt(III) complexes are exceptionally stable and give stable geometrical isomers, e.g., *cis* and *trans*-$[Co(en)_2Cl_2]Cl$, and optical isomers, e.g., d and l-$[Co(en)_3]Cl_3$ and d and l-*cis*-$[Co(en)_2Cl_2]Cl$. The carbonyls $Co_2(CO)_8$ and $KCo(CO)_4$ represent the 0 and -1 oxidation states, respectively.

Most of the complexes of nickel are those of nickel(II). Planar complexes such as $[Ni(CN)_4]^{2-}$ are diamagnetic; the octahedral complexes such as $[Ni(NH_3)_6]^{2+}$ have two unpaired electrons. In the solid state the $[NiCl_4]^{2-}$ ion is tetrahedral. A few five-coordinate complexes of nickel(II) have been reported, e.g., $[Ni(P(C_2H_5)_3)_2Br_3]$ and

$$\left[Ni \left(\begin{array}{c} \qquad\qquad (CH_2)_2 As(CH_3)_2 \\ \diagup \\ As\!\!-\!\!(CH_2)_2 As(CH_3)_2 \\ \diagdown \\ \qquad CH_3 \end{array} \right) Cl_2 \right]$$

Nickel carbonyl, $Ni(CO)_4$, is the most stable of the common metal carbonyls.

Ruthenium and osmium form complexes similar to those of iron(II) and iron(III). In addition, many of their complexes can be oxidized to the +4 oxidation state. Oxidation of ruthenium metal produces RuO_2. Strong oxidation of ruthenium salts in alkaline solution produces RuO_4, an orange liquid above 25°C. The stable oxy anions encountered for ruthenium are the ruthenate(VI) ion, RuO_4^{2-}, and ruthenate(VII) or perruthenate ion, RuO_4^-. Osmium tetraoxide, OsO_4, is obtained by the direct oxidation of the metal or the compounds of osmium. It melts at 40°C and boils at about 100°. The oxy anions of osmium are less stable than those of ruthenium because of the ease of formation of OsO_4. Mild reduction of OsO_4 in alkaline solution produces osmate salts such as K_2OsO_4.

Most of the simple and complex salts of rhodium are those of rhodium(III). The +3 state is also the most stable state of iridium, although some of its octahedral complex halides can be oxidized to the +4 state.

The important compounds of palladium and platinum are those of the +2 and +4 oxidation states, primarily their complexes. The palladium compounds are generally planar complexes of palladium(II), e.g., $K_2[PdCl_4]$ and $[Pd(NH_3)_4]Cl_2$. Even $PdCl_2$ in the solid state contains chains of planar $PdCl_4$ units. Oxidation of $K_2[PdCl_4]$ with Cl_2 or aqua regia produces $K_2[PdCl_6]$. The platinum complexes are very similar to those of palladium. Platinum(II) is the metal ion which gives the most stable planar complexes, giving rise to geometrical isomerism as exemplified by *cis* and *trans*-$[Pt(NH_3)_2Cl_2]$. The +4 state is much more stable for platinum than for palladium. The octahedral complexes of platinum(IV) give particularly stable geometrical isomers of the type mentioned for cobalt(III).

No emf diagrams are included for the Group VIII metals because the most important and interesting aspects of the chemistry of these metals involve their complexes. The emf diagrams given for other periodic groups are for hydrated or oxy ions. Appendix E includes important emf values for many of the Group VIII metals.

GENERAL REFERENCES

Hume-Rothery, W., *Atomic Theory for Students of Metallurgy* (London: Institute of Metals, 1960).

Azaroff, L. V., *Introduction to Solids* (New York: McGraw-Hill Book Co., 1960).

Eméleus, H. J., and J. S. Anderson, *Modern Aspects of Inorganic Chemistry* (Princeton: D. Van Nostrand Co., Inc., 1960).

Remy, H., *Treatise on Inorganic Chemistry* (translated by J. S. Anderson), Vols. I and II (Amsterdam: Elsevier Publishing Company, 1956). Probably the best "short" treatise available.

Sidgwick, N. V., *The Chemical Elements and Their Compounds*, Vols. I and II (London: Oxford University Press, 1950).

Wells, A. F., *Structural Inorganic Chemistry* (3rd ed., London: Oxford University Press, 1962).

Ives, D. J. C., *Principles of the Extraction of Metals* (London: Royal Institute of Chemistry Monographs for Teachers, 1960).

Peacock, R. D., "Some Fluorine Compounds of the Transition Metals," in *Progress in Inorganic Chemistry,* Vol. II, F. A. Cotton, ed. (New York: Interscience Publishers, Inc., 1960) p. 193.

Nyholm, R. S., "Stereochemistry of Group VIII Elements," *Quart. Rev. (London),* **3**, 321 (1949).

Douglas, B. E., "Stabilization of Oxidation States Through Coordination," *J. Chem. Educ.,* **29**, 119 (1952).

Kleinberg, J., *Unfamiliar Oxidation States and Their Stabilization* (Lawrence: University of Kansas Press, 1950).

Dunitz, J. D., and L. E. Orgel, "Stereochemistry of Ionic Solids," in *Advances in Inorganic Chemistry and Radiochemistry*, Vol. 2, A. J. Eméleus and A. G. Sharpe eds. (New York: Academic Press, Inc., 1960) p. 1. An excellent review with discussions of crystal field effects.

Jolly, W., "Metal-Ammonia Solutions," in *Progress in Inorganic Chemistry,* Vol. I, F. A. Cotton, ed. (New York: Interscience Publishers, Inc., 1959) p. 235.

Symons, M. C. R., "Solutions of the Alkali Metals in Liquid Ammonia," *Quart. Rev. (London),* **13**, 99 (1959).

Coates, G. E., *Organometallic Compounds* (2nd ed., London: Methuen and Company, Ltd., 1960); *Metal-Organic Compounds* (Advances in Chemistry Series, No. 23), (Washington, D.C.: American Chemical Society, 1959). A collection of papers.

Zeiss, H. H., ed., *Organometallic Chemistry,* A.C.S. Monograph No. 147 (New York: Reinhold Publishing Corporation, 1960). A collection of review articles.

Kharasch, M. S., and O. Reinmuth, *Grignard Reactions of Non-Metallic Substances* (London: Constable and Company, London, and New York: Prentice-Hall, 1954).

Asprey, L. B., and B. B. Cunningham, "Unusual Oxidation States of Some Actinide and Lanthanide Elements," in *Progress in Inorganic Chemistry,* Vol. II, F. A. Cotton, ed. (New York: Interscience Publishers, Inc., 1960) p. 267.

Spedding, F. H., and A. M. Daane, eds., *The Rare Earths* (New York: John Wiley and Sons, Inc., 1961).

Hindman, J. C., T. K. Keenan, B. B. Cunningham, and G. T. Seaborg, *J. Chem. Educ.,* **36**, 15 (1959). Review articles on the actinide elements.

Katz, J. J., and G. T. Seaborg, *The Chemistry of the Actinide Elements* (London: Methuen and Company, Ltd., 1957).

Mason, B., *Principles of Geochemistry* (2nd ed., New York: John Wiley and Sons, Inc., 1958).

Problems

1. Give a reasonable explanation of the "valences" exhibited in each of the following compounds: (*a*) TiH_2; (*b*) TiN; (*c*) VC; (*d*) Fe_4C; (*e*) $FeAl$.

2. Sketch the curves for the distribution of energy states and their electron populations for a metallic conductor, an insulator, and a semi-conductor.

3. Predict the effect on the magnetic properties of alloying (*a*) Mn and Fe; (*b*) Fe and Co; (*c*) Co and Ni. Explain your approach.

4. Using the Pauling approach calculate the number of "metal bonds per atom" in an alloy having 8.5 electrons/atoms on the valence level.

5. Discuss possible effects of extreme pressure on a metal and a nonmetal.

6. Give equations and describe conditions for the preparation of:

(*a*) Cs	(*e*) $TiBr_3$
(*b*) Na_2CO_3	(*f*) $ZrCl_3$
(*c*) MgF	(*g*) $VOCl_3$
(*d*) C_2H_5HgBr	(*h*) K_2WO_4

7.   Give two properties which illustrate the diagonal relationship between Li and Mg and two properties which illustrate the properties of Li as a member of Group I. Explain the factors which are important in each case.

8.   Predict the following for Fr:

(*a*) the product of the burning of Fr in air;

(*b*) an insoluble compound of Fr;

(*c*) the structure of FrCl;

(*d*) the relative heats of formation of FrF and FrI.

9.   Sketch the structure of the silicate anion in beryl.

10.   Describe the packing of oxide ions and give the coordination number of Mg^{2+} in forsterite, Mg_2SiO_4.

11.   Explain why Al and Ti, among the most abundant metals, became important metals so late in man's history.

12.   Give equations for reactions which could be used to separate Zn^{2+}, Cd^{2+}, and Hg^{2+} present in solution.

13.   Can one obtain:

(*a*) Hg^{2+} salts free of Hg_2^{2+}?

(*b*) Hg_2^{2+} salts free of Hg^{2+}?

Explain.

14.   Give an example of:

(*a*) an acidic oxide of a metal;

(*b*) an amphoteric oxide of a transition metal;

(*c*) a diamagnetic rare earth metal ion;

(*d*) a compound of a metal in the +8 oxidation state;

(*e*) a liquid metal chloride.

15.   Would the removal of Hf from Zr be important in most applications of zirconium compounds? In the use of Zr metal in flash bulbs?

16.   What properties of tungsten make it so suitable for filaments for light bulbs?

17.   Discuss the factors involved in determining the following solubility patterns: LiF is much less soluble than LiCl, but AgF is much more soluble than AgCl.

18.   The metal perchlorates have been referred to as "universal solutes." What properties are important in causing most metal perchlorates to be quite soluble in water and several other solvents?

19.   How can one account for the color of the following:

(a) Fe_3O_4	(c) $KFeFe(CN)_6$	(e) $Ti(H_2O)_6^{3+}$
(b) Ag_2S	(d) $KMnO_4$	(f) $Cu(NH_3)_4^{2+}$

CHAPTER X

Coordination Compounds. I.
Structure and Bonding

Introduction

Probably the student's first obvious encounter with a coordination compound or complex ion is that involving the formation of the deep blue $[Cu(NH_3)_4]^{2+}$ ion on addition of aqueous ammonia solution to a solution of a copper(II) salt. The reaction is usually described by Equation 10.1, however, Equation 10.2 is a more complete representation.* The copper ion in solution is already a complex ion – an aquo or water complex.

$$Cu^{2+} + 4NH_3 \rightleftharpoons [Cu(NH_3)_4]^{2+} \qquad (10.1)$$
$$[Cu(H_2O)_4]^{2+} + 4NH_3 \rightleftharpoons [Cu(NH_3)_4]^{2+} + 4H_2O. \qquad (10.2)$$

The reaction is not an addition reaction, but rather a substitution reaction in which ammonia displaces water from the coordination sphere. The *coordination sphere* includes those molecules or ions bonded directly to the metal ion.

If one adds acid to the solution of $[Cu(NH_3)_4]^{2+}$, the protons combine with NH_3 to give NH_4^+ and the ammonia complex is destroyed, i.e., the ammonia molecules are removed by the stronger acid H^+ and the less basic water molecules take their place to give $[Cu(H_2O)_4]^{2+}$. When a minimum amount of hydrochloric acid is added to neutralize the ammonia, the solution will have the pale blue color of the $[Cu(H_2O)_4]^{2+}$ ion. If an excess of concentrated hydrochloric acid is added, the solution becomes green because, in the presence of an excess of Cl^-, some of the yellow $[CuCl_4]^{2-}$ ion is formed. The intermediate species $[Cu(H_2O)Cl_3]^-$, $[Cu(H_2O)_2Cl_2]$, and $[Cu(H_2O)_3Cl]^+$ will also be present in varying amounts depending on the concentration of Cl^-. The $[Cu(H_2O)_4]^{2+}$ ion is never completely converted to $[CuCl_4]^{2-}$, even in concentrated hydrochloric acid solution, because the concentration of water is still greater than that of Cl^- and the Cl^- is a poorer coordinating agent or ligand than water. Since coordination can be interpreted as a Lewis acid–base reaction, this is equivalent to saying that the Cl^- is a weaker base than water. On dilution, the green solution becomes blue again because the Cl^- loses out in the competition when the chloride ion concentration is not

---

* Actually these representations for both the aquo and ammonia complexes are also inaccurate. The Cu^{2+} ion usually has four molecules held rather strongly and two more held more loosely. The ammonia complex might have two molecules of water attached or one or two additional ammonia molecules, depending on the concentrations.

very great. If one adds HBr or NaBr to a solution of $[Cu(H_2O)_4]^{2+}$, the solution becomes green and finally, in the presence of a high Br^- concentration, dark brownish-green because of the formation of some brown $[CuBr_4]^{2-}$. This complex ion also can be destroyed by dilution.

The chemistry of metals in solution is essentially the chemistry of their complexes. A metal ion in solution will be coordinated to water molecules or to other ligands. The transition metal ions are fairly good Lewis acids and their complexes are quite stable. The cations of the more electropositive metals such as the alkali metals and alkaline earth metals are weaker Lewis acids and form fewer complexes. They are hydrated in solution, but the interaction with water is much weaker than in the case of transition metal ions. Reactions of ions generally require that the water layers (hydration spheres) be stripped away so that the reactants can come together.

Metal ions are almost never encountered without effective shielding. In solution the shielding is provided by the solvent or some other ligand. In the solid state, cations are always surrounded by anions. For an ionic substance such as NaCl, the interaction between the Na^+ and the 6 surrounding Cl^- ions is almost entirely electrostatic. The tendency of the more acidic metal ions such as Cd^{2+} and Pd^{2+} to form lattices in which the interactions are not the same in all directions has been mentioned (see p.

121). $CuCl_2$ crystallizes as the dihydrate, which contains planar
$$H_2O-\overset{\displaystyle Cl}{\underset{\displaystyle Cl}{\mid}}{\overset{\mid}{\underset{\mid}{Cu}}}-OH_2$$

units. In many cases the complexes which exist in the well ordered crystal do not persist in solution because of competition with the solvent.

Analytical Applications

Equilibria involving complex formation are frequently encountered in analytical chemistry. Ag^+ is separated from Hg_2Cl_2 and $PbCl_2$ in the qualitative analysis scheme by dissolving it as $[Ag(NH_3)_2]^+$. Antimony, arsenic, and tin sulfides are separated from the remaining Group II sulfides because they dissolve in the presence of an excess of sulfide ion as the complexes SbS_4^{3-}, AsS_4^{3-}, and SnS_3^{2-}. Organic reagents which give insoluble complexes are widely used for the separation and determination of metals. Two of the most familiar examples are dimethylglyoxime, which is a fairly specific reagent for nickel, and 8-hydroxyquinoline, which precipitates many metals. These compounds are usually insoluble because the metal is incorporated in a large organic molecule and the resulting complex has no net charge. Complexes in which the negative charge on the ligand(s) just balances the charge on the metal ion are called *inner complexes*. Some inner complexes are fairly volatile and can be sublimed, e.g., Fe-(acetylacetonate)$_3$ can be purified by sublimation at reduced pressure. Inner complexes

Bis(8-hydroxyquinolinato)zinc(II)

are often insoluble in water but soluble in organic solvents. For this reason they are used also for separations based on solvent extraction procedures. At an appropriate pH one can get reasonable separations of a metal such as Ga(III) from others by extracting the 8-hydroxyquinoline complex with chloroform. The equilibria involved are as follows:

$$HQ \rightleftharpoons H^+ + Q^- \qquad K_a = \frac{[H^+][Q^-]}{[HQ]} \tag{10.3}$$

$$3Q^- + M^{3+} \rightleftharpoons MQ_3(aq) \qquad K_f = \frac{[MQ_3(aq)]}{[M^{3+}][Q^-]^3} \tag{10.4}$$

$$MQ_3(aq) \rightleftharpoons MQ_3(org) \qquad K_{ext} = \frac{[MQ_3(org)]}{[MQ_3(aq)]} \tag{10.5}$$

K_a depends only on the complexing agent. K_f depends on the specific metal ion and the complexing agent. K_{ext} depends on the solvation of the complex in the two solvents. K_{ext} is particularly dependent on the choice of the organic solvent. At low pH (low concentration of Q^-) only the more stable complexes (high K_f) will be formed to be extracted.

Acetylacetone also forms complexes which can be used in solvent extraction procedures. Acetylacetone exists in the keto, $CH_3\overset{\overset{O}{\|}}{C}CH_2\overset{\overset{O}{\|}}{C}CH_3$, and enol, $CH_3\overset{\overset{OH}{|}}{C}=CH\overset{\overset{O}{\|}}{C}CH_3$, forms. The enol form coordinates through both oxygen atoms with the loss of a proton to form a *chelate ring* (see Figure 10.1). The term chelate (crab's claw) was first used by Morgan* to describe the formation of similar complexes. The term chelate is now used to refer to the compounds formed as a result of chelation. Chelating ligands must have two or more points of attachment. Ammonia, with only one point of attachment, is a unidentate ligand. Ligands such as acetylacetone and ethylenediamine ($NH_2C_2H_4NH_2$) are bidentate. Some common multidentate ligands are shown in Table 10.1. For the rules of nomenclature as applied to ligands and coordination compounds the student is referred to Appendix B.

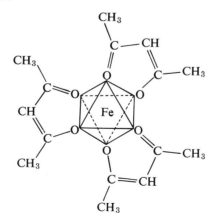

FIGURE 10.1. *Chelate rings in the tris(acetylacetonato)iron(III) compound.*

* Morgan, G. T., and H. D. A. Drew, *J. Chem. Soc.*, **117**, 1456 (1920).

TABLE 10.1
Some Common Multidentate Ligands

Name	Formula	Abbreviation	Classification
Carbonato	CO_3^{2-}		Bidentate
Oxalato	$C_2O_4^{2-}$	ox	Bidentate
Ethylenediamine	$NH_2C_2H_4NH_2$	en	Bidentate
1,2-Propanediamine	$NH_2CH(CH_3)CH_2NH_2$	pn	Bidentate
Acetylacetonato	$CH_3-\overset{\overset{\displaystyle O^-}{\displaystyle \vert}}{C}=CH\overset{\overset{\displaystyle O}{\displaystyle \Vert}}{C}-CH_3$	acac	Bidentate
8-Hydroxyquinolinato		oxine	Bidentate
2,2'-Dipyridyl		dipy	Bidentate
1,10-Phenanthroline		phen	Bidentate
Glycinato	$NH_2CH_2CO_2^-$	gly	Bidentate
Diethylenetriamine	$NH(C_2H_4NH_2)_2$	dien	Tridentate
Triethylenetetramine	$(-CH_2NH_2C_2H_4NH_2)_2$	trien	Quadridentate
Nitrilotriacetato	$N(CH_2CO_2)_3^{3-}$	NTA	Quadridentate
Tetraethylenepentamine	$NH(C_2H_4NHC_2H_4NH_2)_2$	tetraen	Quinquidentate
Ethylenediamine-tetraacetato	$[-CH_2N(CH_2CO_2)_2]_2^{4-}$	EDTA	Sexadentate

Many titration procedures now use EDTA in the determination of metals. These procedures usually involve competition for the metal between EDTA and a dye that can also serve as a ligand. One of the common oxidation–reduction indicators, ferroin, is a complex. Ferroin contains the $[Fe(phen)_3]^{2+}$ ion, which is deep red, while the Fe(III) compound is pale blue. In a suitable oxidation–reduction titration the removal of the color of the ferroin is an indication that the end point has been reached. The ferroin is oxidized only after the reducing agent being titrated is completely oxidized.

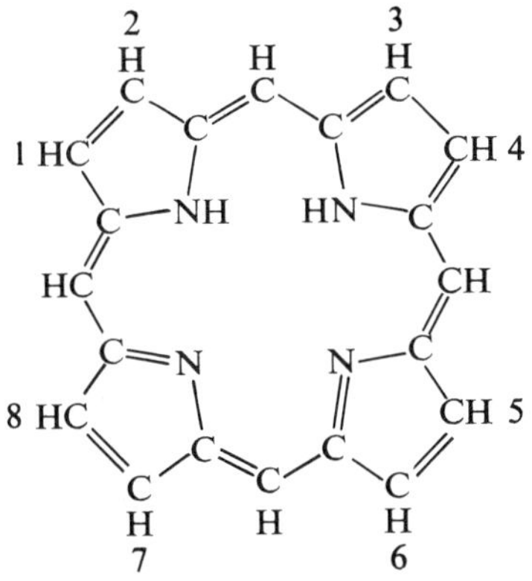

Porphin

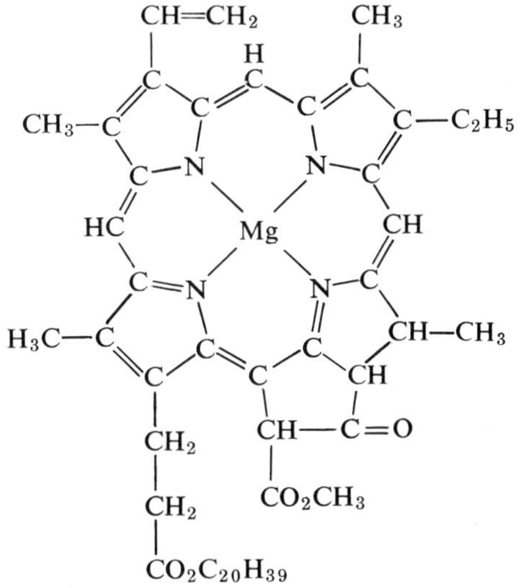

Chlorophyll A

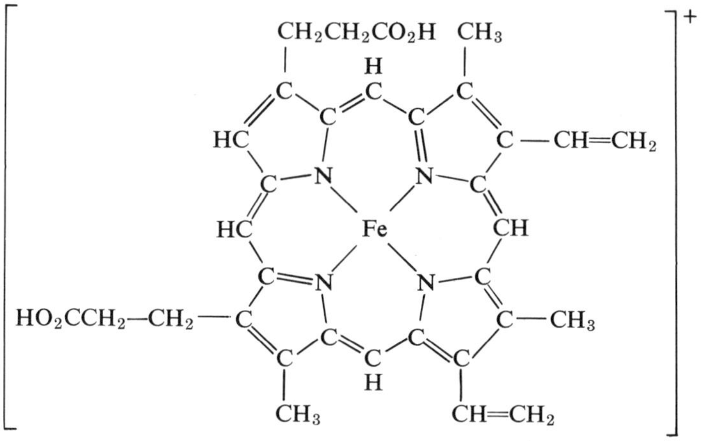

Hemin

FIGURE 10.2. *Porphin and porphyrin complexes.*

Coordination Compounds in Nature

A number of coordination compounds are of biological importance. Chlorophyll is a magnesium compound in which the magnesium is coordinated to four nitrogens which are part of a coplanar fused ring system. The parent fused ring compound to which chlorophyll is related is porphin, shown in Figure 10.2. The substituted compounds are known as porphyrins. The blood pigments are related iron compounds. The structure of hemin is shown in Figure 10.2. Upon reduction and association with the protein material globin, hemoglobin is formed. Hemoglobin is responsible for oxygen transport in the body. Most essential trace metals probably function through coordination processes.

Bonding in Coordination Compounds

Werner's Views

The Germans use the term "compounds of a higher order" to refer to compounds formed by combination of two or more molecules, each of which has satisfied its usual valence requirements. These include coordination compounds such as the ammonia complexes, molecular addition compounds and those which involve hydrogen bonding, e.g., $NaF \cdot HF$, and other types of interaction, e.g., $KI \cdot I_2$. Before the development of modern theories of valence, the interactions in the various compounds of higher order were vague, but those in the coordination compounds were especially puzzling. Compounds we would now consider to be coordination compounds have been known for more than 150 years, but no satisfactory explanation for their formation was available until the imaginative work of Alfred Werner.

In 1893 Werner formulated his coordination theory, which provided the basis for modern theories. In order to appreciate Werner's insight, it must be remembered that the electron, the basis for all modern theories of chemical bonding, was unknown at the time. He suggested that each metal has two kinds of valence: primary or ionizable valence, which may be satisfied only by negative ions as in simple salts, e.g., $CrCl_3$, and secondary valence, which may be satisfied by negative ions or neutral molecules. The secondary valences are responsible for the addition of ammonia to give compounds such as $CrCl_3 \cdot 6NH_3$. Each metal has a characteristic number of secondary valences directed in space to give a definite geometrical arrangement. On the other hand, the primary valences are nondirectional. The arrangement for six secondary valences was assumed to be octahedral (see Figure 10.3). When a uninegative ion is in the inner coordination sphere, it satisfies one of the primary, as well as one of the secondary, valences of the metal (see Figure 10.4). When two anions are in the coordination sphere, the directional character of the secondary valences gives rise to *cis* and *trans* isomers, e.g., $CrCl_3 \cdot 4NH_3$ (see Figure 10.4). Only the negative ions outside of the coordination sphere are readily ionizable. Thus, the molecule $CrCl_3 \cdot 3NH_3$ should be a nonelectrolyte and the chloride ion should not be precipitated by silver nitrate, except as it is displaced from the coordination sphere.

Werner's productive life was spent in placing his coordination theory on a firm experimental basis. He had compiled such an impressive amount of evidence for the octahedral configuration from the isomerism and reactions of 6-coordinate complexes that his configuration was generally accepted long before it had been confirmed by modern structural investigations.

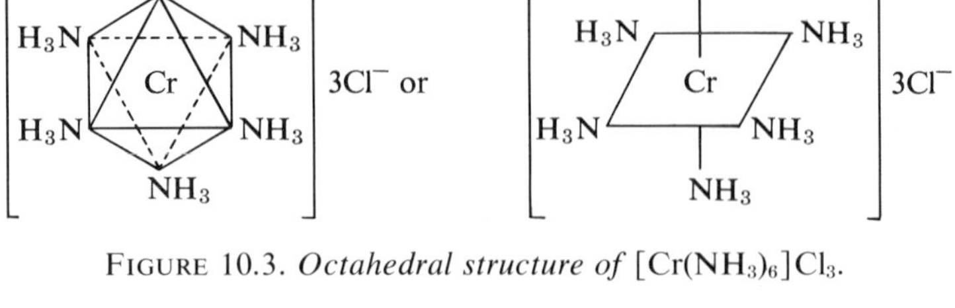

FIGURE 10.3. *Octahedral structure of* $[Cr(NH_3)_6]Cl_3$.

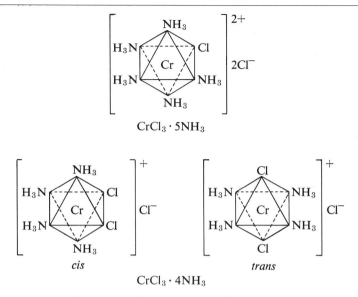

CrCl₃ · 5NH₃

cis *trans*

CrCl₃ · 4NH₃

FIGURE 10.4. *Octahedral structures of chromium ammines.*

Some critics were skeptical of the optical activity attributed to the octahedral arrangement around a central ion in a complex such as [Co(en)₃]Cl₃. The optical isomers are represented in Figure 10.5 by showing the octahedra as trigonal antiprisms in order to illustrate that the *dextro* and *levo* isomers are really right- and left-handed spirals and are not superimposable. The isomer with the left-handed spiral has been shown by x-ray methods to be the D isomer (also designated as Λ), which exhibits a positive rota-

tion at the sodium D line. Werner prepared and resolved $\left[Co \left\{ \begin{matrix} OH \\ \\ OH \end{matrix} \right\} Co(NH_3)_4 \right]^{6+}$,

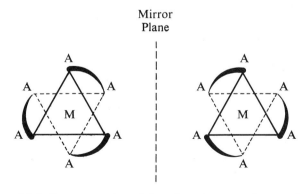

FIGURE 10.5. *Representation of the mirror images of a complex of the type* M(AA)₃ *as right- and left-handed spirals.*

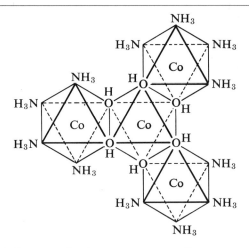

FIGURE 10.6. *A completely inorganic optically active complex ion.*

which contains no carbon (see Figure 10.6) to answer the criticism that the optical activity of [Co(en)$_3$]Cl$_3$ might be caused by carbon in some way.

Valence Bond Interpretation

The nature of secondary valence was interpreted by G. N. Lewis* in terms of the coordinate covalent bond in which the ligand atom, e.g., N in NH$_3$, furnishes an electron pair, which is shared with the central metal ion. Sidgwick considered the coordination process as providing the opportunity for a transition metal ion to reach an inert gas configuration, or the effective atomic number of an inert gas. The *effective atomic number* (EAN) of a metal ion is calculated as the total of the electrons of the metal ion and those shared with it through coordination. In [Co(NH$_3$)$_6$]$^{3+}$ the cobalt(III) ion has 24 electrons plus the 6 electron pairs from the ammonia molecules to give a total of 36 electrons, the configuration of krypton. Quite a few metals, but not all, achieve the EAN of an inert gas through coordination (see Table 10.2). The EAN concept has been particularly successful for the metal carbonyls, which are considered to contain the metal in the zero oxidation state and for the π complexes such as ferrocene (p. 382). In general, it can be taken only as a rough guide. Most of the complexes of Ni give EAN values, which are 34 (C.N. 4) or 38 (C.N. 6) rather than 36.

Much of the modern valence bond treatment of coordination compounds was developed by Pauling. Although the crystal field and molecular orbital treatments (see p. 359) now appear to be more generally useful, it is still desirable to be familiar with the valence bond treatment and its terminology. It would be a great mistake to fail to recognize the importance of the qualitative valence bond model in fostering the development of this field to its present status. The success of the crystal field theory would not be so impressive if it were not for the large body of experimental results, which has been accumulated because of the stimulation and simplicity of the valence bond approach.

* Lewis, G. N., *J. Am. Chem. Soc.*, **38**, 762 (1916).

TABLE 10.2

Complex	Number of Electrons on M^{n+}	Number of Electron Pairs from Ligands	EAN
$Co(NH_3)_6{}^{3+}$	27-3	6	36 (Kr)
$Pt(NH_3)_6{}^{4+}$	78-4	6	86 (Rn)
$Fe(CN)_6{}^{4-}$	26-2	6	36
$Fe(CO)_5$	26-0	5	36
$Cr(CO)_6$	24-0	6	36
$Ni(CO)_4$	28-0	4	36
$Ni(NH_3)_6{}^{2+}$	28-2	6	38
$Ni(CN)_4{}^{2-}$	28-2	4	34
$Cr(NH_3)_6{}^{3+}$	24-3	6	33

Coordination compounds are interpreted as resulting from the use of available bonding orbitals on the metal for the formation of coordinate covalent bonds. The coordination number and configuration are determined by size and charge effects in part, but also to a great extent by the orbitals available for bonding. The common hybridized orbitals encountered in coordination compounds are shown in Table 10.3. The orbitals which might be used for forming strong π bonds are also shown.

TABLE 10.3[a]

Coord. Number	Hybridized Orbitals (σ)	Configuration	Strong π Orbitals	Examples
2	sp	Linear	p^2, d^2	$Ag(NH_3)_2{}^+$
3	sp^2	Trigonal plane	p, d^2	BF_3, $NO_3{}^-$, $Ag(R_3P)_3{}^+$
4	sp^3	Tetrahedral		$Ni(CO)_4$, $MnO_4{}^-$, $Zn(NH_3)_4{}^{2+}$
4	dsp^2	Planar	d^3, p	$Ni(CN)_4{}^{2-}$, $Pt(NH_3)_4{}^{2+}$
5	$d_{z^2}sp^3$ or d^3sp	Trigonal bipyramid	d^2	TaF_5, $CuCl_5{}^{3-}$
5	$d_{x^2-y^2}sp^3$, d^2sp^2, d^4s, or d^4p	Tetragonal pyramid	d	IF_5, $[Ni(PEt_3)_2Br_3]$
6	d^2sp^3	Octahedral	d^3	$Co(NH_3)_6{}^{3+}$, $PtCl_6{}^{2-}$
7	d^5sp or d^3sp^3	Pentagonal bipyramid	—	$ZrF_7{}^{3-}$
7	d^4sp^2 or d^5p^2	Trigonal prism with an extra atom in one tetragonal face	—	$TaF_7{}^{2-}$, $NbF_7{}^{2-}$
8	d^4sp^3	Dodecahedral	d	$Mo(CN)_8{}^{4-}$, $Zr(C_2O_4)_4{}^{4-}$
8	d^5p^3	Antiprismatic	—	$TaF_8{}^{3-}$, $Zr(acac)_4$

[a] Kimball, G. E., *J. Chem. Phys.*, **8**, 188 (1940).

The chromium(III) ion has 3 unpaired d electrons, so the remaining two $3d$ orbitals and the $4s$ and $4p$ orbitals are available for the sharing of electron pairs furnished by six ligands to give an octahedral complex with d^2sp^3 hybrid bonds, as in $[Cr(NH_3)_6]^{3+}$. The cobalt(III) ion (or the isoelectronic Fe^{2+} ion) has six $3d$ electrons and one would expect 4 unpaired electrons in the free ion. However, if six strong bonds can be formed through coordination, there should be enough gain in energy to force the electrons to pair off in just three of the d orbitals, leaving the d^2sp^3 orbitals available for bond formation. The cobalt(III) complexes, such as $[Co(NH_3)_6]Cl_3$, are diamagnetic, indicating that the electrons have indeed become paired.

The cobalt(II) ion has seven $3d$ electrons, so that two d orbitals cannot be vacated by electron pairing. Pauling suggested that the orbitals are made available by pairing six of the d electrons and promotion of the seventh electron to a higher energy orbital. The promoted electron would be expected to be easily lost to give a cobalt(III) complex. In fact, simple cobalt salts are those of Co(II), but in most cobalt complexes the $+3$

TABLE 10.4

Ion or Complex	3d					4s	4p			4d or 5s	Structure
Cr^{3+}	↑	↑	↑	—	—	—	—	—	—		
$Cr(NH_3)_6^{3+}$	↑	↑	↑	[↑↓	↑↓	↑↓	↑↓	↑↓	↑↓]		Octahedron
Co^{3+}	↑↓	↑	↑	↑	↑	—	—	—	—		
$Co(NH_3)_6^{3+}$	↑↓	↑↓	↑↓	[↑↓	↑↓	↑↓	↑↓	↑↓	↑↓]		Octahedron
Co^{2+}	↑↓	↑↓	↑	↑	↑	—	—	—	—		
$Co(NH_3)_6^{2+}$	↑↓	↑↓	↑↓	[↑↓	↑↓	↑↓	↑↓	↑↓	↑↓]	↑	Octahedron
Zn^{2+}	↑↓	↑↓	↑↓	↑↓	↑↓	—	—	—	—		
$ZnCl_4^{2-}$	↑↓	↑↓	↑↓	↑↓	↑↓	[↑↓	↑↓	↑↓	↑↓]		Tetrahedron
$Zn(NH_3)_6^{2+}$ "Ionic"	↑↓	↑↓	↑↓	↑↓	↑↓	—	—	—	—		Octahedron
$Zn(NH_3)_6^{2+}$ "Outer Orbital"	↑↓	↑↓	↑↓	↑↓	↑↓	[↑↓	↑↓	↑↓	↑↓	↑↓ ↑↓]	Octahedron
Fe^{3+}	↑	↑	↑	↑	↑	—	—	—	—		
$Fe(C_2O_4)_3^{3-}$	↑	↑	↑	↑	↑	} Ionic or					Octahedron
$Ni(NH_3)_6^{2+}$	↑↓	↑↓	↑↓	↑	↑	} Outer Orbital					Octahedron
Cu^+	↑↓	↑↓	↑↓	↑↓	↑↓	—	—	—	—		
$Cu(CN)_4^{3-}$	↑↓	↑↓	↑↓	↑↓	↑↓	[↑↓	↑↓	↑↓	↑↓]		Tetrahedron
$Ni(CN)_4^{2-}$	↑↓	↑↓	↑↓	↑↓	[↑↓	↑↓	↑↓	↑↓]	—		Square Plane
$Cu(NH_3)_4^{2+}$	↑↓	↑↓	↑↓	↑↓	[↑↓	↑↓	↑↓	↑↓]		↑	Square Plane

oxidation state is much more stable than +2. Some electronic configurations of simple metal ions and complexes are shown in Table 10.4. An ion such as Zn^{2+} has ten $3d$ electrons and hence the $3d$ orbitals are not available for bond formation. The s and p orbitals can be used for the formation of a tetrahedral complex such as $[ZnCl_4]^{2-}$.

Magnetic susceptibility measurements have been widely used to determine the number of unpaired electrons in complexes and from this information the number of d orbitals used for bond formation usually can be inferred for those ions which contain 4–8 d electrons. The complexes in which the d electrons are forced to pair off to allow bond formation were referred to as covalent complexes by Pauling. Those complexes in which the inner d orbitals are not used for bond formation as in $[Zn(NH_3)_6]^{2+}$, $[Ni(NH_3)_6]^{2+}$, or $[Fe(C_2O_4)_3]^{3-}$ (5 unpaired electrons) were referred to as "ionic" complexes. The terms *low-spin* (or spin-paired) and *high-spin* (or spin-free) are preferred since they describe the population of the d orbitals without any assumptions concerning the nature of the bonding.

INNER AND OUTER ORBITAL COMPLEXES

The complexes such as $[Zn(NH_3)_6]^{2+}$ and $[Fe(C_2O_4)_3]^{3-}$ need not be considered to be completely lacking in covalent character. The $4d$ orbitals should be low enough in energy in a positive transition metal ion to be used for covalent bond formation. These complexes are often referred to as outer orbital complexes to indicate that the bonding can involve the sp^3d^2 orbitals instead of the d^2sp^3 orbitals as in $[Co(NH_3)_6]^{3+}$, which is referred to as an inner orbital complex.

The choice of structures for Zn^{2+} is between the tetrahedral and the outer orbital octahedral complexes. The tetrahedral complexes would be more likely for large or charged ligands because of ligand–ligand repulsion, e.g., $[ZnCl_4]^{2-}$. Nickel(II) forms outer orbital octahedral complexes with ligands such as H_2O and NH_3. However, with ligands such as CN^-, which have a greater tendency to form strong covalent bonds, diamagnetic planar complexes involving dsp^2 bonding are formed with nickel(II). Planar complexes are also common for Pd^{2+}, Pt^{2+}, Cu^{2+}, and Au^{3+}. The necessary d orbital is available or can be made available by electron pairing in all of these ions except Cu^{2+}. The interpretation applied above to the $[Co(NH_3)_6]^{2+}$ would lead to the prediction that the 9th d electron in $[Cu(NH_3)_4]^{2+}$ would be promoted and might easily be lost to give a Cu^{3+} complex. In fact, the Cu^{2+} complexes are not at all easily oxidized. The interpretation of the planar Cu^{2+} complexes as outer orbital complexes is also unsatisfactory because of the great stability of the complexes and because the bonding does not seem to be particularly different from that in planar nickel complexes. The failure to offer a really satisfactory account of the bonding in the very stable Cu(II) complexes is a major weakness of the valence bond treatment.

ELECTRONEUTRALITY PRINCIPLE

One objection to the coordinate bond treatment of coordination compounds has been that it might seem to imply the accumulation of negative charge on a metal atom. The formal charge on Fe in $[Fe(H_2O)_6]^{3+}$ is −3 and the formal charge on Fe in $[Fe(H_2O)_6]^{2+}$ or $[Fe(CN)_6]^{4-}$ is −4. Pauling has shown that these unlikely situations need not arise. His electroneutrality principle (see p. 59) would lead one to expect the metal atom to be neutral or bear only a partial positive charge. In the cationic aquo or ammonia complexes most of the positive charge can be spread over the H atoms so that no atom has more than a small partial positive charge. In an anionic complex the negative charge should be spread over the electronegative atoms present. The charge distribution is much different from that implied by the formal charges because the bonds are polar, i.e., they have partial ionic character. The formal charge on Fe in $[Fe(H_2O)_6]^{3+}$ would be -3 assuming 100% covalent character. If the Fe—O bonds were only 50% covalent the charge on the Fe would be zero. In $[Fe(H_2O)_6]^{2+}$ the Fe would have zero charge if the Fe—O bonds were 33.3% covalent, which is a reasonable approximation. The Fe—O bond in $[Fe(H_2O)_6]^{3+}$ should be slightly more covalent than that in $[Fe(H_2O)_6]^{2+}$, because the higher oxidation state of Fe increases its electronegativity.

The application of the electroneutrality principle leads to useful correlations and predictions concerning the stabilization of various oxidation states of transition metals with different ligands. The oxidation state common to all of the metals of the first transition series is $+2$, as encountered in the aquo complexes. The approximately $\frac{1}{3}$ covalent character of the M—O bond for divalent transition metals leads to zero formal charge on the metal. The M—N bond should be more covalent (closer to 50%) than the M—O bond because of the smaller difference in electronegativity of M and N, compared to M and O, resulting in more charge transfer to the metal. This would favor a higher oxidation state in ammonia complexes in order to prevent a negative formal charge on the metal. The striking difference in the $+2$ and $+3$ oxidation states of cobalt in the aquo and ammonia complexes has already been mentioned. The difference is not so great for other first transition series ions, but, in general, coordination with ligand atoms less electronegative than oxygen stabilizes oxidation states higher than that of the most stable aquo ion, unless other factors are involved.

DOUBLE BONDING

There are notable exceptions to the generalization that higher oxidation states are stabilized in compounds containing ligand atoms of low electronegativity. The most striking common examples are compounds of CO, CN^-, 1,10-phenanthroline. Some examples are given in Table 10.5.

TABLE 10.5

Complex	Oxidation State of M	Comment
$Ni(CO)_4$, $Fe(CO)_5$, $Cr(CO)_6$	0	Stable
$Ni(CN)_4^{4-}$, $Pd(CN)_4^{4-}$	0	Easily oxidized
$Ni(CN)_4^{3-}$, $Mn(CN)_6^{5-}$	$+1$	Easily oxidized
$Fe(CN)_6^{4-}$	$+2$	Fe(III) slightly stabilized
$Fe(phen)_3^{2+}$	$+2$	Fe(II) more stable than Fe(III)

An atom such as C (CO and CN^- coordinate through C normally) could give a predominately covalent bond with a transition metal atom, leading to the accumulation of negative charge on the metal atom. The Ni—C bond distance in $Ni(CO)_4$, however, is shorter than that expected for a single bond, which suggests that the bond has an

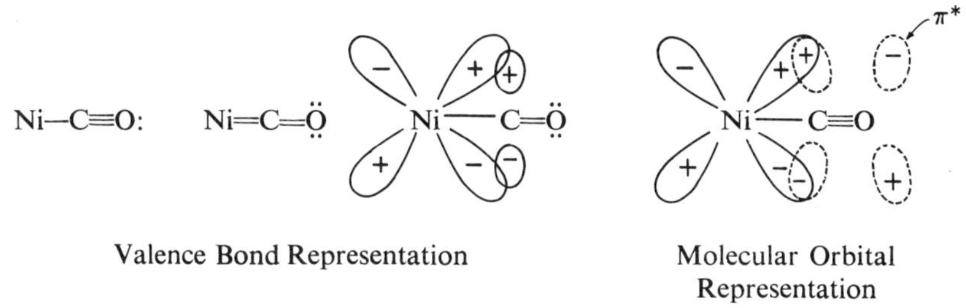

Valence Bond Representation

Molecular Orbital
Representation

FIGURE 10.7. *Metal–carbon double bonding.*

appreciable amount of double bond character. The valence bond representation of the metal–carbon double bond requires that the carbon–oxygen bond be changed to a double bond in order to vacate a p orbital for d-p-π bonding (Figure 10.7). The molecular orbital representation affects the carbon–oxygen bond only indirectly. A filled d orbital of nickel can overlap with an empty π^* (antibonding) molecular orbital of CO. Occupying the π^* orbital lowers the bond order and weakens the bond of CO. The cyanide complexes offer similar opportunities for double bonding.

The situation is different for 1,10-phenanthroline, but the conjugated system permits M—N double bonding. Resonance structures can be written with the extra pair of electrons, furnished by the metal, located at various positions around the rings. This is another way of saying that this pair of electrons is a part of the total π electron cloud of the molecule. The heterocyclic ring involving the Fe becomes a part of the conjugated system (see Figure 10.8). Such charge delocalization enhances the stability of the complex. The molecular orbital representation would utilize an empty π^* orbital of the ligand for overlap with a filled d orbital.

The complexes which involve metal–ligand double bonds are more likely to be those with filled, or nearly filled, d orbitals. Hence, in compounds of this type the lower oxidation states are usually favored. This "back bonding," in which the metal shares a pair of its own electrons with the ligand, offsets the accumulation of negative charge on the metal. If the Ni—C bonds in $Ni(CO)_4$ are 75% covalent, the net charge on the nickel without π bonding would be $-\frac{3}{4} \times 4 = -3$. The M—C bond order would have to be close to 2 to offset the accumulation of negative charge on Ni.

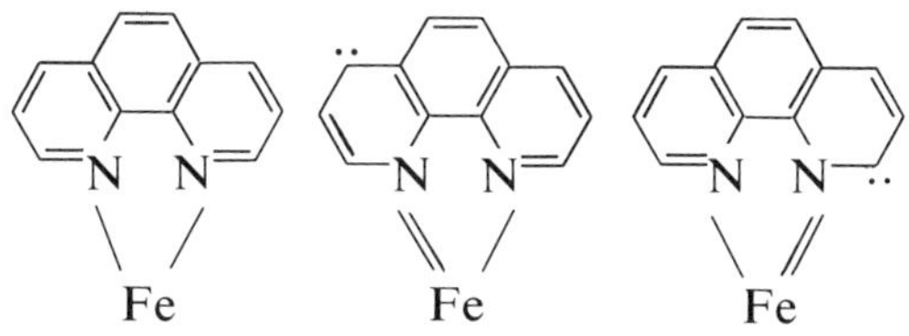

FIGURE 10.8. *Metal–ligand double bonding in a conjugated system.*

Simple Electrostatic Approach to Bonding

The electrostatic interpretation of the interaction between metal ions and ligands in complexes has developed concurrently with the covalent bond approach. In the early 1920's the formation of complexes such as AlF_6^{3-} was discussed in terms of the attraction between oppositely charged ions. Water (aquo) and ammonia complexes were considered in terms of ion–dipole interaction. This approach leads to the correct prediction that large cations of low charge such as Na^+ and K^+ have little tendency to form complexes. In Group IIA the larger cations show little tendency to form stable complexes, but Be^{2+} forms complexes, such as BeF_4^{2-} and others, some of which have great stability. The *ionic potential* (the charge to size ratio) permits ions of different charges to be compared. Ions with high ionic potentials, such as Be^{2+}, Al^{3+}, and many of the transition metal ions, are expected to form stable complexes. The simple electrostatic interpretation, however, does not account for the great stability of complexes of some cations, such as Hg^{2+}, for which the ionic potential is small, compared to Mg^{2+} which forms few stable complexes and for which the ionic potential is large.

The permanent dipole moment of the water molecule is greater than that of ammonia and consequently the aquo complexes would be expected to be considerably more stable than those of ammonia. Ammonia complexes of the alkaline earth and alkali metals are unstable in aqueous solution in accordance with this expectation. Nevertheless, the ammonia complexes are much more stable than the aquo complexes for many of the transition metal ions, such as Ni^{2+}. Ni^{2+} and Mg^{2+} have about the same ionic potentials, so the difference in the relative stabilities of the aquo and ammonia complexes of these ions is not explicable in terms of simple electrostatic theory.

The simple electrostatic treatment considers metal ions and ligands as rigid and undistorted. The picture can be improved by taking polarization of the ligands into account so that the reversal in the stabilities of water and ammonia complexes can be explained. Further refinement, to include polarization of the cation as well as that of the ligand, is required to explain the relative stabilities of some of the halide complexes. The observed stabilities of many complexes agree reasonably well with "bond" energies obtained by taking into account polarization effects. The differences among the transition metals require that crystal field splitting of the d orbitals be taken into account. These refinements in the electrostatic treatment will be considered briefly.

LIGAND POLARIZATION

The stability of complex ions containing neutral ligands is dependent on the ionic potential of the cation and the total dipole moment of the ligand, which includes the permanent (μ) and induced (μ_i) dipole moments.

$$\text{Total dipole moment} = \mu + \mu_i$$

The induced dipole moment is given by the relationship, $\mu_i = \alpha q/r$, where q/r (charge/distance between charges) represents the strength of the electrical field and α is the electronic polarizability of the molecule. The energy of interaction (E) (mutual polarization neglected) is given by

$$E = \frac{q}{r}(\mu + \mu_i)$$
$$= \frac{q}{r}\mu + \frac{q^2}{r^2}\alpha \tag{10.6}$$

The permanent dipole moment of the water molecule is greater than that of ammonia, but the ammonia molecule is more polarizable and the induced dipole moment in a strong field can be quite large. Cations with small ionic potential form stable complexes with water because of its high permanent dipole moment. Cations with high ionic potential form more stable ammonia complexes because both α and E are large and make considerable contributions to the total dipole moment of the ammonia molecule. Thus the total dipole moment of the ammonia molecule can be greater than that of water in a strong electric field.

MUTUAL POLARIZATION OF CATION AND ANION

The polarization of the ligand molecule is not sufficient to account for the differences in the stabilities of the complexes of the metals in Groups IA and IIA compared to those of Groups IB and IIB. Even for metals with about the same ionic potential (e.g., Na^+ and Cu^+, Ca^{2+} and Cd^{2+}), the B subgroup metals form much more stable complexes than the A group metals. The polarization of the B subgroup cations themselves must be considered in order to account for the differences in the coordinating ability of ions such as Na^+ and Cu^+. Inert gas type cations with an outer shell of eight electrons are not easily deformable, but polarization effects are quite important for cations which have the pseudo-inert gas type configuration (18 electrons in the outer shell) or those with similar configurations [$(n-1)s^2p^6d^{10}ns^2$, or an almost complete group of d orbitals in the outer shell] (see p. 90). Cation polarization is particularly important because it decreases the screening of the nuclear charge of the cation and decreases the metal–ligand distance. Both factors favor increased polarization of the ligand. The mutual polarization of the cation and of the ligand accounts for the greater stability of the complexes of ammonia, compared to the aquo complexes, for the metals near the end of, and just following, the transition series.

Halide complexes of cations with inert gas type configurations decrease in stability in the order:

$$F^- > Cl^- > Br^- > I^-$$

This is the order expected on the basis of the anion sizes, the smaller anions releasing more energy (q_1q_2/r) due to the closer approach to the cation. The reverse order of stability is observed for cations such as Hg^{2+}, for which mutual polarization of the cation and anion favors combination with the larger, more polarizable anions.

Alkyl substitution in H_2O and NH_3 (an alkyl group is represented by R) decreases the tendency toward complex formation in the order:

$$H_2O > ROH > R_2O$$
$$NH_3 > RNH_2 > R_2NH > R_3N$$

The order corresponds to a decrease in the dipole moments of the molecules. Alkyl substitution *increases* the tendency toward complex formation for H_2S and PH_3, corresponding to the order of *increasing* dipole moment in the series:

$$H_2S < RSH < R_2S$$
$$PH_3 < RPH_2 < R_2PH < R_3P$$

The electrostatic approach, including polarization effects, permits one to predict the "bond" energies for many complexes. Table 10.6 compares the calculated and experimental energies per bond for the reaction:

$$M^{m+}(g) + nL(g) \longrightarrow ML_n^{m+}(g) \qquad (10.7)$$

TABLE 10.6[a]

Complex	Energy per bond (Calc.)	Energy per bond (Exp.)	Energy per bond Crystal Field Corrected
$[Fe(H_2O)_6]^{2+}$	50 kcal	58 kcal	52 kcal
$[Fe(H_2O)_6]^{3+}$	109	116	109
$[K(H_2O)_6]^+$	13	16	13
$[Cr(H_2O)_6]^{3+}$	111	122	120
$[Co(NH_3)_6]^{3+}$	117	134	125
$[AlF_6]^{3-}$	212	233	212
$[Zn(NH_3)_4]^{2+}$	86	89	86

[a] From F. Basolo and R. Pearson, *Mechanisms of Inorganic Reactions* (New York: John Wiley and Sons, Inc., 1958) p. 50.

The metals of the first transition series have nearly the same radii and hence the electrostatic treatment predicts that the complexes formed by these metals in the same oxidation state would be of about the same stability. Failure to account for the striking differences among the complexes of the transition metals is one of the greatest weaknesses of the simple electrostatic approach. The $[Cr(NH_3)_6]^{3+}$ and $[Co(NH_3)_6]^{3+}$ complexes are very stable, but manganese and iron do not form ammonia complexes which are stable in aqueous solution. Such differences among the transition metal complexes can be explained by application of the crystal field theory. It is seen that the corrected values are in closer agreement with the experimental values than the uncorrected values for those complexes in Table 10.6 for which crystal field corrections are applicable. The crystal field corrections are important in accounting for differences among the transition metal complexes, but it should be noted that the simple electrostatic attraction accounts for most of the bond energy.

The Ligand Field Theory (Crystal Field Theory)

The five *d* orbitals are degenerate and of equal energy in the gaseous metal ions. The simple electrostatic approach failed to predict differences among complexes of different transition metals because it did not take into account the fact that the degeneracy of the *d* orbitals may be removed in the electrostatic field created by the presence of the ligands. The symmetrical field caused by the ligands is similar to the electric field around ions in ionic crystals. This similarity accounts for the name, the *crystal field theory*. Although crystal field theory was first proposed by Bethe in 1929, its application to coordination compounds is quite recent.*

* Orgel, L. E., *J. Chem. Soc.*, **1952**, 4756; *J. Chem. Phys.*, **23**, 1004, 1819, 1824 (1955); *An Introduction to Transition Metal Chemistry* (London: Methuen and Company, Ltd., 1960).

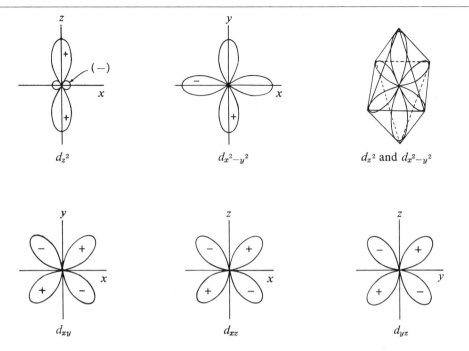

FIGURE 10.9. *The d orbitals.*

Octahedral Complexes

In an octahedral complex oriented as shown in Figure 10.9, two of the d orbitals, d_{z^2} and $d_{x^2-y^2}$, are directed toward the ligands. The repulsion caused by the ligands raises the energy of these orbitals (e_g*)† more than that of the other three orbitals, d_{xy}, d_{xz}, and d_{yz} (t_{2g}), which are directed at 45° to the axes (see Figure 10.10). The stronger the field due to the ligands, the greater the splitting of the energy levels $(10Dq)$. There is no change in the energy of the system due to the splitting if all five orbitals are equally occupied. The t_{2g} level is lowered by $4Dq$ and the e_g* level is raised by $6Dq$ relative to the average energy of the d orbitals. Hence, for a d^{10} ion with

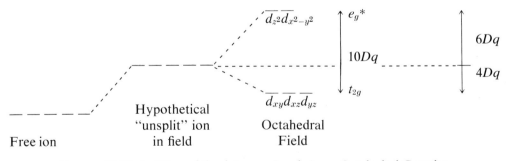

FIGURE 10.10. *Splitting of the d Energy Levels in an Octahedral Complex.*

† See footnote p. 356 for a brief explanation of the molecular orbital notation. The e_g* orbital carries the asterisk to indicate that this is really an antibonding molecular orbital. The asterisk is usually omitted in the literature because the "pure" crystal field theory treatment does not recognize either bonding or anti-bonding interactions.

$6t_{2g}$ and $4e_g$ electrons the net change is zero. Similarly, no stabilization results from the

$$6(-4Dq) + 4(+6Dq) = -24Dq + 24Dq = 0$$

splitting for a d^5 configuration if each orbital is singly occupied. For all configurations other than d^0, d^5 (high-spin), and d^{10}, the splitting lowers the total energy of the system. The decrease in energy caused by the splitting of the energy levels is the *crystal field stabilization energy* (CFSE).

The electrons will enter the t_{2g} orbitals in accordance with Hund's rule for d^1, d^2, and d^3 configurations. Thus $[Cr(NH_3)_6]^{3+}$ will have three unpaired electrons with CFSE of $3(-4Dq) = -12Dq$. The CFSE results since the three electrons can occupy orbitals which are lower in energy than in the free ion because of the splitting in the field created by the ligands. The CFSE for any octahedral chromium(III) complex is $12Dq$, but the value of Dq varies with the ligand. There are two possible configurations for a d^4 ion in the ground state, $t_{2g}(3)e_g^*(1)$ and $t_{2g}(4)$ (see Figure 10.11). In the first case the fourth electron occupies the e_g^* level to give four unpaired electrons. The CFSE is $3(-4Dq) + 1(6Dq) = -6Dq$. This is referred to as the weak field case, since the splitting is not great, or the high-spin case, since there is the maximum number of unpaired electrons. Here the splitting is small enough (implying a weak field or small value of Dq) so that the possible gain in CFSE which would result if the fourth electron were placed in the t_{2g} level is not great enough to provide the pairing energy which would be required. If Dq were large (strong field), the energy required to pair two electrons would be less than the gain in CFSE which results. The $t_{2g}(4)$ configuration, with two unpaired electrons, is referred to as the strong field case (also called the low-spin or spin-paired case). The CFSE for this case is $4(-4Dq) = -16Dq$ and Dq is larger than in the weak field case. The net energy gain is less than $-16Dq$ by the amount of energy which must be expended for pairing the electrons. Other configurations can be treated similarly as shown in Table 10.7. The maximum CFSE is obtained for the d^6 configura-

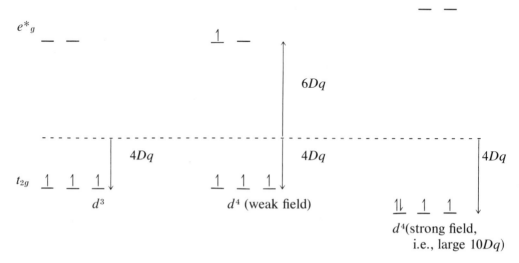

FIGURE 10.11. *Occupation of d orbitals in octahedral complexes for d^3 and d^4 configurations.*

TABLE 10.7.
Crystal Field Stabilization Energy of Octahedral Complexes

Configu-ration	Examples	Strong Field t_{2g}	e_g	No. of un-paired e^-	CFSE $(-Dq)$	Weak Field t_{2g}	e_g	No. of un-paired e^-	CFSE $(-Dq)$
d^0	Ca^{2+}, Sc^{3+}	0	0	0	0	0	0	0	0
d^1	Ti^{3+}	1	0	1	4	1	0	1	4
d^2	V^{3+}	2	0	2	8	2	0	2	8
d^3	Cr^{3+}, V^{2+}	3	0	3	12	3	0	3	12
d^4	Cr^{2+}, Mn^{3+}	4	0	2	16	3	1	4	6
d^5	Mn^{2+}, Fe^{3+}	5	0	1	20	3	2	5	0
d^6	Fe^{2+}, Co^{3+}	6	0	0	24	4	2	4	4
d^7	Co^{2+}	6	1	1	18	5	2	3	8
d^8	Ni^{2+}	6	2	2	12	6	2	2	12
d^9	Cu^{2+}	6	3	1	6	6	3	1	6
d^{10}	Cu^+, Zn^{2+}	6	4	0	0	6	4	0	0

tion in a strong field since the lower t_{2g} levels are completely occupied and the high energy levels are empty.

The order of field strength for common ligands is approximately:

$$CN^- > \text{pyridine} > C_2O_4{}^{2-} > H_2O > F^- > RCO_2{}^- > OH^- > Cl^- > Br^- > I^-.$$

The order is approximately that to be expected from electrostatic effects. However, there are a few notable exceptions which require that covalent character, particularly π bonding, be taken into account. The name *ligand field theory* is used to refer to the approach in present use which is essentially the same as the pure crystal field approach, but with covalent character taken into account when necessary. The high crystal field effect of CN^- and 1,10-phenanthroline is attributed to π bonding in which the metal donates electrons from one of the filled t_{2g} orbitals to a vacant p orbital of the attached ligand atom. This type of π bonding further stabilizes the t_{2g} orbitals and shortens the M—X distance. The donation of electrons from the metal increases the effective positive charge on the metal ion. All three factors tend to increase the splitting. Perhaps the greatest surprise in the order is the fact that the crystal field strength is greater for H_2O than for OH^-. Generally, charged ligands are expected to give greater splitting than neutral ligands because of the stronger interaction between a positive metal ion and a negative ligand. The observed order for OH^- and H_2O has been explained as the result of ligand to metal π bonding in OH^- complexes. The oxygen atom of the negative OH^- ion can share a pair of electrons in a filled p orbital with an empty t_{2g} metal orbital, if available for bond formation. Such bonding would raise the energy level of the t_{2g} orbital and lower the effective charge on the metal. Both effects tend to decrease the crystal field splitting. If the t_{2g} orbitals are filled, the interaction with the filled p orbitals results only in repulsion. Such interaction would be more important for the negative OH^- ion than for H_2O.

Cyanide and 1,10-phenanthroline complexes usually have low-spin corresponding to a large splitting of the energy levels and maximum occupancy of the t_{2g} orbitals. Hydrated ions and halide complexes are usually high-spin complexes. The splitting ($10Dq$), for the same ligand, increases for the second and third transition series metals compared to the first transition series. The pairing energy decreases for the second and third transition series metals compared to those of the first transition series. Both trends are the consequence of the larger size of the $4d$ and $5d$ orbitals compared to the $3d$ orbitals. The larger orbitals, which extend further from the central atom, are affected to a greater extent by the ligands. Also, less energy is required to force two electrons into one of the larger orbitals. The splitting increases as the charge on the metal ion increases, as one might expect, because the cation radius decreases with increasing charge and the ligands would be more strongly attracted by the higher charge.

The magnitude of the crystal field splitting can be evaluated from spectra. For a d^1 ion, such as $[Ti(H_2O)_6]^{3+}$, only one transition, from t_{2g} to e_g^*, is expected. The dif-

TABLE 10.8

Crystal Field Splitting for Some Octahedral Complexes[a]
(10 Dq values in italics indicate low-spin complex)

Ligands Metal Ion	6Br⁻	6Cl⁻	6H₂O	6NH₃	3 en
Ni(II)	7,000 cm⁻¹	7,200 cm⁻¹	8,500 cm⁻¹	10,800 cm⁻¹	11,500 cm⁻¹
Cr(III)	–	13,800	17,400	21,600	21,900
Co(III)	–	–	*18,200*	*22,900*	*23,200*
Rh(III)	*19,000*	*20,300*	*27,000*	*34,100*	*34,600*

[a] Jørgensen, C. K., *Absorption Spectra and Chemical Bonding in Complexes* (London: Pergamon Press Limited, 1962) pp. 110-111, used with permission.

ference in energy between t_{2g} and e_g^* is $10Dq$. One absorption band is observed with a maximum at 20,400 cm⁻¹ (490 mμ),† which is taken as the value of $10Dq$. The theoretical (calculated) values of $10Dq$ can be used as approximations, but the spectral values are more reliable.

There are more electronic transitions possible for ions which contain several d electrons, and the spectra are generally more complex than for $[Ti(H_2O)_6]^{3+}$. The observed transitions can usually be evaluated in terms of Dq, although additional parameters are needed in some cases. The usefulness of the ligand field theory in the interpretation of spectra of transition metal complexes has been one of its greatest advantages over the valence bond treatment. It also provides for a more detailed understanding of magnetic properties of such complexes. The application of ligand field theory to these two areas has led to a real breakthrough in the understanding of electronic structure and bonding for these compounds.

† The crystal field splitting is usually obtained from spectra and is expressed in wave numbers (cm⁻¹) because the value in wave numbers is directly proportional to energy, 10,000 cm⁻¹, or 1000 mμ, corresponds to 28.6 kcal/mole; 20,000 cm⁻¹, or 500 mμ, corresponds to 57.2 kcal/mole.

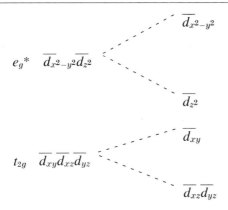

FIGURE 10.12. *Splitting of the energy levels in a distorted octahedral (tetragonal) field.*

Distorted Octahedral Complexes

The discussion of crystal field splitting of the d orbitals into two levels applies for a regular octahedral arrangement with six identical ligands. In many cases some distortion of the octahedron can increase the stability of the complexes. Just as the removal of the degeneracy of the five d orbitals can result in crystal field stabilization, further removal of the degeneracy of the d orbitals can result in additional stabilization. The Jahn–Teller theorem predicts that distortion will occur whenever the resulting splitting of energy levels yields additional stabilization. If the octahedron is elongated along the z axis by increasing the metal–ligand distances along this axis, the degeneracy of the t_{2g} and $e_g{}^*$ levels is removed. The d_{z^2} orbital is lowered in energy because the crystal field of the ligand decreases rapidly as the distance is increased. The $d_{x^2-y^2}$ orbital is raised in energy (see Figure 10.12). The withdrawal of the ligands along the z axis would decrease the ligand–ligand repulsion and would tend to shorten the metal–ligand distances along the x and y axes. The splitting is such that no stabilization results if the two $e_g{}^*$ orbitals are equally occupied. The t_{2g} orbitals are affected to a much smaller extent by the distortion because they are not directed toward the ligands.

Copper(II) complexes (d^9 ion) are generally tetragonal (four short M—X distances in a plane and two long M—X distances perpendicular to the plane) as expected from the Jahn–Teller effect. The high energy $d_{x^2-y^2}$ orbital is only singly occupied so that the additional stabilization over the regular octahedron is $+\beta - 2\beta = -\beta$ as shown in Figure 10.13. The t_{2g} levels are filled so no stabilization results from their splitting.

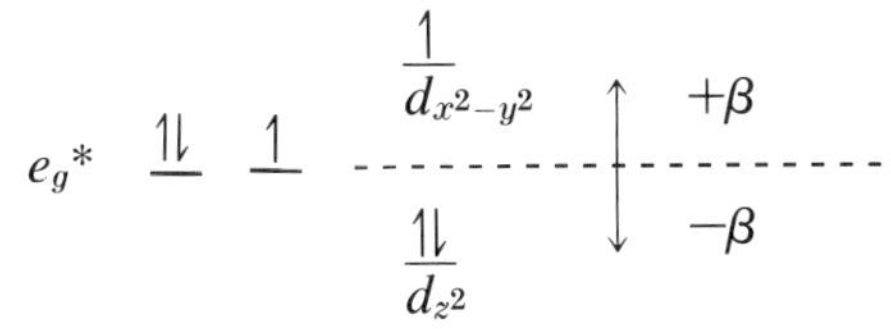

FIGURE 10.13. *Splitting of the $e_g{}^*$ levels in tetragonal Cu^{2+} complexes.*

No additional stabilization results for a high-spin d^8 ion (Ni^{2+}) because the two e_g* levels are both singly occupied. Of course, no crystal field stabilization occurs for d^0, d^5 (high-spin), or d^{10} ions for regular or distorted octahedra. Distorted octahedral complexes are expected for low-spin d^7 ions and for high-spin d^4 ions (one electron in d_{z^2} in each case). Slight distortion is expected for complexes which involve unequal occupancy of the t_{2g} orbitals, but the effect is not great because of the smaller splitting of these orbitals.

Planar Complexes

If the ligands along the z axis are removed completely to form a planar complex, the splitting is greatly increased. The most favorable electronic configuration for planar complexes is that of a d^8 ion, e.g., Ni^{2+}, Pt^{2+}, and Au^{3+}, in which the splitting is great enough to bring about pairing of all electrons. The very high energy $d_{x^2-y^2}$ orbital is left vacant (see Figure 10.14). Planar complexes are also expected for d^7 and d^9 ions. In a planar complex of a d^7 ion such as Co^{2+} the highest energy orbital is vacant and the next to the highest energy orbital is singly occupied. A planar copper(II) (d^9) complex will have a single electron in the highest energy orbital.

The radius ratio ($r_+/r_- \geq 0.414$) required for a square planar arrangement is identical to that for an octahedral complex. Since the octahedral complex is favored by the additional energy released from the interaction with the two extra ligands, the higher coordination number is to be expected. The square planar arrangement is encountered only in cases where the additional splitting of the levels is most advantageous or where the planar configuration is imposed by the geometry of the ligand. The copper phthalocyanine complex (see Figure 10.15) can be sublimed *in vacuo* at about 580°C without decomposition and it is not decomposed by strong mineral acids. The planar fused ring system is similar to that of the porphyrins. The divalent metal ions that give planar complexes with this ligand (e.g., Cu, Be, Mn, Fe, Co, Ni, and Pt) include several which normally form tetrahedral complexes.

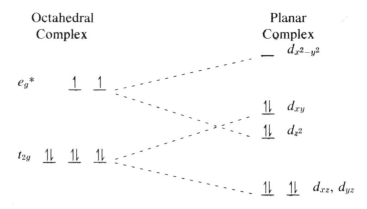

FIGURE 10.14. *Energy levels for square planar nickel(II) complexes.*

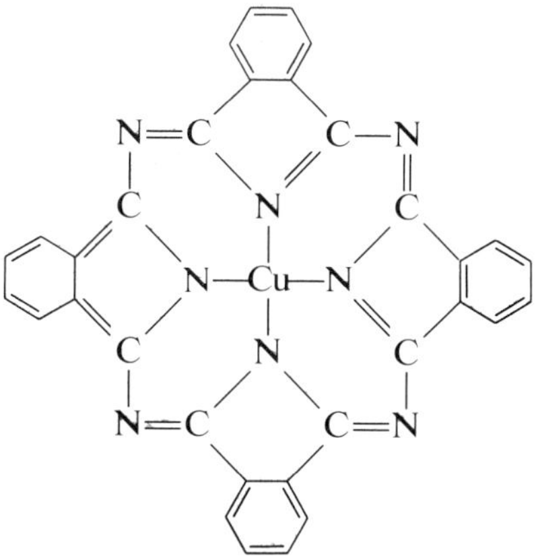

FIGURE 10.15. *The planar copper(II) phthalocyanine complex.*

Tetrahedral Complexes

A tetrahedral arrangement is the configuration of least ligand–ligand repulsion for a four-coordinated metal ion. Further, this is the configuration expected for a complex with a radius ratio between 0.225 and that required for an octahedral complex. The crystal field splitting is less important in tetrahedral complexes since $10Dq$ is only $\frac{4}{9}$ of that of a regular octahedral arrangement for the same ligands. This is because the ligands do no approach along the direction of any of the orbitals. The axes, chosen for convenience, are the twofold symmetry axes which bisect the six edges of the tetrahedron. The high energy orbitals are the d_{xy}, d_{xz}, and d_{yz} orbitals directed most nearly toward the ligands (see Figure 10.16). Because of the smaller crystal field splitting, tetrahedral complexes are not commonly expected in cases where the crystal field stabilization is great for octahedral or planar complexes. Tetrahedral complexes are more likely for nontransition metals and transition metals with no crystal field stabilization (d^0, high-spin d^5, and d^{10}). There is crystal field stabilization for tetrahedral complexes of d^2, d^4 (low-spin), and d^7 ions. However, in some cases the crystal field stabilization of octahedral or planar complexes can be even greater, as in the case of planar Co(II) (d^7) complexes. Large ligands or those with high negative charge might favor the formation of tetrahedral complexes over planar or octahedral complexes in

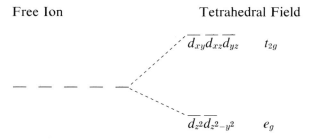

FIGURE 10.16. *Crystal field splitting for tetrahedral complexes.*

order to minimize ligand–ligand repulsion. The oxy anions and chloro complexes such as those shown in Table 10.9 are common examples.

TABLE 10.9

Examples of Regular Tetrahedral Complexes

d^0	d^2	d^5 (*high-spin*)	d^7 (*high-spin*)	d^{10}
$AlCl_4^-$ $TiCl_4$ MnO_4^- CrO_4^{2-}	FeO_4^{2-}	$FeCl_4^-$	$CoCl_4^{2-}$	$ZnCl_4^{2-}$ $GaCl_4^-$

Crystal field stabilization greatly favors planar complexes for Cu(II) and Ni(II), but $CuCl_4^{2-}$, $NiCl_4^{2-}$, and a few other complexes of these metals are tetrahedral. The importance of covalent bonding and particularly π bonding may be difficult to assess in many cases. Planar nickel complexes are usually those with an appreciable amount of π bonding (e.g., $[Ni(CN)_4]^{2-}$) and it seems likely that the π bonding is essential in order to give the necessary splitting for spin pairing. Although the pure crystal field treatment does not take covalent character into account, increased covalent character or π bonding can often be handled in terms of the effect of giving a stronger crystal field. Tetrahedral complexes are to be expected for Ni(II) and Cu(II) only for ligands which give a weak field, for complexes in which ligand–ligand repulsion is great, or for complexes such as those of tris-(2-aminoethyl)amine, $(NH_2C_2H_4)_3N$, where the tetrahedral configuration is imposed by the geometry of the ligand. Previous reports of tetrahedral complexes of Pt(II) with this ligand, however, have proven to be in error.* Low-spin tetrahedral complexes are not expected because of the small CF splitting.

Molecular Orbital Treatment

In an LCAO molecular orbital treatment of bonding in a complex the atomic orbitals of the metal ion are grouped by symmetry. For an octahedral complex the metal orbitals are designated as: s, a_{1g}; p_x, p_y and p_z, t_{1u}; $d_{x^2-y^2}$ and d_{z^2}, e_g; and d_{xy}, d_{xz}, and d_{yz}, t_{2g}.† The ligands have p or s-p hybrid orbitals available for σ bonding. The nature of the hybridization of these ligand orbitals is not important for the present discussion. Combination ligand orbitals can be obtained having e_g, a_{1g}, and t_{1u} symmetry. Each of the six combination orbitals plus a metal orbital of the same symmetry gives a σ molecular orbital. Since no ligand combination orbitals with t_{2g} symmetry are available,

---

* Carlson, R., and T. Cameron, unpublished work.

† The symbolism used for molecular orbitals is based on the degeneracy and symmetry of the orbitals. Thus *a* and *b* refer to nondegenerate orbitals, *e* refers to 2-fold degenerate orbitals, and *t* refers to 3-fold degenerate orbitals. The corresponding capital letters are used for the respective energy states. If a nondegenerate orbital is symmetrical with respect to a rotation of 360° about an *n*-fold axis, *a* (or *A*) is used, if not *b* (or *B*) is used. In the absence of an *n*-fold axis *a* (or *A*) is used. The numerical subscripts may be used to differentiate among molecular orbitals of the same degeneracy, or they may have special meaning. The subscript *g* (for *gerade*) indicates that the orbital has a center of symmetry; *u* (for *ungerade*) designates an orbital for which there is a change or sign on reflection through the center of symmetry (see Appendix C). The *s* and *d* atomic orbitals are *g* and the *p* atomic orbitals are *u*. The asterisk designates antibonding orbitals.

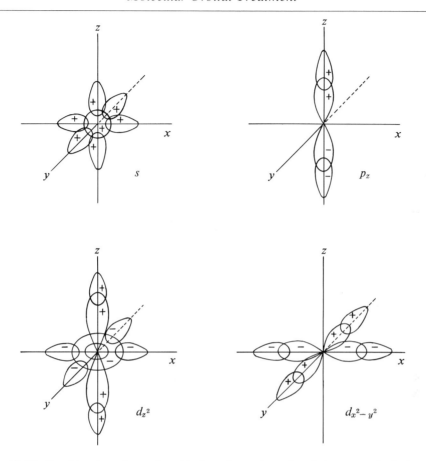

FIGURE 10.17. *Combination of atomic orbitals to form sigma bonds in an octahedral complex.*

the t_{2g} metal orbitals are nonbonding. Figure 10.17 shows a representation of the σ bond formed from the metal s orbital and the ligand combination orbital with a_{1g} symmetry. The wave functions of all six ligand orbitals used for this combination orbital have the same sign (+) as that of the metal s orbital. The corresponding antibonding MO would involve reversal of the sign of the wave function of the combination orbital. The d_{z^2} and $d_{x^2-y^2}$ orbitals combine with combination ligand orbitals of the same symmetry (e_g) with signs as shown in the figure. Each of the metal p orbitals combines with a ligand combination orbital involving two ligands as shown for the p_z orbital. It is noteworthy that the metal bonding orbitals are the same as those involved in the d^2sp^3 hybridization used in the valence bond treatment.

The molecular orbital correlation diagram for an octahedral complex involving only σ bonding is shown in Figure 10.18. The σ bonding orbitals are filled by the 12 electrons from the six ligands. The d electrons of the metal ion occupy the nonbonding t_{2g} level and, if necessary, as for a d^8 ion, the antibonding e_g^* level. The crystal field splitting ($10Dq$) is the difference in energy between these two levels.

When π bonding is involved the pure crystal field and valence bond treatments are inadequate. The ligand field approach can be used since it takes covalent character

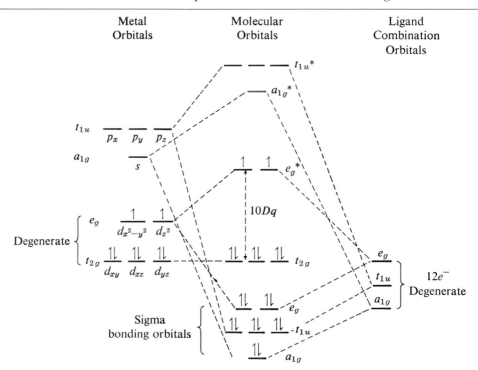

FIGURE 10.18. *Qualitative diagram for the molecular orbitals of an octahedral d^8 complex such as* $[Ni(NH_3)_6]^{2+}$ *(without π bonding).*

into account when the purely electrostatic treatment is not successful. The molecular orbital treatment is the most general and it is the only approach giving a really satisfactory explanation of the bonding in olefin complexes, ferrocene, etc.

The ligand orbitals used for π bonding are generally the p orbitals, which are mutually perpendicular and perpendicular to the metal–ligand σ bond, or molecular π orbitals. The ligand orbitals are combined to give ligand combination orbitals. The combination orbitals obtained from atomic p orbitals, which correspond to the symmetry of available metal orbitals, have t_{1u} and t_{2g} symmetry. A t_{1u} combination ligand orbital is obtained from the p orbitals of four ligands in the same plane as shown in Figure 10.19, the p orbitals being perpendicular to this plane. There will be one such combination orbital for each of the metal p orbitals to give 3 π molecular orbitals with t_{1u} symmetry. Each of the metal t_{2g} orbitals can interact with a ligand combination orbital obtained from the p orbitals of four ligands with all atoms and orbitals in the same plane. The appropriate signs of the wave functions are shown in Figure 10.19. Thus there are a total of six possible π bonding molecular orbitals. The metal t_{1u} orbitals, however, are used for σ bonding and this only leaves the antibonding $t_{1u}{}^*$ level for π interaction with the ligands. π bonding involving these high energy orbitals is not expected to be of great importance.

In the very stable cyanide and 1,10-phenanthroline complexes of d^6 ions such as Fe(II) and Co(III) and also in complexes containing phosphine and arsine ligands, the filled metal t_{2g} orbitals overlap with the empty π orbitals of the ligands. The metal t_{2g}

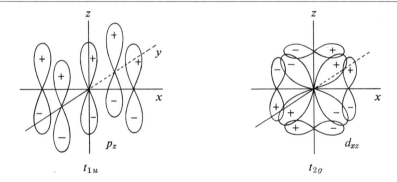

FIGURE 10.19. *The two symmetry types of π bonds in octahedral complexes.*

orbitals are then bonding orbitals and are lowered in energy, thus increasing the CF splitting. Ligands such as OH^- have only filled π orbitals of low energy and any inter-action between filled t_{2g} ligand orbitals and the filled metal orbitals can only result in destabilization (increase in energy) of the metal orbitals. This results in a decrease in the magnitude of $10Dq$ (p. 351).

Comparison of the Different Approaches to Bonding in Coordination Compounds

Research in the field of coordination compounds made rapid progress utilizing the valence bond approach for about 25 years, starting in the early 1930's. As more results were obtained, the qualitative nature of this approach became a serious limitation. Even some of the qualitative predictions of the relative stabilities of complexes based on the availability of low energy orbitals are incorrect, e.g., Cu(ii) and Zn(ii), with no vacant inner d orbitals, form more stable complexes than some of the metals with vacant inner d orbitals.

The crystal field theory offered advantages in that it permitted the interpretation of spectra of complexes, more detailed interpretation and explanation of the magnetic behavior, stability, stereochemistry, and reaction rates of complexes. The pure crystal field approach, which does not consider covalent bonding, might seem to be as limited as the extreme valence bond approach which considers only covalent bonding. The effect of σ bonding, however, can be treated as though it were the result of a very strong crystal field. Without π bonding, the results of the molecular orbital treatment are so similar to the crystal field representation that the latter is adequate for most applications. The important spectral transitions and the differences which result in crystal field stabilization involve the t_{2g} (nonbonding) and e_g^* (antibonding) levels.

For the present, the ligand field theory seems to offer the most practical approach to bonding in coordination compounds. It is essentially the crystal field theory modified to take covalent character into account when necessary. In the application of the ligand field theory one can take advantage of simple pictorial models similar to those which proved so useful in the valence bond approach. The ligand field theory lends itself to simple qualitative applications and predictions, but it also permits quantitative applications.

The molecular orbital theory encompasses the crystal field and valence bond approaches as special cases. Although the molecular orbital theory is the most general, it is difficult to obtain an exact treatment for complexes which contain many atoms. It is to be expected that applications of molecular orbital theory will be particularly promising in the future.

Geometrical Configurations and Isomerism of Coordination Compounds

Simple Types of Isomerism

Reagent chromium chloride, labelled $CrCl_3 \cdot 6H_2O$, is usually a green crystalline compound. It dissolves in water to give a green solution, but on standing for a week or more the solution becomes violet. Violet crystals can be obtained from the solution. These crystals also have the composition $CrCl_3 \cdot 6H_2O$. Actually there are three isomers with this composition. They differ as shown:

$[Cr(H_2O)_6]Cl_3$	Violet
$[Cr(H_2O)_5Cl]Cl_2 \cdot H_2O$	Blue-Green
$[Cr(H_2O)_4Cl_2]Cl \cdot 2H_2O$	Green

In the violet isomer the six water molecules are coordinated to the chromium and the three chloride ions are separate ions in the solid and in solution. In the second isomer one water molecule has been displaced from the coordination sphere by a chloride ion and this water molecule is held as a molecule of water of crystallization. In the third isomer there are two coordinated chloride ions and two molecules of water of crystallization. Commercial chromium chloride is usually a mixture of the two green isomers. This type of isomerism is known as *hydrate isomerism*. The fact that the sum of the number of ionic chlorides and water molecules of crystallization is constant suggests that the water molecules of crystallization serve to fill the anion sites vacated when a chloride ion enters the coordination sphere.

Several other kinds of isomerism are illustrated in Table 10.10. In the polymerization isomers shown, the platinum has a coordination number of four. The first compound

TABLE 10.10

Some Types of Isomerism among Coordination Compounds

Examples	Type of Isomerism
$[Pt(NH_3)_4][PtCl_4]$ and $[Pt(NH_3)_2Cl_2]$	Polymerization
$[Co(NH_3)_6][Cr(CN)_6]$ and $[Cr(NH_3)_6][Co(CN)_6]$	Coordination
$[Co(NH_3)_5(NO_2)]Cl_2$ and $[Co(NH_3)_5(ONO)]Cl_2$	Linkage
$[Pd(bipy)(SCN)_2]$ and $[Pd(bipy)(NCS)_2]$	
$[Pt(NH_3)_4Cl_2]Br_2$ and $[Pt(NH_3)_4Br_2]Cl_2$	Ionization

contains the $[Pt(NH_3)_4]^{2+}$ and $[PtCl_4]^{2-}$ ions and has a molecular weight twice that of the second compound which is a neutral molecule. The compounds $[Pt(NH_3)_3Cl]$-$[Pt(NH_3)Cl_3]$, $[Pt(NH_3)_4][Pt(NH_3)Cl_3]_2$, and $[Pt(NH_3)_3Cl]_2[PtCl_4]$ are also isomers of this series. The coordination isomers involve the exchange of the metal ions between the cation and anion.

Many ligands might conceivably form linkage isomers similar to the nitro complex (coordination through N) and nitrito complex (coordination through O) shown. However, for most ligands coordination normally occurs through the same atom. Cyanide ion seems to coordinate only through C except when it serves as a bridging group. In the clathrate compound $Ni(NH_3)_2(CN)_2C_6H_6$ (p. 93) the six coordinate Ni ions are bonded to two NH_3 and the N atoms of four bridging CN^- ions; the four coordinate Ni ions are bonded to the C of the CN^- ions. The lower coordination number of Ni would be expected when bonded to the less electronegative carbon because more negative charge is transferred to the Ni in the Ni—C bond (see electroneutrality principle, p. 343). The thiocyanate ion seems to coordinate through the nitrogen atom in almost all cases, e.g., $[Co(NCS)_4]^{2-}$, but it can coordinate through S as in $[Hg(SCN)_4]^{2-}$. Two isomers have been obtained for $[Pd(dipy)(SCN)_2]$. The S-bonded isomer is stable in the solid at room temperature, but rearranges to give the N-bonded isomer at elevated temperatures or in solution.* The isomers were assigned from infrared data (p. 453).

The ionization isomers differ only in the exchange of a coordinated anion and one present to maintain charge balance.

STEREOISOMERISM

The most interesting types of isomerism among coordination compounds are those which arise because of differences in the orientation of the groups in space. A much wider variety of stereoisomers is encountered than in the case of carbon compounds because of the various coordination numbers and configurations encountered. The stereochemistry of carbon is concerned primarily with the tetrahedral arrangement. Great complexity can arise because a given compound can contain a large number of carbon atoms connected in many different ways. The stereoisomerism of coordination compounds with coordination numbers four and six is most important and has been investigated most extensively. These coordination numbers and the stereochemistry encountered for them will be discussed before considering the less common coordination numbers.

Coordination Number Four

Coordination compounds with the coordination number four are encountered with tetrahedral and square planar configurations. Both permit stereoisomerism.

TETRAHEDRAL COMPLEXES

Only optical isomerism is encountered among tetrahedral complexes. Many of the complexes are too labile for the optical isomers to be separated. Because of the lability no optical isomers in which four different groups are coordinated to the metal have been prepared. The tetrahedral complexes which have been resolved are those containing unsymmetrical chelating agents. The isomerism encountered is similar to that of the optically active organic spiran compounds. Thus, bis(benzoylpyruvato)beryllium(II) can be separated into the *d* and *l* forms (see Figure 10.20). The complex as shown has no center or plane of symmetry and the two forms are not superimposable. Other

---

* Basolo, F., J. L. Burmeister, and A. J. Poe, *J. Am. Chem. Soc.*, **85**, 1700 (1963).

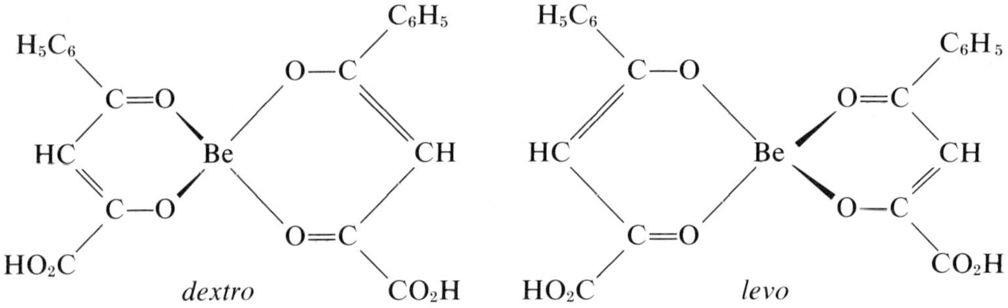

FIGURE 10.20. *Optical isomers of bis(benzoylpyruvato)beryllium.*

tetrahedral complexes of Be, B, Zn, and Cu(II) have been reported to have been re-solved. In many cases the possibility that the Cu(II) and Zn(II) complexes are really six-coordinate (water or an anion coordinated) cannot be ruled out.

SQUARE PLANAR COMPLEXES

Werner (1893) assumed the planar structure for Pt(II) complexes because this struc-ture led to the prediction of the number of isomers encountered. The planar structures of $K_2[PtCl_4]$ and $K_2[PdCl_4]$ were confirmed by x-ray studies in 1922. Pauling (1932) predicted that nickel(II) would form planar complexes also. Many planar complexes are now known for Pt(II), Pd(II), Ni(II), Cu(II), Ag(II), Au(III), and Co(II). Most of the examples of isomerism involve the Pt(II) compounds, which are much more stable than the planar complexes of other metals.

The compounds $[Pt(NH_3)_4][PtCl_4]$ and $[Pt(NH_3)_2Cl_2]$ were cited as examples of polymerization isomers. The structures of these compounds are as follows:

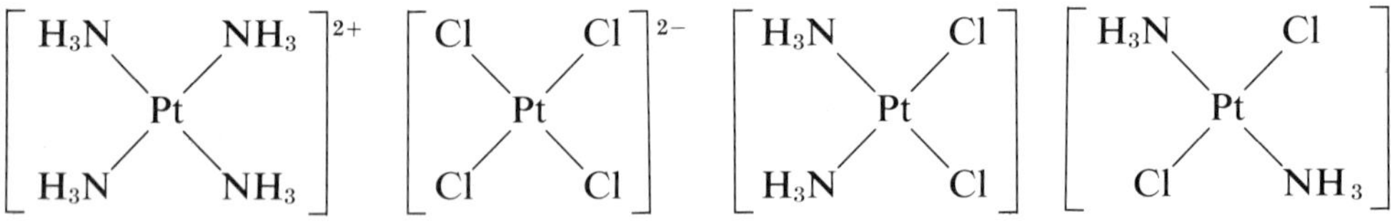

Magnus' Salt   *cis*   *trans*

The second compound exists as *cis* and *trans* isomers. The *cis* isomer has one 2-fold symmetry axis and the *trans* isomer has three 2-fold symmetry axes. (See Appendix C for a discussion of symmetry elements.) The *trans* compound can be made by treating $[Pt(NH_3)_4]Cl_2$ with HCl. The reaction proceeds stepwise and after one Cl^- has been substituted for an NH_3, the remaining NH_3 most readily displaced is the one *trans* to the Cl^- to give the *trans* compound (see Figure 10.21). The difference in the ease of replacement of one of the ammonia molecules in the second step is attributed to the *trans effect*, which is very important in reactions of planar complexes. The group *trans* to a negative group (but CO and C_2H_4 also have very high *trans* directing properties*) is the one most readily replaced. The *cis* isomer is prepared by treating $K_2[PtCl_4]$

---

* See p. 418 for further discussion of the *trans* effect and for a discussion of the various theories of the *trans* effect, see F. Basolo and R. Pearson, *Mechanisms of Inorganic Reactions* (New York: John Wiley and Sons, Inc., 1958) pp. 172-192; and *Progress in Inorganic Chemistry*, Vol. 4, F. A. Cotton, ed. (New York: Inter-science, 1963) p. 381.

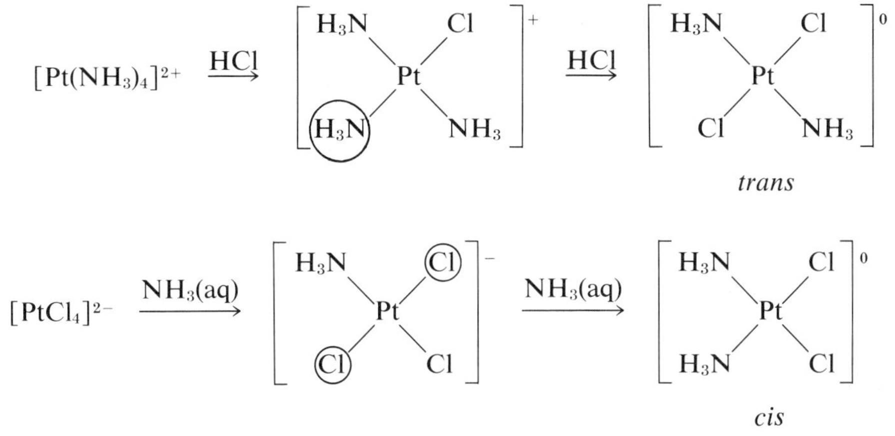

FIGURE 10.21. *Reactions for the formation of cis- and trans-*[Pt(NH₃)₂Cl₂].

with NH_3. After one NH_3 has replaced a Cl^- ion, one of the two remaining Cl^- ions *trans* to another is more readily displaced than the Cl^- *trans* to NH_3, giving the *cis* isomer (see Figure 10.21).

Three isomers have been reported for $[Pt(NH_3)(NH_2OH)(NO_2)(C_5H_5N)]NO_2$, corresponding to the ammonia *trans* to each of the other three groups. The complex ion has a plane of symmetry, but since the four groups are different it has no rotational

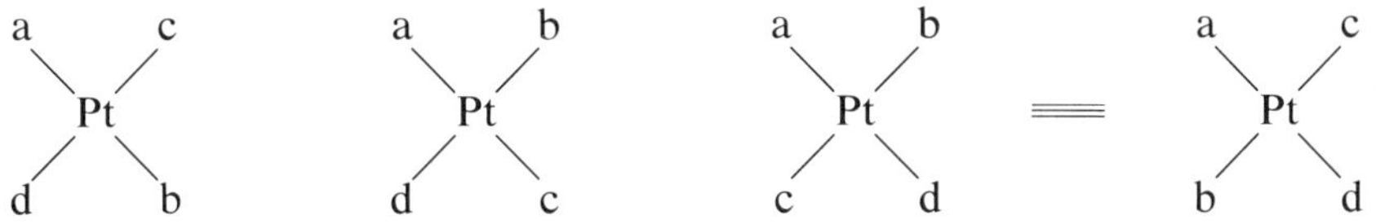

symmetry axis. Fixing any two groups in *trans* positions also fixes the other two positions. The fourth structure shown, in which a is *trans* to d, is identical to the third. Either of these structures can be obtained by rotation of the other through 180° about the axis through a—Pt—d. All possible isomers are easily obtained by selecting one group, a, and seeing how many different groups can be placed *trans* to it. Even four different groups coordinated to the metal ion do not lead to optical isomerism because each isomer has a plane of symmetry (the molecular plane) and hence mirror images are superimposable. Nevertheless, the ingenuity of Mills and Quibell (1935) provided an example of an optically active planar complex. The compound $[Pt(NH_2CHC_6H_5-CHC_6H_5NH_2)(NH_2C(CH_3)_2CH_2NH_2)]Cl_2$ should be optically active if planar because the plane of symmetry is eliminated, but if it were tetrahedral, it would possess a plane of symmetry and hence could not be optically active (Figure 10.22). In the representation of the tetrahedral configuration, the ring to the right would be in the plane of the paper and the one to the left perpendicular to it. The plane of the paper represents a plane of symmetry.

Coordination Number Six

Probably the most common and certainly the most thoroughly studied complexes are those with a coordination number six. Several possible configurations have been considered, but the weight of physical and chemical evidence is so strongly in favor of

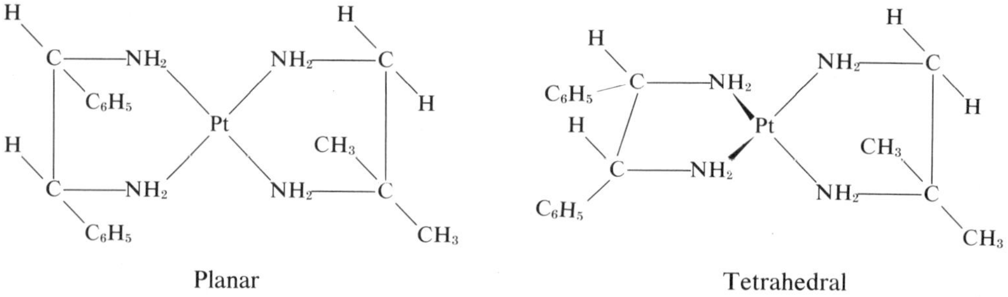

FIGURE 10.22. *Possible configurations of a Pt(II) complex.*

the octahedron that the arguments concerning other possible structures are of historical interest only. MoS_2 and WS_2 are among the few solid compounds in which the metal ion is surrounded by six anions arranged at the apices of a trigonal prism. A structure other than the octahedron has not been found for any discrete six-coordinate complex. The octahedron is sometimes distorted by the structure of the ligands or because of the Jahn-Teller effect (p. 353).

The number of possible isomers for octahedral complexes is very great indeed. Compounds of the type [Mabcdef] with six different ligands have been prepared only for Pt(IV). Only a few isomers have been isolated, but there could be 15 stereoisomers, each of which could exist in d and l forms to give a total of 30 isomers. Most of the complexes for which isomers have been isolated are those of Pt(IV), Co(III), and Cr(III). Octahedral complexes of most other metals are too labile to permit the separation of stereoisomers. Few isomers except optical isomers of other metals are known.

CIS-TRANS ISOMERISM

The octahedron can be represented in many ways. The first representation shown in Figure 10.23 will be used here. The second representation is easier to draw and is commonly used. The metal may be omitted or shown. The axial positions are not unique; any two groups on opposite sides of the octahedron can be chosen for axial positions. The positions are numbered as shown. A *cis* isomer, such as *cis*-[Co(NH₃)₄-Cl₂]⁺, is one in which the two chlorides are in (any) two adjacent positions (see Figure 10.24). *Cis* isomers are designated as 1,2 isomers and *trans* isomers are 1,6 isomers. The difference in color of the isomers of [Co(NH₃)₄Cl₂]⁺ is striking, *cis*-[Co(NH₃)₄-Cl₂]Cl is a beautiful blue-violet color and the *trans* compound is bright green.

A compound of the type [Co(NH₃)₃Cl₃] gives two isomers. In one isomer the Cl⁻ ions are on one triangular face and the NH₃ molecules are on the opposite face. This isomer is called the 1,2,3 or *facial* isomer. The 1,2,6 or *peripheral* isomer has the Cl⁻

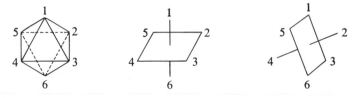

FIGURE 10.23. *Representations of the octahedron.*

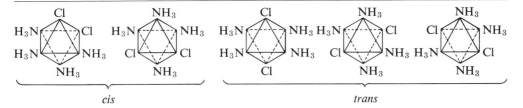

FIGURE 10.24. *Equivalent representations of cis and trans isomers.*

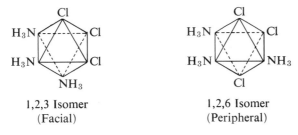

FIGURE 10.25. *Isomers of* [Co(NH$_3$)$_3$Cl$_3$].

ions around an edge of the octahedron with the NH$_3$ molecules around the opposite edge (see Figure 10.25).

COUNTING ISOMERS

With practice one can draw all of the isomers of a complex without duplicating any, but it is sometimes difficult to recognize duplicate isomers which differ in the orientation of the octahedron. Some experience in handling solid models is of very great value in acquiring this facility. Bailar* has suggested a scheme for predicting isomers, which is of value for complicated cases.

Bailar's scheme is fairly simple and it gives the correct number of isomers. However, it deals with the manipulation of symbols and does not emphasize the visualization of the solid models. One can proceed to draw systematically all of the isomers for a given complex by using symmetry as a guide to the expected number of isomers each step along the way. It is important to be able to identify axes and planes of symmetry (see Appendix C); for this purpose it is advantageous to write *cis* and *trans* isomers as shown in Figure 10.26.

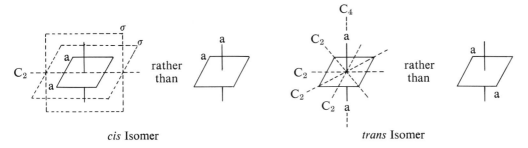

FIGURE 10.26. *Representations of cis and trans isomers of an octahedral complex.*

* Bailar, J. C., Jr., *J. Chem. Educ.*, **34**, 334 (1957).

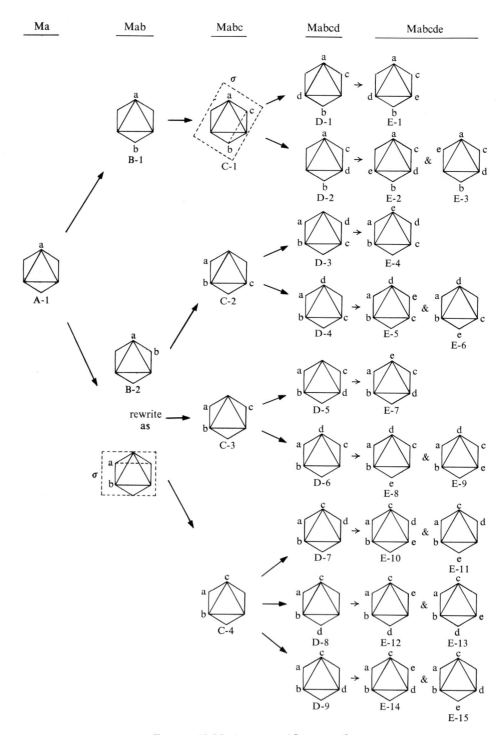

FIGURE 10.27. *Isomers of* [Mabcdef].

We can begin with one group, a, in the 1-position (A-1 in Figure 10.27) and add successively the other groups to give the isomers of [Mabcdef]. The *trans* arrangement for Mab– – – – (B-1) has a 4-fold axis so the 4 remaining positions are equivalent, giving only one isomer (C-1) for Mabc– – –. C-1 has a plane of symmetry so that there are two different positions to yield D-1 and D-2 on the addition of d. D-1 still has a plane of symmetry so the two vacant positions are equivalent and only E-1 is obtained by the addition of e to D-1. D-2 has no plane or axis of symmetry so the two vacant positions are different, yielding E-2 and E-3. B-2 has a plane of symmetry so the positions above and below the plane are equivalent. The addition of c gives the three isomers shown. C-2 and C-3 have planes of symmetry so the axial positions are equivalent. Each can give two isomers on the addition of d. Since C-4 has no plane or axis of symmetry, all three vacant positions are different, giving 3 isomers on addition of d. D-3 and D-5 have planes of symmetry and hence yield only one isomer each on addition of e (E-4 and E-7). D-4, D-6, D-8, and D-9 each yield two isomers on addition of e. After the addition of 5 groups 15 isomers are obtained; the addition of the sixth group does not increase the number of isomers because there is only one vacant position in each case.

For the compound of the type [Mabcde$_2$] the groups can be added in the same way to give D-1-9. Since the e groups are identical, no additional isomers are obtained when they are added. Only four isomers (C-1-4) are obtained for [Mabcd$_3$]. The isomers C-1-4 can be written for [Mabc$_2$e$_2$]. The addition of the second c group to C-1 gives two isomers corresponding to D-1 and D-2 with c = d. The addition of the second c group to C-2 gives the two isomers corresponding to D-3 and D-4. The addition of the second c group to C-3 gives a new isomer corresponding to D-6, but since c = d, D-5 is identical to D-3. Only one new isomer (D-8) is obtained by adding a second c group to C-4. Isomer D-7 is identical to D-6, and D-9 is identical to D-4. The addition of the identical groups e adds no more isomers. The total remains six isomers (Figure 10.28).

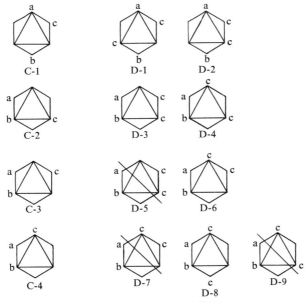

FIGURE 10.28. *Isomers of* [Mabc$_2$c$_2$].

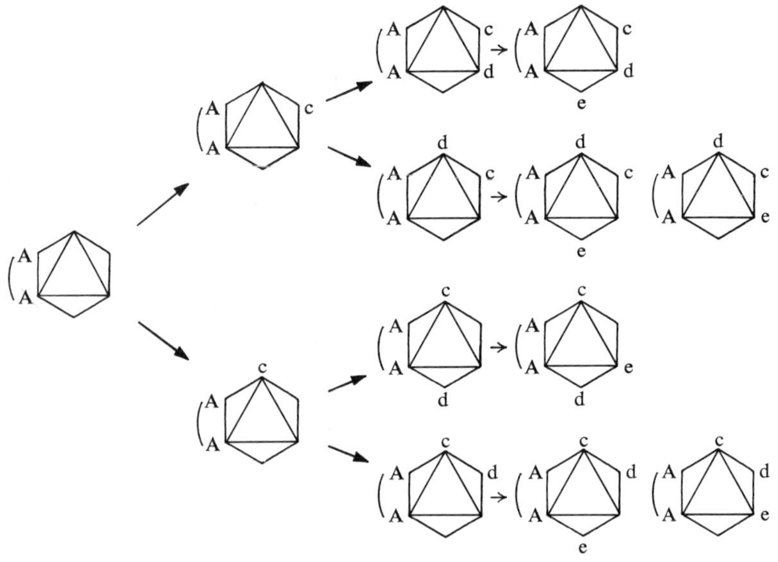

FIGURE 10.29. *Isomers of* [M(AA)bcde].

The compound of the type [M(AA)cdef], where AA is a symmetrical chelate ligand, can be treated in the same way as before for the addition of c-f (c-f corresponds to a-d in Figure 10.28). Of the nine isomers obtained, D-1, D-3, and D-5 can be eliminated since they have only *trans* positions vacant and AA could be expected to occupy *cis* positions. Six isomers would be obtained. If one does not make use of Figure 10.28, the six isomers can be drawn more directly by adding the chelate first, followed by the other ligands in turn (Figure 10.29). If the chelate group were unsymmetrical (AB) the number of isomers would be doubled since A of AB could be *trans* to either of the other groups in the plane of AB for each of the six isomers.

A general approach using group theory for the determination of the number of isomers of inorganic compounds has been presented.*

OPTICAL ISOMERS

If one examines the isomer E-11 (Figure 10.27) with f in the vacant position *trans* to a, it is seen that the groups b, c, d, and e are arranged around a plane in that order proceeding in a clockwise direction, as drawn. The same *trans* pairs are present if the groups b, c, d, and e are arranged in that order proceeding in a counterclockwise direction looking toward a. These isomers are mirror images and, since they are not super-imposable, they represent optical isomers. Each of the 15 isomers shown for [Mabcdef] represents a pair of optical isomers.

The compounds [Co(NH$_3$)$_6$]Cl$_3$ and [Co(en)$_3$]Cl$_3$ are very similar except that the latter can be resolved into optical isomers. The optical isomers (mirror images) are

* Kennedy, B. A., D. A. McQuarrie, and C. H. Brubaker, Jr., *Inorg. Chem.*, **3**, 265 (1964).

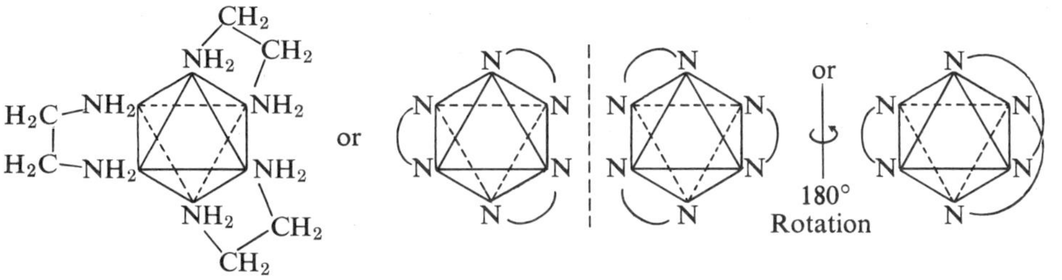

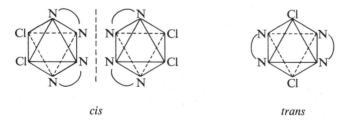

FIGURE 10.30. *Optical isomers of* $M(en)_3^{n+}$.

shown above. The planar representations are of more value once the student has convinced himself that he cannot superimpose the solid models of the mirror images on one another. In Figure 10.30 one of the optical isomers is rotated through 180° to show that it cannot be superimposed on the other one. The optical isomers of a compound of the type $M(AA)_3$ are shown on p. 339 to illustrate the right- and left-handed spiral effects.

The *cis* and *trans* isomers of $[Co(NH_3)_4Cl_2]Cl$ are very similar in color to the *cis* and *trans* isomers of $[Co(en)_2Cl_2]Cl$. Only the *cis*-$[Co(en)_2Cl_2]Cl$ can be resolved into optical isomers (see Figure 10.31). It is the only one of this group that does not possess a center or plane of symmetry. The mirror images of the more symmetrical structures are superimposable. The structures drawn for complexes, or the models, should be examined for elements of symmetry (i.e., a plane, center, or rotation-reflection axis of symmetry) which would rule out optical activity in trying to decide which isomers will be optically active. Complexes of the type $M(AB)_3$, e.g., $Co(gly)_3$, give 1,2,3 and 1,2,6 isomers, each of which could be optically active. All of the isomers shown for [M(AA)cdef] (Figure 10.29) are potentially optically active.

In principle, chelate groups are not required for optical activity in octahedral complexes, but all known examples involve chelate groups because of the greater stability of their complexes. Three of the five possible isomers of $[Pt(NH_3)_2(py)_2Cl_2]^{2+}$ (Figure 10.32) have been prepared. One of the isomers should be optically active. It would be the isomer in which all like groups are *cis* to one another. Two isomers of the complex $[Pt(py)Cl(NH_3)_2(NO_2)_2]Cl$ could exist as *d, l* pairs. These correspond to isomers D-4 and D-6 for $[Mabc_2e_2]$ of Figure 10.28.

cis   *trans*

FIGURE 10.31. *Isomers of* $[Co(en)_2Cl_2]^+$.

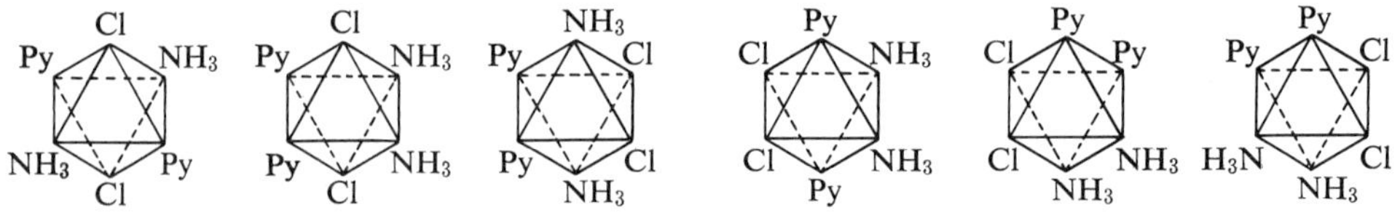

Cl	Cl	NH₃	Py	Py	Py
Py ... NH₃	Py ... NH₃	Py ... Cl	Cl ... NH₃	Cl ... Py	Py ... Cl
NH₃ ... Py	Py ... NH₃	Py ... Cl	Cl ... NH₃	Cl ... NH₃	H₃N ... NH₃
Cl	Cl	NH₃	Py	NH₃	NH₃

FIGURE 10.32. *Isomers of* $[Pt(NH_3)_2(py)_2Cl_2]^{2+}$.

The metals for which octahedral complexes have been resolved are shown in Table 10.11. Some of the gaps in the table are doubtless due to the small amount of work done with metals, other than Pt, beyond the first transition series.

TABLE 10.11

Metals for which Octahedral Complexes have been Resolved

								Al	Si	
	Ti	Cr	Fe	Co	Ni	Cu	Zn	Ga	Ge	As
Y			Ru	Rh			Cd			
			Os	Ir	Pt					

Resolution Procedures. The properties of the *d* and *l* isomers of a complex such as [Co(en)₃]Cl₃ are identical except for the interaction with polarized light. However, if the chloride ions are replaced by optically active ions the resulting salts might differ in properties such as solubility. $[Co(en)_3]^{3+}$ is commonly resolved by replacing two chloride ions by the *d*-tartrate ion, followed by fractional crystallization. The diastereoisomers, *d*-[Co(en)₃]Cl*d*-tart and *l*-[Co(en)₃]Cl*d*-tart, are not mirror images because the tartrate ion has the same configuration in each salt. On crystallization the *d*-[Co(en)₃]Cl*d*-tart separates in the form of large crystals. The *l* complex is much more soluble and the solution becomes a thick gelatinous mass before fine needles begin to crystallize. The diastereoisomers can be converted to the active chloride complexes by treatment with concentrated hydrochloric acid. The active complex is stable in solution for many weeks without racemization.

The antimonyl tartrate ion, SbO*d*-tart⁻, and the *d*-α-bromocamphor-π-sulfonate ion have been useful resolving agents for cationic complexes. Anionic complexes, e.g., $[M(C_2O_4)_3]^{3-}$, are usually resolved using an optically active cation such as those formed by the bases strychnine or brucine. A resolved cationic complex such as *d*- or *l*-[Co(en)₃]³⁺ or *d*- or *l*-[Co(en)₂(NO₂)₂]⁺ can be used as the resolving agent.

Neutral complexes offer more of a challenge for their resolution. They cannot form diastereoisomers in the usual way, but several other methods are possible. The neutral complexes are often reasonably soluble in nonpolar solvents, so that extraction into an optically active organic solvent would provide a possible means of separation. Dwyer achieved partial resolution of [Co(acac)₃] by extraction into an organic solvent from an aqueous solution containing *d*-[Co(en)₃]I₃. The solubilities of the *d*- and *l*-[Co(acac)₃] are not the same in water containing an optically active ion.

Partial resolution of active complexes has also been achieved by differential adsorption on an optically active solid such as quartz, starch, or sugar. Failure to resolve a complex by any one or several means does not justify the conclusion that the complex is not dissymmetric. The method tried might not be applicable for that complex or the complex might racemize so rapidly that the optical isomers cannot be isolated.

A racemic mixture contains equal amounts of the *d* and *l* isomers. Hence, complete resolution would give 50% of the material as the *d* isomer. Dwyer was able to isolate nearly 100% of $[Fe(phen)_3]^{2+}$ as the *l* isomer by fractional crystallization of $[Fe(phen)_3]$-$(SbOC_4H_4O_6)_2$. The complex racemizes at an appreciable rate in solution, but very slowly in the solid. As the *l* isomer crystallizes, the *d* isomer undergoes racemization in solution. Werner (1912) observed a similar situation in the resolution of $[Cr(C_2O_4)_3]^{3-}$ which racemizes rapidly in solution.

The presence of an optically active substance in solution can greatly affect the equilibrium between the *d* and *l* isomers of a complex. Pfeiffer noted that the optical rotation of a solution of zinc *d*-camphor-π-sulfonate changed from +0.98° to +0.09° upon addition of enough 1,10-phenanthroline to form the $[Zn(phen)_3]^{2+}$ ion. The complex ion isolated from the solution is inactive. Presumably the active anion causes a shift in the equilibrium between *d*- and *l*-$[Zn(phen)_3]^{2+}$ in solution, perhaps through ion-pair formation. However, Dwyer has also shown that the rates of racemization of *d*-$[Ni(phen)_3]^{2+}$ and *l*-$[Ni(phen)_3]^{2+}$ differ when in the presence of optically active anions *or cations*. The usual ion-pair interactions cannot be responsible in the latter case.

Stereospecific Effects. If the ligands are optically active the number of possible isomers of the complex formed is increased. A complex of the type $M(AA)_3$, where AA is a "symmetrical" optically active chelate group (e.g., *trans*-cyclohexanediamine) would be expected to have 8 isomers:

D*ddd*	L*lll*
D*ddl*	L*lld*
D*dll*	L*ldd*
D*lll*	L*ddd*

where D and L refer to the optical rotation of the complex, and *d* and *l* refer to the optical rotation of the asymmetric ligand. However, generally only one pair of isomers is obtained. In the case of *trans*-1,2-cyclohexanediamine (chxn), the cobalt complexes isolated are D-$[Co(l\text{-chxn})_3]^{3+}$ and L-$[Co(d\text{-chxn})_3]^{3+}$. Only recently have complexes containing the same ligand in different configurations been isolated. Dwyer has separated D$[Pt(d\text{-pn})_2(l\text{-pn})]Cl_4$ and L$[Pt(d\text{-pn})_2(l\text{-pn})]Cl_4$. The situation involving propylenediamine is further complicated by the fact that geometrical isomers are also possible. The methyl groups can be arranged on a face or around an edge.

Corey and Bailar* have given a very detailed discussion of stereospecific effects. The configuration of the chelate ring in an ethylenediamine complex can be compared to the chair form of cyclohexane. The substituents on the puckered ring can be classified as approximately axial or equitorial. In a square planar complex of the type $M(en)_2^{n+}$ the two puckered rings can be arranged as shown in Figure 10.33. In the lower drawing (kk′ form) the two en rings are mirror images. The clockwise sequence from above in the chelate ring for k is Meaea and for k′ it is Maeae. The kk form shown has three mutually perpendicular 2-fold axes. The kk form, with the hydrogens staggered around both rings, is expected to be more stable than the kk′ form in which the hydrogen atoms on adjacent nitrogen atoms are directly opposed.

* Corey, E. J., and J. C. Bailar, Jr., *J. Am. Chem. Soc.*, **81**, 2620 (1959).

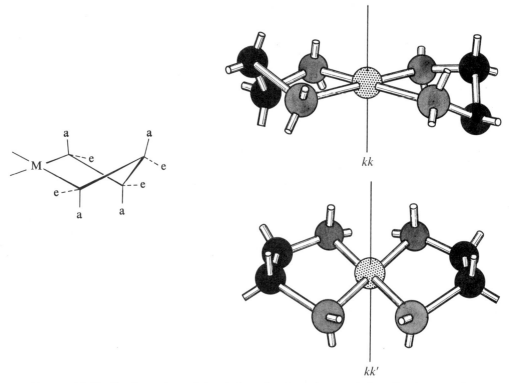

FIGURE 10.33. *Configuration of the chelate ring in a planar ethylenediamine complex.*
[*E. J. Corey and J. C. Bailar, Jr.,* J. Am. Chem. Soc., *81, 2620 (1959).*]

The interactions are not so apparent in octahedral complexes, but the situation is treated similarly. There are four different forms possible for an octahedral complex of the type $M(en)_3^{n+}$, kkk, k'kk, k'k'k, and k'k'k'. The four forms will differ in energy with the energies of k'kk and k'k'k intermediate between those of kkk and k'k'k'. The hydrogen–hydrogen and carbon–hydrogen interactions were evaluated for the kkk and k'k'k' forms. Assuming one configuration of rings about the dissymmetric metal ion, one of these forms is considered to be more stable than the other by about 1.8 kcal/mole. For this discussion kkk will arbitrarily be assumed to be the more stable form. The kkk form is labeled *lel* in Figure 10.34. In it the C—C bonds are approximately parallel to the short trigonal axis shown. In the less stable form, labeled *ob*, the C—C bonds are slanted obliquely, relative to the short trigonal axis.

For an optically active ligand such as 1,2-propylenediamine, the interactions will be more important because a hydrogen on each ligand is replaced by the larger methyl group. The most stable arrangement for $[Co(pn)_3]^{3+}$ is that in which all three chelate rings have the same configuration, with the methyl groups in equatorial positions.* This necessitates that all three ligands be either *d*-pn or *l*-pn. Similar interactions can account for stereospecific effects observed for other optically active ligands.

Bailar and his students have investigated the stereospecific behavior of cobalt com-

---

* The equatorial positions are relative to the chelate rings. Geometrical isomerism (facial and peripheral) is also possible.

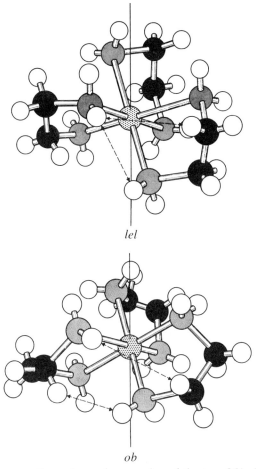

lel

ob

FIGURE 10.34. *Two configurations of a complex of the type* M(en)$_3^{n+}$. [*E. J. Corey and J. C. Bailar, Jr.,* J. Am. Chem. Soc., *81, 2620 (1959).*]

plexes extensively. The treatment of [Co(*l*-pn)$_2$CO$_3$]$^+$ with racemic tartaric acid produces the complexes [Co(*l*-pn)$_2$*d*-tart]$^+$ and [Co(*l*-pn)$_2$*l*-tart]$^+$. The tartrate ion can be replaced by *l*-pn, but the two complexes react at different rates. The *l*-tartrate ion is displaced more rapidly by *l*-pn to achieve partial resolution of racemic tartaric acid. Partial resolution of racemic tartaric acid can also be achieved by using an excess of the acid for the reaction with [Co(*l*-pn)$_2$CO$_3$]$^+$. The rates of substitution differ for *d* and *l*-tartaric acid. The reaction of [Co(en)$_2$CO$_3$]$^+$ with *d*-tartaric acid produces D-[Co(en)$_2$*d*-tart]$^+$ and L-[Co(en)$_2$*d*-tart]$^+$. These complexes react at different rates with en so that about 70% yield of D-[Co(en)$_3$]$^{3+}$ can be obtained in this way. The stereospecific effects cause more of one of the isomers to be produced in one (or both) of the substitutions.

Rotatory Dispersion. The optical rotation of most organic compounds does not vary greatly with changes in wavelength of light in the visible region. Djerassi's recent work demonstrates that the rotations do change greatly with wavelength in the ultraviolet region. Most optically active coordination compounds are highly colored and the optical rotation often changes from very high positive values to very high negative

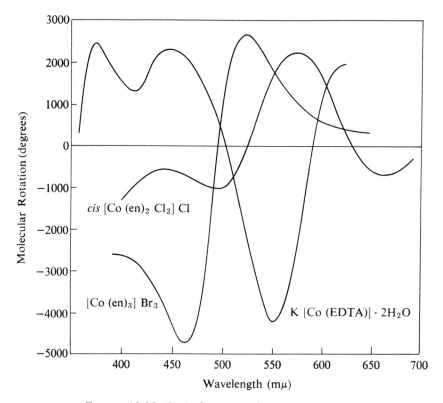

FIGURE 10.35. *Optical rotatory dispersion curves.*

values as the wavelength changes. Typical rotatory dispersion curves are shown in Figure 10.35. The molecular rotations for some complexes are as high as 87,000°. The high rotations are fortunate since it is usually necessary to use very low concentrations because of the high optical density of solutions of the complexes. Rotatory dispersion curves have been useful in assigning configurations to coordination compounds. Similar complexes of the same configurations generally give similar rotatory dispersion curves.

Less Common Coordination Numbers

The very common coordination numbers four and six have been considered in some detail. It is now appropriate to take a brief look at the coordination numbers which are less common, but not so rare as has been assumed in the past.

Coordination Number Two

There are only two possible arrangements for compounds in which there is a coordination number two, linear and angular. The linear arrangement would be expected to be common since it provides minimum ligand–ligand repulsion. Only special circumstances, such as the bond hybridization in the H_2O molecule, would be expected to give an angular arrangement. The linear arrangement is the one encountered among coordination compounds and no stereoisomers are to be expected.

The coordination number two is not encountered for many metals. The $[Ag(NH_3)_2]^+$ ion involves a linear N—Ag—N arrangement and the $[Ag(CN)_2]^-$ ion is linear. Although ethylenediamine complexes are generally much more stable than those of ammonia, this is not true for $[Ag(en)]^+$ compared to $[Ag(NH_3)_2]^+$. The unexpectedly low stability of $[Ag(en)]^+$ is attributed to the fact that the en molecule cannot span the Ag^+ to permit the desired linear arrangement.

In chelate compounds, the 5-membered rings are generally the most stable. Thus, $[Cu(en)_2]^{2+}$ is more stable than the $NH_2CH_2CH_2CH_2NH_2$ complex, $[Cu(1,3-pn)_2]^{2+}$, in which the ligands form six-membered rings. In the case of silver, the trend is reversed because the larger ring can permit less strained bonding to the Ag^+. The Ag^+ compounds containing 6- ,7- , and 8-membered rings are all more stable than $[Ag(en)]^+$.

The coordination number two has been clearly established in the solid state for $[Ag(NH_3)_2]^+$ and $[Ag(CN)_2]^-$. However, Ag^+ can add additional ligands and has been

shown by x-ray studies to have a coordination number four in $\left[Ag\left(SC \underset{CH_3}{\overset{NH_2}{\diagdown}} \right)_4 \right] Cl.$

There is some evidence* that two molecules of water are rather strongly associated with complexes such as $[Ag(NH_3)_2]^+$ to give an effective coordination number four in solution.

A linear arrangement is usually associated with *sp* bonding and this seems reasonable for compounds of Ag^+ and Hg^{2+} since these metals have filled *d* orbitals. Infrared studies of the linear $HgCl_2$, $HgBr_2$, and HgI_2 in the vapor state, however, indicate that the angle bending force constants are extremely low. This suggests that the Hg^{2+} orbitals lack directional properties and seems to be inconsistent with pure *sp* bonding. This view agrees with the fact that linear complexes readily add additional ligands and are probably strongly associated with polar solvents in solution.

Coordination Number Three

Odd coordination numbers are not common. The arrangements expected for C.N. 3 are the trigonal plane (BF_3, NO_3^-) and the trigonal pyramid (NH_3, ClO_3^-). Among the few complexes for which this coordination number is presumed are alkyl phosphines and arsines of Cu^+, Ag^+, and Au^+ of the type $[M(R_3P)_2I]$, and the silver compounds $[Ag(R_3P)_3]^+$ and $[Ag(R_2S)_3]^+$. There is the possibility that some of these compounds might be hydrido complexes with a coordination number four, such as those mentioned in the discussion of the C.N. 5. The hydrogen would not readily be detected by x-ray structural methods and it would make little difference in the analytical results. Nuclear magnetic resonance and infrared studies are the obvious methods to use for the investigation of such possibilities.

---

* Jonassen, H. B., and P. C. Yates, *J. Am. Chem. Soc.*, **74**, 3388 (1952); H. B. Jonassen, T. F. Fagley, C. C. Rolland, and P. C. Yates, *J. Phys. Chem.*, **58**, 286 (1954).

The compounds $K_2[CuCl_3]$ and $Cs_2[AgCl_3]$ contain infinite chains of MCl_4 tetrahedra. It seems reasonable to assume that, in general, if the stoichiometry indicates a coordination number three, but the ligands are potentially bridging groups, such as Cl^-, then bridging will occur to give a higher coordination number.

Coordination Number Five

Coordination compounds with coordination number five are uncommon. As in the case of compounds with an apparent C.N. 3, the stoichiometry should not be taken as valid evidence for a coordination number five. The compound $(NH_4)_3[ZnCl_5]$ has been shown by x-ray studies to contain the $[ZnCl_4]^{2-}$ and Cl^- anions. The compound $Tl_2[AlF_5]$ contains chains of AlF_6 octahedra. The cobalt(II) cyanide complex, $[Co(CN)_5]^{3-}$, has been presumed to represent an example of a compound with coordination number five. The compound has been shown recently to involve a Co—H bond so that the formula should be $[CoH(CN)_5]^{3-}$.

The cobalt(I) compound $[Co(C_6H_5NC)_5]ClO_4$ is 5-coordinate and the planar $[Ni(CN)_4]^{2-}$ ion readily adds a fifth CN^- in concentrated CN^- solution. The complex $[Ni(diarsine)_2](ClO_4)_2$ $\left(\text{diarsine} = \right.$ $\left. \right)$ readily adds 1 mole of Cl^-,

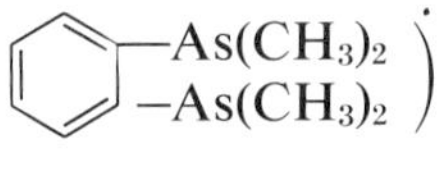

Br^-, or I^- to give a 5-coordinate complex. The corresponding planar Pd(II) and Pt(II) complexes also add a mole of X^- in nitromethane, but these 5-coordinate complexes are largely dissociated to give 4-coordinate complexes in water. Similar 5-coordinate complexes of Ni(III) and Au(III) have been prepared. In the compound $[Ni(triarsine)\text{-}Br_2]Br$ (triarsine $= (CH_3)_2AsC_3H_6As(CH_3)C_3H_6As(CH_3)_2$) the nickel is 5-coordinate with a tetragonal pyramidal structure. The bond to the Br in the apical position is longer than the bonds in the base of the pyramid. The compound $[Ni(P(C_2H_5)_3)_2Br_3]$ has been assigned a square pyramidal structure (p. 435).

Although the compounds just mentioned seem to be well characterized as 5-coordinate complexes, it is possible that some of the compounds believed to be 5-coordinate may turn out to be hydride complexes. Several of the very stable hydride complexes which have been prepared are phosphine compounds, e.g., $trans\text{-}[PtH(Cl)(PR_3)_2]$ and $[RuH(Cl)(PR_2C_2H_4PR_2)]$.

The compounds $Fe(CO)_5$, $TaCl_5$, $MoCl_5$, and the $CuCl_5^{3-}$ ion have the trigonal bipyramidal arrangement. The discrete anion $[SbF_5]^{2-}$ exists in $K_2[SbF_5]$, but the reason that bridging does not occur to give a higher coordination number is that the structure is essentially that of an octahedron with one position occupied by a lone pair of electrons (Figure 10.36). The lone pair–bonding pair repulsion is so important that the Sb is about 0.3 Å below the equatorial plane, rather than above it as one might expect if

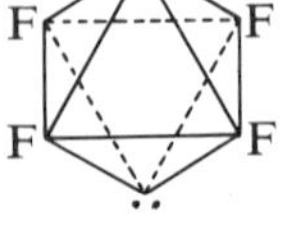

FIGURE 10.36. *Structure of* $[SbF_5]^{2-}$.

the important repulsion were among the F atoms (see p. 61 for a discussion of lone-pair interactions).

From a valence bond or molecular orbital viewpoint, the d^8 ions (Fe[0], Co[I], Ni[II], Pd[II], Pt[II], and Au[III]) would be expected to be most likely to form 5-coordinate complexes. The tendency to give 5-coordinate complexes seems to decrease in the order Fe[0] > Co[I] > Ni[II] and Ni[II] > Pd[II] > Pt[II]. The structures of the Fe[0] and Ni[II] compounds indicate that they differ in bonding, with Ni(II) showing a definite tendency toward the formation of planar complexes (since the apical bond is long). The stabilization of the planar complexes is apparently even greater for Pd(II) and Pt(II) so that the apical group is easily removed.

The coordination number five is important in the consideration of the intermediate formed by a dissociation mechanism in substitution reactions of octahedral complexes. The structures considered most likely are the tetragonal pyramid and the trigonal bipyramid. The tetragonal pyramid results from the removal of one group from the octahedron without rearrangement. The trigonal bipyramid requires that three groups in the plane of the leaving group rearrange to give 120° bond angles in the plane.

In addition to organometallics such as pentaphenylantimony, some of the coordination compounds of Si and Sn(IV) seem to show a coordination number of 5. R. West and J. Y. Corey have found that Ph_3SiI forms a complex with 2,2'-bipyridine, $Ph_3Si(bipy)I$, with ionized I^- in solution.

Coordination Number Seven

The molecule IF_7 has the structure of a pentagonal bipyramid. The $[ZrF_7]^{3-}$ ion was originally reported to have a structure which can be described as an octahedron with a seventh F^- added in the center of one expanded face. However, it has been shown to have the same structure as UO_2F_5 and $[UF_7]^{3-}$, which is that of a pentagonal bipyramid. The $[NbF_7]^{2-}$ and $[TaF_7]^{2-}$ ions have a structure which can be related to a trigonal prism with a seventh F^- added to one of the tetragonal faces, with subsequent distortion to diminish anion–anion repulsion. This results in a configuration which can be represented by the F^- ions arranged to give coincident 4- and 3-fold axes (Figure 10.37). The compound $(NH_4)_3[SiF_7]$ contains the $[SiF_6]^{2-}$ and F^- anions rather than a 7-coordinate species.

Until recently the only known examples of complexes with a coordination number seven were fluorides of large cations. Hoard* has shown by x-ray structural methods

$UF_7{}^{2-}$

FIGURE 10.37. *Structures of* $UF_7{}^{2-}$ *and* NbF_7.

* Hoard, J. L., G. S. Smith, and M. Lind, in *Advances in the Chemistry of the Coordination Compounds*, edited by S. Kirschner (New York: Macmillan Company, 1961) p. 296.

that iron gives a 7-coordinate complex $[Fe(H_2O)(EDTA)]^-$. The arrangement of the seven atoms around the iron is approximately that of a pentagonal bipyramid. Hoard has also studied a 7-coordinate manganese(II) complex, $[Mn(H_2O)(HEDTA)]^-$, in which one of the coordinated carboxylate groups is protonated. The configuration around the manganese is essentially the same as that of $[NbF_7]^{2-}$. The 7-coordinate anion is encountered in the salt $Mn[Mn(H_2O)(HEDTA)]_2 \cdot 8H_2O$. The other manganese ion is 6-coordinate, being coordinated to $4H_2O$ and 2 carbonyl oxygens of the EDTA.

It appears likely that 7-coordinate complexes are not as rare as has been believed, particularly in solution. It is probably significant that both of the examples cited (Mn^{2+} and Fe^{3+}) are high-spin d^5 ions with no crystal field stabilization. Octahedral complexes with strong crystal field stabilization, e.g., Cr^{3+} (d^3) and low-spin Co^{3+} (d^6) complexes, are probably not likely to expand the coordination sphere.

The 7-coordinate intermediate or transition state which has been considered most generally for substitution reactions in octahedral complexes by a second order process (p. 405) is the pentagonal bipyramid. A 7-coordinate transition state with the $[NbF_7]^{2-}$ configuration has been proposed for the base catalyzed racemization of d-$[Co(EDTA)]^-$ (p. 415).

Coordination Number Eight

After coordination numbers six and four, the coordination number eight is most common. The only structures verified for this coordination number are the Archimedes tetragonal antiprism ($[TaF_8]^{3-}$) and the dodecahedron with triangular faces ($[Mo(CN)_8]^{4-}$) (see Figure 10.38). The same dodecahedral arrangement of 8 oxygen atoms around Zr^{4+} occurs in $ZrSiO_4$ (zircon). The cube has been considered as a likely possibility, but no complexes with this structure have been obtained. The cube would be a less favorable structure from the standpoint of anion–anion repulsion. The $[U(C_2O_4)_4]^{4-}$ ion has been reported to have been resolved into two pairs of optical isomers. These results rule out the cube. The structure of $[Zr(C_2O_4)_4]^{4-}$ has been shown to be that of a dodecahedron. It is interesting to note that the complexes $[Th(acac)_4]$ and $[Zr(acac)_4]$ with larger chelate rings have the antiprismatic structure.

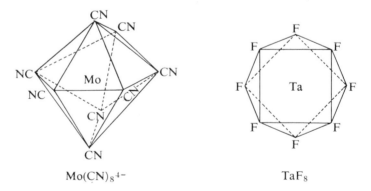

$Mo(CN)_8{}^{4-}$ TaF_8

FIGURE 10.38. *Complexes with a coordination number eight.*

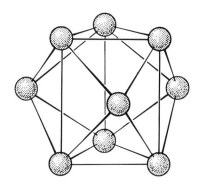

FIGURE 10.39. *Structure of* $Nd(H_2O)_9^{3+}$.

Coordination Number Nine

The only known coordination number greater than eight which has been demonstrated by structural methods for a complex is nine. The compound $Nd(BrO_3)_3 \cdot 9H_2O$ has been shown to contain the $[Nd(H_2O)_9]^{3+}$ ion, where the Nd^{3+} is at the center of a trigonal prism with an additional water molecule in each tetragonal face (Figure 10.39). Similar 9-coordinate aquo ions of La^{3+}, Ce^{3+}, and Y^{3+} have been reported on the basis of incomplete x-ray studies. The ReH_9^{2-} and TcH_9^{2-} ions have similar structures.*

Pi Bonded Complexes

Olefin Complexes

The bonding in the complexes already discussed can be understood in terms of dative bonding or in terms of electrostatic interactions. The compound $K[Pt(C_2H_4)Cl_3]$, known as Zeise's salt, was discovered in 1827. The ethylene molecule cannot form dative bonds in the usual way, because it has no unshared electrons. Ethylene would not be expected to be a good ligand from the electrostatic point of view; it is neutral with a dipole moment of zero. Nevertheless, a variety of interesting metal compounds involving olefins and cyclic unsaturated molecules are known.

Zeise's salt was first prepared by boiling platinum(IV) chloride with alcohol, and adding potassium chloride. Platinum–olefin complexes can be prepared generally by treating anhydrous platinum(IV) chloride or bromide with the olefin in an anhydrous solvent. The olefin molecule can be displaced by other ligands such as Cl^- or pyridine; the unchanged olefin can be recovered quantitatively by displacement with cyanide ion. The metals which form olefin complexes are primarily those with d^8 or d^{10} configurations, notably Pt(II), Pd(II), Rh(I), Ag(I), Cu(I), and Hg(II). Platinum(II) forms the most stable olefin complexes.

* Abrahams, S. C., A. P. Ginsberg and K. Knox, *Inorg. Chem.*, **3**, 558 (1964); A. P. Ginsberg, *ibid.*, **3**, 567 (1964).

The infrared and ultraviolet spectra of olefin complexes indicate that the double bond remains intact although the bond is somewhat lengthened. X-ray structural studies indicate that the C_2H_4 molecule is approximately perpendicular to the plane of the $PtCl_3$ group in Zeise's salt and is symmetrically arranged with respect to the Pt atom. Double bonding between the metal and olefin is suggested by the similarity between olefin complexes and those of CO, and by the fact that only metals with filled, or nearly filled, *d* orbitals form stable complexes.

The bonding in platinum–ethylene complexes can be described as the resonance hybrid of the contributing structures shown in Figure 10.40. The first two structures

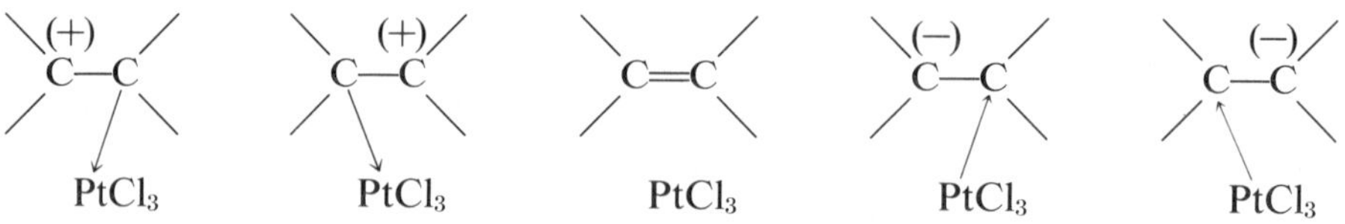

FIGURE 10.40

involve dative bonding from one carbon atom, the third structure is a "no bond" structure in which the carbon–carbon double bond is retained, and the last two involve donation of a pair of *d* electrons from the Pt to a carbon atom. The molecular orbital description as developed by Dewar and Chatt is more satisfactory. Electrons of the ethylene are shared with the platinum by the overlap of the π orbital of the olefin with a $5d6s6p^2$ hybrid orbital of the platinum. The electrons from the platinum are shared with the olefin through the overlap of a filled hybridized $5d6p$ orbital (a hybridized orbital is used to provide better overlap than with the d_{xz} or the d_{yz} orbital) with the antibonding π^* orbital of the olefin (Figure 10.41). The π^* orbital is antibonding with respect to the bonding in the olefin molecule and its use should weaken the C—C bond, but its overlap with a Pt orbital would strengthen the Pt–olefin bond.

The stabilities of the various substituted styrene–platinum complexes have been investigated by studying the displacement of 1-dodecene by the styrenes in alcohol solution containing 0.01 mole HCl/liter. The equilibrium constants were evaluated spectrophotometrically and are shown in Figure 10.42 plotted against the Hammett

$$X—C_6H_4CH=CH_2 + [C_{12}H_{24}PtCl_3]^- = [X—C_6H_5CH=CH_2PtCl_3]^- + C_{12}H_{24}$$

sigma constants for the substituents (see p. 197). The rather surprising result is that both electron releasing and electron withdrawing substituents *increase* the stability of

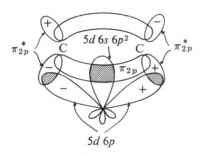

FIGURE 10.41. *Bonding in a Pt–ethylene compound.*

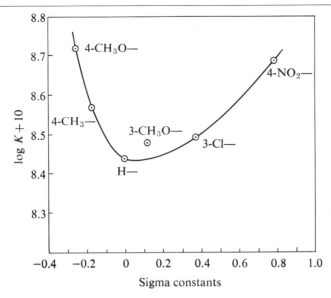

FIGURE 10.42. *Plot of stability constants of substituted* Pt–*styrene complexes vs. sigma values for the substituents* [*J. R. Joy and M. Orchin,* J. Am. Chem. Soc., *81, 308 (1959)*].

the complex relative to styrene. An appealing explanation was presented. The substituents with negative σ constants increase the electron density in the olefinic linkage and increase the strength of the coordinate σ bond. An increasing positive σ constant of the substituent decreases the electron density in the olefinic linkage and decreases the strength of the σ bond, but it also increases the strength of the Pt–ligand d-p-π bond. An alternative explanation based on orbital overlap and energies of molecular orbitals was also presented.

The bonding in Ag$^+$–olefin complexes presumably differs from that in the Pt compounds since the orbital that overlaps with the π orbital of the olefin is an s orbital or an sp hybrid orbital, because the d orbitals are filled. The bonding in stable Hg^{2+}–olefin complexes which have been obtained apparently involves breaking of the carbon–carbon double bond, with Hg attaching to one carbon and another group, e.g., OH, attaching to the other carbon atom.

Metal–olefin complexes are also of practical interest. Olefins can be separated from saturated hydrocarbons by absorption in aqueous solutions containing Cu(I), Ag(I), Hg(II), or Pt(II) salts. Hydration and polymerization reactions are catalyzed by heavy metal salts. The most important applications involve the polymerization of olefins. The Ziegler process for the production of polyethylene by low pressure polymerization utilizes a catalyst obtained from the reaction of TiCl$_4$ with aluminum trialkyls. The exact nature of the active catalyst and how it functions are not well understood. It seems likely that bridged complexes of Al with Ti or other di- or tri-valent transition metal halides are essential for catalytic activity. Metals, such as platinum, which give very stable metal–olefin complexes do not produce effective catalysts with aluminum alkyls. Stereospecific polymerization, e.g., head to tail chains, can be achieved with metal catalysts to duplicate characteristics of natural polymers.

Acetylene complexes similar to those of ethylene have been prepared for Pt and several other metals. Cyclopropane was reported to form a compound in which it was believed to behave as an unsaturated ligand, like ethylene. However, it has been shown by infrared studies to involve opening of the cyclopropane ring.* The solid compound formed from H_2PtCl_6 and C_3H_6 is a polymer involving Cl bridges between

$$H_2C \underset{CH_2}{\overset{CH_2}{\diagup \diagdown}} PtCl_2$$

units to give Pt a coordination number of six. The polymer dissolves in aqueous HCl or NaCl solution. The solid adds two molecules of pyridine per Pt to give an octahedral complex with the pyridine molecules in *trans* positions. It is surprising that the cyclopropane ring opens in the complex, since cyclopropane is displaced quantitatively from the polymer or from the pyridine complex by aqueous KCN solution.

Cyclopentadienyl Compounds

Bis(cyclopentadienyl)iron(II), $Fe(C_5H_5)_2$, was first prepared by the reaction of $FeCl_3$ and C_5H_5MgBr,† and independently by the reaction of reduced iron, in the presence of K_2O, with cyclopentane in nitrogen at 300°C.‡ The product, now known as ferrocene, is an orange solid melting at 172.5–174°C with sublimation. Ferrocene is soluble in alcohol, ether, and benzene. It is insoluble in water, 10% NaOH solution, or concentrated HCl. It is easily oxidized to a blue cation, $Fe(C_5H_5)_2^+$. Ferrocene is diamagnetic and the cation obtained by oxidation contains one unpaired electron. Cyclopentadienyl compounds have now been prepared for many of the transition metals in a variety of oxidation states (Table 10.12). In the most general preparation, the anhydrous metal halide is treated with a solution of sodium cyclopentadienide in tetrahydrofuran or a polyether.

TABLE 10.12
Cyclopentadienyl Compounds

No. of Electrons[a]	12	13	14	15	16	17	18		19	20
	$TiCp_2^{2+}$	$TiCp_2^+$	$TiCp_2$			$FeCp_2^+$	$FeCp_2$	$CoCp_2^+$	$CoCp_2$	
	$ZrCp_2^{2+}$	VCp_2^{2+}	VCp_2^+	VCp_2		$RuCp_2^+$	$RuCp_2$	$RhCp_2^+$	$NiCp_2^+$	$NiCp_2$
	$NbCp_2^{3+}$		$MoCp_2^{2+}$		$CrCp_2$		$OsCp_2$	$IrCp_2^+$		$PdCp_2$
	$TaCp_2^{3+}$									

[a] Number of outer electrons of metal (*d* and *s*) plus 10 electrons for the two Cp radicals.

The crystal structure of ferrocene leads to the staggered "sandwich" configuration shown in Figure 10.43. Ruthenocene has the eclipsed configuration in the crystal. In both compounds the rings are probably freely rotating at higher temperatures, since the energy barrier to free rotation is apparently very small. Dipole moments of substituted

* Adams, D. M., J. Chatt, and R. G. Guy, *Proc. Chem. Soc.*, **1960**, 179.
† Kealy, T. J., and P. L. Pauson, *Nature*, **168**, 1039 (1951).
‡ Miller, S. A., J. A. Tebboth, and J. F. Tremaine, *J. Chem. Soc.*, **1952**, 632.

Ferrocene   Ruthenocene

FIGURE 10.43.

acetylferrocenes are approximately those to be expected assuming free rotation of the rings about the symmetry axis.

The bonding in ferrocene has been described by Pauling* in terms of 560 resonance structures! For nickelocene, $Ni(C_5H_5)_2$, a total of 4100 structures were considered!! In these situations the simple pictorial value of the valence bond approach is completely lost. The molecular orbital description is much more appealing. Moffitt arrived at a description of the bonding in ferrocene from combinations of the orbitals of two cyclopentadienyl radicals and an iron atom using arguments based on the symmetry of the orbitals. If two cyclopentadienyl radicals are brought into their final positions on each side of an iron atom, they repel electrons of the iron in the region directed toward the cyclopentadienyl rings. The d_{z^2} and s orbitals of iron can combine to give a lower energy orbital (h_{ag}), in which an electron pair can be concentrated in a ring around the metal between the cyclopentadienyl rings, and an orbital of higher energy (k_{ag}) directed along the z axis. Of these two orbitals, only the one of lower energy is occupied in ferrocene. The unfavorable k_{ag} orbital should be comparable in energy to the $4p$ orbitals of the iron atom.

The iron–carbon bonding is the result of the overlap of the d_{xz} and d_{yz} metal orbitals with the π orbitals of the rings. Combination of the d_{xz} and d_{yz} orbitals gives two cup shaped lobes about z as a symmetry axis. These orbitals overlap with the π ring orbitals which encompass all ten carbon atoms. There is essentially one electron pair bond to each ring, permitting free rotation of the rings. The bonding orbitals are represented in Figure 10.44, and the approximate energy level diagram is shown in Figure 10.45. The b_{eg} orbitals are the bonding orbitals. In ferrocene additional stability is achieved because an electron pair can occupy the h_{ag} orbital, which is lower in energy than the

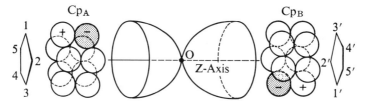

FIGURE 10.44. *Bonding orbitals in ferrocene* [*W. Moffitt*, J. Am. Chem. Soc., *76, 3389 (1954)*].

* Pauling, L., *The Nature of the Chemical Bond* (3rd Ed., Ithaca: Cornell University Press, 1960) pp. 387-390.

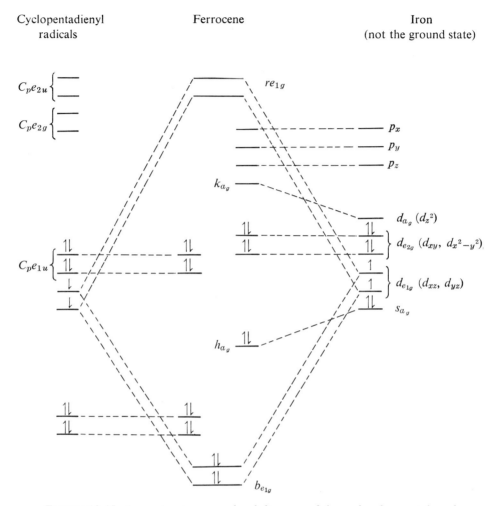

FIGURE 10.45. *Approximate energy level diagram of the molecular, metal, and cyclopentadienyl orbitals in ferrocene (after Moffitt).*

atomic orbitals from which it is derived. Nickelocene has two additional electrons which will occupy (singly) two of the orbitals of the group k_{ag}, p_x, and p_z. These two electrons will be unpaired because these orbitals are of comparable energy. Later papers have modified the Moffitt description, but these changes do not alter the essential features and his representation can be related to the simple pictorial description.

Mixed cyclopentadienyl carbonyl compounds have been obtained for many metals. The reaction of $Co_2(CO)_8$ and C_5H_6 at 25° gives $(C_5H_5)Co(CO)_2$. Carbon monoxide replaces one cyclopentadienyl ring in $V(C_5H_5)_2$ at elevated temperature and under CO pressure to give $(C_5H_5)V(CO)_4$. Although manganese dicyclopentadienide, $Mn(C_5H_5)_2$, is ionic like $Mg(C_5H_5)_2$, and unlike ferrocene, the carbonyl compound, $(C_5H_5)Mn(CO)_3$, presumably involves π bonding to the C_5H_5 ring.

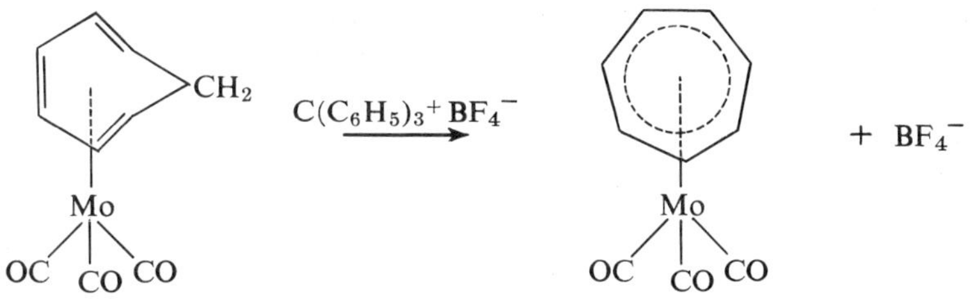

(C_7H_8) Mo $(CO)_3$ $\quad\quad\quad\quad\quad\quad (C_7H_7)$ Mo $(CO)_3{}^+$ BF$_4{}^-$

FIGURE 10.46. *Two six-electron donors.*

Metal Compounds of Benzene and Other Cyclic Systems

Fischer and Hafner* obtained dibenzenechromium, $Cr(C_6H_6)_2$, by reaction of benzene with chromium(III) chloride in the presence of aluminum chloride and powdered aluminum at an elevated temperature to produce $Cr(C_6H_6)_2{}^+$, followed by reduction with sodium dithionite. $Cr(C_6H_6)_2$ is decomposed by air although it is the most stable of the benzene compounds. It is a sandwich compound, as shown by an x-ray structure investigation. The dibenzene compounds so far prepared are given in Table 10.13. Several metal compounds of diphenyl and mesitylene have been prepared also. As in the case of the cyclopentadienyl compounds, a number of mixed carbonyl–benzene compounds such as $(C_6H_6)Cr(CO)_3$ have been obtained.

After cyclopentadienyl and benzene complexes of a variety of metals had been prepared it became of interest to learn just how general the formation of π complexes might be. The mixed hydrocarbon–metal carbonyl compounds have yielded the greatest variety of compounds containing unsaturated hydrocarbons. The most common of these are the "piano stool" compounds, which contain a cyclic hydrocarbon and three CO molecules bonded to the metal. Cycloheptatriene, C_7H_8, gives compounds similar to those of benzene, serving as a 6-electron donor (see Figure 10.46). Six of the carbon atoms are presumably in a plane to give an approximately cyclic π electron system, bypassing the out-of-plane CH_2 group. The cycloheptatriene compound of molyb-

* Fischer, E. O., and W. Hafner, *Z. Naturforsch.,* **10b**, 665 (1955); *Z. Anorg. Allgem. Chem.,* **286**, 146 (1956).

TABLE 10.13
Metal Benzene Compounds

No. of Electrons[a]	16	17		18		20
	VBz$_2{}^+$	VBz$_2$		FeBz$_2{}^{2+}$	CoBz$_2{}^{3+}$	CoBz$_2{}^+$
		CrBz$_2{}^+$	CrBz$_2$	RuBz$_2{}^{2+}$	RhBz$_2{}^{3+}$	
		MoBz$_2{}^{2+}$	MoBz$_2$			
			ReBz$_2$			

[a] Number of outer electrons of metal plus 12 electrons for the two benzene rings.

denum, $[Mo(C_7H_8)(CO)_3]$, reacts with triphenylmethyl fluoroborate to give a cationic complex, $[Mo(C_7H_7)(CO)_3]^+$, in which the seven protons are found to be equivalent by nuclear magnetic resonance studies. Azulene, $C_{10}H_8$, is a planar molecule consisting of fused 5- and 7-membered rings containing a total of 10 π electrons. The iron compound, $[C_{10}H_8Fe_2(CO)_5]$, presumably has an $Fe(CO)_2$ group above the 7-membered ring and an $Fe(CO)_3$ group below the 5-membered ring.

The cycloheptatriene compounds demonstrate that benzene is not the only 6-electron π donor. Likewise the cyclopentadienyl radical is not the only 5-electron π donor, the cyclohexadienyl radical can also serve as a 5-electron donor in the compound $[Mn(C_6H_7)(CO)_3]$. The cationic complex $[Mo(C_7H_7)(CO)_3]^+$ can be considered to be a molybdenum(0) derivative of the tropylium cation, $C_7H_7^+$, or a molybdenum(I) derivative of the cycloheptatrienyl radical.

The series of donors can be extended to include those which contribute 1–7 electrons (see Table 10.14). The alkyl groups can be considered as 1-electron donors. Most common ligands are 2-electron donors, but in this series monoolefins, such as ethylene, serve as better examples. The allyl group has been shown to be symmetrically bonded

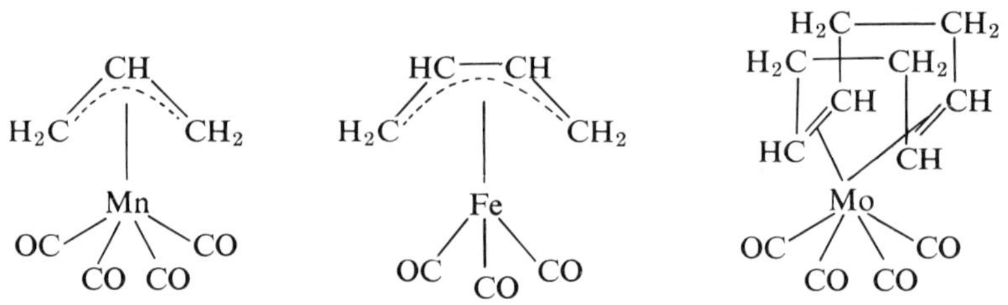

FIGURE 10.47. *Three- and four-electron donors.*

in some compounds such as $[Mn(CH_2CHCH_2)(CO)_4]$ (see Figure 10.47). The allyl group can be considered to be a 3-electron donor. The most common 3-electron donor is NO. Butadiene serves as a 4-electron donor involving delocalized bonding. Cyclooctadiene is another 4-electron donor, but it functions as a diolefin without delocalization in the hydrocarbon ring. Cyclobutadiene is not known, but evidence has been obtained for the formation of metal derivatives of cyclobutadiene.

TABLE 10.14

Number of Electrons Donated	Ligands	Complexes
1	H, CH_3	$HCo(CO)_4$, $H_2Fe(CO)_4$, $CH_3Mn(CO)_5$
2	CO, CN^-, C_2H_4	$HCo(CO)_3C_2H_4$, $Ni(CO)_4$, $Cr(CO)_6$
3	NO, CH_2CHCH_2	$(C_5H_5)Ni(NO)$, $(C_5H_5)Cr(CO)_2(NO)$, $(CH_2CHCH_2)Mn(CO)_4$
4	C_4H_6, C_8H_{12}	$(C_4H_6)Fe(CO)_3$, $(C_8H_{12})Mo(CO)_4$
5	C_5H_5, C_6H_7	$(C_5H_5)_2Fe$, $(C_5H_5)Mn(CO)_3$, $(C_6H_7)Mn(CO)_3$
6	C_6H_6, C_7H_8	$(C_6H_6)_2Cr$, $(C_6H_6)Cr(CO)_3$, $(C_7H_8)Cr(CO)_3$
7	C_7H_7	$(C_7H_7)Mo(CO)_3^+$

The Effective Atomic Number Principle has been very successful in predicting new π complexes. Not all of the known π compounds obey the EAN rule; even ferrocene (EAN = 36) can be oxidized to the 1+ cation (EAN = 35). However, the most stable

Charge

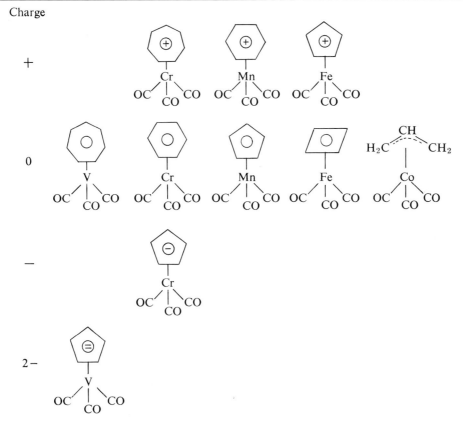

FIGURE 10.48. *Tricarbonyl compounds (after P. L. Pauson,*
The University of Strathclyde, Glasgow).

compounds obey this rule. Manganese, which needs 11 electrons to attain the EAN of krypton, gives the compounds $CH_3Mn(CO)_5$, $(CH_2CHCH_2)Mn(CO)_4$, and (C_5H_5)-$Mn(CO)_3$. Iron, which needs 10 electrons, gives the compounds $(C_4H_6)Fe(CO)_3$, $(C_5H_5)_2Fe$, $(C_6H_6)_2Fe^{2+}$, and $(C_7H_8)Fe(CO)_2$. Some examples of compounds containing various donors are given in Table 10.14. Figure 10.48 summarizes the compounds of the tricarbonyl type.

The investigation of π complexes has progressed at a remarkable pace in the last few years. The great interest in this area continues and many new developments can be anticipated.

REFERENCES

Bailar, J. C., Jr., ed., *The Chemistry of Coordination Compounds* (New York: Reinhold Publishing Corporation, 1956).
Lewis, L., and R. G. Wilkins, eds., *Modern Coordination Chemistry* (New York: Interscience Publishers, Inc., 1960).

Orgel, L. E., *An Introduction to Transition-Metal Chemistry, Ligand-Field Theory* (London: Methuen and Company, Ltd., 1960).

Ballhausen, C. J., *Introduction to Ligand Field Theory* (New York: McGraw-Hill Book Company, Inc., 1962).

Jørgensen, C. K., *Absorption Spectra and Chemical Bonding in Complexes* (London: Pergamon Press, 1961).

Basolo, F., and R. G. Pearson, *Mechanisms of Inorganic Reactions* (New York: John Wiley and Sons, Inc., 1958).

Martell, A. E., and M. Calvin, *Chemistry of the Metal Chelate Compounds* (New York: Prentice-Hall, Inc., 1952).

Gray, H. B., "Molecular Orbital Theory for Transition Metal Complexes," *J. Chem. Educ.,* **41,** 2 (1964).

Sutton, L. E., "Some Recent Developments in the Theory of Bonding in Complex Compounds," *J. Chem. Educ.,* **37,** 498 (1960).

Liehr, A. D., "Molecular Orbital, Valence Bond, and Ligand Field," *J. Chem. Educ.,* **39,** 135 (1962).

Manch, W., and W. C. Fernelius, "The Structure and Spectra of Nickel(II) and Copper(II) Complexes," *J. Chem. Educ.,* **38,** 192 (1961).

Hoard, J. L., with J. V. Silverton and G. L. Glen, *Inorg. Chem.,* **2,** 235, 243, 250 (1963). Excellent coverage of compounds with coordination number eight.

Woldbye, F., "Technique of Optical Rotatory Dispersion and Circular Dichroism," in *Technique of Inorganic Chemistry,* H. Jonassen and A. Weissberger, Eds. (New York: Interscience Publishers, Inc., 1965). A comprehensive review of work with optically active coordination compounds.

Wilkinson, G., and F. A. Cotton, "Cyclopentadienyl and Arene Metal Compounds," in *Progress in Inorganic Chemistry,* Vol. I, F. A. Cotton, ed. (New York: Interscience Publishers, Inc., 1959).

Duhn, T. M., D. S. McClure, and R. G. Pearson, *Some Aspects of Crystal Field Theory* (New York: Harper and Row, Publishers, 1965).

Problems

1. Name the following compounds according to the modified IUPAC rules (see Appendix B):

K_2FeO_4

$[Cr(NH_3)_6]Cl_3$

$[Cr(NH_3)_4Cl_2]Cl$ $Fe(C_5H_5)_2$

$K[PtCl_3(C_2H_4)]$ $(CO)_5Mn-Mn(CO)_5$

$K_3[Al(C_2O_4)_3]$

$K_2[Co(N_3)_4]$ $[(NH_3)_4\,Co \overset{\displaystyle OH}{\underset{\displaystyle NH_2}{\diagup\diagdown}} Co(en)_2]Cl_4$

$K[Co(EDTA)]$

$[Cr(NH_3)_2(H_2O)_3(OH)](NO_3)_2$

2. Sketch all of the possible geometrical isomers for the following complexes and indicate which of these would exhibit optical activity.

$[Co(en)(NH_3)_2BrCl]^+$

$[Co(NH_2CH_2CO_2)_2NH_3Cl]^+$

$[Pt(NH_3)BrCl(NO_2)]^-$

[Co(trien)Cl₂]⁺ (consider the different ways of linking trien to Co).

$$[(gly)_2 Co \overset{OH}{\underset{OH}{\diamond}} Co(gly)_2]$$

3. Draw *all* possible isomers for Ma₂bcd assuming the complex forms a square pyramid.

4. How might one distinguish between the following isomers?
  (*a*) [Co(NH₃)₅Br]SO₄ and [Co(NH₃)₅SO₄]Br
  (*b*) [Co(NH₃)₃(NO₂)₃] and [Co(NH₃)₆] [Co(NO₂)₆]
  (*c*) *cis-* and *trans-* [CoCl₂ en₂]Cl
  (*d*) *cis-* and *trans-* NH₄ [Co(NO₂)₄(NH₃)₂]
  (*e*) *cis-* and *trans-* [Pt(gly)₂]

5. Give the formula of the most stable compound of the type M(Ol)(CO)ₓ to be expected for each of the following metals with each of the olefins listed.

Metals	Ligands
Cr, Mn, and Fe	CH₂CHCH₂, C₅H₅, C₆H₆, and C₇H₇

6. Discuss briefly the factors working *for* and *against* the maximum spin state of *d* electrons in transition metal complexes.

7. For a square planar complex with the ligands lying along the *x* and *y* axes, indicate all of the metal orbitals which may participate in σ bonds. Sketch one ligand combination orbital which could enter into a σ_g molecular orbital and one which could enter into a σ_u molecular orbital. Repeat the above, this time for π bonds.

8. The molecular orbitals formed by the six p π orbitals in benzene may be depicted as shown below (top half only shown, the sign of ψ reverses on going through the plane of the sheet of paper).

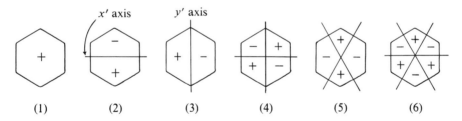

(1)	(2)	(3)	(4)	(5)	(6)

Consider a molecule of bis(benzene)chromium as having a chromium atom at the origin of a set of Cartesian axes with a benzene ring on each side, centered on, and perpendicular to the *z* axis. (*a*) Indicate below each of the above figures the metal orbital(s) which would combine with the group orbitals of the ligands and the type of molecular orbital (σ_g, δ_u, etc.) that would be formed. Draw an energy level diagram showing ligand orbitals, metal orbitals, and molecular orbitals with appropriate labeling.

9. Using published ligand field energy level diagrams, predict which trivalent rare earth metals should give particularly stable octahedral complexes with (*a*) high spin and (*b*) low spin. Which of these spin states are expected for the rare earths? Why? Are tetrahedral or octahedral complexes more likely? Are coordination numbers higher than 6 likely? Reference: Friedman, II. G., Jr., G. R. Choppin, and D. G. Feuerbacher, *J. Chem. Educ.*, **41**, 354 (1964).

CHAPTER XI

Coordination Compounds. II.
Stability and Reaction Mechanisms

Factors That Influence the Stability of Coordination Compounds

The coordination process can be regarded as an acid–base reaction. The factors affecting acidity and basicity have already been discussed (Chapter VI). In general, an increase in basicity of the ligand and/or an increase in the acidity of the metal enhances the stability of the complexes formed. The general properties of metals and ligands, which contribute to the stability of the complexes formed, are most clearly identified in the ligand field approach (see p. 348). It is now appropriate to consider some additional factors, which contribute to stability, and some specific effects that do not conform to the general pattern.

When one speaks of an organic compound such as ethanol as being stable, this might refer to the thermodynamic stability with respect to the elements carbon, hydrogen, and oxygen, or it might refer to the kinetic stability – the fact that ethanol can be handled under ordinary circumstances without decomposition. Ethanol is kinetically stable in air even though the products of the reaction with O_2, (CO_2 and H_2O) are more stable thermodynamically. The stability of a metal complex, MX_m^{n+}, is usually expressed in terms of the formation constant, β_m, for the reaction:

$$M^{n+} + mX = MX_m^{n+} \qquad \beta_m = \frac{[MX_m^{n+}]}{[M^{n+}][X]^m}. \qquad (11.1)$$

The β_m expresses the thermodynamic stability since it is an equilibrium constant from which one can calculate a free energy change for the formation of the complex. It is often worthwhile to consider the constants for each step in the formation of the complex:

$$M^{n+} + X = MX^{n+} \qquad K_1 = \frac{[MX^{n+}]}{[M^{n+}][X]} \qquad (11.2)$$

$$MX^{n+} + X = MX_2^{n+} \qquad K_2 = \frac{[MX_2^{n+}]}{[MX^{n+}][X]} \qquad (11.3)$$

$$MX_{m-1}^{n+} + X = MX_m^{n+} \qquad K_m = \frac{[MX_m^{n+}]}{[MX_{m-1}^{n+}][X]} \qquad (11.4)$$

$$\beta_2 = K_1 K_2$$

$$\beta_m = K_1 K_2 \cdots K_m \tag{11.5}$$

Most ligands are bases, e.g., $NH_2C_2H_4NH_2$, or anions of weak acids, e.g., $C_2O_4^{2-}$. For consistency, the basicity of the ligand is expressed in terms of the pK ($-\log K$) of the acid dissociation constant for its conjugate acid. The symbols HL, HL^+, H_2L, etc., are used to indicate the species to which the pK refers:

$$H_2C_2O_4 = H^+ + HC_2O_4^- \quad K(H_2L) = \frac{[H^+][HC_2O_4^-]}{[H_2C_2O_4]} \quad pK(H_2L) = -\log K(H_2L) \tag{11.6}$$

$$HC_2O_4^- = H^+ + C_2O_4^{2-} \quad K(HL^-) = \frac{[H^+][C_2O_4^{2-}]}{[HC_2O_4^-]}$$

$$^+NH_3C_2H_4NH_3^+ = H^+ + NH_2C_2H_4NH_3^+ \quad K(H_2L^{2+}) = \frac{[H^+][NH_2C_2H_4NH_3^+]}{[NH_3C_2H_4NH_3^{2+}]}$$

$$NH_2C_2H_4NH_3^+ = H^+ + NH_2C_2H_4NH_2 \quad K(HL^+) = \frac{[H^+][NH_2C_2H_4NH_2]}{[NH_2C_2H_4NH_3^+]}$$

The formation constants are evaluated by the usual methods for determining equilibrium constants. These methods include: potentiometric titrations, spectrophotometric methods, polarography, electrode potential measurements, solubility measurements, ion exchange procedures, etc.

Statistical Factor

Even if there were no change in the ΔH^0 of reaction for the successive stepwise addition of ligands, the change of symmetry of the complex would bring about a change in ΔS^0, and since $\Delta F^0 = \Delta H^0 - T\Delta S^0$, the free energy change would differ. This would, of course, cause K_n to differ from K_{n+1}. The equation below shows this variation of K_n and K_{n+1}, which is called the statistical factor:[*]

$$\frac{K_n}{K_{n+1}} = \frac{(N - n + 1)(n + 1)}{(N - n)n} \quad \text{where } N = \text{C.N.} \tag{11.7}$$

The above equation assumes all available points to be equivalent. More precisely, the relationship is found in terms of the symmetry of $ML_n(H_2O)_{m-n}$ and $ML_{n+1}(H_2O)_{m-n-1}$.[†]

Effect of Metal Ion

NATURAL ORDER OF STABILITY

The stabilities of the complexes formed by various metals follow some regular trends, such as those involving size and charge effects. Although there are pronounced differences among metals in the tendencies to form complexes with various ligand atoms (p. 398), there are some helpful trends within groups of similar metals. For a variety of

[*] Bjerrum, J., *Metal Ammine Formation in Aqueous Solution* (Copenhagen: P. Haase and Son, 1941).
[†] See S. W. Benson, *J. Am. Chem. Soc.*, **80**, 5151 (1958) for a more complete discussion of statistical factors.

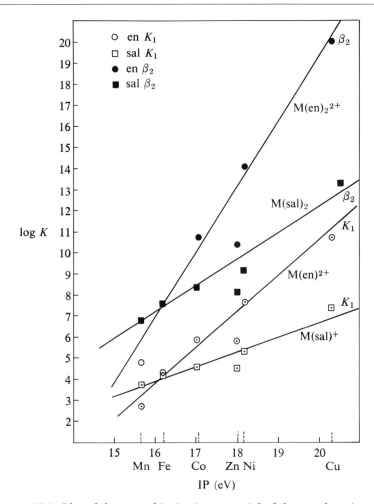

FIGURE 11.1. *Plot of the second ionization potential of the metal against the formation constants (as log K) of some complexes.*

ligands, the divalent metals in the first transition series show an increase in formation constants from Mn^{2+} through Cu^{2+} followed by a drop at Zn^{2+}. The order $Mn^{2+} < Fe^{2+} < Co^{2+} < Ni^{2+} < Cu^{2+} > Zn^{2+}$ is referred to as the *natural order* of stability.* Since the major contribution to the bond energy is the simple electrostatic interaction, one should examine the size and charge effects. The charges are the same, but the increase in atomic number through the series results in a slight increase in effective nuclear charge. The radii decrease slightly through the transition series with a very small increase at Zn^{2+}. Except for the decrease at Zn^{2+}, the *natural order* is not surprising, but the actual differences in stability are much greater than would be expected on this simple basis. Prior to the resurgence of crystal field theory, attempts were made to correlate the stabilities with ionization potentials (second IP or the sum of the first and second IP)

* Mellor, D. P., and L. E. Maley, *Nature,* **159**, 370 (1947); M. Calvin and N. C. Melchior, *J. Am. Chem. Soc.,* **70**, 3270 (1948); H. Irving and R. J. P. Williams, *Nature,* **162**, 146 (1948); *J. Chem. Soc.,* **1953**, 3494.

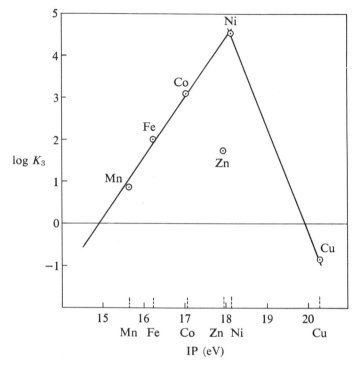

FIGURE 11.2. *Plot of the second ionization potential of the metal against the formation constants (as log K_3) of complexes of the type* M(en)$_3^{2+}$.

and electronegativities. Each of these properties might be expected to be related to the tendency toward complex formation since they are measures of the attraction for electrons. The fact that such correlations exist implies that there is a covalent contribution involved in complex formation. The covalent contribution is not incompatible with the crystal (or ligand) field treatment, but it is handled purely in terms of the effect of increasing the splitting of the energy levels.

The correlation between the second ionization potential and the log K values* for the ethylenediamine and salicylaldehyde complexes of the metals Mn^{2+}–Zn^{2+} is fairly good as shown in Figure 11.1. The greatest deviation from a straight line plot is shown by zinc in each case. A variety of ligands follows the same trend for M(AA) and M(AA)$_2$ high-spin complexes. A plot of log K_3 *vs.* the second ionization potential (Figure 11.2) shows a very regular pattern from Mn–Ni, but Cu and Zn show large deviations. The negative value of log K_3 for [Cu(en)$_3$]$^{2+}$ can be attributed to the greater stability of a planar complex compared to a regular octahedral arrangement for Cu(II). The low value of log K_3 for [Zn(en)$_3$]$^{2+}$ suggests a different reaction for the formation of the tris complex of Zn(II) as compared to those of Mn, Fe, Co, and Ni. The [M(en)$_2$]$^{2+}$ complexes of the latter metals are probably octahedral with two water molecules of coordination. [Zn(en)$_2$]$^{2+}$ might be a tetrahedral complex even in aqueous solution. The conversion

---

* Values of log K are a measure of ΔF for complex formation. Since the entropy changes in a series of similar complexes might be expected to be comparable, the log K values can be used as roughly proportional to the ΔH values for the formation of such a series of similar complexes.

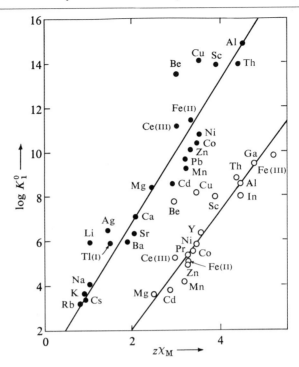

FIGURE 11.3. *Log* $K_1(30°C)$ *as a function of* $z\chi_M$ *for dibenzoylmethanato (closed circles) and acetylacetonato (open circles) complexes* [*from F. J. C. Rossotti, Chapter I in* Modern Co-ordination Chemistry, *edited by J. Lewis and R. G. Wilkins (New York: Interscience Publishers, Inc., 1960) p. 43*].

from a tetrahedral complex to an octahedral complex with increased ligand–ligand repulsion could account for the low value of log K_3.

The ionization potential for a metal from another transition series does not place that metal correctly in the Mn^{2+}–Zn^{2+} series (see problem 11.2). More success has been achieved in extending the series by using electronegativities instead of ionization potentials. The log K_1 values of a variety of dibenzoylmethanato and acetylacetonato complexes of an extensive series of metal ions, varying in charge from 1+ to 4+, are plotted in Figure 11.3 against the product of the ionic charge, Z, and the Allred–Rochow electronegativities.* The data are from Fernelius and co-workers. This relationship also breaks down for the six-coordinate complexes, such as $M(acac)_3$, but many of these are low-spin complexes.

The formation of a complex in aqueous solution is a displacement reaction which may be represented as

$$[M(H_2O)_6]^{n+}(aq) + 6L(aq) \rightleftharpoons [ML_6]^{n+}(aq) + 6H_2O(l) \qquad \Delta H_c \qquad (11.8)$$

for a six-coordinate complex formed by a neutral ligand. This reaction can be broken down into more fundamental thermochemical steps as in a Born–Haber cycle. George and McClure have considered it in terms of the reactions

$$M^{n+}(g) + 6H_2O(l) \longrightarrow [M(H_2O)_6]^{n+}(aq) \qquad \Delta H_H \qquad (11.9)$$

* Allred, A. L., and E. G. Rochow, *J. Inorg. Nucl. Chem.*, **5**, 264 (1958).

and

$$M^{n+}(g) + 6L(aq) \longrightarrow [ML_6]^{n+}(aq) \qquad \Delta H_L \qquad (11.10)$$

such that $\Delta H_L = \Delta H_c + \Delta H_H$ or $\Delta H_c = \Delta H_L - \Delta H_H$. Hence, the heat of formation of the complex in solution (ΔH_c) is the difference between two large numbers (ΔH_L and ΔH_H). Since the heats of hydration of $[M(H_2O)_6]^{n+}$ and $[ML_6]^{n+}$ should be comparable (for the same charge type) and the heats of hydration of L and of H_2O should be comparable, ΔH_c for aqueous solution should not be greatly different from the heat of formation in the gaseous state from $[M(H_2O)]^{n+}(g) + 6L(g)$.

The thermodynamic quantities ΔH_H and ΔH_L for the formation of the six coordinate complexes of the metals in the series Mn^{2+}–Zn^{2+} do not vary in the same way as the ionization potentials, as seen in Figure 11.4. These values (ΔH_H and ΔH_L) for six-coordinate complexes include all stereochemical effects, such as those of Cu(II), resulting in fairly flat maxima at Ni and Cu (see also Figure 11.6).

CRYSTAL FIELD STABILIZATION ENERGY

The variation in the hydration energies of the transition metal ions and the heat of formation of their complexes can be related to the crystal field stabilization energy (CFSE) of the complexes. The CFSE is zero for d^0, d^5, and d^{10} ions, but the hydration energies would be expected to increase from Ca^{2+} to Mn^{2+} to Zn^{2+} as the ionic radii decrease. The hydration energies for the divalent and trivalent metal ions of the first transition series are shown in Figure 11.5. When the CFSE values are subtracted from the observed hydration energies, the corrected values fall almost on the lines through

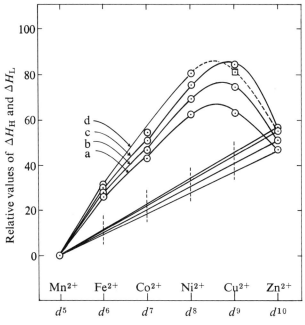

FIGURE 11.4. *The values of* ΔH_H *(a) and of* ΔH_L *for the mono-, bis-, and tris-(ethylenediamine) complexes (b, c, and d, respectively) of* Fe^{2+}, Co^{2+}, Ni^{2+}, Cu^{2+}, *and* Zn^{2+} *relative to the corresponding values for* Mn^{2+} *[from P. George and D. S. McClure, in* Progress in Inorganic Chemistry, *Vol. I, edited by F. A. Cotton (New York: Interscience Publishers, Inc., 1959), p. 46].*

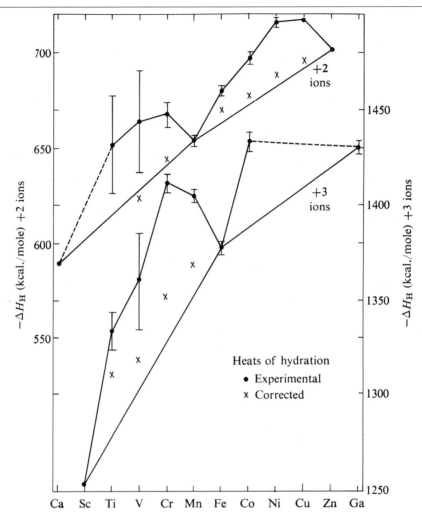

FIGURE 11.5. *The hydration energies of the divalent and trivalent ions of the first transition series. The uncorrected values are connected by dotted lines, the corrected values are connected by solid lines. (See reference for Figure 11.4, p. 418.)*

the points for the ions with no CFSE. Similarly, the vertical distance between a particular point and the straight line joining the values of the heats of formation of the complexes in solution from the gaseous metal ion (ΔH_L) for Mn^{2+} and Zn^{2+} in Figure 11.6 would be expected to be the CFSE for the particular complex. The CFSE obtained from optical spectra are subtracted from the ΔH_L values in Figure 11.6 to demonstrate that the deviation from the straight line is due primarily to CFSE.

The formation constants are given in Table 11.1 for some divalent metal complexes of ethylenediaminetetraacetate ion (EDTA).* For EDTA the formation constants

* The Co(III) complex, Rb[Co(EDTA)], has been shown by x-ray crystallography to be sexadentate. The two oxygens in the plane of the nitrogens, because of the constraint of the three chelate rings, are at a greater distance than the other two. There is no assurance that the EDTA coordinates in the same way with the divalent metal ions. In fact, the Fe(II) and Mn(II) complexes have been shown to be 7-coordinate in the solid (p. 378). The CFSE discussed here is for regular octahedral complexes.

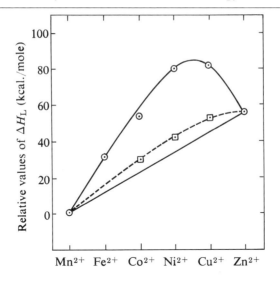

FIGURE 11.6. *A plot of the ΔH_L values (relative to Mn^{2+}) of the tris (ethylenediamine) complexes of the metals in the series Mn^{2+}–Zn^{2+}. The CFSE obtained from optical spectra for Co^{2+}, Ni^{2+}, and Cu^{2+} are subtracted to give the corrected curve (dotted line). (See reference for Figure 11.4, p. 456.)*

increase linearly from Ca^{2+} to Mn^{2+} to Zn^{2+}. The interpolated values for the other metal ions are compared to the experimental values. The differences are attributed to the CFSE. The difference in the CFSE of $[Ni(EDTA)]^{2-}$ and $[Ni(H_2O)_6]^{2+}$ from spectra (5.5 kcal/mole) is in reasonable agreement with the value from Table 11.1, $2.3RT \times 3.4 = 4.6$ kcal/mole. The crystal field stabilization of the en complexes (Figure 11.4) is greater than that of the EDTA complexes in accordance with the greater crystal field strength of en. For regular octahedral complexes, the crystal field theory predicts that Ni^{2+} complexes would be more stable than those of Cu^{2+}. The strong tetragonal field in the Cu^{2+} complexes is responsible for the greater tendency for Cu^{2+} to add one or two bidentate ligands, and yet a much smaller tendency to add a third ligand.

The "natural order" applies to high-spin (or low crystal field) complexes. The order is quite different for low-spin complexes and it is not related directly to the ionization

TABLE 11.1[a]

	M^{2+}	EDTA $\log K_1$	$\log K_1$ Interpolated	Stabilization ($\log K$ units)
d^0	Ca	10.6	10.6	0
d^3	V	12.7	12.3	0.4
d^5	Mn	13.4	13.4	0
d^6	Fe	14.2	14.0	0.2
d^7	Co	16.1	14.5	1.6
d^8	Ni	18.5	15.1	3.4
d^9	Cu	18.4	15.6	2.4
d^{10}	Zn	16.2	16.2	0

[a] Bjerrum, J., and C. K. Jørgensen, *Rec. Trav. Chim.*, **75**, 658 (1956).

potential or the electronegativity. For divalent metals, the maximum stability of low-spin complexes is expected for d^6 ions (maximum CFSE). The most stable 1,10-phenanthroline complex of the divalent metals of the first transition series is $[Fe(phen)_3]^{2+}$, a diamagnetic d^6 ion.

Generally, the stability of complexes decreases with increasing atomic number for the electropositive metals, e.g., Group IIA, and increases with increasing atomic number for the more noble metals, following the general trend for the ionization potentials and also the trend expected from the ligand field theory. The ionic charge density is the determining factor for electropositive metal ions (d^0), but the magnitude of the crystal field splitting must be considered for d^1–d^9 ions, and the polarizabilities of the cations must be considered for d^{10} ions.

Effect of Ligand Atom

CLASSIFICATION OF METAL ACCEPTOR PROPERTIES

It has been mentioned that for the more electropositive metals the order of stability of the halide complexes is $F > Cl > Br > I$, but that the reverse order is observed for highly polarizing (and also polarizable) metal ions such as Hg^{2+}. The most electropositive metals show a great preference for forming complexes with ligands such as F^- or oxygen-containing ligands. As the electropositive character of the metals decreases, the nitrogen complexes increase in stability with respect to those of oxygen. Still more electronegative (or more noble) metals show a preference for S and P over O and N, respectively. The noble metals show the greatest tendency to form stable olefin complexes.

Metals have been classified according to their acceptor properties as shown in Table 11.2. The metals of class (a) show affinities for ligands which are roughly proportional to the basicities of the ligands. The class (b) acceptors are the ones which form stable olefin complexes (see p. 379). The border regions are not well defined in all cases and,

TABLE 11.2

Classification of Metals According to Acceptor Properties[a]

| | | | Class (a) | | Class (b) | | Border Region |

[a] Ahrland, S., J. Chatt, and N. R. Davies, *Quart. Rev.*, **12**, 265 (1958).
[b] Lanthanides.
[c] Actinides.

of course, the classification depends on the oxidation state of the metal ion. Copper(I) is a class (b) acceptor, but copper(II) is in the border region. Class (a) acceptors form the most stable complexes with the ligand atom in the second period (N, O, or F), while class (b) acceptors form their most stable complexes with ligand atoms from the third or a later period. Thus, trimethyl gallium shows the following tendencies toward complex formation involving alkyls of the ligand atoms from Groups V and VI: N > P > As > Sb and O > S < Se > Te. On the other hand, for platinum(II) the order is apparently N ≪ P > As > Sb and O ⋘ S ≫ Se < Te. The order of stability of halide complexes has already been discussed (p. 347).

BASICITY AND STRUCTURE OF THE LIGAND

The increase in stability of complexes with increasing basicity of ligands is illustrated in Figure 11.7. The $\log \beta_2$ ($\log K_1 K_2$) values for Ag^+ are plotted as a function of the $pK(HL^+)$ values for a variety of primary and heterocyclic amines. Most metals other than silver do not tend to form linear bonds and their complexes of chelate groups, e.g., $NH_2C_2H_4NH_2$, are much more stable than those of unidentate groups, e.g., NH_3. This

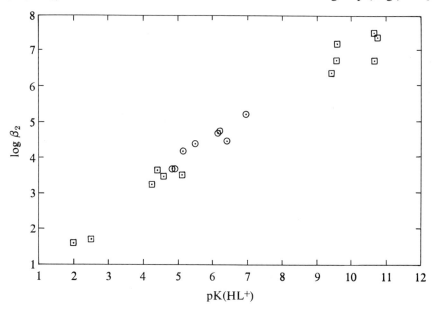

FIGURE 11.7. *Plot of $\log \beta_2$ of silver complexes vs. pK of the protonated ligand.*

	pK of HL+	log β_2		pK of HL+	log β_2
p-nitroaniline	2.0	1.6	ethylamine	10.81	7.30
m-nitroaniline	2.5	1.7	n-butylamine	10.71	7.48
β-naphthylamine	4.28	3.23	quinoline	4.98	3.67
o-toluidine	4.43	3.61	3-methoxypyridine	4.91	3.67
aniline	4.62	3.47	pyridine	5.21	4.16
p-toluidine	5.12	3.48	β-picoline	5.52	4.35
2-methoxyethylamine	9.45	6.34	4-methoxypyridine	6.47	4.44
benzylamine	9.62	7.14	α-picoline	6.20	4.68
ethanolamine	9.60	6.68	γ-picoline	6.26	4.70
methylamine	10.72	6.68	2,4-lutidine	6.99	5.18

enhanced stability is referred to as the *chelate effect*. The greater the number of chelate rings, the greater the stability of the complex. The log of the formation constant for the addition of four ammonia molecules to Cu^{2+} is 11.9, for the addition of two en molecules it is 20.0, and for triethylenetetraamine (4 coordinated nitrogen atoms with 3 chelate rings) it is 20.4.

The chelate rings of greatest stability are generally five-membered rings because one of the bond angles in the ring is 90° for planar or octahedral complexes.

Six-membered rings are most often encountered in organic compounds and they are more stable than 5-membered rings in complexes of heterocyclic ligands or ligands involving conjugation in the chelate ring. Rings of more than six members are rare and only a few ligands, e.g., CO_3^{2-}, give four-membered rings.

The chelate effect is predominately an entropy effect for nontransition metal ions, but there may be an enthalpy effect for transition metal ions* where crystal field stabilization effects are important. After one end of an ethylenediamine molecule has attached to a metal ion, the "effective concentration" of the other $-NH_2$ group is increased because its motion is restricted to a small volume in the vicinity of the metal ion. Each ethylenediamine molecule replaces two water molecules, increasing the total number of particles in the system and hence the entropy is increased.

Adamson† has suggested that the chelate effect is more apparent than real. The effect practically disappears if one changes the standard states for the solute from the hypothetical one molal state to the hypothetical mole fraction unity state. Nevertheless, as concentrations and stability data are usually handled, the effect is important and useful.

Most alkaline earth metal complexes are not very stable. However, ethylenediaminetetraacetate ion (EDTA) forms quite stable complexes with metals such as Ca^{2+}. The EDTA can wrap around a metal ion displacing as many as six coordinated water molecules. These complexes of the alkaline earth metal ions form primarily because of entropy effects as a consequence of the increase in the number of particles in the system and the neutralization of charge on M^{2+} and $EDTA^{4-}$. Neutralization of charge brings about a very favorable entropy change in a polar solvent because it removes a large part of the ordering of the solvent molecules caused by the ions.

FORCED CONFIGURATIONS

A ligand such as porphyrin or phthalocyanine (see pp. 337, 355), which has a completely fused planar ring system, forms extraordinarily stable complexes with metal ions that tend to give planar complexes, e.g., Cu^{2+}. These ligands impose planar configurations on metal ions that have no tendency to form planar complexes with unidentate ligands, e.g., Be^{2+} and Zn^{2+}.

The ligands tris(2-aminoethyl)amine, $N(CH_2CH_2NH_2)_3$, tren, and triethylenetetraamine, $(NH_2C_2H_4NHCH_2-)_2$, trien, are both quadridentate, but only trien can assume a planar or nearly planar configuration. From the pK values of the ligands, tren would be expected to form more stable complexes as, indeed, is the case for Zn^{2+}, which can form tetrahedral complexes (Table 11.3). The Ni^{2+} complex of tren is only slightly more stable than that of trien, and Cu^{2+}, which tends to form planar complexes or octahedral complexes with two long bonds, gives a slightly more stable complex with trien

* Spike, C. G., and R. W. Parry, *J. Am. Chem. Soc.,* **75**, 2726, 3770 (1953).
† Adamson, A. W., *J. Am. Chem. Soc.,* **76**, 1578 (1954).

in spite of its lower basicity. Although it has sometimes been assumed that tren would give tetrahedral complexes even with Pt(II), the ligand cannot span the tetrahedral positions around a large cation. For large cations it is more likely to fill four positions in an octahedral complex, or to form polymeric complexes by serving as a bridging ligand.

TABLE 11.3

	Tren	*Trien*
Ni^{2+} ($\log K_1$)	14.8	14.0
Cu^{2+} ($\log K_1$)	19.1	20.4
Zn^{2+} ($\log K_1$)	14.65	12.1
pK (HL^+)	10.29	9.92

Other Steric Effects

Bulky groups substituted on the ligand atom, e.g., *N*-alkylethylenediamines, or adjacent to the ligand atom, e.g., 8-hydroxyquinoline with substituents in the 2 position, can result in complexes of lower stability, or even prevent complex formation. Thus, substitution of methyl or phenyl groups in 8-hydroxyquinoline has little effect on the stability of the complexes formed except when the substitution is in the 2 position, which prevents chelation with aluminum. The effect of the substituent in the 2 position is very important for the small Al^{3+} ion, and less important for even slightly larger ions, so that chelation still occurs for Cr^{3+}, Fe^{3+}, Ga^{3+}, Cu^{2+}, and Zn^{2+}. Such steric considerations can be valuable in obtaining specific or selective organic analytical reagents.

Substitution in the 6 and 6′ positions of 2,2′-bipyridine lowers the stability of the complexes formed because the substituents crowd the metal ion. Substitution in the 5,5′ or 4,4′ positions affects the stability of the complexes formed only slightly, and in the way expected from the effect on basicity. Substitution in both the 3 and 3′ positions causes steric hindrance because the two substituents prevent the pyridine rings from lying in the same plane for favorable π orbital overlap among the two pyridine rings and the chelate ring.

2,2′-bipyridine (dipyridyl)

The stability of the 2,2′-bipyridine and 1,10-phenanthroline complexes such as those of Fe^{2+} are greatly enhanced by such π bonding.

Rates and Mechanisms of Substitution Reactions

The substitution of one ligand for another in a coordination compound often takes place in a time interval comparable to the time required to mix the reactants. Complexes that undergo such rapid substitution reactions are classified as *labile* complexes. Compounds that undergo slow substitution reactions (half-life > 1 min) are called *inert* complexes. Since labile complexes rapidly reach equilibrium with their environment, the properties of their solutions are independent of the previous history of the solution, whereas the same is not true for inert complexes. The classical method of establishing the configuration of a complex by isolating the expected number of isomers may be used with inert complexes, but not with labile complexes due to rapid changes in these complexes in solution.

Taube's Classification

Taube,* in an extensive review of the data then available, pointed out a striking correlation between the electronic configuration and rates of reaction of *inner orbital* (Valence Bond terminology, see p. 340) octahedral complexes. Inner orbital complexes having one or more remaining empty inner *d* orbitals are labile, those with no empty inner *d* orbitals are inert—even though the *d* orbitals may be singly occupied (see Table 11.4). The most striking feature of Table 11.4 is the sharp distinction between inert and labile complexes of the same metal in different oxidation states. As we have noted previously (p. 346), the stability of a complex generally increases with

TABLE 11.4
Six-Coordinate "Inner Orbital" Complexes

Electronic Configuration			Central Metal Ions
Valence Bond	*Molecular Orbital*		
	t_{2g}	$e_g{}^*$	Labile Complexes
$d^0d^0d^0D^2SP^3$	000	00	Sc(III), Y(III), rare earths(III), Ti(IV), Zr(IV), Hf(IV), Ce(IV), Th(IV), Nb(V), Ta(V), Mo(VI), W(VI)
$d^1d^0d^0D^2SP^3$	100	00	Ti(III), V(IV), Mo(V), W(V), Re(VI)
$d^1d^1d^0D^2SP^3$	110	00	Ti(II), V(III), Nb(III), Ta(III), W(IV), Re(V), Ru(VI)
			Inert Complexes
$d^1d^1d^1D^2SP^3$	111	00	V(II), Cr(III), Mo(III), W(III), Mn(IV), Re(IV)
$d^2d^1d^1D^2SP^3$	211	00	Cr(CN)$_6^{4-}$, Mn(CN)$_6^{3-}$, Re(III), Ru(IV), Os(IV)
$d^2d^2d^1D^2SP^3$	221	00	Mn(CN)$_6^{4-}$, Re(II), Fe(CN)$_6^{3-}$, Fe(phen)$_3^{3+}$, Ru(III), Os(III), Ir(IV)
$d^2d^2d^2D^2SP^3$	222	00	Fe(CN)$_6^{4-}$, Fe(phen)$_3^{2+}$, Ru(II), Os(II), Co(III) (except CoF$_6^{3-}$), Rh(III), Ir(III), Pd(IV), Pt(IV)

* Taube, H., *Chem. Rev.,* **50**, 69 (1952).

increasing charge on the central atom and it might seem surprising to find W(III) and Mo(III) complexes classified as inert and those of the same metals in the higher oxidation states classified as labile. This difficulty does not arise, however, if one considers that the rate is controlled by entry of the new ligand rather than by the leaving of the old ligand. Taube proposed that the transition state for the labile inner orbital complexes involves a coordination number of seven, and the empty d orbital is used in accepting the electron pair of the incoming ligand and forming a new bond. The proposed mechanism is similar in some respects to the S_N2 mechanism proposed for displacement reactions on carbon atoms.*

$$H:\ddot{\underset{\cdot\cdot}{O}}:^- + H\!-\!\overset{\overset{\displaystyle H}{|}}{\underset{\underset{\displaystyle H}{|}}{C}}\!-\!Br \longrightarrow [HO\!-\!\overset{\overset{\displaystyle H}{|}}{\underset{\underset{\displaystyle H}{|}}{C}}\!-\!Br]^- \longrightarrow HO\!-\!\overset{\overset{\displaystyle H}{}}{\underset{\underset{\displaystyle H}{}}{C}}\!-\!H + Br^-$$

Nucleophile   Transition state

It differs in that the coordination number of M can be increased more easily than that of C and, accordingly, an unstable intermediate may be formed in the reaction of labile inner orbital complexes.

$$H_2O \;+\; \underset{\underset{\displaystyle L}{L\diagup\;|\;\diagdown L}}{\overset{\overset{\displaystyle L}{L\diagdown\;|\;\diagup L}}{M}} \;\rightleftharpoons\; H_2O\!-\!\underset{\underset{\displaystyle L}{L\diagup\;|\;\diagdown L}}{\overset{\overset{\displaystyle L}{L\diagdown\;|\;\diagup L}}{M}} \;\rightleftharpoons\; H_2O\!-\!\underset{\underset{\displaystyle L}{L\diagup\;\diagdown L}}{\overset{\overset{\displaystyle L}{L\diagdown\;\diagup L}}{M}}\!-\!L \;+\; L$$

Nucleophile   Unstable intermediate
(or perhaps transition state)

Due to the extremely fast rates of reaction of these compounds, it has not been possible to determine whether an intermediate exists in these reactions, or indeed, even to establish the kinetic order of these reactions. Application of the relaxation methods of Eigen et al. (see p. 458) should prove fruitful in this area.

Taube further pointed out that when a central ion forms both inner and outer orbital complexes (as determined from magnetic measurements) the inner orbital complexes will be inert and the outer orbital complexes will be labile.† Thus $[FeF_6]^{3-}$ is labile and $[Fe(CN)_6]^{3-}$ is inert. The decrease in rates of hydrolysis with increasing charge on the central "ion" in the series $AlF_6{}^{3-}$, $SiF_6{}^{2-}$, $PF_6{}^-$, and SF_6 led Taube to propose an S_N1 mechanism for the substitution reactions of these complexes. An S_N1 substitution reaction for an octahedral complex involves an unimolecular dissociation process as the rate determining step to give a five-coordinate intermediate or transition state, followed by the rapid addition of the new ligand.

---

* The abbreviation S_N2 stands for substitution (S) by a nucleophile (N) (a positive seeking group, i.e., a Lewis base) in a bimolecular (2) reaction.
† Ions with two vacant inner d orbitals in the ground state are assumed to give inner orbital complexes. Outer orbital complexes include high-spin complexes of d^4, d^5, and d^6 ions and complexes of d^7, d^8, d^9, and d^{10} ions.

$$MX_6 \underset{\text{fast}}{\overset{\text{slow}}{\rightleftharpoons}} MX_5 + X$$

$$MX_5 + Y \overset{\text{fast}}{\rightleftharpoons} [MX_5Y]$$

The cases where a mechanism was clearly predicted by Taube could not be studied until recently because of the fast rates. The results of nuclear magnetic resonance studies (p. 447) and relaxation methods (p. 460) in the last few years are consistent with Taube's expectations. Connick (p. 447) has found the rates of substitution of H_2O by SO_4^{2-} to be comparable to the rates of H_2O exchange for an extensive series of divalent metals. These results suggest an S_N1 mechanism.

Taube's original classification used Valence Bond terminology. The inner orbital complexes are those for which two d orbitals (e_g) are assumed to be used for covalent bonding. Molecular orbital terminology would add that these are complexes for which the $e_g{}^*$ orbitals are vacant. The vacant t_{2g} orbital which is considered to be necessary for the formation of a seventh bond in labile inner orbital complexes is a nonbonding orbital in octahedral complexes. One of these orbitals, however, would be involved in bonding in the formation of a 7-coordinate intermediate or transition state. Any metal electrons present in this orbital would have to occupy the resulting antibonding orbital, making the formation of the 7-coordinate complex less favorable. Thus, Taube's classification of inner orbital complexes can be restated in molecular orbital terminology. Those complexes with vacant $e_g{}^*$ orbitals will be labile if one of the t_{2g} orbitals is empty and inert if all three t_{2g} orbitals are occupied. Similarly, Taube's outer orbital complexes can be considered as those with one or more $e_g{}^*$ electrons. The formation of a seventh bond would not be expected because it would increase the number of antibonding electrons. A dissociation mechanism would seem to be more likely since this could reduce the number of antibonding electrons.

CRYSTAL FIELD INTERPRETATION

No bonding orbitals are considered in the "pure" crystal field approach (see p. 348). The low energy orbitals occupied first in the build up of the configuration of an octahedral complex are the t_{2g} orbitals directed toward the edges of the octahedron, between the ligands. An incoming group would be expected to approach between the ligands and hence it would be influenced by the t_{2g} electrons. If the $e_g{}^*$ orbitals are vacant but all three of the t_{2g} orbitals are occupied, the incoming group will be repelled by the electrons directed toward it, resulting in a high activation energy. These complexes are expected to be inert. The most inert complexes should be those of d^6 ions, e.g., $[Co(NH_3)_6]^{3+}$ and $[Pt(NH_3)_6]^{4+}$ in which all three t_{2g} orbitals are doubly occupied. If one or more of the orbitals is singly occupied, then the activation energy should be lower because the incoming group can approach in the direction of an orbital of lower electron density. The complexes of d^0, d^1, and d^2 ions should be labile because at least one of the t_{2g} orbitals is not occupied, providing a low energy approach for a seventh ligand and hence a low activation energy.

Further comparisons are possible using the crystal field interpretation and the interpretation is not restricted to a particular mechanism. An estimate of the activation energy for a particular mechanism can be obtained from a comparison of the crystal field stabilization energy (CFSE) of the initial octahedral complex and the CFSE of the transition state, using an assumed configuration for the activated complex. A 5-coordinate transition state might have the configuration of a trigonal bipyramid or that of a square pyramid. The crystal field effects favor a square pyramid. The pentagonal bipyramid is used commonly as the configuration for the 7-coordinate transition state.

The removal of a ligand from an octahedral complex to form a square pyramid should alter the splitting of the energy levels of the d orbitals in very much the same way as for a tetragonal complex (an octahedral complex with two long bonds, see p. 353). If this change causes a great loss in CFSE, a high activation energy should be encountered and the octahedral complex should be inert. If there is little or no loss in CFSE, the complex should be labile.* Estimates of the contribution (ΔE_a) to the total activation energy from crystal field effects are given in Table 11.5. In those cases where the CFSE of the square pyramid is greater than that for the octahedral complex, the ΔE_a is given as zero. This situation arises in part because the values given are for *regular* octahedral complexes and in several cases (p. 353) additional stabilization results from distortion of the octahedron. Only the ΔE_a values are given for the displacement mechanism, the CFSE values used to obtain these values are given in the reference.

---

* It should be noted that for a dissociation mechanism the activation energy must be equal to, or greater than, the bond dissociation energy. The CFSE is only one factor in determining this energy and when the change in CFSE is small other factors might be more important. This should apply particularly to complexes involving π bonding.

TABLE 11.5
Crystal Field Activation Energies[a]

System	Dissociation Mechanism						Displacement Mechanism	
	Octahedron $\to$ Square Pyramid						Oct. $\to$ Pent. Bipy.	
	Strong Field			Weak Field			Strong Field	Weak Field
	Oct.	Sq. Py.	ΔE_a	Oct.	Sq. Py.	ΔE_a	ΔE_a	ΔE_a
d^0	0 Dq	0 Dq	0 Dq	0 Dq	0 Dq	0 Dq	0 Dq	0 Dq
d^1	4	4.57	0	4	4.57	0	0	0
d^2	8	9.14	0	8	9.14	0	0	0
d^3	12	10.00	2.00	12	10.00	2.00	4.26	4.26
d^4	16	14.57	1.43	6	9.14	0	2.98	1.07
d^5	20	19.14	0.86	0	0	0	1.70	0
d^6	24	20.00	4.00	4	4.57	0	8.52	0
d^7	18	19.14	0	8	9.14	0	5.34	0
d^8	12	10.00	2.00	12	10.00	2.00	4.26	4.26
d^9	6	9.14	0	6	9.14	0	1.07	1.07
d^{10}	0	0	0	0	0	0	0	0

[a] From F. Basolo and R. G. Pearson, *Mechanisms of Inorganic Reactions* (New York: John Wiley and Sons, Inc., 1958) p. 109.

It is seen from Table 11.5 that regardless of the assumed mechanism, d^0, d^1, d^2, and d^{10} ions never lose CFSE and hence their complexes should be labile, as also predicted from the valence bond interpretation. The valence bond theory assumes an S_N2 mechanism, but from the table it is apparent that the ΔE_a values are always higher for an S_N2 process. Experimental results so far obtained for inert complexes strongly favor an S_N1 mechanism. There is agreement between the CF and VB theories with respect to strong field (inner orbital) complexes of d^3, d^4, d^5, and d^6 ions being inert. Either mechanism can be assumed for the CFT, permitting the order of decreasing lability to be obtained: $d^5 > d^4 > d^3 > d^6$.

The two theories disagree only with respect to the prediction of the relative rates of reactions of d^8 ions. By either mechanism the ΔE_a values for d^8 ions would lead one to expect relatively slow substitution reactions. The octahedral d^8 complexes encountered are the weak field complexes of nickel(II). Low-spin complexes of d^8 ions are square planar, e.g., Ni(II), Pd(II), Pt(II), and Au(III). The weak field (high-spin) complexes of nickel(II) usually react much more rapidly than those of d^3 or d^6 ions, but they are slow in comparison to reactions of Cu(II), Co(II), and Zn(II) complexes (p. 447).* The VBT does not permit a prediction to be made with respect to the relative rates of reaction for these ions.

The crystal field theory does not limit the prediction of reaction rates to a particular assumed mechanism, although it offers some support to the S_N1 mechanism. A major advantage of the CFT over the VBT is that the former theory permits comparisons to be made within a classification in order to predict relative rates for inert complexes.

The Mechanisms of Substitution in Cobalt Complexes

The most extensively studied complexes have been those of Co(III) and Cr(III). A few typical examples of some reactions of Co(III) will now be discussed. One of the most common types of reaction of complexes of the type $[Co(NH_3)_5Cl]^{2+}$ involves replacement of the Cl^- by H_2O, a process known as *aquation* or acid hydrolysis:

$$[Co(NH_3)_5Cl]^{2+} + H_2O \longrightarrow [Co(NH_3)_5H_2O]^{3+} + Cl^- \tag{11.11}$$

The reaction is found to be first order, since the rate is dependent only on the concentration of the complex (to the first power). This observation does not permit one to conclude that an S_N1 reaction is involved. Since the solvent is present in large excess, the reaction would appear to be first order even if a bimolecular reaction involving H_2O were involved. In order to arrive at a reasonable mechanism (a mechanism can be shown to be consistent with all of the facts, but it cannot be proven conclusively), some of the characteristics of the complex can be varied to see the effect on the rate.

EFFECT OF CHARGE ON THE COMPLEX

The rate of aquation of $[Co(NH_3)_5Cl]^{2+}$ is much slower than the rate of aquation of either *cis* or *trans*-$[Co(NH_3)_4Cl_2]^+$ (Table 11.6). The second step of the aquation of $[Co(NH_3)_4Cl_2]^+$ is slower by a factor of about 100 than the first step. The following

* Basolo, F., and R. G. Pearson, *Mechanisms of Inorganic Reactions* (New York: John Wiley and Sons, Inc., 1958) pp. 111, 204.

equations apply for an assumed S_N1 mechanism:

$$[Co(NH_3)_4Cl_2]^+ \underset{\text{fast}}{\overset{\text{slow}}{\rightleftharpoons}} [Co(NH_3)_4Cl]^{2+} + Cl^- \qquad (11.12)$$

$$\text{fast} \downarrow \begin{array}{l} H_2O \\ \text{adds} \end{array}$$

$$[Co(NH_3)_4(H_2O)Cl]^{2+}$$

$$[Co(NH_3)_4(H_2O)Cl]^{2+} \underset{\text{fast}}{\overset{\text{slow}}{\rightleftharpoons}} [Co(NH_3)_4H_2O]^{3+} + Cl^- \qquad (11.13)$$

$$\text{fast} \downarrow \begin{array}{l} H_2O \\ \text{adds} \end{array}$$

$$[Co(NH_3)_4(H_2O)_2]^{3+}$$

TABLE 11.6
Rates of Aquation of Some Cobalt(III) Complexes at pH 1[a]

Ion[b]	$k \times 10^4$ (min^{-1})	Ion	$k \times 10^4$ (min^{-1})
cis-$[Co(NH_3)_4Cl_2]^+$	very fast	$[Co(NH_3)_5Cl]^{2+}$	4.0
cis-$[Co(en)_2Cl_2]^+$	150	cis-$[Co(en)_2(NH_3)Cl]^{2+}$	0.85
cis-$[Co(trien)Cl_2]^+$	90	cis-$[Co(trien)(NH_3)Cl]^{2+}$	0.40
trans-$[Co(NH_3)_4Cl_2]^+$	1100	$[Co(en)(dien)Cl]^{2+}$	0.31
trans-$[Co(en)(NH_3)_2Cl_2]^+$	130		
trans-$[Co(en)_2Cl_2]^+$	19		

[a] Pearson, R. G., C. R. Boston, and F. Basolo, *J. Phys. Chem.*, **59**, 304 (1955).
[b] Substitution of first chloride ion only.

Since bond breaking is the important process in an S_N1 reaction, it should be easier to remove a Cl^- ion from a 2+ ion (remaining) than from a 3+ ion. The reverse order would be expected for the addition of a ligand (S_N2) although the effect should be smaller for the addition of a neutral ligand such as H_2O (see Figure 11.8). Aside from

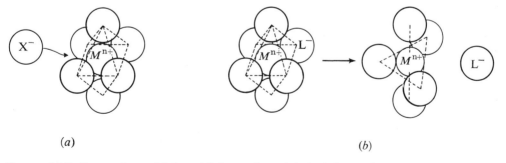

(a)   (b)

FIGURE 11.8. *Comparison of S_N1 and S_N2 reactions. (a) An S_N2 attack is accelerated by an increase in positive charge on the metal or on the complex ion. (b) An S_N1 attack is retarded by an increase in positive charge on the metal or on the complex ion.*

the ease of bond breaking for an S_N1 mechanism, the change in charge from the initial complex to the transition state is important. Since the energy of charging a sphere varies as q^2, the change in electrostatic energy on going from the six- to five-coordinated state is $1^2 \rightarrow 2^2$ or 3 for (11.12) and $2^2 \rightarrow 3^2$ or 5 for (11.13). Hence (11.12) would be expected to proceed more rapidly than (11.13) on the basis of both charge effects. The observation that the complexes with $+2$ charge react more slowly than the $+1$ complexes is consistent with an S_N1 mechanism. It rules out an S_N2(lim) mechanism,* but it cannot be concluded that bond making is of no importance. See Table 11.7 for a comparison of the effects of various changes on rates.

TABLE 11.7

Effect of Sizes and Charges on Rates of S_N1 and S_N2 Reactions[a]

	S_N1(*lim*) *and* S_N1 *Rate*	S_N2 *Rate*	S_N2(*lim*) *Rate*
Increased positive charge of central atom	decrease	opposing effects	increase
Increased size of central atom	increase	increase	increase
Increased negative charge of entering group	no effect	increase	increase
Increased size of entering group	no effect	decrease	decrease
Increased negative charge of leaving group	decrease	decrease	decrease
Increased size of leaving group	increase	opposing effects	decrease
Increased negative charge of other ligands	increase	opposing effects	decrease
Increased size of other ligands	increase	decrease	decrease

[a] From F. Basolo and R. G. Pearson, *Mechanisms of Inorganic Reactions* (New York: John Wiley and Sons, Inc., 1958) p. 103.

EFFECT OF CHELATION

Replacement of NH_3 by en, trien, dien, or other chelate groups slows down the rate of aquation as seen in Table 11.6, but not to the same extent as for a change in the charge of the complex ion. The effect of chelation might be expected to shorten the Co—N bond distance and to transfer more charge to the cobalt in the chelate complexes compared to those of NH_3. This effect should enhance the aquation process in the chelate complexes, so obviously some other factor must be more important. It has been suggested† that the transition state requires solvation for stabilization and the solvation is less efficient for the chelate complexes because of their larger size. However, the differences in the rates are much larger than might be expected on the basis of such changes in solvation, unless they are more specific. Thus the alkyl groups could

* The S_N2(lim) mechanism is the limiting case in which only bond making is important in the rate determining step. A reaction would be classified as S_N2(lim) only if evidence for a seven-coordinated intermediate could be obtained.
† Basolo, F., and R. G. Pearson, *Mechanisms of Inorganic Reactions* (New York: John Wiley and Sons, Inc., 1958) p. 118.

interfere with hydrogen bonding between N and the solvent. Perhaps the rate differences are great enough to suggest that the solvent assists in the removal of the Cl⁻ ion by direct interaction with the cobalt and that this solvation is diminished by the presence of the alkyl groups. Such a mechanism could still be somewhere between the S_N1(lim) and S_N2(lim) cases. It might still be labeled an S_N1 process if bond breaking is more important than bond making.

EFFECT OF SUBSTITUTION ON ETHYLENEDIAMINE

Substitution of one methyl group on a nitrogen atom of en slows down the rate of aquation of $[Co(AA)_2Cl_2]^+$ slightly, in line with some sort of solvation effect as discussed above. Nevertheless, the effect of substitution on the carbon atoms or of substitution of more bulky groups on N is to increase the rate of aquation. This strongly suggests that a dissociation mechanism is involved and that the rate increases because of steric factors. The formation of a five-coordinated transition state relieves steric strain, while the formation of a seven-coordinated transition state increases steric strain (see Figure 11.9).

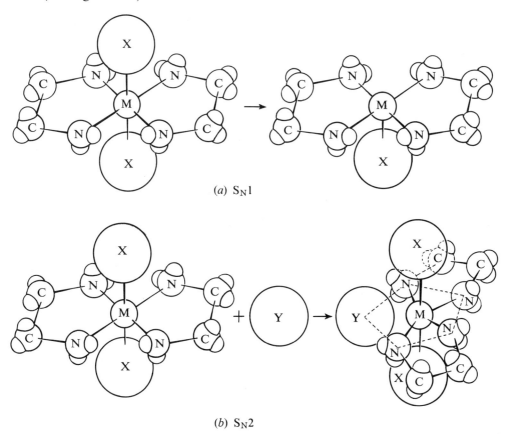

(a) S_N1

(b) S_N2

FIGURE 11.9. (a) *Strained (crowded) complex gives a less strained transition state (shown as an intermediate) by an S_N1 process. (b) Strained complex becomes more strained in the transition state by an S_N2 process.*

CHANGE OF LEAVING GROUP

The rate of aquation of $[Co(NH_3)_5X]^{2+}$ varies with the nature of X as would be expected if bond breaking is of great importance in the rate determining step. The observed order* is $HCO_3^- > NO_3^- > I^- > Br^- > Cl^- > SO_4^{2-} > F^- > CH_3COO^- > SCN^- > NO_2^-$. This order corresponds to the order of decreasing thermodynamic stability of the complexes of these groups.

The results of the various investigations are consistent with an S_N1 mechanism. Bond breaking is important in the activated complex, but it cannot be said to be more important than bond making. Only the $S_N2(lim)$ mechanism can be ruled out.

RATE OF EXCHANGE OF CHLORIDE ION

The chloride ion exchange in $[Co(en)_2Cl_2]^+$ is a first order process. The rate of exchange with radioactive *Cl$^-$ is independent of the chloride ion concentration. The reaction proceeds through two steps, the first of which is an aquation process:

$$[Co(en)_2Cl_2]^+ + H_2O \longrightarrow [Co(en)_2(H_2O)Cl]^{2+} + Cl^-$$
$$[Co(en)_2(H_2O)Cl]^{2+} + {^*Cl^-} \longrightarrow [Co(en)_2{^*ClCl}]^+ + H_2O$$

Apparently substitution reactions of this type are common.

RATE OF BASE HYDROLYSIS

The replacement of a ligand by OH^- is referred to as base hydrolysis. In cobalt complexes of the type $[Co(NH_3)_5X]^{2+}$ and $[Co(en)_2X_2]^+$, the base hydrolysis is much faster than the acid hydrolysis and the reaction is *second order*, first order in complex and first order in OH^-. The fact that a reaction is second order suggests a bimolecular reaction, but it does not prove it. Studies of variables such as those discussed above for aquation reactions indicate that the mechanism which obtains for the base hydrolysis is different from that for aquation, but the results cast doubt on an S_N2 process. The OH^- ion reacts much more rapidly than other ligands and seems to be unique in its reactions in water.

The mechanism suggested for the base hydrolysis reactions† involves the following steps:

$$[Co(NH_3)_5Cl]^{2+} + OH^- \overset{fast}{\rightleftharpoons} [Co(NH_3)_4NH_2Cl]^+ + H_2O \qquad (11.14)$$

$$[Co(NH_3)_4(NH_2)Cl]^+ \longrightarrow [Co(NH_3)_4(NH_2)]^{2+} + Cl^- \qquad (11.15)$$

$$[Co(NH_3)_4(NH_2)]^{2+} + H_2O \overset{fast}{\longrightarrow} [Co(NH_3)_5OH]^{2+} \qquad (11.16)$$

The first step involves the removal of a proton by OH^- in a rapid acid–base equilibrium to give a complex ion of lower charge which then loses a Cl^- more rapidly than the

---

* Basolo, F., and R. G. Pearson, *Mechanisms of Inorganic Reactions* (New York: John Wiley and Sons, Inc., 1958) pp. 121-22.
† Basolo, F., and R. G. Pearson, *Mechanisms of Inorganic Reactions* (New York: John Wiley and Sons, Inc., 1958) pp. 124–132.

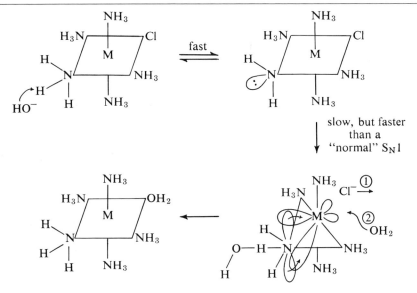

FIGURE 11.10. *The S_N1CB mechanism.*

starting complex. The last step is relatively fast, so the second step is rate determining. This mechanism is referred to as an S_N1CB mechanism, indicating that it involves an S_N1 reaction of the conjugate base of the starting complex (see Figure 11.10).

The rate law for the base hydrolysis is

$$\text{Rate} = k[\text{complex}][\text{base}] \tag{11.17}$$

This can easily be shown to be consistent with the S_N1CB mechanism if Equation 11.14 is an equilibrium. The rate law for Equation 11.15 would be first order in conjugate base ($[\text{Co(NH}_3)_4(\text{NH}_2)\text{Cl}]^+$), but the concentration of the conjugate base can be related to the concentrations of the inital complex and OH^-. Consider the hydrolysis reaction:

$$\text{Complex} + OH^- \rightleftharpoons \text{Conjugate base} + H_2O$$

$$K_h = \frac{K_a}{K_w} = \frac{[\text{Conjugate base}]}{[\text{Complex}][OH^-]}$$

$$[\text{Conjugate base}] = \frac{K_a}{K_w}[\text{Complex}][OH^-] \tag{11.18}$$

Since

$$\text{Rate} = k'[\text{Conjugate base}]$$

$$\text{Rate} = k'\frac{K_a}{K_w}[\text{Complex}][OH^-] \tag{11.19}$$

Equation 11.19 is the observed rate law (Equation 11.17) where

$$k = k'\frac{K_a}{K_w}.$$

One important prediction of the $S_N 1CB$ mechanism should be mentioned here. This mechanism requires a moderately acidic proton in the starting complex. A complex without an acidic proton should react with OH^- much more slowly and the rate of the reaction would be expected to be independent of OH^-. In fact, this is what is observed for the base hydrolysis of $[Co(CN)_5Br]^{3-}$ and *trans*-$[Co(py)_4Cl_2]^+$.

Although the $S_N 1CB$ mechanism is in better agreement with the results than is an $S_N 2$ mechanism, it cannot be proven and it is not the only possible mechanism.

A novel approach to distinguish between $S_N 2$ and $S_N 1CB$ mechanisms has been presented.* This depends on the fact that HO_2^- is much more reactive than OH^- for typical $S_N 2$ reactions but HO_2^- is a much weaker base than OH^-. The equilibrium constant for the reaction

$$OH^- + H_2O_2 = H_2O + HO_2^- \qquad (11.20)$$

is 150 in conventional units. If a base hydrolysis reaction occurs by an $S_N 2$ mechanism, the addition of excess H_2O_2 to a reaction mixture of substrate and OH^- will increase the rate by a factor which may be as large as 10^4 because of the greater reactivity of HO_2^-. If the reaction occurs by an $S_N 1CB$ mechanism, the H_2O_2 will reduce the rate by a factor as large as 150 for one molar H_2O_2. The rate is reduced in this case because of the above equilibrium which greatly reduces the concentration of OH^-. The rate of an $S_N 1CB$ reaction is directly proportional to OH^-. The addition of H_2O_2 to reaction mixtures of $[Co(NH_3)_5Cl]^{2+}$ and OH^- caused a decrease in the rate constant by a factor of 3.6 for 0.018 M H_2O_2. The calculated factor for the rate reduction for these concentrations assuming an $S_N 1CB$ mechanism is 3.7.

The base hydrolysis of $[Co(EDTA)]^-$ appears to be one of the few $S_N 2$ reactions which has been established for an octahedral complex (see p. 415). The rate of the base hydrolysis of $[Co(EDTA)]^-$ is proportional to hydroxide ion and a conjugate base mechanism is ruled out because there are no acidic protons in the complex ion. Surprisingly, the base hydrolysis of $[Co(PDTA)]^-$ (where PDTA is the 1,2-propylenediaminetetraacetate ion) is not dependent on OH^- concentration. This has been explained† on the basis of the greater crowding in the PDTA complex so that a 7-coordinate intermediate or transition state is less stable than for the EDTA complex. Presumably the base hydrolysis of $[Co(PDTA)]^-$ occurs by an $S_N 1$ mechanism.

SUBSTITUTION WITHOUT BREAKING THE METAL–LIGAND BOND

In acid solution, carbonato complexes such as $[Co(NH_3)_5CO_3]^+$ are converted to aquo complexes with the release of CO_2. When the reaction is carried out in the presence of oxygen-18 labeled water, none of the ^{18}O is found in the resulting aquo complex. Hence the Co—O bond must be retained during the reaction. The reaction presumably involves protonation of the oxygen attached to the Co followed by removal of CO_2. The complex $[Co(NH_3)_4CO_3]^+$, in which the CO_3^{2-} is bidentate, is converted to *cis*-$[Co(NH_3)_4(H_2O)_2]^{3+}$ in acid solution. If the reaction is carried out in the presence of $H_2^{18}O$, the product is found to have derived half of its oxygen from the solvent. Pre-

* Pearson, R. G., and D. N. Edgington, *J. Am. Chem. Soc.*, **84**, 4608 (1962).
† Busch, D. H., D. W. Cooke, K. Swaminathan, and Y. A. Im, in *Advances in the Chemistry of the Coordination Compounds*, edited by S. Kirschner (New York: Macmillan Co., 1961) p. 139; D. W. Cooke, Y. A. Im, and D. H. Busch, *Inorg. Chem.*, **1**, 13 (1962).

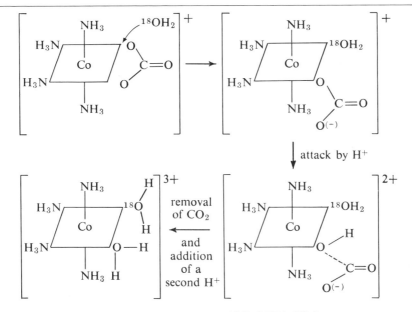

FIGURE 11.11. *Aquation of* $[Co(NH_3)_4CO_3]^+$.

sumably the first step in the reaction involves breaking the chelate ring with a H_2O molecule substituting for the O of the CO_3^{2-} ion. The second step involves removal of CO_2 without rupture of the Co—O bond as in the case of $[Co(NH_3)_5CO_3]^+$ (see Figure 11.11).

REACTIONS IN NONAQUEOUS SOLVENTS

One obvious way to avoid some of the uncertainty of participation of the solvent water in substitution reactions is to work in another solvent. Most charged complexes, however, are soluble only in polar solvents, where solvent interaction is still likely, although perhaps less important than for water. Some studies carried out in methanol illustrate the difficulty of deciding on a mechanism, even in the absence of water.

The substitution of a chloride ion in *cis*-$[Co(en)_2Cl_2]^+$ by several anions was investigated in methanol using chemical, radiochemical, polarimetric, and spectrophotometric methods.* The observed rates are shown in Figure 11.12. The rates were the same for substitution by SCN^-, Br^-, Cl^-, and NO_3^- and were independent of the concentration of the entering group. These substitution reactions were interpreted as involving an S_N1 mechanism. Other evidence also pointed to an S_N1 mechanism, but all of the results could be interpreted also in terms of an S_N2 mechanism involving the solvent.

The anions NO_2^-, N_3^-, and CH_3O^- react more rapidly than the other reagents and the rate law is second order. The mechanism was interpreted to be S_N2. The reaction with CH_3O^- can be interpreted also as an S_N1CB mechanism. Studies in buffered solu-

* Brown, D. D., and C. K. Ingold, *J. Chem. Soc.*, **1953**, 2674.

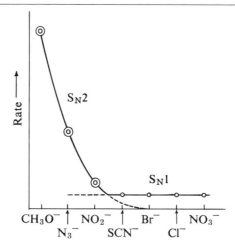

FIGURE 11.12. *Relative rates and assumed mechanism for the reaction of various anions with* cis[Co(en)$_2$Cl$_2$]$^+$ *in methanol (from D. D. Brown and C. K. Ingold,* J. Chem. Soc., *1953, 2693).*

tions* have shown that the reactions with N$_3^-$ and NO$_2^-$ can be interpreted as dissociation mechanisms in which the dissociation is assisted by ion-pair formation (S$_N$1IP mechanism). On the basis of the information available, the S$_N$2 and S$_N$1IP mechanisms are indistinguishable.

ISOMERIZATION AND RACEMIZATION REACTIONS

Substitution reactions involving *cis*, *trans*, or optical isomers can be useful in shedding light on the mechanism of substitution reactions because in some cases it is possible to draw conclusions about the symmetry of intermediates. Isomerization and racemization reactions are also of interest in themselves. The optically active complex *d-cis*-[Co(en)$_2$Cl$_2$]$^+$ is converted to the *trans* isomer in methanol, but the rate of loss of optical activity is greater than the rate of conversion to the *trans* isomer.† Either process can be accounted for by the dissociation of a Cl$^-$ to give a five-coordinate intermediate, either a trigonal bipyramid or a tetragonal pyramid. One of the possible trigonal bipyramidal configurations leads to racemization, but not to conversion to the *trans* isomer. All mechanisms that result in conversion to the *trans* isomer also result in loss of optical activity. As long as there are any other reaction paths leading to racemization, the loss of optical activity should be greater than the rate of conversion to the *trans* isomer.

The rates of racemization of [Ni(phen)$_3$]$^{2+}$ and [Ni(bipy)$_3$]$^{2+}$ have been shown to be the same as the rates of the respective dissociations and the activation energies are the same for the two processes. Hence, the racemization is concluded to occur through a dissociation mechanism for these complexes. However, the rate of racemization is greater than the rate of dissociation for [Fe(phen)$_3$]$^{2+}$ and [Fe(bipy)$_3$]$^{2+}$. In these

* Pearson, R. G., P. M. Henry, and F. Basolo, *J. Am. Chem. Soc.,* **79**, 5379, 5382 (1957); F. Basolo and R. G. Pearson, *Mechanisms of Inorganic Reactions* (New York: John Wiley and Sons, Inc., 1958) pp. 141-151.
† Brown, D. D., and R. S. Nyholm, *J. Chem. Soc.,* **1953**, 2696.

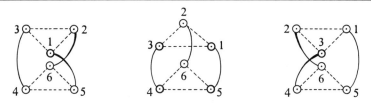

FIGURE 11.13. *Conversion of d to l isomer of an octahedral complex* M(AA)₃ *by an intramolecular process.*

complexes at least some of the racemization must occur through an intramolecular process.

The oxalato complexes $[Co(C_2O_4)_3]^{3-}$ and $[Cr(C_2O_4)_3]^{3-}$ undergo racemization fairly rapidly in solution although no dissociation can be detected and no exchange with tagged oxalate ion is observed in the time required for racemization. The racemization could involve the breaking of one Co—O bond without complete removal of the oxalate ion, followed by rearrangement of the five bonds before the oxalate ion reattaches as a chelate ligand. It is also possible for racemization to occur through the twisting of bonds in such a way that a symmetrical trigonal bipyramid is formed. This can be pictured as the twisting of one triangular face of an octahedron through 60° so that it comes into the eclipsed position with the opposite face of the octahedron. If the same face is twisted through another 60° an octahedral configuration is obtained which is the mirror image of the starting configuration (Figure 11.13). This same mechanism can bring about *cis* to *trans* conversion. The initial complex has 1 and 6 in *trans* positions, but they are in *cis* positions in the final complex as shown.

The thermal racemization of $[Co(EDTA)]^-$ presumably proceeds by an intramolecular process (Figure 11.14a). The base catalyzed racemization of $[Co(EDTA)]^-$ presumably proceeds through a symmetrical 7-coordinate intermediate (Figure 11.14b).

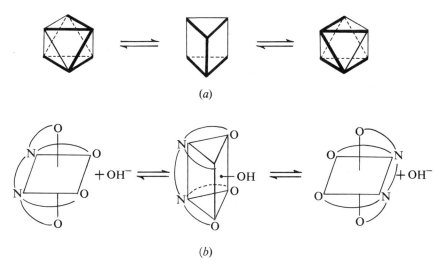

FIGURE 11.14. *(a) Intramolecular racemization of* $[Co(EDTA)]^-$; *(b) Base catalyzed racemization of* $[Co(EDTA)]$ *[from D. W. Cooke, Y. A. Im, and D. H. Busch,* Inorg. Chem., *1, 14 (1962)].*

The 7-coordinate intermediate appears reasonable in the light of 7-coordinate EDTA complexes, which have been found. The complex d-$[Co(l\text{-}PDTA)]^-$ does not undergo racemization or mutarotation under similar conditions. It was mentioned (p. 412) that these complexes undergo base hydrolysis by different mechanisms.

OXIDATION–REDUCTION REACTIONS

Equations for oxidation–reduction reactions are usually balanced by the ion–electron method, which focuses attention on the electron transfer process. No one expects a complicated oxidation–reduction equation to describe the mechanism of the reaction. Some reactions really do involve direct electron transfer, but many reactions, particularly reactions of oxy anions, involve atom transfer. Dwyer* has shown that optically active $[Ru(dipy)_3]^{2+}$ can be oxidized to $[Ru(dipy)_3]^{3+}$ with Ce^{4+} and then reduced with $FeSO_4$ to regenerate the original complex without loss in rotation. In this case the oxidation and reduction processes involve simple electron exchange with little rearrangement of the octahedral complex.

Electron exchange reactions are fast in cases such as $[Fe(CN)_6]^{4-}$–$[Fe(CN)_6]^{3-}$ where the two octahedral complexes are very similar. They are both low-spin complexes and the bond distances must be very nearly the same. Electron exchange also occurs between MnO_4^- and MnO_4^{2-} without rearrangement of the coordination sphere. Electron exchange is slow for complexes such as $[Co(NH_3)_6]^{3+}$–$[Co(NH_3)_6]^{2+}$ where one of the complexes $[Co(NH_3)_6]^{3+}$ is a low-spin complex and one is a high-spin complex and where the Co—N distances are quite different.

The factors affecting rates of *direct* electron transfer have been summarized by Halpern† as follows:

(*1*) Electrostatic Repulsion – the contribution to the free energy of activation ranges from 15% to 50% of the total for such *direct* electron transfer reactions as $[Co(NH_3)_6]^{3+}$, $Cr^{2+}(aq)$. Other reactions such as $[Fe(phen)_3]^{2+}$–$[Fe(phen)_3]^{3+}$ are very fast. The high dielectric constant of water plus secondary solvation effects greatly reduce electrostatic repulsion.

(*2*) Reorganization Energy – the bond lengths in MnO_4^- and MnO_4^{2-} differ and the activated complex for exchange between these must involve a "stretched" MnO bond in MnO_4^-. Slow reactions are expected where the oxidized and reduced form of the reagent have greatly different bond lengths, geometries, or solvation shells. For octahedral complexes, bond lengths are changed more drastically when e_g electrons are involved in the transfer as compared to t_{2g} electrons in the d orbitals.

(*3*) Electrical Conductivity – metal orbitals may be delocalized to some extent over π-conjugated systems. The cross section for electron transfer of complexes is increased by π-bonding ligands such as CN^- and phen. Unsaturated ligands such as terephthalate ion, HO_2C—C_6H_4—CO_2^-, also serve as effective bridges for electron transfer.

(*4*) The greater the negative free energy change for the overall reaction the faster the reaction will proceed. This is somewhat similar to Hammond's postulate regarding fast exothermic reactions.

This discussion has dealt with metal complexes exclusively. For the halogenate ions the observed order of chemical reactivity is $IO_3^- > BrO_3^- > ClO_3^-$. This order is also the order of increasing π-bonding between the halogen and oxygen (see p. 251).

* Dwyer, F. P., and E. C. Gyarfas, *J. Proc. Roy. Soc. N. S. Wales*, **83**, 174 (1950).
† Halpern, J., *Quart. Rev.*, **15**, 207 (1961).

Many cases of atom transfer are known, but only examples involving a novel approach will be discussed here. Taube has taken advantage of the fact that Cr(II), which forms very labile complexes, is a good reducing agent and on oxidation the Cr(III) complexes formed are inert.

Anhydrous $CrCl_3$ is not wet by water and dissolves very slowly except in the presence of a catalyst such as Cr(II). The species obtained on dissolution is $[Cr(H_2O)_5Cl]^{2+}$ rather than $[Cr(H_2O)_6]^{3+}$, which might be expected if equilibrium were established rapidly. The reaction is presumed to be

$$CrCl_3 + *Cr^{2+} \longrightarrow Cr^{2+} + *CrCl^{2+} + 2Cl^-$$

where * is used to follow the course of a particular Cr and does not mean a tagged isotope of Cr. The aquation of $[Cr(NH_3)_5Cl]^{2+}$ in acid solution produces $[Cr(NH_3)_5(H_2O)]^{3+} + Cl^-$, except in the presence of Cr^{2+} as a catalyst when the reaction is

$$[(NH_3)_5CrCl]^{2+} + 5H^+ \xrightarrow{Cr^{2+}} 5NH_4^+ + [Cr(H_2O)_5Cl]^{2+}$$

The reaction rate is independent of acidity, but first order in the Cr(III) complex and in the catalyst Cr^{2+}. The halogen atom presumably forms a bridge $[(NH_3)_5Cr-Cl-Cr(H_2O)_5]^{4+}$ and in the process of being transferred oxidizes the Cr(II) to Cr(III) and reduces the Cr(III) complex to a labile Cr(II) complex, which dissociates. The data in Table 11.8 indicate that F^- serves as the poorest electron transfer agent and that I^- is the best for the complexes shown. Electron exchange between $[Cr(H_2O)_6]^{2+}$ and $[Cr(H_2O)_6]^{3+}$ is very slow, but exchange between $[Cr(H_2O)_6]^{2+}$ and $[Cr(H_2O)_5Cl]^{2+}$ is very fast, since in the latter case the Cl can form a bridged complex and serve as a more effective electron transfer agent than water. In the reduction of $[Co(NH_3)_5Cl]^{2+}$ with Cr(II), if a radioactive isotope of Cl^- is used, $[Co(NH_3)_5*Cl]^{2+}$, the activity appears almost completely in the product $[Cr(H_2O)_5*Cl]^{2+}$. If untagged $[Co(NH_3)_5Cl]^{2+}$ is used, but the reaction is carried out in the presence of tagged $*Cl^-$, no activity appears in the Cr(III) ion $[Cr(H_2O)_5Cl]^{2+}$. In these instances it is clear that the oxidation–reduction process is accomplished by atom transfer without exchange with the solvent or with free Cl^- present in solution.

TABLE 11.8

Rates of Reaction of Cr^{2+} with Various Cr(III) Complexes[a]

Oxidant	k ($M^{-1}\ sec^{-1}$)	Temp. (°C)
$[Cr(H_2O)_5F]^{2+}$	2.6×10^{-2}	27
$[Cr(H_2O)_5Cl]^{2+}$	8.3 ± 2	0
$[Cr(H_2O)_5Br]^{2+}$	> 60	0
$[Cr(NH_3)_5F]^{2+}$	2.7×10^{-4}	25
$[Cr(NH_3)_5Cl]^{2+}$	5.1×10^{-2}	25
$[Cr(NH_3)_5Br]^{2+}$	3.2×10^{-1}	25
$[Cr(NH_3)_5I]^{2+}$	5.5 ± 1.5	25

[a] Taube, H., *Advances in Inorganic Chemistry and Radiochemistry*, Vol. 1, H. J. Eméleus and A. G. Sharpe, eds. (New York: Academic Press, 1959) p. 24.

Substitution Reactions in Planar Complexes — The Trans Effect

The extent to which the solvent participates in substitution reactions is often difficult to determine. In the case of planar complexes the role of the solvent is also often uncertain. Certainly the opportunity for bonding between the metal and the solvent or other ligands is much greater for planar complexes because of the poor shielding of the metal above and below the plane of the complex. It is probably safe to assume that substitution in planar complexes does not proceed by an $S_N1(lim)$ mechanism which would require a three-coordinated intermediate.

One of the most important considerations in substitution reactions in planar complexes is the *trans effect* (p. 362). Substitution in planar complexes containing *trans* directing groups generally occurs in the position *trans* to that group. An approximate order of increasing *trans* directing influence is $H_2O < OH^- < NH_3 < Cl^- < Br^- < I^-$, NO_2^-, $PR_3 < NO$, CO, C_2H_4, CN^-.

Several theories have been proposed for the explanation of the *trans effect*.* Only two theories representing different approaches will be discussed here.

POLARIZATION THEORY

A highly polarizable ligand (Y) might be expected to distort the induced dipole in a planar complex (MX_3Y) as shown in Figure 11.15. The mutual polarization of M and Y results in a diminished positive charge on the central ion directly opposite Y. This might be expected to result in a weakening of the bond to the group *trans* to Y. Substitution might then be more likely in this position.

The order of increasing *trans* effect for the halide ions is the same as the order of increasing polarizability ($Cl^- < Br^- < I^-$). Nevertheless, the total electrostatic effect should give the reverse order because of the change in charge density. Thus the polarization theory offers a simple model for the explanation of the *trans effect*, but it does not permit one to make reliable predictions of the relative *trans* directing influence of

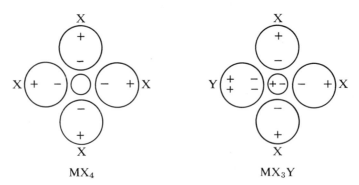

FIGURE 11.15. *Unsymmetrical induced dipole in MX_3Y as compared to MX_4. Y is a highly polarizable ligand.*

* Basolo, F., and R. G. Pearson, *Mechanisms of Inorganic Reactions* (New York: John Wiley and Sons, Inc., 1958) Chap. 4; "The Trans Effect," in *Progress in Inorganic Chemistry*, Vol. IV, F. A. Cotton, ed. (New York: Interscience Publishers, 1962) pp. 381–453.

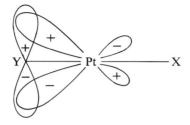

FIGURE 11.16. *Formation of a d-p-π bond between* Pt *and* Y. *The complex* PtA₂XY *is in the xy plane perpendicular to the plane of the paper.*

groups in many cases. The electrostatic approach has also been applied to a kinetic treatment with some degree of success, but it fails to explain the high *trans effect* of neutral ligands such as ethylene and CO.

π BONDING THEORY

The very high *trans effect* of the ligands C_2H_4, CO, and CN^- suggests that π bonding is probably important. Such ligands have a vacant orbital for *d-p-π* bonding using a filled d orbital (d_{xz} or d_{yz}) of the metal (Figure 11.16). The formation of the π bond increases the electron density in the direction of Y and diminishes it in the direction of the group *trans* to Y. The incoming ligand (X′) should approach from the direction of lower electron density, resulting in the displacement of X. The π bonding does not necessarily weaken the Pt—X bond, but it lowers the activation energy for the formation of a five-coordinated transition state.

In the absence of π bonding, a theory based on electrostatic or polarization effects is needed. The failure of the polarization theory to predict the correct order of *trans* directing influence can often be attributed to the importance of π bonding. Hence both approaches are useful. Unfortunately it is not always possible to predict *a priori* the relative importance of π bonding and polarization effects.

REFERENCES

Stability

George, P., and D. S. McClure, "The Effect of Inner Orbital Splitting on the Thermodynamic Properties of Transition Metal Compounds and Coordination Complexes," in *Progress in Inorganic Chemistry*, Vol. I, F. A. Cotton, ed. (New York: Interscience Publishers, Inc., 1960) p. 381.

Rossotti, F. J. C., "The Thermodynamics of Metal Ion Complex Formation in Solution," in *Modern Coordination Chemistry*, J. Lewis and R. G. Wilkins, eds. (New York: Interscience Publishers, Inc., 1960) Chapter 1.

Bailar, J. C., Jr., ed., *The Chemistry of Coordination Compounds* (New York: Reinhold Publishing Corp., 1956).

Bjerrum, J., G. Schwarzenbach, and L. G. Sillén, *Stability Constants of Metal-ion Complexes*, Revised ed. (London: The Chemical Society, 1964). The most extensive compilation of stability constants and acid dissociation constants available.

Rossotti, F. J. C., and H. Rossotti, *The Determination of Stability Constants* (New York: McGraw-Hill Book Co., Inc., 1961). A comprehensive review of methods for the determination of formation constants.

Rates and Mechanisms

Basolo, F., and R. G. Pearson, *Mechanisms of Inorganic Reactions* (New York: John Wiley and Sons, Inc., 1958).

Basolo, F., and R. G. Pearson, "Mechanisms of Substitution Reactions of Metal Complexes," in *Advances in Inorganic Chemistry and Radiochemistry*, Vol. III (New York: Academic Press, 1961) p. 1.

Pearson, R. G., "Crystal Field Theory and Substitution Reactions of Metal Ions," *J. Chem. Educ.*, **38**, 164 (1961).

Eigen, M., "Fast Elementary Steps in Chemical Reaction Mechanisms," in *Coordination Chemistry* (London: Butterworths, 1963) p. 97.

Stranks, D. R., "The Reaction Rates of Transitional Metal Complexes," in *Modern Coordination Chemistry*, J. Lewis and R. G. Wilkins, eds. (New York: Interscience Publishers, Inc., 1960) Chapter 2.

Stranks, D. R., and R. G. Wilkins, "Isotopic Tracer Investigations of Mechanism and Structure in Inorganic Chemistry," *Chem. Rev.*, **57**, 743 (1957).

Wilkins, R. G., "Kinetics and Mechanism of Replacement Reactions of Coordination Compounds," *Quart. Rev.*, **16**, 316 (1962).

Halpern, J., "Mechanism of Electron Transfer Processes," *Quart Rev.*, **15**, 207 (1961).

Taube, H., in *Advances in Inorganic Chemistry and Radiochemistry*, Vol. I, H. J. Emeléus and A. G. Sharpe, eds. (New York Academic Press, 1960) p. 1.

Problems

1.   The solubility of AgBr is about 7×10^{-7} mole per liter. It dissolves in 1% $Na_2S_2O_3$ solution to the extent of 0.35 g per 100 g of solution. Calculate the equilibrium constant for the reaction between Ag^+ and $S_2O_3^{2-}$ on the assumption: (*a*) that the reaction is $Ag^+ + 2S_2O_3^{2-} \rightleftharpoons Ag(S_2O_3)_2^{3-}$, (*b*) that the reaction is $Ag^+ + S_2O_3^{2-} \rightleftharpoons Ag(S_2O_3)^-$. In 10% $Na_2S_2O_3$ solution, the solubility of AgBr is 3.50 g per 100 g of solution. Is assumption (*a*) or (*b*) correct? (Rough calculation, assuming perfect solutions, will be adequate.)

2.   Look up the values for log K_1 for the complexes of salicylaldehyde with Cd^{2+}, Mg^{2+}, and Pb^{2+}. Plot these values against the first ionization potentials of these metals and compare to the complexes of Figure 11.1. Replot the log K_1 values for these three ions and several of those from Figure 11.1 against the electronegativities of the ions. (See Bjerrum, Schwarzenbach, and Sillén (references) for log K_1 values).

3.   Predict whether the following complexes would be labile or inert. Indicate the basis for your choice. The magnetic moment (in Bohr magnetons) is indicated after each complex (see Chapter XII).

   (*a*) Ammonium oxopentachlorochromate(v) (1.82 BM); (*b*) potassium hexaiodomanganate(iv) (3.82 BM); (*c*) potassium hexacyanoferrate(iii) (2.40 BM); (*d*) Hexamineiron(ii) chloride (5.45 BM).

4. The following mechanism has been proposed for the hydrolysis of triarylgermanium halides in mixed aqueous solvents

$$\phi_3GeX + H_2O \underset{2}{\overset{1}{\rightleftharpoons}} \phi_3Ge\overset{OH_2}{\underset{X}{\diagup}} \underset{4}{\overset{3}{\rightleftharpoons}} \phi_3GeOH_2^+ + X^-$$

$$\downarrow\uparrow fast$$

$$\phi_3GeOH + H^+$$

On the basis of this mechanism predict the effect of the following changes on the rate of step 1, step 3, and the over-all reaction.

(*a*) Decreasing the dielectric constant of the solvent (i.e., by adding some dioxane); (*b*) adding LiX to the solution; (*c*) adding LiY to the solution; (*d*) adding *ortho* alkyl substituents to the phenyl groups; (*e*) adding *para* nitro substituents to the phenyl groups.

Under what circumstances, if any, would the reaction appear to be kinetically first order? Second order?

How might one distinguish experimentally between the above mechanism and an S_N1 or S_N2 mechanism? [See F. Basolo and R. G. Pearson in *Advances in Inorganic Chemistry and Radiochemistry*, Vol. 3, H. J. Eméleus and A. G. Sharpe, eds. (New York: Academic Press, 1961) p. 57, or see D. H. Johnson and E. A. Schmall, *J. Am. Chem. Soc.*, **80**, 2931 (1958) for original paper.]

5. Explain how one might use the optical activity of a ligand as a means for following the rate of ligand exchange. [B. Bosnich, F. P. Dwyer, and A. M. Sargeson, *Nature*, **186**, 966 (1960).]

6. Indicate the selection you would make (and why) for the most favorable circumstances for observing an S_N2 substitution process:

(*a*) C.N. and configuration about the metal ion; (*b*) nature of M^{n+}; (*c*) nature of the incoming ligand; (*d*) nature of the ligands present in the original complex; (*e*) choice of solvent.

7. From the relative *trans* directing influence of Cl^- and NH_3, predict the product of substitution of

(*a*) two Cl^- ions in $[Pt(NH_3)_4]^{2+}$; (*b*) two NH_3 molecules in $[PtCl_4]^{2-}$; (*c*) NH_3 and then NO_2^- in $[PtCl_4]^{2-}$; (*d*) NO_2^- and then NH_3 in $[PtCl_4]^{2-}$.

8. Pyridine and other amines have about the same *trans* effect as NH_3. Using the *trans* directing influence of the ligands, give synthetic routes for the synthesis of the three isomers of $[Pt(NH_3)(NH_2OH)(py)(NO_2)]^+$ from $[PtCl_4]^{2-}$. [Check with Basolo and Pearson, *Progr. Inorg. Chem.*, **4**, 384 (1962)].

CHAPTER XII

Experimental Methods
for the Elucidation of Structure
and Bonding of Chemical Compounds

X-ray Crystallography

The most powerful tool available for the study of the structure of inorganic compounds is x-ray crystallography. X rays were discovered by Röentgen in 1895. In 1912 Laue suggested that crystals should serve as three-dimensional diffraction gratings for x rays, since the spacing between atoms is comparable to the wavelengths of x rays. By 1913 his prediction had been verified when it was shown that crystals produced dif-

FIGURE 12.1. *A Laue diffraction photograph of a tungsten single crystal (courtesy of Y. A. Yackob and H. Weik, Department of Physics, The University of Cincinnati).*

422

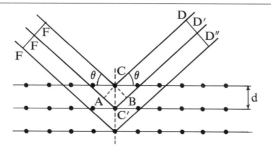

FIGURE 12.2. *Diffraction of a beam of x rays from the layers of atoms in a crystal.*

fraction patterns on photographic plates. A crystal placed between an x-ray source (collimated to give a narrow beam) and a photographic plate produced a dark spot, caused by the undeflected x rays, surrounded by a symmetrical pattern of spots caused by the diffraction of the x-ray beam by the crystal. The pattern produced depends on the geometrical arrangement of the atoms in the crystal. A Laue diffraction photograph is shown in Figure 12.1.

Laue diffraction photographs are taken with "white" radiation, i.e., continuous x rays covering a range of wavelengths. Most modern techniques use monochromatic radiation, such as the K_α radiation (1.54 Å) obtained from an x-ray tube using Cu as the target. The K_β radiation (1.39 Å) can be removed by using nickel foil as a filter. Nickel strongly absorbs the shorter wavelength radiation, but not the K_α radiation because the adsorption edge of nickel (1.48 Å) falls between these two wavelengths. The adsorption edge of an element, which corresponds to the energy required to remove a $1s$ electron, generally falls between the wavelengths of the K_α and K_β radiation of the element of next higher atomic number.

Bragg's Law

If one imagines a beam of monochromatic x rays impinging on a crystal at an angle θ, some of the rays will be diffracted by the layers of atoms in the crystal (see Figure 12.2). The wave front F consists of a bundle of rays in phase. The wave front after diffraction is at DD'D″. The path length for the rays diffracted from the first layer is FCD and that from the second layer is FC'D'. The path length FC'D' is longer than FCD by AC'B which is equal to 2(AC'). Since AC' = $d \sin \theta$, the difference in path length is $2d \sin \theta$. The ray will be diffracted without destructive interference only if the difference in path length is equal to an integral number of wavelengths ($n\lambda$) or

$$2d \sin \theta = n\lambda \text{ (Bragg's Law)} \tag{12.1}$$

Bragg's Law permits the spacing between layers (d) to be calculated if λ is known and θ is measured. Similarly, the wavelength of monochromatic x rays can be determined using a crystal of known layer spacing.

Miller Indices

The faces of a crystal and the internal layers of atoms are identified by a set of three numbers known as *Miller Indices*. The center face shaded in Figure 12.3a is parallel to

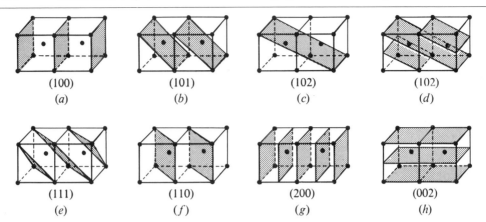

(100)   (101)   (102)   (102)
(*a*)   (*b*)   (*c*)   (*d*)

(111)   (110)   (200)   (002)
(*e*)   (*f*)   (*g*)   (*h*)

FIGURE 12.3. *Miller indices of planes in a body-centered cubic lattice.*

the *b* and *c* axes (the intercepts are taken as ∞) and intercepts the *a* axis at a distance which is one unit cell length. The Miller indices are the reciprocals of the intercepts, 1/1, 1/∞, 1/∞, or (100). The indices are referred to in the general case as (*hkl*). The parallel face through the atoms in the center of the cubes would cut the *a* axis at $(\frac{1}{2})a$, the Miller indices being (200). The face in the plane of the paper is parallel to the *a* and *c* axes and cuts the *b* axis at one unit cell length. The Miller indices are 1/∞, 1/1, 1/∞, or (010). The plane shaded in Figure 12.3*b* has the intercepts 1, ∞, and 1 and the indices (101). The plane shaded in Figure 12.3*c* has the indices $\frac{1}{2}$, 1/∞, 1/1, or multiplying by 2 to give whole numbers, (102). The lower parallel plane shaded in (*d*) gives the indices (102) directly. Equivalent parallel planes are identified by the set of indices containing the smallest whole numbers. The indices of several other planes are shown in the figure.

The reflections from a set of equivalent planes in a crystal is referred to by the Miller indices of the planes, i.e., the (100) reflection, the (111) reflection, etc. Higher orders ($n > 1$) of the reflections from the same planes are equivalent to reflections from parallel planes which are more closely spaced. Thus the second-order reflection ($n = 2$) from the (100) planes would occur at the same angle(θ) as a reflection from a (200) plane. This reflection is referred to as the (200) reflection. The third-order reflection from the (111) plane would be the (333) reflection.

Intensities of the Reflections

The intensities of the reflections depend on the scattering power of the atoms within the planes and on the extent of destructive interference. Reflections corresponding to all possible combinations of (*hkl*) are observed for a simple cubic structure. The situation is quite different for a face-centered lattice such as that of sodium chloride or potassium chloride. When x rays scattered from the (100) planes are in phase the reflections from the (200) planes are retarded by exactly half a wavelength, causing destructive interference. One of these planes contains metal ions and the other contains chloride ions. The cation and anion are isoelectronic in the case of potassium chloride and have essentially the same scattering power, so interference is complete and the reflection is missing. The scattering power of sodium ion is less than that of chloride ion and hence the interference is not complete, so the (100) reflection is observed, but weak. Because of the scattering equivalence of K^+ and Cl^-, similar systematic absences are noted for all planes containing odd values of h, k, or l. The intensities of the corresponding reflections for NaCl will be weak. The second-order reflection from the (100) planes will be exactly in phase with the first-order reflection from the (200) planes, so that the (200) reflection will be very strong (twice as many planes scattering) for both NaCl and KCl. The reflections observed for KCl are the same as those which would be expected for a simple cubic structure with a unit cell of length $a/2$.

Experimental Methods

The Laue method uses a single crystal in the path of a beam of "white" radiation x rays. A number of reflections are observed in a single photograph because the x rays cover a range of wavelengths to produce reflections from most of the planes, which are properly oriented with respect to the beam, even though the spacings vary. If the beam were monochromatic only a few planes would have the proper spacing to produce reflections from the crystal in a fixed position.

The powder method uses monochromatic x rays, but the powdered sample contains many tiny crystals randomly oriented. Some of the crystals will be properly oriented for all observable reflections. The random orientations of the crystals produce diffraction rings or cones rather than spots. The powder method is commonly used for identification purposes by comparing the observed spacing of the arcs recorded on a strip of film surrounding the crystal. Extensive files of spacings from powder photographs are available for comparison. Systematic absences of reflections as discussed for KCl are particularly helpful for identification. The method is not usually used for detailed structural analysis except in the simplest cases (primarily the cubic system) because of the difficulty in assigning indices to all of the planes for crystals of low symmetry.

There are a variety of methods available for recording diffraction patterns from single crystals which are oscillated or rotated. In some cases the rotation of the crystal is synchronized with the motion of the film so that one can obtain, in a single photograph, all of the reflections observable for the crystal mounted with one axis perpendicular to the x-ray beam. The crystal must be remounted on the other axes for a complete record of all reflections. One such method which is currently being used produces a photograph from which the assignment of indices to particular reflections is relatively simple (Figure 12.4).

Interpretation of the Diffraction Patterns

The intensities of the spots on the film are obtained experimentally and then one tries to reconstruct a structure which would produce the observed diffraction pattern. It is often a relatively simple task to obtain the dimensions and symmetry (space group) of the unit cell and the number of molecules in the unit cell. The assignment of individual atoms or molecules to particular positions in the crystal lattice is usually much more difficult.

Each reflection is characterized by a term called the structure factor $F(hkl)$. The structure factor is a summation of waves from all of the atoms in the unit cell. The

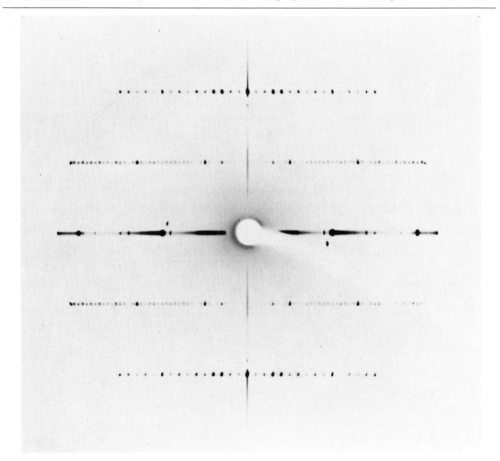

FIGURE 12.4. *Photograph of the reciprocal lattice of tridymite (a polymorph of SiO_2) from Lakeview, Oregon, taken with x-radiation of wavelength 1.54 A. (Technically, this is a zero-level precession photograph made with the 110+ axis of the crystal as the precessing axis, and with the precession angle $\mu = 25°$, exposed 16 hours.)*

amplitudes and phases of the waves differ. The experimentally determined quantity is the intensity of the reflection. The intensity is proportional to the square of the amplitude. Thus the amplitude of the structure factor for a given reflection is obtainable, but not the phase of the scattered wave. The structure factor may be expressed as the summation of a number of sine and cosine terms which are functions of the scattering powers of the individual atoms and the positions of the atoms in the unit cell. If it is possible to make reasonable guesses concerning the positions of the atoms in the unit cell, the structure factors can be calculated and from them the expected intensities of the reflections. The assumed positions can be varied until one obtains reasonable agreement between the calculated and observed intensities.

In practice, one usually tries to make reasonable guesses for atomic positions from combined chemical and structural information available. The observed intensities can be used to obtain the amplitudes of the structure factors and the assumed positions can be used to assign reasonable phase contributions for each atom. An electron density map is obtained from these structure factors using a Fourier series, which involves the summation of a number of sine and cosine terms. The resulting electron density map is likely to show some atoms in positions which are different from those assumed and hence suggests changes in positions which are likely to improve the agreement between calculated and observed intensities.

Guesses of atomic positions might be of little value for complex structures. Systematic methods which are used in such cases are discussed at length in books on x-ray crystallography. In applying these methods the use of all available chemical and physical information and "chemical intuition" are invaluable in simplifying the task.

The heavy atom method has been applied with success in a number of cases. If a

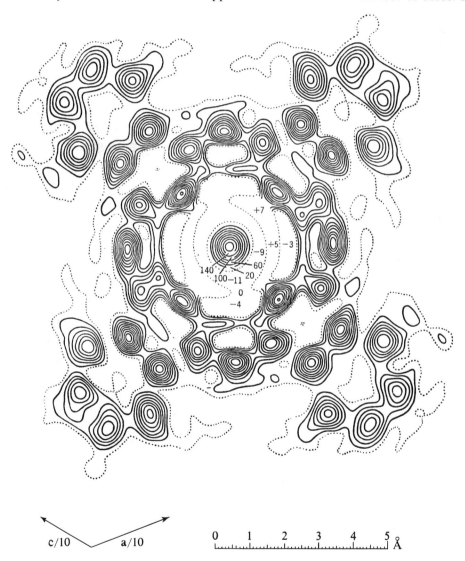

FIGURE 12.5. *An electron density map of the platinum phthalocyanine molecule (from J. M. Robertson and I. Woodward, J. Chem. Soc., 1940, 36).*

heavy atom, such as Pt or I, is incorporated in an organic compound, the scattering caused by the heavy atoms will be much greater than that of the light atoms for most reflections. The intensities for many reflections will be determined almost entirely by the heavy atoms. This simplifies the problem in that, at least for these reflections, it is necessary to adjust only the positions of the heavy atoms in order to achieve reasonable agreement between the observed and calculated intensities. The location of the heavy atoms which contribute strongly to the intensities of most reflections greatly simplifies the task of locating the other atoms. The electron density map of the platinum phthalocyanine molecule is shown in Figure 12.5. The structure determination for such a large molecule was greatly simplified because of the presence of Pt and because of the planarity of the fused ring system.

The replacement of an atom by a heavier one in a compound that gives crystals that are isomorphous with those of the first compound can facilitate the structure determination. The replacement of Se for S in $CuSO_4 \cdot 5H_2O$ causes some of the reflections to change in intensity very greatly. These reflections are ones to which the Se (or S) contribute strongly and this simplifies the assignment of the positions of Se or S.

Location of Hydrogen Atoms

Hydrogen atoms are usually not located by x-ray methods because of the very low scattering caused by the hydrogen atom. In some recent applications where the positions of all other atoms (no heavy atoms present) have been obtained very accurately, the hydrogen atoms have been located from a difference synthesis. Essentially this amounts to using the calculated positions and observed intensities to obtain an electron density map. Another Fourier synthesis is performed in which the contributions of the other atoms to the electron density are subtracted out to give, in very favorable situations, an electron density map in which the positions of the hydrogen atoms appear. The difference synthesis is also useful for the refinement of structures since an incorrectly assigned position is likely to show up as a region of negative density in the difference map.

Accuracy of Results of X-ray Investigations

Modern computers have greatly facilitated the tedious task of obtaining accurate structural information from x-ray diffraction data. The structures of very complex molecules such as vitamin B_{12}, penicillin, and some proteins have been obtained using modern techniques and group efforts.

The accuracy of the results of x-ray investigations vary widely. The early work, concerned primarily with fairly simple structures, was much less accurate than most present work. The interatomic distances obtained were probably not reliable to more than a few tenths of an Angstrom unit. The dimensions of a unit cell can be measured to within about 1 part in 1000 using modern techniques, so that internuclear separations in cubic crystals might be accurate to within ± 0.002 Å or slightly better. The internuclear separations are not obtained with an accuracy much better than ± 0.01 Å in most other cases.

The reliability of an x-ray structure determination is judged by the agreement between the structure factors (F_c) calculated from the assigned atomic positions and those obtained from the observed intensities (F_o). The agreement, which is never perfect, is usually expressed as the reliability index or residual, R, where

$$R = \frac{\Sigma \left| |F_o| - |F_c| \right|}{\Sigma |F_o|} \qquad (12.2)$$

The value of R which is considered to indicate reasonable agreement depends on the simplicity of the structure. A very accurate structure analysis is likely to include standard deviations for the bond lengths.

Neutron Diffraction

Neutron diffraction by crystals was demonstrated as early as 1936, but the method did not become important until the advent of nuclear piles. Fast neutrons produced in a nuclear pile are slowed down by collisions within a "moderator" (D_2O or graphite) to produce thermal neutrons, i.e., neutrons for which the range of kinetic energies is determined by the temperature of their surroundings. If the temperature is 100°, the peak energy corresponds to 0.0305 eV and a velocity of 2.4×10^5 cm sec^{-1}. The wavelength (1.63 Å) is given by the following relationships:

$$\lambda = \frac{h}{mv}$$

or

$$\lambda = \frac{0.081}{E} \times 10^{-8} \text{ cm} \qquad (12.3)$$

where E is the energy in electron volts. The wavelengths of thermal neutrons, which are in the same range as those of x rays, are suitable for diffraction by crystals.

The spectrum of the beam of neutrons which emerges from a nuclear pile is continuous, the wavelength range covering several Angstroms. A monochromatic beam, which is used for neutron crystallography, is obtained by reflection at a flat crystal surface. Wide beams, with cross-sectional areas of a few square inches, are used in order to obtain a sufficiently high counting rate in the detector. The large size and expense of neutron spectrometers combined with the need for a nuclear pile rule out this as a tool which one might consider adding to the list of fairly standard pieces of equipment for a laboratory. The difficulty of obtaining single crystals of sufficient size is not the least of the problems for many substances. The detector on a neutron spectrometer is usually a boron trifluoride counter. The counter actually records the α particles emitted in the $^{10}B(n,\alpha)^7Li$ nuclear reaction. Since the isotopic abundance of ^{10}B is low (about 20%), the efficiency of the counter can be greatly increased by using $^{10}BF_3$ rather than BF_3 containing the boron isotopes in the normal ratio.

Neutron diffraction differs from x-ray diffraction in a number of respects. The mass absorption coefficients of elements for x rays usually increase with increasing atomic number, but there is no such regular trend to be observed for neutron absorption. The neutron absorption coefficients are usually much smaller than those for x rays, but Table 12.1 shows that the variation is great. The x-ray scattering power increases fairly regularly with increasing atomic number, but there is no regular trend for neutron scattering. The neutron scattering power does not vary greatly (by less than an order of magnitude), while the x-ray scattering power increases from H to the heavy elements by about three orders of magnitude. Just about the maximum range of scattering power is encountered for two isotopes of nickel. It is exceptionally low for ^{62}Ni and exceptionally high for ^{58}Ni. Similar large differences are encountered for adjacent elements in the periodic table. Nevertheless, the scattering powers of most nuclides are of the same order of magnitude.

TABLE 12.1

X-ray and Neutron Absorption Coefficients (from J. Thewlis, Ann. Repts., 1950, 423)

| Element | At. No. | Mass Absorption Coefficient | |
		X rays	Neutrons
		($\lambda = 1.93$ Å)	($\lambda = 1.8$ Å)
Li	3	1.5	5.8
B	5	5.8	38.4
C	6	10.7	0.00023
Fe	26	72.8	0.026
Ag	47	402	0.32
Cd	48	417	13.0
Gd	64	199	183.0
Pb	82	429	0.0006

The differences between neutron and x-ray scattering offer great advantages and equally great disadvantages to neutron crystallography. The major advantage is that light elements, such as H or D, which cannot be located by x-ray diffraction can be located by neutron diffraction because they are comparable in neutron scattering power to the heavy elements. The great disadvantage is that the background scatter is likely to be much more serious because different isotopes of the same element, which would be expected to be randomly distributed among the sites for that element, might differ greatly in their scattering power. A nickel crystal should appear to contain a disordered array of atoms of greatly different scattering power occupying the sites of the lattice. This disadvantage might be turned into an advantage if one had a case where isotopic ordering should occur.

Neutrons, which possess magnetic moments, interact with nuclei which have magnetic moments to produce further background scattering for substances for which the nuclear spins are randomly oriented. The spin-disorder scattering is so great for hydrogen in comparison with the ordered scattering that deuterated compounds are often used for neutron diffraction studies if possible. Paramagnetic materials also contribute to the general background scattering because of the interaction of the magnetic moments of neutrons with the randomly oriented orbital magnetic moments of the atomic electrons. The magnetic moments of neighboring atoms are oriented in the same direction in ferromagnetic substances. The magnetic moments of neighboring pairs of atoms are opposed in antiferromagnetic substances. Neutron diffraction offers a tool for the investigation of the orientation of atomic magnetic moments in such substances. Manganese(ii) oxide is an antiferromagnetic substance with the sodium chloride structure. Neutron diffraction has shown that the magnetic "superlattice" is a cube twice as long on edge as the chemical unit cell.

It is to be expected that neutron diffraction will be reserved for special applications for which it can yield information not obtainable from x-ray diffraction studies. The neutron diffraction investigation in many cases is likely to follow an x-ray investigation or some other structural study that suggests that the neutron diffraction study would be worthwhile. One intriguing possibility has been suggested concerning the electron distribution in molecules and crystals. X rays are scattered by electrons and neutrons are scattered by atomic nuclei. If the electron distribution is not spherically symmetrical about each atom this would affect the x-ray diffraction, but not the neutron diffraction. Neutron diffraction results might help in the refinement of x-ray data in order to obtain information concerning the distribution of electrons in chemical bonds.

Electron Diffraction

The fact that electrons possess wave properties as well as corpuscular properties was demonstrated by the diffraction of a beam of electrons by a crystal of nickel in 1927 by Davisson and Germer. Davisson and Kunsman had observed interference effects in the scattering of electrons by nickel in 1921, but at the time the wave nature of electrons had not been proposed. It was 1924 before de Broglie proposed that electrons should have wave properties and obey the equation

$$\lambda = \frac{h}{mv} \quad \text{(de Broglie's equation)}$$

The wavelength of a beam of electrons is also given by

$$\lambda = \frac{150}{E} \times 10^{-8} \text{ cm} \tag{12.4}$$

where E is the potential in volts.

An electron beam with a wavelength of 1 Å would correspond to an energy of 150 V. The scattering of such low energy electrons is caused by interaction with the outer electrons of atoms as well as with the nuclei. The treatment of the scattering of high energy electrons is less complex because the scattering is caused primarily by interaction with atomic nuclei. Electron diffraction studies generally utilize electrons with energies of the order of 40,000 V (0.06 Å). The samples to be studied are usually gases or very thin films since electrons are very strongly absorbed by matter. It is also possible to investigate surfaces by reflection of the electron beam. However, the most important application involves the study of the diffraction of electrons by substances as vapors at low pressures (as low as 10^{-5} mm). The strong interaction of electrons with the molecules of the sample plus a very great effect on the photographic plate combine to require very short exposure time (of the order of tenths of a second).

The diffraction of x rays by a crystal depends on the spacing between layers. The diffraction of electrons by gaseous molecules depends on the distances between atoms in the molecule. Since the gaseous molecules will be randomly oriented relative to the electron beam, the diffraction pattern, like that of an x-ray powder photograph, consists of concentric rings. There is an appreciable amount of background scatter of the electron beam and, in early photographs at least, the diffraction bands are poorly resolved. New experimental techniques have greatly improved the resolution of the bands.

Electron diffraction studies are most useful for the evaluation of bond lengths and bond angles in relatively simple molecules. As the number of atoms increases, one soon reaches the situation where the number of pieces of information available (the spacings of the resolved diffraction rings) is not great enough to evaluate all of the necessary structural parameters. The number of electron diffraction rings observed is usually much less than the number of x-ray diffraction spots observed in an x-ray crystal study. This fact combined with the absence of information such as external crystal habit, which is such a help in an x-ray investigation, make the assumed model much more important in electron diffraction studies. The chance of an incorrect model giving reasonable agreement with the observed diffraction pattern is much greater in electron diffraction studies as compared to x-ray crystallography.

The accuracy of bond lengths and bond angles obtained from electron diffraction studies is probably comparable to that obtained in x-ray studies (usually not better than ± 0.01 Å, but as good as ± 0.002 Å in the best work) for simple molecules. The low electron scattering power of hydrogen makes it difficult to locate hydrogen atoms except when hydrogen is combined only with light elements, e.g., B_2H_6.

Electric Dipole Moment

In a diatomic molecule formed by two atoms of the same element, e.g., H_2, F_2, or N_2, the centers of positive and negative charge coincide. The H_2 molecule placed between charged plates does not have a preferred orientation with respect to the direction of the field. Two opposite charges ($\pm q$) separated by a distance d constitute an electric dipole with a moment which is given by qd. The dipole moment is a vector quantity directed from the positive to the negative charge. A molecule such as HF possesses a dipole moment because of the polarity of the bond resulting from the greater electronegativity of F compared to that of H. The electrons are shared between H and F, but the charge is displaced toward F. It was mentioned earlier (p. 88) that the dipole moment of HF is 1.98 Debye units rather than 4.4 Debye units as would be expected for the separation of unit charges ($e = 4.80 \times 10^{-10}$ esu) by the bond length (0.917 Å). The Debye unit (D) is 10^{-10} Å-esu or 10^{-18} cm-esu.

Dielectric Constants

The dipole moment of a molecule is usually obtained from dielectric constant measurements. The dielectric constant, ϵ, of a substance is the ratio of the capacitance of a capacitor with the substance (an insulator or dielectric) between the plates to that of the empty capacitor (vacuum).

$$\epsilon = \frac{C}{C_0} \tag{12.5}$$

The introduction of the substance into the capacitor results in a reduction of the field strength between the plates because of polarization of the dielectric. The attraction between two opposite charges ($\pm q$) separated by the distance d is q^2/d^2 in a vacuum, but $q^2/\epsilon d^2$ in the medium of dielectric constant ϵ. The dielectric constant is related to the molar polarization, P, by the Clausius-Mosotti Law:

$$P = \frac{\epsilon - 1}{\epsilon + 2} \cdot \frac{M}{\rho} \tag{12.6}$$

where M is the molecular weight of the substance and ρ is its density.

Determination of Dipole Moments

There are three contributions to the molar polarization, the electronic polarization, P_E, the atomic polarization, P_A, and the orientation polarization, P_O. The electronic polarization is caused by induced dipoles resulting from the distortion of the electron clouds of the molecules. The atomic polarization is caused by the displacement of the

$$P = P_E + P_A + P_0 \tag{12.7}$$

nuclei by the applied field. The orientation polarization is due to the effect of the field in trying to orient the dipoles. For some purposes P_E and P_A are combined as the induced polarization. Debye derived the equation

$$P = \frac{4\pi N}{3}\alpha_0 + \frac{4\pi N}{3}\frac{\mu^2}{3kT} \tag{12.8}$$

where N is Avogadro's number, α_0 is the molecular polarizability (the sum of the electronic and atomic susceptibilities), k is the Boltzmann constant, and T is the absolute temperature. The first term is independent of temperature, but the second term, the orientation polarization, is temperature dependent since thermal motion tends to oppose the orientation of the molecule in the field. If the dielectric constant is measured as a function of T, and P is plotted against $1/T$, a straight line is obtained. The intercept is $\frac{4}{3}\pi N\alpha_0$ and the slope is $4\pi N\mu^2/9k$. The dipole moment is calculated from the slope of the line.

For many substances the dielectric constant cannot be studied over a sufficiently wide temperature range for the method above to be applied. The dipole moment can also be obtained from dielectric constant and refractive index measurements. The Maxwell relation, $\epsilon = n^2$ (where n is the refractive index), holds for substances with $\mu = 0$ if n is measured in the infrared region. Combination of the Lorentz–Lorenz and

$$R = \frac{n^2 - 1}{n^2 + 2} \cdot \frac{M}{\rho} \quad \text{Lorentz–Lorenz Law} \tag{12.9}$$

Clausius–Mosotti laws shows that R (the molecular refractivity) is equal to P. Since the relationship holds for $\mu = 0$,

$$R = P = P_E + P_0$$

The low frequencies (500–5000 kc/sec) used for dielectric constant measurements permit the alternating field to influence P_E, P_A, and P_O. In the infrared region the alternating field of the electromagnetic radiation influences the electronic and atomic polarizations, but the permanent dipoles cannot change their orientation quickly enough to follow the high frequency. In the visible region even the atomic nuclei cannot follow the very high frequencies, but the light electrons are able to do so. Hence, only the electronic polarization is affected by visible light. The refractive index measured in the infrared region gives the molecular refractivity, which can be taken as equal to $P_E + P_A$ or $\frac{4}{3}\pi N\alpha_0$.

If the dielectric constants of dilute solutions of a polar substance dissolved in a non-polar solvent are measured as a function of concentration, one can calculate the apparent polarization. The molar refractions of the solutions can be calculated from the refractive indices (measured in the infrared region) of the pure liquids. The difference between the apparent polarizations and the molar refractions give the apparent molar orientation polarization, $4\pi N\mu^2/9kT$. Extrapolation to infinite dilution gives the true molar orientation polarization, from which the dipole moment may be calculated. The refractive indices in the visible region may be used if the atomic polarization can be evaluated or approximated. Usually P_A is only about 10% of P_E.

Dipole Moments and Molecular Structure

The dipole moment of a polyatomic molecule can be obtained by the addition of the vectors of the individual bond moments. The C—O bonds in CO_2 are somewhat polar, but the two equal vectors are directed at 180° to each other to give a net moment of zero. In a symmetrical molecule such as CCl_4 the vector representing one bond moment is exactly balanced by the sum of the components (directed at 180° to the first bond) of the vectors of the other three bonds. The zero dipole moment of BF_3 indicates that the molecule has a symmetrical planar structure. A pyramidal structure would have an appreciable dipole moment directed toward the center of the base of the pyramid.

The calculation, from bond moments, of the dipole moment of a molecule such as H_2O or NH_3 is complicated by the fact that the lone pairs on O or N also contribute to the total moment. This makes the use of dipole moments as a measure of percentage of ionic character questionable in such cases (see p. 89). Even though S has an unshared electron pair in SO_2, the bond polarity is great enough to give a dipole moment of 1.60 D.

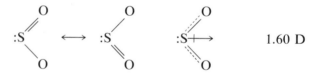

Hydrogen peroxide has been studied by electron diffraction, but only the O—O distance can be determined since the hydrogens cannot be located. X-ray crystallography is of little value for H_2O_2 itself, but the crystalline addition compound with urea, $CO(NH_2)_2 \cdot H_2O_2$, has provided valuable information. In addition to giving the O—O distance, the angle between the O—H bonds can be determined because of the formation of hydrogen bonds to urea. The structure can be represented by imagining the oxygen atoms (O—O distance 1.46 Å) along the line joining the pages of an open book with the O—H bonds (0.96 Å) in the planes of the pages opened to an angle of 106°. The O—O—H bond angle is 101°30'. This structure is consistent with the dipole moment of 2.13 D. It has also been confirmed from microwave studies. Even in the absence of other structural information the dipole moment would eliminate the planar structure with the H atoms on opposite sides of the O—O bond and it would also eliminate a structure involving free rotation about the O—O bond.

Dipole moments are helpful in distinguishing between different configurations or between geometrical isomers of coordination compounds. A four coordinate complex of the type MA_2B_2 might give a tetrahedral or planar configuration. If the complex is planar, two isomers, *cis* and *trans*, are possible. The differences between the dipole moments of the *cis* and *trans* planar arrangements should be very great. A tetrahedral configuration should give an intermediate dipole moment. The complex $[PtBr_2(Et_3P)_2]$ gives two isomers (in itself suggesting a planar arrangement). The isomer with zero dipole moment is obviously the *trans* isomer. The other isomer (*cis*) has a dipole moment of 11.2 D. Two isomers are also obtained for $[PtCl_2(Pr_2S)_2]$ (Pr = propyl), but neither has zero dipole moment (2.35 and 9.5 D). The dipole moment of the *trans* isomer should be lower than that of the *cis* isomer, but not zero in this case because the alkyl sulfide has its own moment (because of the lone pair on S) which is not directed along the Pt—S bond.

Nickel(III) forms a complex, $[Ni\{P(Et)_3\}_2Br_3]$, which is soluble in benzene. The molecular weight indicates that it is an undissociated monomer. As a 5-coordinate complex, the structures which are considered reasonable are shown in Figure 12.6. The expected dipole moments are shown for each structure. The observed dipole moment, 2.5 D, indicates that the correct structure is (*d*). The net dipole moment within the tetragonal plane for (*d*) should be approximately zero, so the expected dipole moment is that of the Ni—Br bond.

The cyclopentadienyl rings are staggered in ferrocene in the solid although there is a great deal of thermal motion. The dipole moment of diacetylferrocene (4.23 D) indicates that there is free rotation of the rings. Apparently the energy barrier to prohibit free rotation is small.

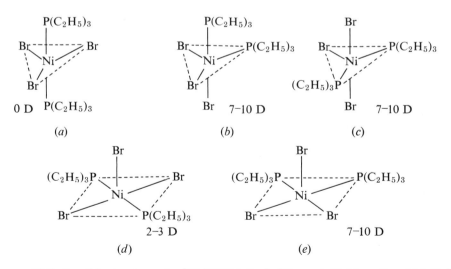

FIGURE 12.6. *Possible structures for* $[Ni\{P(Et)_3\}_2Br_3]$. [*From A. E. Martell and M. Calvin,* Chemistry of the Metal Chelate Compounds *(Englewood Cliffs: Prentice-Hall, Inc., 1952) p. 323.*]

Magnetic Properties

Magnetic Susceptibility

Atoms and molecules interact with an electric field because the atoms are made up of positively charged nuclei and negatively charged electrons. The motion of the electrons causes an interaction with an external magnetic field which is formally similar to the interaction with an electric field. If a sample is placed in a magnetic field of strength H, a certain intensity of the magnetization (I) is induced inside the sample. The ratio I/H is the *magnetic susceptibility* (per unit volume), κ. The specific or per gram susceptibility is given by $\chi_g = \kappa/\text{density}$ and the molar susceptibility (χ_M) is equal to $\chi_g \times$ Mol. Wt. The molar susceptibility is also given by Equation 12.10 which is similar in form to Equation 12.8 for the molar polarization in an electric field.

$$\chi_M = N\alpha + \frac{N}{3kT}\beta^2\mu_M^2 \tag{12.10}$$

N is Avogadro's number, α is the diamagnetic constant, k is the Boltzmann constant, T is the absolute temperature, β is the Bohr magneton $\left(\dfrac{eh}{4\pi mc} = 9.27 \times 10^{-21}\ \text{erg/oersted}\right.$ per atom or 5585 erg/oersted per gram-atom), and μ_M is the magnetic dipole moment expressed in Bohr magnetons. The diamagnetic constant represents the induced magnetic field in the sample. Since the induced field is opposed to the applied field, α is given a negative sign. Like the induced dipole moment, α is expected to be independent of temperature. In practice, however, small temperature effects on diamagnetic bodies may be observed due to secondary causes, such as change in hydrogen bonding or other physical forces of association. The contribution of the magnetic dipole moment to χ_M varies inversely with T because the tendency for the magnetic dipole to line up with the field is opposed by thermal motion.

If a substance has zero magnetic moment (no unpaired electrons), the second term is zero and $\chi_M = N\alpha$. Such substances are *diamagnetic* and, since the induced magnetization acts in an opposite sense to the applied field, the sample tends to be repelled by or pushed out of a magnetic field. All substances have the diamagnetic contribution, but when unpaired electrons are present $\mu_M \neq 0$ and the interaction of the magnetic dipole with the field is so great that this overshadows the diamagnetic contribution. Such substances are *paramagnetic* and the sample is drawn into the magnetic field (the magnetic field is stronger within the sample than outside the sample and acts in the same sense as the applied field).

Diamagnetism and paramagnetism are properties of individual atoms or molecules. The magnetic dipoles within a domain are lined up to act as little magnets in some substances. Such substances, e.g., Fe, Ni, and a number of alloys, are *ferromagnetic*. The force acting to draw a ferromagnetic substance into the magnetic field is much greater (perhaps $10^6\times$) than for paramagnetic substances. Adjacent magnetic dipoles are paired (opposed) in *antiferromagnetic* substances. The present discussion will be limited to diamagnetic and paramagnetic substances.

The magnetic susceptibility of a sample can be determined by several experimental approaches, but the Gouy method is one of the most simple in principle and in opera-

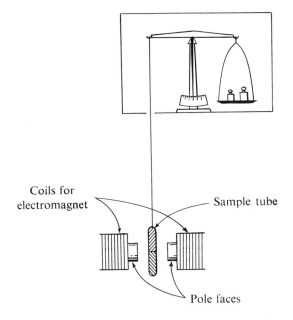

Coils for electromagnet

Sample tube

Pole faces

FIGURE 12.7. *Gouy magnetic balance.*

tion (see Figure 12.7). An analytical balance is modified so that a long thin sample tube can be hung from the left pan hook through a hole in the bottom of the balance. One type of sample tube is divided into two parts so that the sample being studied is placed in one end and a reference standard in the other end. The sample tube is suspended between the pole faces of a magnet (5,000–15,000 gauss*) so that the sample is in the upper (or lower) part of the field and the reference is in the lower (or upper) part of the field. The sample tube is weighed with the field on and with the field off (the current turned off in an electromagnet, or the magnet moved out of place in the case of a permanent magnet). If the sample (in the upper part of the tube) is more strongly paramagnetic than the reference, the apparent weight of the sample tube will be greater with the field on than with the field off. The difference in the weight gives the force acting to draw the sample into the magnetic field. This force (ΔW [in grams] times g [the gravitational constant]) is related to the volume susceptibilities of the sample (κ) and reference (κ_r) by the equation:

$$\text{Force} = \frac{(\kappa - \kappa_r)H^2A}{2} \qquad (12.11)$$

where H is the strength of the field (gauss) and A is the cross-sectional area of the sample tube. The molar susceptibility, calculated from $\kappa \times$ mol.wt./density or from the known concentration of a solution, is substituted in Equation 12.10 for the evaluation of μ_M. The diamagnetic contribution, α, can be calculated from tabulated atomic diamagnetic contributions for all of the atoms present. If χ_M is determined at several temperatures, μ_M can be obtained as the slope of the straight line given by the plot of χ_M *vs.*

* One gauss (or one oersted) is the field strength, which acts on a unit magnetic pole with a force of one dyne.

$1/T$ since Equation 12.10 is of the form

$$\chi_M = N\alpha + \text{const}\,\frac{\mu_M{}^2}{T} \qquad (12.12)$$

Spin and orbital motions of unpaired electrons contribute to the magnetic moment of most paramagnetic substances. The unpaired electrons of the rare earth metal ions are $4f$ electrons, which are well shielded from the influence of the fields of neighboring atoms and ions. Observed moments for these metals agree very well with those calculated from the expected orbital and spin contributions. The unpaired electrons in paramagnetic transition metal ions are the outer d electrons and the effect of the fields of neighboring ions and molecules is to quench the orbital contribution. The observed magnetic moments often agree reasonably well, particularly for members of the first transition series, with the moments expected from the spin contribution alone. The magnetic moment (in Bohr magnetons) is calculated from the spin only formula:

$$\mu_M = \sqrt{n(n+2)} \qquad (12.13)$$

where n is the number of unpaired electrons.

Magnetic moments are generally useful in determining the number of unpaired electrons to provide information about the population and relative energies of the d levels in complex ions (see p. 350). In the case of nickel(II) compounds magnetic moments may be used almost always to distinguish between planar complexes which are diamagnetic and tetrahedral or octahedral complexes which are paramagnetic with 2 unpaired electrons. More detailed magnetic studies allow the distinction to be made between octahedral and tetrahedral complexes in favorable cases because the orbital contribution is not quenched to the same extent in the two cases. Copper(II) complexes

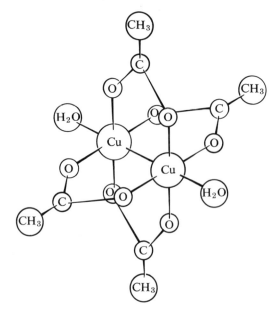

FIGURE 12.8. *Structure of* $Cu(CH_3CO_2)_2 \cdot H_2O$.

are expected to be paramagnetic with one unpaired electron. Surprisingly, the compound $Cu(CH_3CO_2)_2 \cdot H_2O$ is diamagnetic. The x-ray structure shows the presence of a dimer with the two copper atoms close enough to form a metal–metal bond (see Figure 12.8), which might be a δ-bond.

The magnetic properties of odd electron molecules and free radicals provide a means of detecting and following these substances. The paramagnetism of O_2 serves as the basis for an analytical method for the determination of oxygen in the presence of diamagnetic gases. Oxygen is the only common gas which is paramagnetic. Other paramagnetic gases (NO, NO_2, or ClO_2) are not likely to be present, but if they are present they can be easily removed because of their great reactivity.

Magnetic Resonance Spectroscopy

Paramagnetic resonance and nuclear magnetic resonance are really applications of microwave (wavelength in mm or cm range, frequency in kilomegacycles) and radiowave (wavelength in m or km range, frequency in kilocycles) spectroscopy. Since they also involve the magnetic properties of substances, they will be discussed before other applications of spectroscopy.

PARAMAGNETIC RESONANCE

When an ion with resultant angular momentum, J, is placed in a magnetic field, Zeeman splitting of electronic energy levels occurs. The measurement of the magnetic susceptibility involves the determination of the interaction of one energy state (usually the ground state) with the magnetic field. Electron paramagnetic resonance (EPR) (also called electron spin resonance) is concerned with the determination of the energy changes involved in transitions from one of these states to another for a paramagnetic ion or molecule. The energies of the levels corresponding to the various spatial orientations of J in a magnetic field H are given by

$$E_H = g\beta H M \tag{12.14}$$

where g is the spectroscopic splitting factor, β is the Bohr magneton, and M is the electronic magnetic quantum number. Transitions corresponding to the selection rule, $\Delta M = \pm 1$, can be observed using microwave radiation with the magnetic vector polarized perpendicular to the field H. The energies of the quanta absorbed are given by

$$h\nu = g\beta H$$

or

$$\nu \text{ (Megacycles)} = 1400 \ gH \text{ (kilogauss)} \tag{12.15}$$

For most paramagnetic ions and free radicals g is about 2 ($g = 2.0023$ for a free electron spin), the value to be expected if the orbital contribution is quenched. If $g = 2$ and $H = 10$ kilogauss, $\nu = 28,000$ Mc and $\lambda = 21.42/gH = 1.07$ cm.

Paramagnetic resonance measurements are obtained by detecting the change in transmitted or reflected power of microwave radiation for a sample in a wave guide or cavity resonator placed in a magnetic field. One could obtain a spectrum by changing the frequency of microwave radiation, but it is easier experimentally to work at constant frequency and vary the magnetic field strength. The wavelength used is likely to be in the range of 1–3 cm with field strengths sweeping through the range of 0–15 kilogauss. The equipment is similar to that used for nuclear magnetic resonance shown in Figure 12.9.

Paramagnetic resonance studies, like magnetic susceptibility measurements, permit one to determine the number of unpaired electrons present in an ion, but the method is capable of providing much more detailed information. The splitting factor, g, depends on the orbital and spin contributions. Variations of g (from $g = 2$ for $L = 0$ or for complete quenching of the orbital contribution) can be taken as an indication of the orbital contribution. This permits one to distinguish between possible configurations of paramagnetic rare earth ions such as $5f^n6d^1$ and $5f^{n+1}6d^0$. If the orbital contribution is not quenched, it might also be possible to decide whether an electron has been promoted from a $3d$ to a $4d$ orbital in a coordination compound for which covalent bonding involving the d orbitals is possible (see p. 343).

Distorted octahedral complexes such as those of Cu^{2+} give different g values depending on the orientation of a crystal in the magnetic field. The variation in the g values provides information concerning the nature of the distortion of the octahedral field. It is interesting that the octahedral complex $[Cu(H_2O)_6]^{2+}$ is flattened (along the z axis) according to measurements made at 290°K and elongated according to measurements made at 90°K.*

Nuclear magnetic moments (for nuclei with nonzero spins) interact with the electron spin magnetic moment to produce hyperfine splitting. Such splitting in the paramagnetic resonance spectrum of $[IrCl_6]^{2-}$ (caused by ^{35}Cl and ^{37}Cl) is interpreted to mean that the unpaired electron is spread over the whole complex ion in antibonding molecular orbitals.† Similar splitting is caused by Cl in the copper complex of tetraphenylporphyrin with Cl substituted in the para position of each phenyl group. Here also the unpaired electron occupies a molecular orbital extending over the whole molecule.‡ Such EPR studies provide a basis for determining the extent of delocalization of electrons and gives real meaning to discussions of the "degree" of covalent bonding.

The EPR method can be applied to the study of electron exchange reactions which occur in time intervals of 10^{-3}–10^{-9} sec. Line width measurements permit the study of the rates of very rapid substitution reactions of paramagnetic ions.

NUCLEAR MAGNETIC RESONANCE

The existence of nuclear spin was demonstrated by Dennison in 1924 when he showed that there were two molecular species of H_2, one with the nuclear spins parallel, *ortho*-hydrogen, and one with the spins opposed, *para*-hydrogen. A spinning nucleus, since it is charged, has a magnetic moment which interacts with an applied magnetic field. The magnetic properties of substances have been discussed earlier in terms of the interaction between electrons, particularly unpaired electrons, and a magnetic field. The magnetic moments of nuclei are only of the order of 1/2000 that of electronic magnetic moments because of the much greater mass of nuclei. Nuclear magnetic

* Owen, J. J., in *Chemistry of the Co-ordinate Compounds* (London: Pergamon Press, 1958) pp. 433-434.
† Bleaney, B., *J. Phys. Chem.*, **57**, 508 (1953).
‡ Ingram, D. J. E., J. E. Bennett, P. George, and J. M. Goldstein, *J. Am. Chem. Soc.*, **78**, 3545 (1956).

moments, μ, are given in nuclear magnetons (1 nm $= eh/4\pi M$, where M is the mass of the proton). The magnetic moment of the proton is 2.79276 nm and that of the neutron is -1.9135 nm.*

Nuclei are characterized by nuclear spin numbers, I, which have the values $0, \frac{1}{2}, 1, \frac{3}{2}, \ldots$ (expressed in quantum units $h/2\pi$). Those with even atomic numbers and even mass numbers, e.g., $^{12}_{6}C$, $^{16}_{8}O$, $^{28}_{14}Si$, and $^{32}_{16}S$, have spin numbers of zero. Such nuclei can be considered to have no mechanical spin and the nuclear magnetic moment is zero. Nuclei with spin numbers of $\frac{1}{2}$, e.g., ^{1}H, ^{13}C, ^{15}N, ^{19}F, ^{29}Si, and ^{31}P, can be considered to have a magnetic moment because of the mechanical spin of the nuclei for which the charge distribution is symmetrical. When $I > \frac{1}{2}$, ($I = 1$ for ^{2}H and ^{14}N, $I = \frac{3}{2}$ for ^{33}S, ^{35}Cl, ^{37}Cl, and ^{79}Br, $I = \frac{5}{2}$ for ^{17}O and ^{127}I), the nuclei possess magnetic moments because of the spin, but they also possess nuclear quadrupole moments, Q, which can be pictured as the result of an asymmetric distribution of charge in the nucleus. The greatest interest for nuclear magnetic studies has been in nuclei with $I = \frac{1}{2}$ and $Q = 0$. The spectra are more complex for substances containing nuclei with nuclear quadrupole moments.

The total angular momentum of a nucleus is $(h/2\pi)\,[I(I+1)]$. The spinning nucleus in a magnetic field precesses about the direction of the field. There are $(2I + 1)$ possible orientations (corresponding to $I, I - 1, \ldots, -I$) with respect to the direction of the applied field. Thus, if $I = \frac{1}{2}$ there are two orientations ($I = \pm\frac{1}{2}$); there are three possible orientations if $I = 1$ ($I = 1, 0,$ or -1). The potential energy difference between adjacent (with respect to energy) orientations in a strong uniform magnetic field, H_0, is $\mu H_0/I$. Consequently, the frequency of radiant energy required to bring about such a transition is

$$h\nu_0 = \mu H_0/I$$

or

$$\nu_0 = 0.7625\ \mu H_0/I \tag{12.16}$$

where ν_0 is the resonance frequency in Mc/sec and H_0 is in kgauss. The resonance frequency is 42.6 Mc/sec, which is in the radio-frequency range, for a bare nucleus in a magnetic field of 10 kgauss. This corresponds to the energy needed to flip a spinning proton from an orientation in which its magnetic vector is aligned with the applied field to the orientation in which its alignment is opposed to the field. Since the energy required to go from the lower energy orientation to one corresponding to higher energy is very small, it is not too surprising that, because of thermal agitation, the population of the two states is not greatly different even in a strong magnetic field. The excess number of protons in the lower energy state is only about 7 in 1 million (corresponding to 1,000,007 in the lower state and 999,993 in the higher state) in a field of 10 kgauss at room temperature.

Equipment. A nuclear magnetic resonance spectrometer is very similar to a paramagnetic resonance spectrometer. A sample in a strong homogeneous magnetic field (directed along the x axis as identified in Figure 12.9) is subjected to a radio-frequency signal, which imposes a small oscillating field (directed along the y axis) on the sample. The magnetic field is varied by the sweep generator. At the appropriate field strength

---

* The fact that the neutron, even though it is neutral, has a magnetic moment has been explained in terms of a model consisting of a proton and a negative meson.

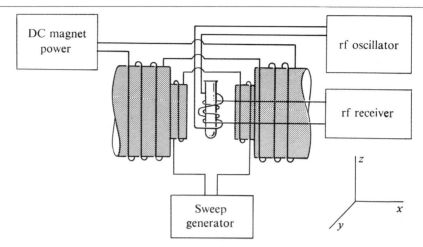

FIGURE 12.9. *NMR spectrometer.*

the oscillating magnetic field will cause absorption of energy by the sample and will produce an oscillating magnetic field in the z direction. This alternating field induces a current in the receiver coil, which is amplified as the NMR signal. The magnetic field must be very homogeneous. The field strength might be as high as 14 kgauss. The radio-frequency oscillator might operate at about 40 Mcycles, the frequency used depending on the nuclear species being studied.

Chemical Shift. The remarkable rapidity with which NMR has been applied to chemical problems (NMR was discovered in 1946) attests to the importance of this structural tool. Perhaps the most unusual feature of the information gained from NMR is the great sensitivity to small changes in chemical environment. The resonance frequency for the bare proton was discussed earlier, but in stable compounds hydrogen is never encountered as a bare proton. Nuclei are shielded by electrons so that in an applied magnetic field, H_{appl}, the effective field at the nucleus is given by

$$H_0 = H_{appl}(1 - \sigma) \tag{12.17}$$

where σ is a measure of the shielding of the nucleus from the external field. Sigma varies from just a few parts per million for H to about 2% for some metals. The shielding of the nucleus depends on the chemical environment, so the position of the resonance peak provides valuable chemical information. The change in the position of an NMR peak is referred to as the *chemical shift*. Since the chemical shift, δ, depends on the field strength, it is defined as

$$\delta = \frac{H_{sample} - H_{ref}}{H_{ref}} \times 10^6 \tag{12.18}$$

where H_{ref} is the field strength at which resonance occurs for some reference substance (for protons it is commonly H_2O, benzene, or tetramethylsilane) and H_{sample} is the field strength at which resonance occurs for the compound being examined.

The chemical shift of CH_3 protons in C_2H_5OH is different from that of CH_2 protons because of the differences in shielding and both differ from that of the OH proton.*

---

* The term proton is used because it is the nucleus which is being studied. It does not imply ionization.

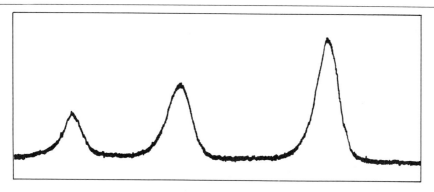

FIGURE 12.10. *The low resolution spectrum of ethanol (40Mc)* [*from L. M. Jackman,* Applications of Nuclear Magnetic Resonance Spectroscopy in Organic Chemistry *(London: Pergamon Press Limited, 1959) p. 20, reprinted with permission*].

The low resolution NMR spectrum of C_2H_5OH is shown in Figure 12.10. The areas under the three peaks are in the approximate ratio 1:2:3, corresponding to the number of protons of each type.

The chemical shift has been shown to give a satisfactory correlation with electronegativities of the halogens in compounds such as the ethyl halides. Useful correlations with Hammett's constants (see p. 197) have also been obtained.

Spin–Spin Interactions. A high resolution NMR spectrogram of ethanol shows that the CH_3 peak is a triplet and the CH_2 peak is a quartet (see Figure 12.11). The explanation of the splitting observed for the ethyl group is found in the interaction between the spins of the protons of adjacent groups. The methyl protons will be affected by the spins of the methylene protons, which can be combined at any time in one of four possible combinations (see Figure 12.12). The CH_3 protons will have slightly different

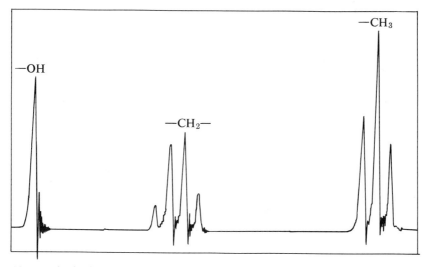

FIGURE 12.11. *The high resolution spectrum of ethanol obtained at 40 Mc with a sample containing a trace of acid* [*from L. M. Jackman,* Applications of Nuclear Magnetic Resonance Spectroscopy in Organic Chemistry *(London: Pergamon Press Limited, 1959) p. 20, reprinted with permission*].

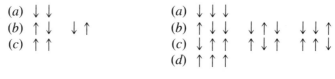

(a) ↓ ↓   (a) ↓ ↓ ↓

(b) ↑ ↓   ↓ ↑   (b) ↑ ↓ ↓   ↓ ↑ ↓   ↓ ↓ ↑

(c) ↑ ↑   (c) ↓ ↑ ↑   ↑ ↓ ↑   ↑ ↑ ↓

                                 (d) ↑ ↑ ↑

Spin arrangements for   Spin arrangements for
protons in CH_2 protons in CH_3

FIGURE 12.12

chemical shifts depending on the particular combination of proton spins of the CH_2 group and, since two of these combinations are equivalent (b), three peaks are observed. The areas under the peaks are in the ratio 1:2:1 in accordance with the fact that one of the combinations (b) is twice as likely to occur as either (a) or (c). The CH_2 peak is a quartet because, although there are eight possible combinations for the protons of the adjacent CH_3 group, there are only four nonequivalent combinations (Figure 12.12). The areas under the peaks correspond to the probabilities of these combinations, 1:3:3:1. The absence of splitting in the OH band is attributed to the rapid exchange of the OH proton in the presence of traces of acid or base. A highly purified sample of ethanol does give the expected splitting of the OH into a triplet with further splitting of the CH_2 peaks.

Spin–spin interactions are usually important only for atoms separated by not more than one or two bonds. The interaction can be pictured as being transmitted by the bonding electrons. There is a tendency for an electron spin to couple with the spin of a nucleus when the electron is close to that nucleus. The repulsion between electrons would suggest that one probable instantaneous arrangement for the electrons in a chemical bond puts one electron near each of the bonded nuclei. The tendencies for the coupling between each nucleus and the nearest electron and the necessary coupling between electron pairs leads to an indirect influence of the nuclei on one another. Diamagnetic substances are usually used for NMR studies as far as possible because of the interaction between electron and nuclear spins and because of the much greater magnitude of electron magnetic moments.

Most of the applications of NMR so far have been to organic compounds. The method is ideally suited to the investigation of stereochemical problems of C—H compounds. Hydrogen is a desirable nucleus ($I = \frac{1}{2}$) and ^{12}C and ^{16}O have zero nuclear magnetic moments ($I = 0$) so that only proton–proton interactions are observed. The resulting spectra are relatively simple even for fairly complex molecules. Applications have also been made to the study of equilibria such as the keto–enol conversion. The kinetics of keto–enol conversions and of other reactions have also been studied.

Inorganic applications of NMR are appearing with increasing frequency. The spectra of B_2H_6 and other boron–hydrogen compounds have yielded useful information, but the situation is more complex because of the moments of the B isotopes. NMR has provided useful structural information concerning the oxyacids of phosphorus. The pos-

$$P—O—H \quad \text{and} \quad P \overset{\displaystyle O}{\underset{\displaystyle H}{<}}$$

sible arrangements P—O—H and P can be distinguished because of the spin–spin

interaction between ^{31}P and ^1H (both have $I = \frac{1}{2}$). The species present in a mixture of

H_2O, HF, and P_2O_5 were identified using the ^{31}P spectrum. In Figure 12.13 there are single peaks for each of two phosphoric acid species, doublets for each of the two species containing one F for each P, and a triplet for $(HO)(O)PF_2$.

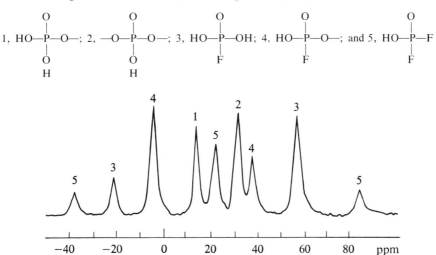

$$1, \; HO—\overset{\overset{\displaystyle O}{|}}{\underset{\underset{\displaystyle H}{|}}{P}}—O—; \quad 2, \; —O—\overset{\overset{\displaystyle O}{|}}{\underset{\underset{\displaystyle H}{|}}{P}}—O—; \quad 3, \; HO—\overset{\overset{\displaystyle O}{|}}{\underset{\underset{\displaystyle F}{|}}{P}}—OH; \quad 4, \; HO—\overset{\overset{\displaystyle O}{|}}{\underset{\underset{\displaystyle F}{|}}{P}}—O—; \quad and \; 5, \; HO—\overset{\overset{\displaystyle O}{|}}{\underset{\underset{\displaystyle F}{|}}{P}}—F$$

FIGURE 12.13. *The ^{31}P spectrum of a sample prepared from P_2O_5, HF, and H_2O. Chemical shifts are relative to 85% H_3PO_4. [After D. P. Ames, S. Ohashi, C. F. Callis, and J. R. Van Wazer, J. Am. Chem. Soc., 81, 6350 (1959).]*

NMR studies have shown that the solid complex believed to be $K_3[Rh(C_2O_4)_3] \cdot 4\frac{1}{2}H_2O$ is, in fact, $K_6[Rh(C_2O_4)_3][Rh(C_2O_4)_2(HC_2O_4)(OH)] \cdot 8H_2O$.* Studies of the ^1H and ^{19}F magnetic resonance of the HF_2^- ion indicate that the ion is symmetrical with the H^+ within ± 0.06 Å of the center of the ion axis.†

Other Applications. Cobalt complexes can be studied using the only natural nuclide, ^{59}Co. The chemical shifts (Table 12.2) are among the largest which have been observed. The unusually large shifts for diamagnetic cobalt(III) complexes are believed to be caused by a second order paramagnetic effect. The shifts and their temperature dependencies have been correlated with the electronic absorption spectra. Symmetrical complexes gave excellent agreement with the crystal field effects, but the unsymmetrical complexes did not.

Broad line (low resolution) NMR spectra also provide useful structural information. Ferrocene gives narrow, liquid-like NMR lines, supporting the assumption of free rotation at room temperature. The lines broaden at lower temperatures, indicating greater restriction of rotation.‡ Substitution of organic groups for H in one or both rings causes line broadening because of some restriction in rotation. The bridged compound in which two rings are joined gives very broad, solid-like lines indicating little or no motion of the rings. The NMR spectra of dibenzenechromium show a greater broadening effect as the temperature is decreased. The close-packed cubic structure of dibenzenechromium (ferrocene is monoclinic) might be expected to make it easier to "freeze out" the rotation.

* Porte, A. L., H. S. Gutowsky, and G. M. Harris, *J. Chem. Phys.,* **34**, 66 (1961).
† Waugh, J. S., F. B. Humphrey, and D. M. Yost, *J. Phys. Chem.,* **57**, 486 (1953).
‡ Mulay, L. N., E. G. Rochow, and E. O. Fischer, *J. Inorg. Nucl. Chem.,* **4**, 231 (1957); L. N. Mulay, E. G. Rochow, E. O. Stejskal, and N. E. Weliky, *ibid.,* **16**, 23 (1960).

TABLE 12.2

^{59}Co *Chemical Shifts in Some Cobalt*(III) *Complexes* [a]

Compound	$\delta(ppm)$
$K_3Co(CN)_6$	0
$[Co(dipy)_3](ClO_4)_3$	−6620
cis-$[Co(NH_3)_4(NO_2)_2]NO_3$	−6880
trans-$[Co(NH_3)_4(NO_2)_2]NO_3$	−7150
$[Coen_3]Cl_3$	−7180
$[Copn_3]Cl_3$	−7220
$[Co(NH_3)_5NO_2]Cl_2$	−7460
$Na_3Co(NO_2)_6$	−7490
$Co(NH_3)_6Cl_3$	−8220
$[Co(NH_3)_5Cl]Cl_2$	−9070
$Co(CH_3COCHCOCH_3)_3$ (benzene solution)	−12,700

[a] From Paul C. Lauterbur, in *Determination of Organic Structures by Physical Methods*, Vol. 2, F. C. Nachod and W. D. Phillips, eds. (New York: Academic Press, 1962) p. 532; see references cited there.

It was mentioned that the nuclear quadrupole resonance (NQR) spectra are more complex than NMR spectra. Nevertheless, since the quadrupole moment arises because of an asymmetric distribution of charge in the nucleus, coupling with the external field might give direct evidence of the asymmetry of the field. Such evidence could be of great importance in providing detailed information about bonding and electron distribution in molecules.

If a proton is exchanged between two species (HA and HB) so that the average lifetime in either species is long compared to the reciprocal of the chemical shift, two lines will be observed. If the average lifetime is short compared to $1/\delta$, a single line will be observed between the peaks for the species HA and HB. Intermediate lifetimes will result in broadening of the lines (Figure 12.14). The broadening of the lines can be used for studying the rate of such exchange processes. The line broadening technique for nuclei with quadrupole moments has been used for studying the rates of formation of the complexes $CdBr^+$, $CdBr_2$, and $CdBr_3^-$ (7×10^8, 1.8×10^7, and 1.4×10^7 $M^{-1}sec^{-1}$, respectively) and the formation of I_3^- from I_2 and I^- (4.1×10^{10} $M^{-1}sec^{-1}$) in references given by Strehlow.

Studies of proton exchange involving hydrated metal ions are uncertain with respect to this as a water exchange or simple proton exchange process. Connick has studied the water exchange of paramagnetic ions in water enriched in O^{17}. The width of the resonance of O^{17} is increased by interaction with paramagnetic ions. The broadening can be related to the rate of the exchange process. The results for the transition metal ions* are in reasonable agreement with those obtained by relaxation methods (p. 460). Connick has also studied the replacement of H_2O by SO_4^{2-} for a series of metals and found the rates to agree closely with those for H_2O exchange, suggesting that the displacement of H_2O is the rate controlling process in both cases. Connick was able to obtain

* Connick, R. E., and E. D. Stover, *J. Phys. Chem.*, **65**, 2075 (1961).

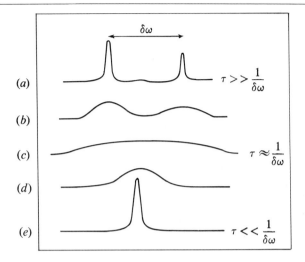

FIGURE 12.14. *NMR spectrum of two proton exchanging substances HA and HB for different rates of exchange. The chemical shift is δ and τ is the average lifetime of the proton in a given species* [from H. Strehlow, in Investigations of Rates and Mechanisms of Reactions, S. L. Friess, E. S. Lewis, and A. Weissberger, eds., Vol. VIII, Part II of Technique of Organic Chemistry, A. Weissberger ed. (New York: Interscience Publishers, Inc., 1963) p. 877].

rate constants for the stepwise displacement of H_2O by Cl^- from $Ru(H_2O)_6^{3+}$ to give complexes up to and including $RuCl_6^{3-}$. The results even included rate constants for conversions from the *trans*-$[Ru(H_2O)_4Cl_2]^+$ to the *cis* isomer and the two routes for further substitution of Cl^- in the *cis* isomer.*

Line broadening techniques have been applied to the study of the exchange of a number of ligands for divalent transition metal ions.† The rates for Ni^{2+} are slow as expected from ligand field theory (p. 406) and also as found for H_2O exchange. The data for Cu^{2+} support an S_N2 mechanism. Presumably the incoming ligand can approach along one of the axial directions to bond to the copper before the displacement of the leaving ligand.

Absorption Spectroscopy

Paramagnetic and nuclear magnetic resonance have been mentioned as applications of microwave and radiowave spectroscopy. It is now appropriate to consider other applications of spectroscopy which provide information concerning structure and bonding of chemical compounds. Emission spectroscopy will not be discussed, although it is of great value in providing information concerning atomic energy levels and excited states of complex organic molecules.

The kind of chemical information involved in each spectral region is determined by the energy per quantum. The electromagnetic spectrum is represented in Figure 12.15.

* Connick, R. E., and D. A. Fine, *J. Am. Chem. Soc.*, **83**, 3414 (1961); R. E. Connick in *Advances in the Chemistry of Coordination Compounds*, S. Kirschner, ed. (New York: The Macmillan Company, 1961) p. 17.
† Pearson, R. G., paper presented at the 145th Meeting of the American Chemical Society, New York, September, 1963, reported in *Chem. Engr. News*, Sept. 16, 1963, p. 74.

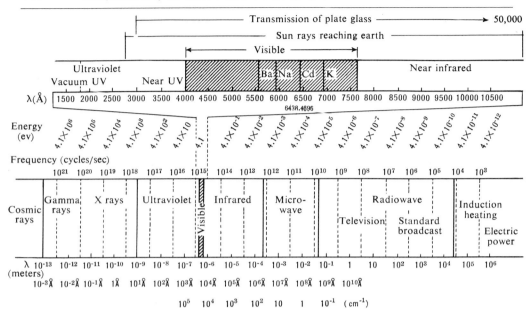

FIGURE 12.15. *The electromagnetic spectrum.*

The smallest amounts of energy absorbed in transitions between molecular energy levels involve pure rotational transitions. Since the energies involved are of the order of 10^{-3} eV, rotational spectra are observed in the far infrared and microwave regions. Transitions between vibrational levels involve energies of about 0.1 eV, which places the vibrational spectra in the infrared region. The absorption of light in the visible range (the energy corresponds to a few electron volts) involves electronic transitions. Color (due to the absorption of visible light) is associated with substances for which the differences between electronic energy levels is small. Most substances that involve atoms with closed configurations are colorless, but absorb in the ultraviolet region (10–100 eV). The absorption of x rays (10^3–10^4 eV) results in the promotion to higher energy levels or removal of the innermost electrons.

An energy level diagram for a molecule is shown in Figure 12.16 with the energy levels designated by quantum numbers. Two electronic states for the molecule are shown, the ground state, $n = 1$, and the first electronically excited state, $n = 2$. For each electronic state several vibrational states ($v = 0, 1, 2, 3, \ldots$) are shown. The rotational states for each of the vibrational states are designated by the quantum number J ($J = 0, 1, 2, 3, \ldots$).

Rotational Spectra

Pure rotational spectra are observed in the far infrared or microwave region for molecules which have permanent dipole moments. Transitions occur only between adjacent quantum levels ($\Delta J = 1$). The rotational energy for each of the permitted levels (J) of a diatomic molecule (AB) treated as a rigid rotator is

$$E_J = \frac{h^2 J(J + 1)}{8\pi^2 I} \qquad (12.19)$$

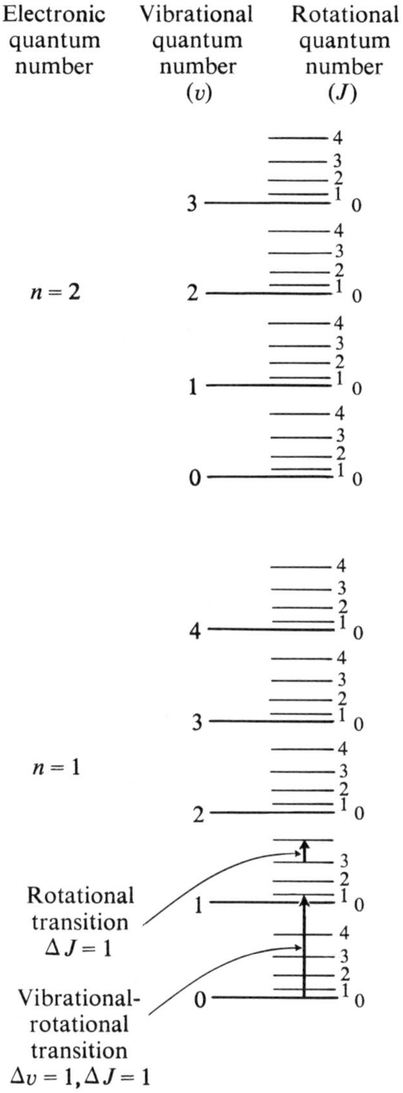
Electronic quantum number
Vibrational quantum number (v)
Rotational quantum number (J)
n = 2
n = 1
3
2
1
0
4
3
2
1
0
4 3 2 1 0
Rotational transition ΔJ = 1
Vibrational-rotational transition Δv = 1, ΔJ = 1

FIGURE 12.16. *Molecular energy level diagram.*

where h is Planck's constant and I is the moment of inertia of the molecule. The moment of inertia for a molecule AB is

$$I = \frac{m_A m_B}{m_A + m_B} r^2 \tag{12.20}$$

where m_A and m_B are the respective masses of the atoms separated by the distance r. The moment of inertia is the same as that of a point mass, μ, at a distance r from the axis of rotation. Mu, the reduced mass of the molecule, is given by

$$\mu = \frac{m_A m_B}{m_A + m_B} \tag{12.21}$$

Equation 12.20 can be written as $I = \mu r^2$.

Since the selection rule restricts transitions to those for which $\Delta J = 1$, the energy involved in the transition is

$$\Delta E = \frac{h^2}{4\pi^2 I} J \qquad (12.22)$$

and, since $\Delta E = h\nu$, the rotational frequency for a rigid rotator is

$$\nu = \frac{h}{4\pi^2 I} J \qquad (12.23)$$

where J is any integer. The frequencies are approximately evenly spaced,* the differences between frequencies being $h/4\pi^2 I$. If the frequencies are expressed in wave numbers (cm^{-1}), the spacing is $h/4\pi^2 cI$, where c is the velocity of light. Thus it is possible to calculate the moment of inertia from the spacing of the rotational lines without knowing the value of J. The internuclear distance, r, can be calculated from I and μ using $I = \mu r^2$. The interpretation of rotational spectra of polyatomic molecules containing more than two atoms is similar, but more complex.

The spacing between rotational lines for HCl is 20.68 cm^{-1}.†

$$20.68 \text{ cm}^{-1} = \frac{h}{4\pi^2 cI} = \frac{55.96 \times 10^{-40}}{I}$$

$$I = 2.71 \times 10^{-40} \text{ gcm}^2$$

Since the reduced mass for $H^{35}Cl$ is 1.62×10^{-24} g (from Equation 12.21), and using $I = \mu r^2$,

$$r = \sqrt{\frac{2.71 \times 10^{-40}}{1.62 \times 10^{-24}}} = \underline{1.30 \times 10^{-8} \text{ cm}} = \underline{1.30 \text{ Å}}$$

The far infrared region presents serious experimental problems because of the small amounts of energy involved, poor resolution, and the great difficulty caused by stray radiation. Pure rotational absorption occurs in the microwave region for heavy molecules. The instrumentation in the microwave region permits resolutions of about 1 part in 10^7 as compared to resolutions of about 1 part in 10^3 in the infrared region. The very high resolution in the microwave region permits interatomic distances to be determined with an accuracy as great as ± 0.002 Å.

Vibrational-Rotational Spectra

Only molecules that undergo a change in dipole moment on going from the ground state to the excited state exhibit vibrational spectra. The oscillating polarity of the molecule is essential to the absorption of a quantum of energy of electromagnetic radiation of the appropriate frequency. Pure vibrational spectra are not usually observed

---

* Real molecules do not behave as perfect rigid rotators. The molecule AB can stretch as a result of the centrifugal force, increasing its moment of inertia. Since the moment of inertia increases with increasing frequency of rotation, the spacing between lines decreases slightly with increasing wave number.
† Herzberg, G., *Molecular Spectra and Molecular Structure*, Vol. I, *Spectra of Diatomic Molecules* (6th ed., Princeton, D. Van Nostrand Company, Inc., 1950) p. 81.

because the selection rules indicate $\Delta v = 1$ and $\Delta J = \pm 1$. Consequently, the transitions are from one rotational level of a vibrational state to the next higher or lower rotational level of the next vibrational state. The differences in energy between vibrational levels is much larger (about 100×) than the differences between the rotational levels. At room temperature most molecules will be in the lowest vibrational state, $v = 0$, but various rotational levels will be populated. The most important vibrational transition is from $v = 0$ to $v = 1$, but this is accompanied by quite a few different rotational transitions, e.g., $v = 0, J = 1 \rightarrow v = 1, J = 0$ or 2; $v = 0, J = 2 \rightarrow v = 1, J = 1$ or 3.

The vibrational-rotational absorption bands are usually expressed in wave numbers (cm^{-1} or $1/\lambda$ in cm) or (less often) microns ($1\mu = 10^{-6}$m $= 10^4$ Å). The region covered is the near infrared, in the approximate range 4000 cm^{-1} to 400 cm^{-1}.

If a molecule A-B is treated as a simple harmonic oscillator, the frequency of oscillation, ν_{osc}, is given by

$$\nu_{osc} = \frac{1}{2\pi} \sqrt{\frac{k}{\mu}} \tag{12.24}$$

where μ is the reduced mass of the molecule (Equation 12.21) and k, the *force constant*, is the restoring force in dynes per centimeter displacement from the equilibrium position. The force constant is a measure of the "stiffness of the spring" or the resistance to displacement from the equilibrium position. The classical oscillator can oscillate with any frequency, but quantum mechanics restricts the frequencies, and hence the energies, to certain discrete values. The energies allowed by quantum mechanics are given by

$$E_{osc} = \left(v + \frac{1}{2}\right)h\nu_{osc} = \left(v + \frac{1}{2}\right)\frac{h}{2\pi}\sqrt{\frac{k}{\mu}} \tag{12.25}$$

where v is the vibration quantum number $(0, 1, 2, \ldots)$. It is obvious that the lowest vibrational state $(v = 0)$ corresponds to $\frac{1}{2}$ quantum of vibrational energy. This is known as the zero point energy, which is the vibrational energy of the molecule at 0°K.

The change in energy from $v = 0$ to $v = 1(\Delta J = 0)$ would be $(h/2\pi)\sqrt{k/\mu}$, but the vibrational transitions are accompanied by rotational transitions $(\Delta J = \pm 1)$, so the energy changes expected for the simple harmonic oscillator are

$$\Delta E = \frac{h}{2\pi}\sqrt{\frac{k}{\mu}} + \frac{h^2}{4\pi^2}\frac{J}{I} \tag{12.26}$$

where J is either $+1$ or -1 and I is the moment of inertia of the molecule (p. 449).

The vibrational-rotational energy levels for the simple harmonic oscillator treated as a simple rotor should be equally spaced. The representation of a molecule as a simple harmonic oscillator, however, is reasonably good only for small vibrational amplitudes. The restoring force for large amplitudes is not proportional to the displacement, as is required of a simple harmonic oscillator. In fact, if the vibrational amplitude is great enough the molecule dissociates. The anharmonicity of the molecule is allowed for in the expression for the vibrational energy by including additional terms (a power series in $[v + \frac{1}{2}]$):

$$E_{vib} = h\nu\left[\left(v + \frac{1}{2}\right) - x\left(v + \frac{1}{2}\right)^2 + y\left(v + \frac{1}{2}\right)^3 - \cdots\right]$$

where $x, y, \ldots$ are the anharmonicity constants. It is unnecessary for many purposes to consider the anharmonicity and when it is necessary the first anharmonic term $[(v + \frac{1}{2})^2]$ is usually sufficient. One effect of the anharmonicity is to change the spacing of the energy levels so that the differences between levels decreases with increasing v. The anharmonicity also partially breaks down the selection rules so that transition other than $\Delta v = 1$ occur, but with a lower probability (and hence lower intensity) than for $\Delta v = 1$.

The vibrations of polyatomic molecules are classified as characteristic modes of vibration. There are $(3n - 6)$ vibrational modes for molecules containing more than two atoms, except for linear molecules for which there are $(3n - 5)$ modes (n is the number of atoms in the molecule). A linear triatomic molecule should have 4 vibrational modes, but there are only three different vibrational frequencies. The bending vibration, ν_3, is doubly degenerate, occurring with the same frequency in the plane of the paper and in the plane perpendicular to the paper (see Figure 12.17). For a symmetrical molecule such as CO_2, ν_1 is inactive in the infrared (no infrared absorption occurs at this frequency) because the symmetrical charge distribution remains unchanged during the vibration. All three frequencies would be observed for an unsymmetrical linear molecule such as $O{=}C{=}S$.

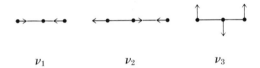

$$\nu_1 \qquad\qquad \nu_2 \qquad\qquad \nu_3$$

FIGURE 12.17. *Vibrational modes for a linear triatomic molecule (e.g., CO_2).*

An infrared spectrometer is now a standard piece of equipment for chemical research, particularly in organic chemistry. A number of functional groups can be identified by characteristic group frequencies. The carbonyl group, $-\overset{\overset{\displaystyle O}{\|}}{C}-$, has a strong characteristic absorption peak at about 1700 cm^{-1}. The frequency is shifted only slightly in going from aldehydes to ketones to carboxylic acids. Characteristic group frequencies are tabulated* for easy identification of observed bands.

The carbonyl frequency has been a valuable aid in the investigation of complexes of ethylenediaminetetraacetic acid† (EDTA) which can function as a sexadentate ligand. It is not always easy to determine if the ligand is attached through both nitrogens and all four carboxylate groups. The carbonyl band occurs at about 1730 cm^{-1} in aliphatic carboxylic acids, but the absorption is shifted to about 1600 cm^{-1} in the carboxylate anions. The large shift is attributed to the lower bond order of the two equivalent carbon–oxygen bonds in $-CO_2{}^-$. The bond order is 2 in $R\overset{\overset{\displaystyle O}{\|}}{C}OH$, but it should be about

* Weissberger, A., W. West, ed., *Technique of Organic Chemistry*, Vol. IX (New York: Interscience Publishers, Inc., 1956) pp. 250-251.
† Busch, D. H., and J. C. Bailar, *J. Am. Chem. Soc.*, **75**, 4574 (1953); M. L. Morris and D. H. Busch, *ibid.*, **78**, 5178 (1956).

$1\frac{1}{2}$ in $(R\!-\!\overset{\displaystyle O}{\underset{\displaystyle O}{C}})^-$. The carbonyl band in EDTA complexes of most divalent metal ions
is very near 1600 cm^{-1}, indicating that the carboxylate group remains essentially un-
changed. In a complex such as that of cobalt(III), K[Co(EDTA)], the carbonyl band
occurs at about 1650 cm^{-1}, indicating that the C—O bond order has increased (relative to —CO$_2^-$) because of more localization of the π electron pair, but not to as great
an extent as for a carboxylic acid. One free carboxylic acid group is present in complexes such as Na[Co(HEDTA)Cl] and a second band appears at 1750 cm^{-1}. This
complex can be converted to Na$_2$[Co(EDTA)Cl] in which there is an uncoordinated
carboxylate ion which absorbs at 1600 cm^{-1}. The extent of the shift of the coordinated
carbonyl band in EDTA complexes has been interpreted as a measure of the extent of
the covalency of the M—O bond.

Chamberlain and Bailar* demonstrated that one can readily determine whether
SCN$^-$ is uncoordinated, coordinated through the S (thiocyanato complex), or coordinated through N (isothiocyanato complex) using the C—N and C—S infrared stretching frequencies. The work was extended by others to include Raman data and many
other compounds. The C—S stretching frequencies, relative to those of KSCN, are
lower for complexes involving M—SCN bonding and higher for M—NCS complexes
(see Table 12.3). The shifts in the C—N stretching frequencies are somewhat variable
and they are in the same direction for both types of bonding. However, the increases in
frequencies are generally greater for the M—SCN compounds. In complexes where
SCN$^-$ bridges two metals, the frequency increases for C—S are less than for the
M—NCS complexes and the C—N frequencies increase somewhat more than in either
of the other cases.

TABLE 12.3
Infrared Frequencies (cm^{-1}) of the Thiocyanate Group

Compound	C—N stretch	C—S stretch
KSCN	2049	748
K$_2$Pt(SCN)$_6$	2122, 2115	694
K$_2$Pt(SCN)$_4$	2127, 2098	705
K$_2$Hg(SCN)$_4$	2132, 2119	716
K$_3$Cr(NCS)$_6$·4H$_2$O	2106	820
(NH$_4$)[Cr(NH$_3$)$_2$(NCS)$_4$]	2120, 2055	823
trans-[Co(NH$_3$)$_4$(NCS)$_2$]Cl	2112	803
K$_2$Co(NCS)$_4$	2085	819
K$_2$Zn(NCS)$_4$·4H$_2$O	2105, 2093, 2080	821, 816
(Hg—SCN—Zn)		
Zn[Hg(SCN)$_4$]	2157, 2146	786
(Hg—SCN—Cr)		
Hg$_3$[Cr(NCS)$_6$]$_2$	2134	801
HNCS	2038	848

* Chamberlain, M. M., and J. C. Bailar, Jr., *J. Am. Chem. Soc.*, **81**, 6412 (1959).

The C—S frequency shifts for the M—NCS complexes indicate that the C—S bond order is increased, relative to the free SCN^- ion, which is to be expected since electrons will tend to be displaced toward N. The lower C—S bond order indicated by the frequency shifts for the M—SCN complexes is also to be expected since coordination through the sulfur should reduce the tendency of S to participate in π bonding. Nothing conclusive can be said about the C—N bond order since the CN stretching frequencies overlap for the thiocyanato and isothiocyanato complexes.

Infrared spectra have been used to determine the manner of coordination of oxy anions such as CO_3^{2-}, NO_3^-, and SO_4^{2-}. The tetrahedral (T_d) SO_4^{2-} ion has four normal modes of vibration, only two of which (ν_3 and ν_4) are infrared active. If the SO_4^{2-} ion functions as a unidentate ligand the symmetry is lowered to C_{3v} (see Appendix C) causing ν_1 and ν_2 to become infrared active and ν_3 and ν_4 to split into two components each. If the SO_4^{2-} ion is bidentate, or if it serves as a bidentate bridging ligand, the symmetry is lowered to C_{2v} increasing the number of components of ν_3 and ν_4 to three each. All four situations have been observed. Simple sulfates show only two infrared bands (ν_3 and ν_4). The complex $[Co(NH_3)_6]_2(SO_4)_3 \cdot 5H_2O$ shows the ν_3 and ν_4 bands and a very weak ν_1 band, which presumably appears because of perturbations in the crystal. The complex $[Co(NH_3)_5SO_4]Br$ shows the expected six peaks and

$$\left[(NH_3)_4Co \underset{SO_4}{\overset{NH_2}{\diagdown\diagup}} Co(NH_3)_4 \right] (NO_3)_3$$

shows the expected eight peaks. The 900–1200 cm^{-1} region is shown in Figure 12.18. The infrared spectrum of $[Co(en)_2SO_4]Br$ shows the expected C_{2v} symmetry also for the bidentate sulfate ion. Infrared spectra do not distinguish between sulfate ion in a mononuclear complex and in a binuclear complex, but other properties such as molecular weight or conductivity can be used to make this distinction.

Raman Spectra

When a beam of monochromatic light is passed through a homogeneous medium, some of the light may be absorbed, some of it transmitted, and some of it scattered. The wavelength of most of the scattered light is unaltered. However, if a spectrogram of the scattered light is obtained, faint lines on either side of the original line can be observed. This shift in the wavelength of scattered light, known as the *Raman effect*, was discovered by C. V. Raman in 1928.

The shift in the Raman lines to longer wavelengths corresponds to the absorption of some of the energy by the molecules in transitions to higher rotational or vibrational-rotational states. The lines of shorter wavelength are the result of the release of rotational or vibrational-rotational energy by molecules in a high energy state.

The Raman effect has a number of experimental advantages. One can select the wavelength on the basis of convenience. This allows the use of glass optics not possible for infrared work. One would like a line of high intensity, which is easily resolved, not strongly absorbed by the sample, and easily detected, e.g., photographically. These

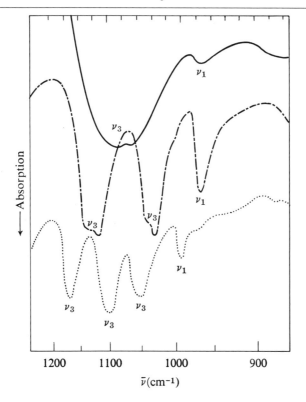

FIGURE 12.18. *Infrared spectra of* $[Co(NH_3)_6]_2(SO_4)_3 \cdot 5H_2O$ *(solid line);* $[Co(NH_3)_5SO_4]Br$

(dot-dash line);
$$\left[(NH_3)_4Co \overset{NH_2}{\underset{SO_4}{\diamond}} Co(NH_3)_4 \right] (NO_3)_3 \textit{ (dotted line).}$$
[From K. Nakamoto,

Infrared Spectra of Inorganic and Coordination Compounds *(New York:*
John Wiley and Sons, Inc., 1963) p. 165.]

limitations pose problems when the sample absorbs strongly in the region of the intense lines of sources such as the mercury arc.

Raman spectra are important because it becomes possible to obtain some information, which could be obtained in the infrared region only with difficulty. The results are also useful because Raman spectra and infrared spectra tend to complement one another. In order for a vibration to be active in the infrared there must be a change in the electric moment of the molecule during the vibration. A vibration is Raman active if there is a change in the polarizability of the molecule during the vibration. Thus many symmetrical vibrations such as ν_1 for CO_2 (p. 452) cannot be observed in the infrared, but they do give rise to Raman lines. The Raman spectra of symmetrical molecules provide valuable information missing from the infrared spectra. Most vibrations of unsymmetrical molecules are active in both infrared and Raman spectra.

Electronic Spectra

DIATOMIC MOLECULES

Electronic transitions can be discussed in a meaningful way using *potential energy curves*. The variation of the potential energy of a diatomic molecule in the ground state as a function of the internuclear distance, r, is shown in Figure 12.19a. The minimum potential energy corresponds to the equilibrium internuclear separation, r_0. In the lowest vibrational level ($v = 0$, corresponding to the zero point energy) the internuclear

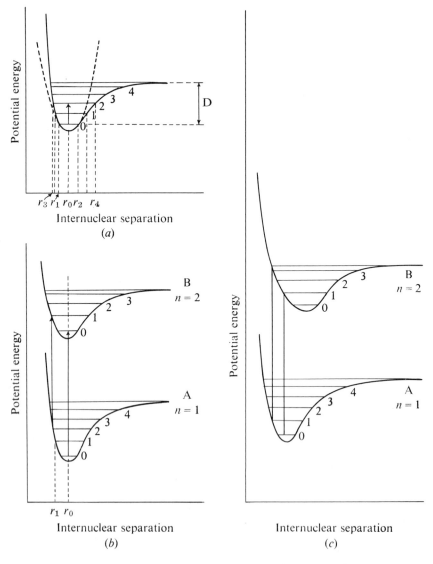

FIGURE 12.19. *Vibrational energy levels in diatomic molecules.*

distance varies from r_1 to r_2 as the atoms vibrate about the equilibrium separation. As the internuclear distance increases from r_1 during a vibration, the potential energy decreases to a minimum at r_0, increases to r_2, and then returns. The variation in potential energy might be represented as a ball rolling back and forth between r_1 and r_2.

The parabola corresponding to simple harmonic motion is shown as the dotted curve. The lower portion of the potential energy curve is approximately parabolic, but, for larger amplitudes of vibration, the motion is anharmonic. Repulsion between the atoms causes the potential energy curve to rise more steeply than the parabola as r becomes small. The real molecule will dissociate if the amplitude of vibration is sufficiently great, so the potential energy curve bends away from the parabola as r increases much above r_0.

The vibrational levels are shown in Figure 12.19, but the rotational levels are omitted for simplicity. The transition from $v = 0$ to $v = 2$ (forbidden for the harmonic oscillator, but only of low probability for the anharmonic oscillator) is represented in the figure. After the transition occurs the molecule vibrates between r_3 and r_4 until some other transition occurs. The sum of the kinetic energy and potential energy of the molecule is constant during the vibration. The vibrational kinetic energy is zero at r_3 or r_4 (the turn-around points). The kinetic energy increases to a maximum at r_0. The vertical distance between $v = 0$ and the asymptote is the dissociation energy (D) of the molecule.

The ground state and the first electronically excited state are shown in Figure 12.19b. Here the equilibrium internuclear separation is the same in both states, but the curves differ slightly in shape. The Franck–Condon principle states that electronic transitions occur so rapidly ($\sim 10^{-16}$ sec) compared to the period of vibration of the nuclei ($\sim 10^{-13}$ sec) that the positions of the nuclei can be assumed to be the same before and after the electronic transition. Since most molecules are likely to be in the lowest vibrational level of the ground state at ordinary conditions, the most probable transitions are from $v = 0$. A transition from $n = 1$, $v = 0$ is most likely to lead to $n = 2$, $v = 0$. The nuclei after the transition will be separated by r_0 and will have kinetic energy most nearly corresponding to the lowest vibrational state. Other transitions occur with lower probability.

Transitions from higher vibrational states ($v > 0$) are considered to occur with greatest probability at one of the turn-around points because the molecules spend the longest time in those positions (where KE. $= 0$). Quantum mechanics leads to the conclusion that the transitions from the lowest vibrational state ($v = 0$) are most probable at the midpoint of the oscillation, ($r = r_0$). The transition from $n = 1$, $v = 2$ is shown in Figure 12.19b. The internuclear separation, r_1, corresponds to $v = 1$ in the electronically excited state so the transition is $n = 1$, $v = 2 \rightarrow n = 2$, $v = 1$.

The equilibrium internuclear separation for the electronically excited state in Figure 12.19c is greater than for the ground state. An electronic transition from the lowest vibrational level would lead to the state $n = 2$, $v = 1$. The electronic transition represented from $v = 1$ would lead to a very high potential energy and the molecule would dissociate.

Since an electronic transition can be accompanied by any one of several vibrational-rotational or rotational transitions, electronic spectra consist of bands comprised of many closely spaced lines. The absorption for most stable molecules occurs in the ultraviolet region. The spectra give information about excited states as well as the ground state. Dissociation energies can be evaluated and vibrational-rotational and rotational transitions can be investigated in favorable cases without having to deal with some of the difficulties encountered in the infrared region.

COLOR IN INORGANIC COMPOUNDS

Most compounds that do not contain unpaired electrons are colorless; the electronic transitions are in the ultraviolet region. It has been mentioned (p. 91) that normally colorless cations and anions can combine to give colored compounds when polarization effects are important. For example, most nontransition metal oxides are colorless, but many of the corresponding compounds formed by the more polarizable sulfide ion are colored. The absorption bands, which give rise to the color of such compounds, are usually *charge transfer bands*. The charge transfer band of a metal sulfide is caused by the transition from the ground state to an excited state in which electronic charge is transferred from the sulfide ion to the metal ion. Usually no net oxidation–reduction occurs because the excited state is short-lived. Paramagnetic molecules, e.g., NO_2, ClO_2, are usually colored because of low lying excited states.

Coordination compounds exhibit a great variety of striking colors. The absorption bands usually involve *d-d* transitions, which can be interpreted using crystal field or molecular orbital energy level diagrams such as those discussed earlier (p. 352). Some complexes for which the bonding involves an appreciable amount of covalent character have charge transfer bands which extend into the visible region in addition to the *d-d* bands. The charge transfer bands require a molecular orbital treatment since the crystal field approach does not take covalent bonding into account.

The effect of resonance on color is most apparent among organic compounds. Normally, transitions involving σ or π bonding electrons are in the ultraviolet region. Hence, most saturated and unsaturated hydrocarbons are colorless. As the length of a conjugated chain increases, the ultraviolet band shifts to longer wavelengths. Resonance stabilizes the ground state of the molecule, but it can be of even greater importance in stabilizing excited states and thereby decreasing the excitation energy. Most colored organic compounds, such as the dyes and indicators, involve rather extensive conjugated systems for which many resonance structures can be written. The yellow to brown color often obtained in organic reactions is probably caused by free radicals which are produced in the reactions.

Methods for the Study of Rapid Reactions

Many organic reactions involving substitution at a carbon atom or rearrangement are slow enough to be studied by classical methods. Reactions of "inert" complexes have been studied extensively using classical methods during the last two decades. Reactions of labile complexes, however, and many other inorganic reactions until recently were described as "instantaneous," "immeasurably fast," or "complete within the time of mixing." The classical methods were limited to time ranges of one second or greater. This lower limit has been extended somewhat by flow methods. New techniques for the study of rapid reactions have filled the gap between the classical methods and the spectroscopic range in the last few years. The spectroscopic range (10^{-10} to 10^{-15} sec) is important for the study of electron motion and the vibration and rotation of molecules, but ordinary chemical reactions are not expected to fall within this range.

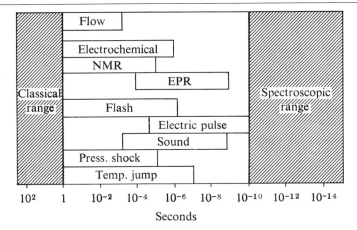

FIGURE 12.20. *Time ranges of relaxation methods compared to some other methods for the study of fast reactions. [Adapted from M. Eigen,* Pure and Appl. Chem., *6, 97 (1963) by permission of the International Union of Pure and Applied Chemistry and Butterworths Scientific Publications.]*

Electrochemical methods, such as polarography, are more familiar than the other techniques and will not be considered here. The important new techniques involve nuclear magnetic resonance (p. 440), electron paramagnetic resonance (p. 439), and relaxation methods. The time ranges covered by several methods are shown in Figure 12.20.

The relaxation methods involve the rapid change of one parameter, e.g., temperature or pressure, causing a shift in the equilibrium or steady state of a system. As an example, if a sudden temperature change caused by an electric discharge brings about a color change because the equilibrium is disturbed, the re-equilibration can be followed spectrophotometrically. Such changes over very short time intervals can be observed on an oscilloscope. The relaxation methods have been developed largely by M. Eigen and co-workers. The change in the external parameter may be effected:

(a) by a sudden rise (e.g., temperature jump or pressure shock in the form of a rectangular step),

(b) by single impulse (e.g., electrical field impulse or flash photolysis), or

(c) periodically (e.g., by a harmonic oscillation such as ultrasonic sound).

The course of the reaction can be followed by measuring changes in optical absorption, optical rotation, conductance, fluorescence, or any other property which changes appropriately and can be followed over very short time intervals.

The shift of equilibrium is characterized by the *relaxation time, τ*. For small deviations from equilibrium the relaxation time is defined by

$$\frac{d\Delta c}{dt} = -\frac{\Delta c}{\tau},$$ (12.28)

where Δc is the deviation of the concentrations from their equilibrium values. For a unimolecular reaction of the type

$$A \underset{k_2}{\overset{k_1}{\rightleftharpoons}} B,$$

from Equation 12.28 and the rate law one obtains the relaxation time

$$\tau = \frac{1}{k_1 + k_2},$$ (12.29)

where k_1 and k_2 are the specific rate constants. For a bimolecular reaction of the type

$$A + B \underset{k_2}{\overset{k_1}{\rightleftharpoons}} AB$$

the relaxation time is given by

$$\tau = \frac{1}{k_2 + k_1 \, [\overline{A}][\overline{B}]}$$ (12.30)

where $[\overline{A}]$ and $[\overline{B}]$ are the equilibrium concentrations. Thus for a unimolecular reaction k_1 and k_2 cannot be evaluated separately, but they can be evaluated for the bimolecular reaction by determining the relaxation time as a function of concentrations of A and B. These relationships are derived and expressions for other reactions are given by Eigen and de Maeyer (see General References). The relaxation time is obtained from the time lag in following the change in the external parameter or from the time required for the re-equilibration process after an impulse. The responses of systems to three types of change in external parameters are shown in Figures 12.21–12.23.

The neutralization of charge by the combination of cations and anions is generally accompanied by an appreciable change in volume, e.g., $H^+ + OH^- \rightarrow H_2O$, $\Delta V_0 = -22$ cm³/mole. Such reactions are sensitive to changes in pressure and can be followed by sound absorption methods. Studies of proton transfer processes have identified $H_9O_4^+$ as a very stable complex ion. This is the species which best represents the hydrated proton in aqueous media. The rate constants (second order) for the combination of $H_9O_4^+$ and inorganic acid anions are of the order of 10^{10}–10^{11} ($M^{-1}sec^{-1}$). Simple hydrolysis reactions ($M^{n+} + OH^-$) are about as fast.

Eigen has used sound absorption as a means of investigating the replacement of water molecules by other ligands for the alkali and alkaline earth metals. The substitution processes occur in 10^{-7}–10^{-8} sec, but discrete complex species could be identified. The ligands included H_2O (an exchange process), OH^-, Cl^-, NO_3^-, SO_4^{2-}, $S_2O_3^{2-}$, CrO_4^{2-}, $C_2H_3O_2^-$, pyridine, polyphosphates, glycinate ion, and several aminopolyacids. The transformation, in the case of nitrilotriacetate ion with the alkali metal ions, involves an ion pair going to a chelated complex with the displacement of several water molecules. The process is slowest for Li^+ and fastest for Cs^+ with small changes in rate within this group of metal ions. The temperature jump method has been used for the investigation of the formation of stable chelate complexes. The final step of complex formation in these cases is dominant and can be followed spectrophotometrically.

The rates of water exchange for divalent metal ions of the fourth period follows the sequence expected from ligand field theory. The rates are high for Ca^{2+}, Mn^{2+}, and Zn^{2+}, which have zero crystal field stabilization energy, and a minimum is observed for Ni^{2+} as predicted (p. 406). Copper(II) ion exchanges water even more rapidly than Zn^{2+}. Presumably the H_2O molecules which are exchanged very rapidly are the ones above and below the plane of four more tightly bound H_2O molecules.

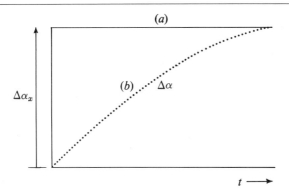

FIGURE 12.21. *(a) Shift in equilibrium ($\Delta\alpha_x$) for a sudden rise in a parameter x; (b) relaxation curve $\Delta\alpha$ in response to the sudden rise in x.*

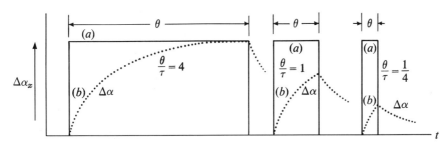

FIGURE 12.22. *Shift in equilibrium ($\Delta\alpha_x$) for rectangular impulses in a parameter x and the relaxation curves $\Delta\alpha$ for various θ values (duration of impulse). [Adapted from M. Eigen, Chapter XVIII in* Rates and Mechanisms of Reactions, *second edition, Volume VIII, Part II of* Technique of Organic Chemistry, *S. L. Freiss, E. S. Lewis, and A. Weissberger, editors (New York: Interscience Publishers, Inc., 1963) p. 922.]*

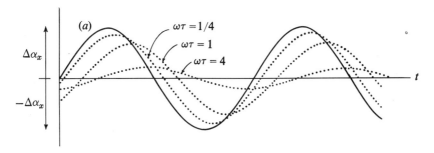

FIGURE 12.23. *Shift in equilibrium ($\Delta\alpha_x$) for a harmonic oscillation (frequency ω) in a parameter x and the relaxation curve $\Delta\alpha$ for $\omega\tau \ll 1$ (solid curve); relaxation curves ($\Delta\alpha$) for various values of $\omega\tau$ (dotted curves). [Adapted from M. Eigen, Chapter XVIII in* Rates and Mechanisms of Reactions, *second edition, Volume VIII, Part II of* Technique of Organic Chemistry, *S. L. Freiss, E. S. Lewis, and A. Weissberger, editors (New York: Interscience Publishers, Inc., 1963) p. 927.]*

REFERENCES

X-Ray Crystallography

McLachlan, D., Jr., *X-Ray Crystal Structure* (New York: McGraw-Hill Book Company, Inc., 1957).

Lipson, H., and W. Cochran, *The Crystalline State*, Vol. III. "The Determination of Crystal Structures" (London: G. Bell and Sons, Ltd., 1953).

Wells, A. F., *Structural Inorganic Chemistry* (3rd ed., London: Oxford University Press, 1952) pp. 197-207.

Barrow, G. M., *Physical Chemistry* (New York: McGraw-Hill Book Company, 1961) pp. 275-278, 424-442.

Moore, W. J., *Physical Chemistry* (2nd ed., New York: Prentice-Hall, Inc., 1955) pp. 369-390.

Jeffrey, G. A., and D. W. J. Cruickshank, *Quart. Rev.,* 7, 335 (1953).

Neutron Diffraction

Thewlis, J., "Neutron Crystallography," *Ann. Rept.,* **1950**, 420-432.

Wells, A. F., *Structural Inorganic Chemistry* (3rd ed., London: Oxford University Press, 1952) pp. 207-210.

Electron Diffraction

Wells, A. F., *Structural Inorganic Chemistry* (3rd ed., London: Oxford University Press, 1952) pp. 210-216.

Barrow, G. M., *Physical Chemistry* (New York: McGraw-Hill Book Company, 1961) pp. 275-286.

Moore, W. J., *Physical Chemistry* (2nd ed., New York: Prentice-Hall, Inc., 1955) pp. 326-331, 271-2.

Dipole Moments

Smyth, C. P., "Dipole Moment, Resonance, and Molecular Structure," in *Chemical Architecture*, R. E. Burk and O. Grummitt, eds. (New York: Interscience Publishers, Inc., 1948) pp. 23-51.

Syrkin, Y. K., and M. E. Dyatkina, *Structure of Molecules and the Chemical Bond* (London: Butterworths Scientific Publications, 1950) Chapter 10.

Barrow, G. M., *Physical Chemistry* (New York: McGraw-Hill Book Company, 1961) pp. 287-303.

Moore, W. J., *Physical Chemistry* (New York: Prentice-Hall, Inc., 1955) pp. 314-322.

Wells, A. F., *Structural Inorganic Chemistry* (3rd ed., London: Oxford University Press, 1952) pp. 250-257.

Magnetic Susceptibility

Mulay, L. N., *Anal. Chem.,* **34**, 343 (1962). A review.

Selwood, P. W., *Magnetochemistry* (2nd ed., New York: Interscience Publishers, Inc., 1956).

Wells, A. F., *Structural Inorganic Chemistry* (3rd ed., London: Oxford University Press, 1952) pp. 241-249.

Figgis, B. N., and J. Lewis, "The Magnetochemistry of Complex Compounds," in *Modern Coor-*

dination Chemistry, J. Lewis and R. G. Wilkins, eds. (New York: Interscience Publishers, Inc., 1960) Chapter 6.

Nyholm, R. S., "Magnetochemistry," in *Chemistry of the Coordinate Compounds* (London: Pergammon Press, 1958) pp. 401-429.

Barrow, G. M., *Physical Chemistry* (New York: McGraw-Hill Book Company, 1961) pp. 303-311.

Paramagnetic Resonance

Gordy, W., "Microwave and Radiofrequency Spectroscopy," in *Technique of Organic Chemistry*, A. Weissberger, ed., Vol. IX, *Chemical Applications of Spectroscopy*, W. West, ed. (New York: Interscience Publishers, Inc., 1956) pp. 126-146.

Owen, J., "Paramagnetic Resonance," in *Chemistry of the Coordinate Compounds* (London: Pergammon Press, 1958) pp. 430-436.

Nuclear Magnetic Resonance

Gordy, W., in *Technique of Organic Chemistry*, Vol. IX (New York: Interscience Publishers, Inc., 1956) pp. 146-180.

Roberts, J. D., *Nuclear Magnetic Resonance* (New York: McGraw-Hill Book Company, Inc., 1959).

Jackman, L. M., *Nuclear Magnetic Resonance Spectroscopy* (London: Pergammon Press, 1959).

Corio, P. L., *Chem. Rev., 60*, 363 (1960).

Brownstein, S., *Chem. Rev., 59*, 463 (1959).

Smith, J. A. S., *Quart. Rev., 7*, 279 (1953).

Absorption Spectroscopy

Barrow, G. M., *The Structure of Molecules* (New York: W. A. Benjamin, Inc., 1963). An introduction to molecular spectroscopy.

West, W., "Introductory Survey of Molecular Spectra," in *Technique of Organic Chemistry*, A. Weissberger, ed., Vol. IX, *Chemical Applications of Spectroscopy*, W. West, ed. (New York: Interscience Publishers, Inc., 1956) Chapter I.

Duncan, A. B. F., "Theory of Infrared and Raman Spectra," *ibid.*, Chapter III.

Jones, R. N., and C. Sandorfy, "Application of Infrared and Raman Spectrometry to the Elucidation of Molecular Structure," *ibid.*, Chapter IV.

Duncan, A. B. F., and F. A. Matsen, "Electronic Spectra in the Visible and Ultraviolet Regions," *ibid.*, Chapter V.

Herzberg, G., *Molecular Spectra and Molecular Structure*, Vol. I, *Spectra of Diatomic Molecules* (2nd ed., Princeton: D. Van Nostrand Company, Inc., 1950).

Herzberg, G., *Molecular Spectra and Molecular Structure*, Vol. II, *Infrared Spectra of Polyatomic Molecules* (Princeton: D. Van Nostrand Company, Inc., 1945).

Moore, W. J., *Physical Chemistry* (2nd ed., New York: Prentice-Hall, Inc., 1955) pp. 331-342.

Nakamoto, K., *Infrared Spectra of Inorganic and Coordination Compounds* (New York: John Wiley and Sons, Inc., 1963).

Cotton, F. A., "The Infrared Spectra of Transition Metal Complexes," in *Modern Coordination Chemistry*, J. Lewis and R. G. Wilkins, eds. (New York: Interscience Publishers, Inc., 1960) Chapter 5.

Dunn, T. M., "The Visible and Ultra-Violet Spectra of Complex Compounds," in *Modern Coordination Chemistry*, J. Lewis and R. G. Wilkins, eds. (New York: Interscience Publishers, Inc., 1960) Chapter 4.

Manch, W., and W. C. Fernelius, "The Structure and Spectra of Ni(II) and Cu(II) Complexes," *J. Chem. Educ.,* **38**, 192 (1961).

Carlin, R. L., "Electronic Spectra of Transition Metal Complexes," *J. Chem. Educ.,* **40**, 135 (1963).

Rapid Reactions

Eigen, M., "Introduction," p. 793; Strehlow, H., "Electrochemical Methods," Chapter XV; Strehlow, H., "Magnetic Resonance Methods," Chapter XVII; Eigen, M., and L. de Maeyer, "Relaxation Methods," Chapter XVIII; in *Investigations of Rates and Mechanisms of Reactions,* S. L. Frieds, E. S. Lewis, and A. Weissberger, eds., Vol. VIII, Part II of *Technique of Organic Chemistry,* A. Weissberger, ed. (New York: Interscience Publishers, Inc., 1963).

Problems

1. The density of NaCl is 2.163 g/cm^3. Calculate:
    (*a*) the molar volume of NaCl (volume occupied by 1 mole);
    (*b*) the volume occupied by one NaCl formula unit;
    (*c*) the number of NaCl units per unit cell for the face-centered cubic structure (count an Na$^+$ shared between 2 cells as $\frac{1}{2}$ Na$^+$, etc.);
    (*d*) the volume of the unit cell;
    (*e*) the cell length, *a*;
    (*f*) the Bragg angle for the 200 reflection using Cu(K$_{\alpha_1}$) radiation ($\lambda = 1.537$ Å).
2. The systematic absences of reflections cause KCl to have the same spacings as for a simple cubic crystal with $a = \frac{1}{2} a(KCl)$. What other alkali metal halides could be indexed as simple cubic crystals on the basis of systematic absences?
3. Calculate the dipole moment expected for unit charges of opposite sign separated by 1.30 Å, the bond length of HCl. The observed dipole moment is 1.03 D. Calculate the approximate percentage of ionic character of the bond.
4. The dipole moments decrease in the series C_2H_5Cl (2.05 D), C_6H_5Cl (1.70 D), HC≡CCl (0.44 D), but the dipole moment of $C_6H_5NO_2$ (4.24 D) is greater than that of alkyl nitro compounds, e.g., $(CH_3)_2CHNO_2$ (3.71 D). Explain the order in each case.
5. Calculate the magnetic susceptibility expected for the triphenylmethyl radical, including the diamagnetic correction made using Pascal's constants (see Selwood's book).
6. Estimate the magnetic moment (spin only) in Bohr magnetons for the following ions:

(*a*) Cr^{3+}	(*f*) Cu^{2+}	(*j*) Fe(CN)$_6^{4-}$
(*b*) Ni^{2+}	(*g*) Cr(NH$_3$)$_6^{3+}$	(*k*) Ag(CN)$_2^-$
(*c*) Fe^{3+}	(*h*) Ni(NH$_3$)$_6^{2+}$	(*l*) Cu(NH$_3$)$_4^{2+}$
(*d*) Fe^{2+}	(*i*) FeF$_6^{3-}$	(*m*) Ni(CN)$_4^{2-}$
(*e*) Ag$^+$		

7. Calculate the spacing between rotational lines for HBr.
8. Calculate the number of modes of vibration for HC≡CH and for NH$_3$. Sketch the modes of vibration (check in Herzberg).
9. The CO bond length is 1.13 Å. Calculate the moment of inertia for CO and the positions of the two lowest frequency absorption lines expected in the microwave absorption spectrum.

Physical Constants[*]

Velocity of light	$c = 2.997925 \times 10^{10}$ cm/sec
Planck's constant	$h = 6.6256 \times 10^{-27}$ erg sec/molecule
Boltzmann constant	$k = 1.38054 \times 10^{-16}$ erg/degree molecule
(gas constant per molecule)	
Gas constant	$R = 8.3143$ abs joules/degree mole
	$= 1.98719$ cal/degree mole
Avogadro's number	$N = 6.02252 \times 10^{23}$ molecules/mole
Electronic charge	$e = 4.80298 \times 10^{-10}$ esu
	$= 1.60201 \times 10^{-19}$ coulombs
Rest mass of the electron	$m_e = 9.1091 \times 10^{-28}$ g
Faraday	$F = 96{,}487$ absolute coulombs
	$= 2.89261 \times 10^{14}$ esu

Conversion Factors

1 kcal/mole $= 349.75$ cm^{-1}
1 electron volt $= 23.063$ kcal/mole
1 electron volt $= 8{,}065.73$ cm^{-1}

---

[*] Consistent set of physical constants based on the new ^{12}C atomic weight scale compiled by the National Academy of Sciences – National Research Council as published in *Chem. Eng. News*, Nov. 18, 44 (1963).

*Nomenclature of Inorganic Chemistry**

Atomic Symbols, Mass, Atomic Number, etc.

The approved symbols and names of the elements are given in Table B.1. The mass number, atomic number, number of atoms, and atomic charge are to be represented as follows:

left upper index	mass number
left lower index	atomic number
right lower index	number of atoms
right upper index	ionic charge

Example: $^{200}_{80}Hg_2^{2+}$ represents the doubly charged ion containing two mercury atoms, each of which has the mass number 200. The charge is to be written as Hg_2^{2+}, not Hg_2^{+2}.

Formulas

The molecular formula is used for compounds which exist as discrete molecules, e.g., S_2Cl_2, not SCl; $Co_2(CO)_8$, not $Co(CO)_4$. If the molecular weight varies with changes in conditions, the simplest formula may be used unless it is desired to indicate the molecular complexity for given conditions, e.g., S, P, and NO_2 may be used instead of S_8, P_4, and N_2O_4.

The electropositive constituent is placed first in the formula, e.g., NaCl, $MgCO_3$. In the case of binary compounds between nonmetals, that constituent should be placed first which appears earlier in the sequence:

$$B, Si, C, Sb, As, P, N, H, Te, Se, S, At, I, Br, Cl, O, F \qquad (1)$$

This sequence roughly follows the order of electronegativities without overlap of periodic groups.

Examples: NH_3, H_2Te, BrCl, Cl_2O, OF_2.

Exceptions to the above order are encountered in compounds in which the sequence of symbols is used to indicate the order in which the atoms are bonded in the molecule or ion, e.g., HOCN (cyanic acid), HONC (fulminic acid), HNCO (isocyanic acid).

* 1957 Report of the Commission on the Nomenclature of Inorganic Chemistry, International Union of Pure and Applied Chemistry (London: Butterworths Scientific Publications, 1959); published with the permission of the International Union of Pure and Applied Chemistry and Butterworths Scientific Publications; also published with notes concerning American usage in *J. Am. Chem. Soc.*, **82**, 5523 (1960).

TABLE B.1

Name	Symbol	Atomic Number	Name	Symbol	Atomic Number
Actinium	Ac	89	Iridium	Ir	77
Aluminum	Al	13	Iron	Fe	26
Americium	Am	95	Krypton	Kr	36
Antimony	Sb	51	Lanthanum	La	57
Argon	Ar	18	Lead	Pb	82
Arsenic	As	33	Lithium	Li	3
Astatine	At	85	Lutetium	Lu	71
Barium	Ba	56	Magnesium	Mg	12
Berkelium	Bk	97	Manganese	Mn	25
Beryllium	Be	4	Mendelevium	Md	101
Bismuth	Bi	83	Mercury	Hg	80
Boron	B	5	Molybdenum	Mo	42
Bromine	Br	35	Neodymium	Nd	60
Cadmium	Cd	48	Neon	Ne	10
Cesium	Cs	55	Neptunium	Np	93
Calcium	Ca	20	Nickel	Ni	28
Californium	Cf	98	Niobium	Nb	41
Carbon	C	6	Nitrogen	N	7
Cerium	Ce	58	Nobelium	No	102
Chlorine	Cl	17	Osmium	Os	76
Chromium	Cr	24	Oxygen	O	8
Cobalt	Co	27	Palladium	Pd	46
Copper	Cu	29	Phosphorus	P	15
Curium	Cm	96	Platinum	Pt	78
Dysprosium	Dy	66	Plutonium	Pu	94
Einsteinium	Es	99	Polonium	Po	84
Erbium	Er	68	Potassium	K	19
Europium	Eu	63	Praseodymium	Pr	59
Fermium	Fm	100	Promethium	Pm	61
Fluorine	F	9	Protactinium	Pa	91
Francium	Fr	87	Radium	Ra	88
Gadolinium	Gd	64	Radon	Rn	86
Gallium	Ga	31	Rhenium	Re	75
Germanium	Ge	32	Rhodium	Rh	45
Gold	Au	79	Rubidium	Rb	37
Hafnium	Hf	72	Ruthenium	Ru	44
Helium	He	2	Samarium	Sm	62
Holmium	Ho	67	Scandium	Sc	21
Hydrogen	H	1	Selenium	Se	34
Indium	In	49	Silicon	Si	14
Iodine	I	53	Silver	Ag	47

TABLE B.1 — *Continued*

Name	Symbol	Atomic Number	Name	Symbol	Atomic Number
Sodium	Na	11	Tin	Sn	50
Strontium	Sr	38	Titanium	Ti	22
Sulfur	S	16	Tungsten	W	74
Tantalum	Ta	73	Uranium	U	92
Technetium	Tc	43	Vanadium	V	23
Tellurium	Te	52	Xenon	Xe	54
Terbium	Tb	65	Ytterbium	Yb	70
Thallium	Tl	81	Yttrium	Y	39
Thorium	Th	90	Zinc	Zn	30
Thulium	Tm	69	Zirconium	Zr	40

The formulas for oxyacids are usually written with the central atom immediately after the hydrogen atom, e.g., H_2CO_3, HNO_3. Hypochlorous acid may be written HOCl or HClO.

Parentheses () or brackets [] are used to improve clarity, e.g., $[Co(NH_3)_6]_2(SO_4)_3$. Hydrates are written as follows: $Na_2SO_4 \cdot 10H_2O$.

The prefixes *cis* and *trans* are italicized and separated from the formula by a hyphen, e.g., *cis*-$[PtCl_2(NH_3)_2]$.

Systematic Names

The name of the electropositive constituent is not modified and is placed first. The name of the electronegative constituent [or the element later in sequence (1) for compounds of nonmetals] is modified to end in -ide if it is monatomic.

Examples: Sodium chloride, magnesium sulfide, lithium nitride, nickel arsenide, silicon carbide, sulfur hexafluoride, and oxygen difluoride.

If the electronegative constituent is polyatomic it should be designated by the termination -ate. Exceptions include OH^-, hydroxide ion; O_2^{2-}, peroxide ion; NH^{2-}, imide ion; NH_2^-, amide ion; and CN^-, cyanide ion.

Complex anions can be named using the name of the characteristic or central atom modified to end in -ate. Ligands attached to the central atom are indicated by the termination -o. The oxidation state of the central atom should be indicated by a Roman numeral (Stock system) or by making the charge on the anion clear by the use of prefixes.

Examples:

$Na_2[SO_4]$ sodium tetraoxosulfate(VI) $Na[SO_3F]$ sodium trioxofluorosulfate(VI)
        or disodium tetraoxosulfate

$Na_2[SO_3]$ sodium trioxosulfate(IV) $Na[ICl_4]$ sodium tetrachloroiodate(III)
        or disodium trioxosulfate

$Na_2[S_2O_3]$ sodium trioxothiosulfate(VI) $Na[PCl_6]$ sodium hexachlorophosphate(V)
        or disodium trioxothiosulfate

Common names of oxy anions and oxy acids may be used (see pp. 470 and 471).

Stoichiometric proportions may be denoted by the use of Greek or Latin numerical prefixes (mono, di, tri, tetra, penta, hexa, hepta, octa, nona, deca, undeca, dodeca) preceding without hyphen the names of the elements to which they refer. The prefix mono may be omitted. Beyond 12 Arabic numerals are used.

Examples:

N_2O	dinitrogen oxide	Fe_3O_4	triiron tetraoxide
N_2O_4	dinitrogen tetraoxide	U_3O_8	triuranium octaoxide
S_2Cl_2	disulfur dichloride		

The proportions of the constituents may also be indicated indirectly by the Stock system, in which Roman numerals are used to represent the oxidation number of an element or central atom. For zero the Arabic 0 is used. Latin names of the elements or Latin stems may be used with the Stock system; such usage is common for complex anions. The charge on the aggregate can be shown by an Arabic numeral in parentheses (Ewens and Bassett system) instead of giving the oxidation number of the central atom.

$FeCl_2$	iron(II) chloride
$FeCl_3$	iron(III) chloride
$SnSO_4$	tin(II) sulfate
MnO_2	manganese(IV) oxide
BaO_2	barium(II) peroxide
$Pb_2^{II}Pb^{IV}O_4$	dilead(II) lead(IV) oxide or trilead tetraoxide
$K_4[Ni(CN)_4]$	potassium tetracyanonickelate(0)
	or potassium tetracyanonickelate(−4)
$K_4[Fe(CN)_6]$	potassium hexacyanoferrate(II)
$K_2[Fe(CO)_4]$	potassium tetracarbonylferrate(−II)
	or potassium tetracarbonylferrate(−2)

The use of the endings -ous and -ic for cations is not recommended.

Trivial Names

The following trivial names are acceptable:

H_2O	water	SiH_4	silane (Si_2H_6, disilane, etc.)
NH_3	ammonia	PH_3	phosphine
N_2H_4	hydrazine	AsH_3	arsine
B_2H_6	diborane	SbH_3	stibine
BH_3	borane		

Names for Ions and Radicals

Cations

Names of monatomic cations are the same as the names of the elements. Oxidation states are designated by use of the Stock system.

Examples: Cu^+, copper(I) ion; Cu^{2+}, copper(II) ion.

Polyatomic cations formed from radicals which have special names use those names without change. Complex cations are discussed later (pp. 473–475).

Examples:

NO⁺	nitrosyl cation	VO²⁺	vanadyl(IV) ion
NO₂⁺	nitryl cation	UO₂²⁺	uranyl(VI) ion

NO^+ nitrosyl cation VO^{2+} vanadyl(IV) ion
NO_2^+ nitryl cation UO_2^{2+} uranyl(VI) ion

Polyatomic cations derived by the addition of protons to monatomic anions are named by adding the ending -onium to the root of the name of the anion.

Examples: phosphonium, arsonium, stibonium, oxonium, sulfonium, selenonium, telluronium, and iodonium ions.

Exceptions: NH_4^+, ammonium ion; $HONH_3^+$, hydroxylammonium ion; $NH_2NH_3^+$, hydrazinium ion; $C_6H_5NH_3^+$, analinium ion; $C_5H_5NH^+$, pyridinium, etc.

Anions

Monatomic anions are named by adding the ending -ide to the stem of the name of the element. *Examples:* H^-, hydride ion; F^-, fluoride ion; Cl^-, chloride ion; Te^{2-}, telluride ion; N^{3-}, nitride ion; Sb^{3-}, antimonide ion, etc.

Certain polyatomic anions have names ending in -ide. These are:

OH^-	hydroxide ion	CN^-	cyanide ion	N_3^-	azide ion
O_2^{2-}	peroxide ion	C_2^{2-}	acetylide ion	NH^{2-}	imide ion
O_2^-	superoxide ion	I_3^-	tri-iodide ion	NH_2^-	amide ion
O_3^-	ozonide ion	HF_2^-	hydrogendifluoride ion	$NHOH^-$	hydroxylamide ion
S_2^{2-}	disulfide ion			$N_2H_3^-$	hydrazide ion

Ions such as HS^- and HO_2^- are named hydrogensulfide ion and hydrogenperoxide ion, respectively. The names of other polyatomic anions consist of the name of the central atom with the termination -ate in accordance with the naming of complex anions.

Example: $[Sb(OH)_6]^-$ hexahydroxoantimonate(V) ion.

Certain anions have names using prefixes (hypo-, per-, etc.) which are well established. These are in accord with the names of the corresponding acids (see p. 471). The termination -ite has been used to denote a lower oxidation state and may be retained in trivial names in the following cases:

NO_2^-	nitrite	SO_3^{2-}	sulfite	ClO_2^-	chlorite
$N_2O_2^{2-}$	hyponitrite	$S_2O_5^{2-}$	disulfite	ClO^-	hypochlorite
NOO_2^-	peroxonitrite	$S_2O_4^{2-}$	dithionite	(and correspondingly for
PHO_3^{2-}	phosphite	$S_2O_2^{2-}$	thiosulfite	the other halogens)
$P_2H_2O_5^{2-}$	diphosphite	SeO_3^{2-}	selenite	
$PH_2O_2^-$	hypophosphite			
AsO_3^{3-}	arsenite			

Other anions which have used the -ite ending, e.g., antimonite, should be named according to the general rule, i.e., antimonate(III).

Radicals

The names ending in -yl of the following radicals are approved:

HO	hydroxyl	SO	sulfinyl (thionyl*)	ClO	chlorosyl
CO	carbonyl	SO₂	sulfonyl (sulfuryl*)	ClO₂	chloryl

* For use in the chlorides only.

NO	nitrosyl	S_2O_5	pyrosulfuryl	ClO_3	perchloryl
NO_2	nitryl	SeO	seleninyl	(and similarly for	
PO	phosphoryl	SeO_2	selenonyl	other halogens)	
VO	vanadyl	CrO_2	chromyl	NpO_2	neptunyl
		UO_2	uranyl	PuO_2	plutonyl, etc.

The prefixes thio-, seleno-, etc., are used for other chalcogens in place of oxygen. *Examples:* PS, thiophosphoryl; CSe, selenocarbonyl, etc. The oxidation state of the characteristic element is denoted by the Stock system. VO may be vanadyl(v), vanadyl(iv), or vanadyl(iii).

Radicals are treated as the positive part of a compound. *Examples:* $COCl_2$, carbonyl chloride; NOS, nitrosyl sulfide; POCl, phosphoryl(iii) chloride, IO_2F, iodyl fluoride, etc.

Acids

Acids giving rise to -ide anions are named as binary and pseudobinary compounds of hydrogen, e.g., hydrogen chloride, hydrogen cyanide, hydrogen azide, etc.

Other acids may be named as pseudobinary compounds of hydrogen, e.g., H_2SO_4, hydrogen sulfate; $H_4Fe(CN)_6$, hydrogen hexacyanoferrate(ii).

Oxy Acids

Most of the common acids are oxy acids commonly named using the -ic and -ous endings in place of the anion endings -ate and -ite, respectively. The acids using the -ous ending should be restricted to those listed for the -ite anions (p. 470).

The prefix hypo- is used to denote a lower oxidation state and the prefix per- is used to denote a higher oxidation state. These prefixes should be limited to the following cases:

$H_4B_2O_4$	Hypoboric acid	HClO	Hypochlorous acid
$H_2N_2O_2$	Hyponitrous acid	$HClO_4$	Perchloric acid
$H_4P_2O_6$	Hypophosphoric acid	(and similarly for	
HPH_2O_2	Hypophosphorous acid	other halogens)	

The prefixes ortho- and meta- may be used to distinguish acids differing in the "content of water" in the following cases:

H_3BO_3	orthoboric acid	H_6TeO_6	orthotelluric acid
H_4SiO_4	orthosilicic acid	$(HBO_2)_n$	metaboric acids
H_3PO_4	orthophosphoric acid	$(H_2SiO_3)_n$	metasilicic acids
H_5IO_6	orthoperiodic acid	$(HPO_3)_n$	metaphosphoric acids

Acids obtained by removing water from H_5IO_6 or H_6TeO_6 and other acids not covered by specific names should be given systematic names, e.g., HIO_4, tetraoxoiodic(vii) acid; H_2ReO_4, tetraoxorhenic(vi) acid; H_2NO_2, dioxonitric(ii) acid; and H_2MnO_4, tetraoxomanganic(vi) acid.

The prefix di- is preferred to the prefix pyro- for $H_2S_2O_7$, disulfuric acid; $H_2S_2O_5$, disulfurous acid; $H_4P_2O_7$, diphosphoric acid; and $H_4P_2O_5$, diphosphorous acid.

The names germanic acid, stannic acid, molybdic acid, etc., may be used for substances of indefinite composition.

Peroxoacids

The prefix peroxo- indicates the substitution of —O— by —O—O— in systematic names (see coordination compounds); peroxy- is used in trivial names.
Examples:

HNO_4 dioxoperoxonitric acid or peroxynitric acid
H_3PO_5 trioxoperoxophosphoric acid or peroxyphosphoric acid
$H_4P_2O_8$ μ-peroxo-bis-trioxophosphoric acid or peroxydiphosphoric acid
H_2SO_5 trioxoperoxosulfuric acid or peroxysulfuric acid
$H_2S_2O_8$ μ-peroxo-bis-trioxosulfuric acid or peroxydisulfuric acid

Thioacids

The prefix thio- indicates the replacement of oxygen by sulfur. The prefixes seleno- and telluro- may be used in a similar manner.
Examples:

$H_2S_2O_2$	thiosulfurous acid	H_3PO_3S	monothiophosphoric acid
$H_2S_2O_3$	thiosulfuric acid	$H_3PO_2S_2$	dithiophosphoric acid
HSCN	thiocyanic acid	H_2CS_3	trithiocarbonic acid

Acids containing ligands other than O and S are generally named as complexes.

Salts and Salt-like Compounds

Simple salts are named as binary compounds using the names as prescribed for ions.

ACID SALTS

Salts which contain acidic hydrogens are named by treating hydrogen as a positive constituent.
Examples:

$NaHCO_3$ sodium hydrogen carbonate
NaH_2PO_4 sodium dihydrogen phosphate
$NaH(HPO_3)$ sodium hydrogen phosphite (HPO_3^{2-} is the phosphite ion)

Double Salts, etc.

CATIONS

Cations are arranged in the order of increasing valence (except H, see above). Within a valence group cations are arranged in alphabetical order.
Examples:

$KMgF_3$	potassium magnesium fluoride
$TlNa(NO_3)_2$	sodium thallium(I) nitrate
$KNaCO_3$	potassium sodium carbonate
$NH_4MgPO_4 \cdot 6H_2O$	ammonium magnesium phosphate hexahydrate (or 6-hydrate)

NaZn(UO$_2$)$_3$(C$_2$H$_3$O$_2$)$_9$·6H$_2$O	sodium zinc triuranyl(VI) acetate hexahydrate or
	sodium zinc triuranyl nonaacetate hexahydrate
NaNH$_4$HPO$_4$·4H$_2$O	ammonium sodium hydrogen phosphate tetrahydrate

ANIONS

Anions are to be cited in the order of the following groups: O^{2-}, OH$^-$, other simple inorganic anions, inorganic anions containing two or more elements (other than OH$^-$), organic anions, H$^-$ (series 2). The order within each group should be alphabetical.
Examples:

NaCl·NaF·2Na$_2$SO$_4$ or Na$_6$ClF(SO$_4$)$_2$	(hexa)sodium chloride fluoride (bis)sulfate*
Ca$_5$F(PO$_4$)$_3$	(penta)calcium fluoride (tris)phosphate*

Basic salts should be treated as double salts, not as oxy or hydroxy salts.
Examples:

Mg(OH)Cl	magnesium hydroxide chloride
BiOCl	bismuth oxide chloride
ZrOCl$_2$·8H$_2$O	zirconium oxide (di)chloride octahydrate
CuCl$_2$·3Cu(OH)$_2$ or Cu$_2$(OH)$_3$Cl	dicopper trihydroxide chloride

Compounds containing radicals assigned special names may be named by either rule, e.g., VOSO$_4$, vanadium(IV) oxide sulfate or vanadyl(IV) sulfate.

Coordination Compounds

The symbol for the central atom is placed first in the formula of coordination compounds followed by anionic, neutral, and cationic ligands in that order. The formula for the complex molecule or ion is enclosed in square brackets [ ]. In names the central atom is placed after the ligands. The anionic ligands are cited in the order given for anions (series 2). Neutral and cationic ligands are cited in the following sequence: H$_2$O, NH$_3$, other inorganic ligands in alphabetical order, organic ligands in alphabetical order.

The oxidation number of the central atom is indicated by the Stock notation. Alternatively, the proportion of constituents may be given by means of stoichiometric prefixes. Formulas and names may be supplemented by italicized prefixes *cis, trans*, etc. Names of complex anions end in *-ate*. Complex cations and neutral molecules are given no distinguishing ending.

NAMES OF LIGANDS

The names for anionic ligands end in -o (-ido, -ito, and -ato commonly).
Examples:

Li[AlH$_4$]	lithium tetrahydroaluminate
K$_2$[OsNCl$_5$]	potassium nitridopentachloro-osmate(VI)
Na$_3$[Ag(S$_2$O$_3$)$_2$]	sodium bis(thiosulfato)argentate(I)
[Ni(C$_4$H$_7$O$_2$N$_2$)$_2$]	bis(dimethylglyoximato)nickel(II)
[Cu(C$_5$H$_7$O$_2$)$_2$]	bis(acetylacetonato)copper(II) or bis(2,4-pentanediono)copper(II)

---

* The prefixes are enclosed in parentheses only to indicate that they may not be necessary if the stoichiometry is obvious. The prefixes bis, tris, tetrakis, etc., are used for anions to avoid confusion with disulfate, etc.

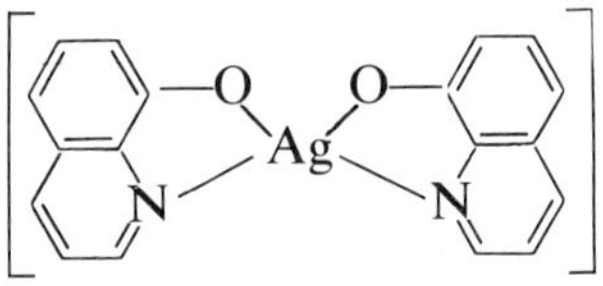

bis(8-hydroxyquinolinato)silver(II)

The following exceptions are recognized:

H^-	hydro	HS^-	thiolo
F^-	fluoro	S^{2-}	thio
Cl^-	chloro	CN^-	cyano
Br^-	bromo	CH_3O^-	methoxo
I^-	iodo	$C_6H_5^-$	phenyl
O^{2-}	oxo	$C_5H_5^-$	cyclopentadienyl
OH^-	hydroxo	Other hydrocarbon anions are also given	
O_2^{2-}	peroxo	radical names without the -o ending.	

Neutral and cationic ligands are given no special endings. Water and ammonia are called aquo and ammine, respectively, in complexes. Groups such as NO, NS, CO, and CS are named as radicals and treated as neutral ligands.

Examples:

$Ba[BrF_4]_2$	barium tetrafluorobromate(III)
$K[CrOF_4]$	potassium oxotetrafluorochromate(V)
$Na[BH(OCH_3)_3]$	sodium trimethoxohydroborate
$[CuCl_2(CH_3NH_2)_2]$	dichlorobis(methylamine)copper(II)
$[Pt\ py_4][PtCl_4]$	tetra(pyridine)platinum(II) tetrachloroplatinate(II)
$[Co\ en_3]_2(SO_4)_3$	tris(ethylenediamine)cobalt(III) sulfate
$K[PtCl_3(C_2H_4)]$	potassium trichloro(ethylene)platinate(II)
$[Al(OH)(H_2O)_5]^{2+}$	hydroxopentaaquoaluminum ion
$[CoCl_3(NH_3)_2(CH_3)_2NH]$	trichlorodiammine(dimethylamine)cobalt(III)
$K_3[Fe(CN)_5NO]$	tripotassium pentacyanonitrosylferrate
$[(CO)_5Mn\!-\!Mn(CO)_5]$	bis(pentacarbonylmanganese)
$K[SbCl_5C_6H_5]$	potassium pentachloro(phenyl)antimonate(V)
$Fe(C_5H_5)_2$	bis(cyclopentadienyl)iron(II)

ALTERNATIVE MODES OF LINKAGE

A ligand which may be attached through different atoms, e.g., SCN^-, may be distinguished as follows:

M—SCN   thiocyanato-S   or   M—NCS   thiocyanato-N

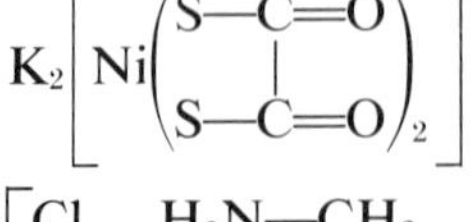

potassium bis(dithiooxalato-S,S')nickelate(II)

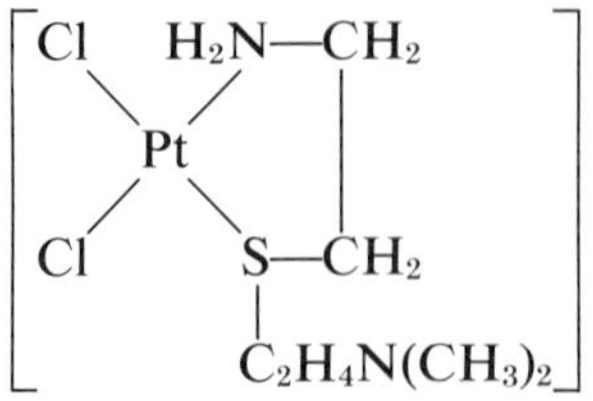

dichloro(*N,N*-dimethylaminoethylaminoethylsulfide-*N'*,S)-platinum(II)

Where special names are recognized for alternative modes of linkage, these may be used, e.g., thiocyanato (—SCN), isothiocyanato (—NCS), nitro (—NO$_2$), and nitrito (—ONO).

Examples:

[Co(NO$_2$)$_3$(NH$_3$)]	trinitrotriamminecobalt(III)
[Co(ONO)(NH$_3$)$_5$]SO$_4$	nitritopentaamminecobalt(III) sulfate
[Co(NCS)(NH$_3$)$_5$]Cl$_2$	isothiocyanatopentaamminecobalt(III) chloride

Di- and Poly-nuclear Compounds

Bridging groups are indicated by adding the Greek letter μ immediately before the names of the groups. Two or more bridging groups of the same kind are indicated by di-μ-, etc. If a bridging group bridges more than two metals, use μ_3, μ_4, etc.

Examples:

[(NH$_3$)$_5$Cr—OH—Cr(NH$_3$)$_5$]Cl$_5$	μ-hydroxo-bis[pentaamminechromium(III)] chloride
[(CO)$_3$Fe(CO)$_3$Fe(CO)$_3$]	tri-μ-carbonyl-bis(tricarbonyliron)
[Au(CN)(C$_3$H$_7$)$_2$]$_4$	*cyclo*-tetra-μ-cyano-tetrakis(dipropylgold)
[Be$_4$O(CH$_3$COO)$_6$]	μ_4-oxo-hexa-μ-acetatotetraberyllium

Extended structures may be indicated by the prefix *catena*-μ, e.g., CsCuCl$_3$ contains the anion

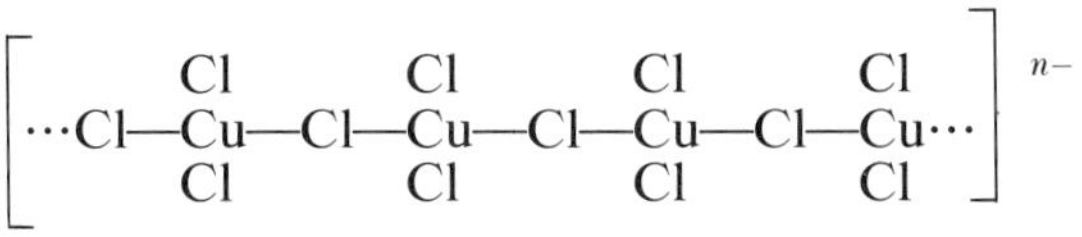

$$\left[\begin{array}{ccccccc} & \text{Cl} & & \text{Cl} & & \text{Cl} & & \text{Cl} \\ \cdots\text{Cl—} & \text{Cu} & \text{—Cl—} & \text{Cu} & \text{—Cl—} & \text{Cu} & \text{—Cl—} & \text{Cu}\cdots \\ & \text{Cl} & & \text{Cl} & & \text{Cl} & & \text{Cl} \end{array} \right]^{n-}$$

The compound may be named cesium *catena*-μ-chloro-dichlorocuprate(II). If the structure were in doubt, however, the substance would be called cesium copper(II) chloride (as a double salt).

For additional examples and for the nomenclature of nonstoichiometric phases and polyacids, see the original report.

Symmetry

The importance of symmetry in inorganic chemistry is apparent from the frequent discussion of symmetry elements in current research papers. Symmetry has long been an important concept in crystal morphology, crystal structure analysis, infrared and Raman spectroscopy, and in the classification of molecular electronic states. Further, symmetry is useful in determining which orbitals of atoms in a molecule can combine to form molecular orbitals and in predicting the number of d-d absorption bands that are observed in coordination compounds.

The absorption spectra of most complexes of transition metal ions contain the important crystal field absorption bands. The d-d transitions responsible for these bands are dependent on the crystal field splitting which, in turn, is dependent on the symmetry of the crystal field. The crystal field symmetry reflects the symmetry of the field at the site of the metal ion. The strength of the field is determined by the ligand atoms attached directly to the metal ion. The crystal field strength and symmetry are not greatly influenced by changing substituents on the ligand atoms, except as these changes influence the basicity of the ligand atoms, the metal–ligand bond distance, etc. The symmetry referred to in the discussion of isomers of coordination compounds is the overall symmetry of the molecule or ion. The overall molecular symmetry is often lower than the crystal field symmetry. The crystal field symmetries of $[Co(NH_3)_6]^{3+}$ and $[Co(en)_3]^{3+}$ are essentially the same, but the overall symmetry of the ethylene-diamine complex is lower than that of the ammonia complex.

Symmetry Elements and Symmetry Operations

The symmetry of a molecule is described in terms of *symmetry elements*, e.g., a plane of symmetry, a center of symmetry, or an axis of symmetry. A *symmetry operation* is the transformation (rotation or reflection) corresponding to a particular symmetry element. The symmetry operation corresponding to a 2-fold symmetry axis, for ex-

ample, involves rotating the molecule through 180° about the symmetry axis. The molecule is left unchanged by the symmetry operation.

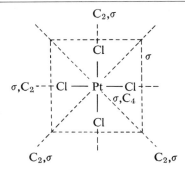

FIGURE C.1. *Symmetry elements of* $PtCl_4{}^{2-}$.

The important elements of symmetry are:

(1) A PLANE OF SYMMETRY (σ)

The two halves of a molecule which has a plane of symmetry must be identical. The symmetry operation involves reflection through the plane. The molecule is said to be transformed into itself or go over into itself on carrying out the symmetry operation. The planar $[PtCl_4]^{2-}$ ion has a plane of symmetry in the plane of the atoms, two σ planes perpendicular to the plane of the ion and through the Pt and two *trans* Cl^- ions, and two σ planes perpendicular to the plane of the complex and bisecting the Cl—Pt—Cl angles (see Figure C.1.)

(2) A CENTER OF SYMMETRY (i)

In a molecule which has a center of symmetry, e.g., $[PtCl_4]^{2-}$, C_2H_4, CO_2, and C_6H_6, a straight line drawn from an atom through the center of symmetry and extended for an equal distance on the other side of the center of symmetry will terminate at an atom identical to the first. The corresponding symmetry operation involves reflection (inversion) through the center of symmetry.

(3) AN AXIS OF SYMMETRY (C_n)

If the arrangement of the atoms in a molecule can be reproduced by rotating the molecule through 180° it is said to have a 2-fold (180° = 360°/2) symmetry axis. The planar BF_3 molecule has a 3-fold symmetry axis perpendicular to the plane of the molecule. An *n*-fold (rotation by $2\pi/n$) axis of symmetry is designated C_n. Benzene has a 6-fold symmetry axis (C_6). A molecule with a C_∞ axis (e.g., HCN, CO_2) must be linear with cylindrical symmetry about the axis.

(4) A ROTATION-REFLECTION AXIS (S_n)

A molecule with an *n*-fold rotation–reflection axis will be transformed into itself by rotation through 360°/*n* about the axis followed by reflection through a plane perpendicular to the axis. The planar ion *trans*-$[PtBr_2Cl_2]^{2-}$ would have a center of symmetry, a plane of symmetry through all five atoms, planes of symmetry perpendicular to the plane of the ion through Cl—Pt—Cl and through Br—Pt—Br, and a C_2 axis

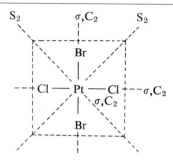

FIGURE C.2. *Symmetry elements of trans-* $[PtBr_2Cl_2]^{2-}$.

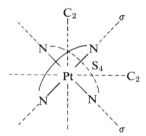

FIGURE C.3. *Symmetry elements of trans-* $[Pt(en)_2]^{2+}$.

perpendicular to the plane of the ion. It also has two 2-fold rotation–reflection axes (S_2) mutually perpendicular along the diagonals shown in Figure C.2. A 2-fold rotation–reflection axis is equivalent to a center of symmetry. If one could prepare the compound $[Pt(en)_2]^{2+}$ in which the ethylenediamine molecules spanned *trans* positions, the molecule would lack the elements of high symmetry possessed by $[PtCl_4]^{2-}$, $[Pt(NH_3)_4]^{2+}$, or $[Pt(en)_2]^{2+}$ in which the en molecules span *cis* positions. However, the *trans* compound would have a 4-fold rotation–reflection axis perpendicular to the plane of the Pt and four nitrogens (see Figure C.3.).

(5) THE IDENTITY (E)

The identity could be regarded as a trivial element of symmetry since any molecule goes into itself if left unchanged. However, the identity operation is important in arriving at a favorable combination of orbitals by the application of group theory. Sometimes it is necessary to carry out two or more symmetry operations consecutively. If the final result can be expressed as equivalent to another symmetry operation the latter is identified. Rotation of the $[PtCl_4]^{2-}$ ion through 90° about the C_4 axis gives an equivalent arrangement, but if we keep track of the individual Cl atoms, the two arrangements are not identical. Four successive rotations of 90° each would be the same as the identity operation.

Some elements of symmetry are implied by or ruled out by the presence of other elements of symmetry. The symmetry of a molecule is described by the minimum number of elements necessary to complete the group. The mathematical *group* consists of a number of elements which are related in that the product of any two of them is identical to one of the elements of the group. For *trans*-$[PtBr_2Cl_2]^{2-}$ rotation about a C_2 axis followed by inversion through the center of symmetry would be equivalent to the identity operation. This is expressed as $C_2 \times i = E$.

The collection of operations that transform a figure or molecule into itself is called a *point group*. The translational symmetry requirement in crystals limits the number of point groups *in crystals* to 32. In molecules additional point groups are possible. Nevertheless, there are fewer than 32 point groups which are commonly encountered in molecules. Herzberg[*] and Barrow[†] give excellent discussions of point groups and the application of symmetry and group theory to the determination of molecular vibrational modes. Mulliken[‡] and Kimball[§] give good discussions of applications of symmetry and group theory to the determination of favorable bonding orbitals. Cotton[||] and Jaffé and Orchin[#] give excellent coverage of symmetry and group theory at a suitable level for chemistry students. They discuss in detail many applications of interest to inorganic chemists.

Point Groups

Some of the more important point groups follow:

C_n. A molecule which has only an *n*-fold axis of symmetry belongs to the point group C_n. A molecule with no symmetry (other than C_1 or E) belongs to the point group C_1. The nonplanar H_2O_2 (p. 434) molecule belongs to the C_2 point group. The only element of symmetry (other than E) is a C_2 axis perpendicular to the O—O bond and in a plane which bisects the angle between the planes containing the O—H bonds.

C_{nv}. The presence of an *n*-fold axis of symmetry and *n* planes of symmetry through the axis characterizes the C_{nv} point group. The principal axis is assumed to be set up vertically, so the planes of symmetry are vertical planes (σ_v). The H_2O molecule belongs to the C_{2v} point group. In addition to the C_2 axis there are two σ_v planes, one in the plane of the 3 atoms and one perpendicular to it. An octahedral complex of the type *cis*-$[Ma_4b_2]$ belongs to the point group C_{2v}. The complex ion *cis*-$[Co(en)_2Cl_2]^+$ belongs to the C_2 point group, but it is often classified as C_{2v} because that is the crystal field symmetry, considering only the coordinating atoms. The NH_3 and PCl_3 molecules are examples of members of the C_{3v} point group. The IF_5 molecule belongs to the C_{4v} point group. Unsymmetrical linear molecules such as HCN, OCS and ICl belong to the $C_{\infty v}$ point group.

The Dihedral Groups D_n. A molecule belongs to the point group D_n if it has an *n*-fold axis and *n* 2-fold axes perpendicular to C_n at equal angles to one another. The most important dihedral group is D_3, which includes octahedral complexes of the type $M(AA)_3$ where AA represents a symmetrical chelate group. The C_3 axis is the spiral axis and each of the three C_2 axes bisects an edge spanned by an AA chelate group (see Figure 10.5).

[*] Herzberg, G., *Molecular Spectra and Molecular Structure*, Vol. II. *Infrared and Raman Spectra of Polyatomic Molecules* (Princeton: D. Van Nostrand Co., Inc., 1945) pp. 1-12, 104-140.
[†] Barrow, G. M., *Molecular Spectroscopy* (New York: McGraw-Hill Book Company, Inc., 1962) Chapter 8.
[‡] Mulliken, R. S., *Phys. Rev.*, **43**, 279 (1933).
[§] Kimball, G. E., *J. Chem. Phys.*, **8**, 188 (1940).
[||] Cotton, F. A., *Chemical Applications of Group Theory* (New York: Interscience, 1963).
[#] Jaffé, H. H., and M. Orchin, *Symmetry in Chemistry* (New York: John Wiley and Sons, Inc., 1965).

C$_{nh}$. If a molecule has an *n*-fold axis and a horizontal plane (σ_h, perpendicular to C$_n$) it belongs to the point group **C**$_{nh}$. In a *trans* planar configuration the H$_2$O$_2$ molecule would belong to the **C**$_{2h}$ point group.

D$_{nd}$. A molecule which has an *n*-fold axis, *n* 2-fold axes perpendicular to C$_n$, and *n* vertical planes of symmetry through the *n*-fold axis belongs to the point group **D**$_{nd}$. The ferrocene molecule with the staggered configuration (p. 383) belongs to the point group **D**$_{5d}$.

D$_{nh}$. If a molecule has an *n*-fold axis of symmetry, *n* vertical planes of symmetry and a horizontal plane of symmetry perpendicular to C$_n$ it belongs to the point group **D**$_{nh}$. These elements of symmetry require *n* C$_2$ axes and, if *n* is even, a center of symmetry. The **D**$_{nh}$ point groups are important in inorganic chemistry. A planar complex ion such as [PtCl$_4$]$^{2-}$ belongs to the point group **D**$_{4h}$ as do octahedral complexes of the type *trans*-[Ma$_4$b$_2$]. The BCl$_3$ (planar) PCl$_5$ (trigonal bipyramid) molecules have **D**$_{3h}$ symmetry. Symmetrical linear molecules such as CO$_2$, N$_2$, and HCCH have **D**$_{\infty h}$ symmetry.

The Tetrahedral Groups T and T$_d$

Molecules belonging to the point group **T** have three mutually perpendicular 2-fold axes and four 3-fold axes. If, in addition to the elements of symmetry of the point group **T**, a molecule has two perpendicular planes of symmetry through each of the 2-fold axes it belongs to the point group **T**$_d$. The tetrahedral NH$_4$$^+$, MnO$_4$$^-$, and ZnCl$_4$$^{2-}$ ions have **T**$_d$ symmetry.

The Octahedral Groups O and O$_h$

If a molecule has three mutually perpendicular 4-fold axes and four 3-fold axes it belongs to the point group **O**. In the more important point group **O**$_h$, in addition to 3 C$_4$ and 4 C$_3$ axes, there is a center of symmetry. These symmetry elements imply the presence of six C$_2$ axes (independent to the C$_4$ axes) and nine planes of symmetry. The SF$_6$ molecule and regular octahedral complexes such as PtCl$_6$$^{2-}$ have **O**$_h$ symmetry.

The Icosahedral Groups I and I$_h$

The icosahedral groups are unusual but they are of interest as the point groups of the highest order of symmetry. In the **I** point group there are six 5-fold axes, ten 3-fold and fifteen 2-fold axes and, in the **I**$_h$ point group, there is also a center of symmetry. The B$_{12}$H$_{12}$$^{2-}$ belongs to the point group **I**$_h$. The B$_{12}$H$_{12}$$^{2-}$ ion can be visualized as related to the staggered ferrocene structure but with the B—H bonds pointed directly away from the center and with an additional B—H group above and one below the pentagonal antiprism (p. 275).

Crystal Systems

Crystals are classified into one of seven crystal systems based on their external symmetry (see Figure C.4). These are:

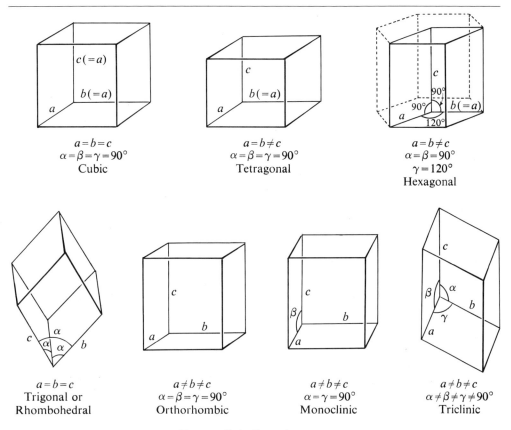

FIGURE C.4. *Crystal systems.*

CUBIC SYSTEM

Crystals belonging to the cubic system have four 3-fold symmetry axes which are the body-diagonals of the cube. The presence of these axes requires the existence of three mutually perpendicular 2-fold axes, which are parallel to the cube edges. The unit cell length is designated $a(a=b=c)$ and the angles between faces of the unit cell are all 90°. These follow from the symmetry. The cube can be primitive (simple), body-centered, or face-centered. The external faces of crystals belonging to the cubic system are not necessarily developed to give a cube. The octahedron and tetrahedron belong to the cubic system since they possess the elements of symmetry listed above.

TETRAGONAL SYSTEM

The tetragonal system is characterized by a single 4-fold symmetry axis. The unit cell has two edges of equal length $(a = b)$ and all angles between faces equal to 90°.

HEXAGONAL AND TRIGONAL SYSTEM

The presence of a single 6-fold or 3-fold rotation axis is characteristic of crystals belonging to the hexagonal system. The hexagonal unit cell has two edges of equal length ($a = b$). The symmetry axis (c) is perpendicular to these two edges which make an angle of 120° with one another. For some crystals it is more convenient to define the unit cell as a rhombohedron with three axes of equal length, meeting at equal angles other than 90°. This unit cell is classified as a member of the *trigonal* or *rhombohedral system*. The symmetry is the same as that of the hexagonal system.

ORTHORHOMBIC SYSTEM

The crystals belonging to the orthorhombic system have three mutually perpendicular 2-fold axes or two perpendicular planes of symmetry without any axes of higher symmetry. The three edges of the unit cell are of unequal length and all angles are 90°.

MONOCLINIC SYSTEM

The monoclinic system is characterized by a single 2-fold axis and a plane of symmetry perpendicular to it, or just one of these elements of symmetry. The unit cell has three edges of unequal length. Two edges form 90° angles and the third angle differs from 90°.

TRICLINIC SYSTEM

The triclinic system is the one of lowest symmetry, there is no simple axis or plane of symmetry. All edges of the unit cell are of unequal length and all angles differ from 90°.

Application of Symmetry to the Derivation of Molecular Orbitals

Dr. E. L. Amma, UNIVERSITY OF SOUTH CAROLINA

When a molecule has a high degree of symmetry, this symmetry can be a powerful tool for simplifying the problem of finding the LCAO molecular orbital wave functions. The two basic premises used in the following argument are: (*1*) that in cases where a molecule has high symmetry there exist sets of equivalent atoms, and the atomic orbitals (AO's) from which the linear combination of atomic orbitals are to be built must contain like AO's on equivalent atoms, and (*2*) that only those orbitals which belong to the same irreducible representations (see below) can mix.

Let us examine a simple case, the molecule diborane, to see what the symmetry of the molecule can tell us about its electronic structure on a qualitative basis. Recent structural data indicate that the molecule has the $\mathbf{D}_{2h}$ configuration given in Figure D.1.

Assume that the relevant boron orbitals are sp^3 hybrids and that each boron has three electrons available for bonding and each hydrogen uses the $1s$ orbital and has one electron available for bonding. Each of the nonbridging B—H bonds can be considered to a first approximation as a normal two-center electron pair bond. This leaves two sp^3 orbitals on each boron and one $1s$ orbital for each bridging hydrogen with a total of four electrons to be considered.

The electronic structure of the bridge and the molecular orbitals involved present the problem. Let us call the sp^3 hybrid orbitals on boron X_1, X_2, X_3, and X_4 and the $1s$ orbitals of hydrogen ϕ_1 and ϕ_2 and define the axes as shown in Figure D.2. These designations are called the representations. But what is desired are linear combinations of these orbitals (representations) that are orthogonal to each other (irreducible representations) so that the energy corresponding to each linear combination can be calculated inde-

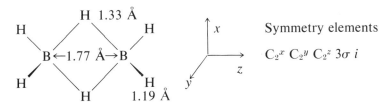

Symmetry elements

$C_2{}^x$ $C_2{}^y$ $C_2{}^z$ 3σ i

FIGURE D.1. *Structure and symmetry elements of diborane.*

FIGURE D.2. *Designation of the orbitals involved in the bridges.*

pendently of the others. This is analogous to the representation of any vector in two-dimensional space being denoted by a linear combination of orthogonal components x and y. Further, as in the two dimensional example the specification of a vector in terms of its orthogonal components is unique, i.e., the breakdown of an arbitrary representation into a linear combination of irreducible representations is unique. The character table will be used in a mechanical way to determine the irreducible representations.

For B_2H_6 we wish to determine the irreducible representations to which the boron and hydrogen bridge orbitals belong. The necessary character tables are listed in numerous standard references as given in Appendix C. The character table for D_{2h} is reproduced in Table D.1. The irreducible representations for D_{2h} are given in the left column using the molecular orbital notation given earlier (p. 356). The result of subjecting the boron orbitals to the symmetry operations of this point group is given in Table D.2.

TABLE D.1.

Character Table Giving the Irreducible Representations for the Point Group D_{2h}

D_{2h}	E	$\sigma(xy)$	$\sigma(xz)$	$\sigma(yz)$	i	$C_2(z)$	$C_2(y)$	$C_2(x)$
A_g	+1	+1	+1	+1	+1	+1	+1	+1
A_u	+1	−1	−1	−1	−1	+1	+1	+1
B_{1g}	+1	+1	−1	−1	+1	+1	−1	−1
B_{1u}	+1	−1	+1	+1	−1	+1	−1	−1
B_{2g}	+1	−1	+1	−1	+1	−1	+1	−1
B_{2u}	+1	+1	−1	+1	−1	−1	+1	−1
B_{3g}	+1	−1	−1	+1	+1	−1	−1	+1
B_{3u}	+1	+1	+1	−1	−1	−1	−1	+1

TABLE D.2.

D_{2h} *Symmetry Operations on Boron Orbitals*

D_{2h}	E	$\sigma(xy)$	$\sigma(xz)$	$\sigma(yz)$	i	$C_2(z)$	$C_2(y)$	$C_2(x)$
X_1	+1	0	+1	0	0	0	0	0
X_2	+1	0	+1	0	0	0	0	0
X_3	+1	0	+1	0	0	0	0	0
X_4	+1	0	+1	0	0	0	0	0
Γ	+4	0	+4	0	0	0	0	0

An entry $+1$ indicates that the orbital is invariant to a particular operation. It is -1 if the operation changes the sign of the orbital and 0 for any other change. The sum of all the columns, Γ, is a representation of the group composed of a linear combination of the basis functions X_1, X_2, X_3, and X_4.

Examining the character table (Table D.1) for $\mathbf{D}_{2h}$ we ask what combination of 4 irreducible representations will add up to our Γ obtained by putting the orbitals through the symmetry operations. The result is

$$\Gamma = A_g + B_{1u} + B_{2g} + B_{3u}$$

The same process is repeated to find the irreducible representations to which the hydrogen orbitals belong (Table D.3). Here, $\Gamma = A_{1g} + B_{3u}$.

TABLE D.3.
$\mathbf{D}_{2h}$ Symmetry Operations on Hydrogen Orbitals

$\mathbf{D}_{2h}$	E	$\sigma(xy)$	$\sigma(xz)$	$\sigma(yz)$	i	$C_2(z)$	$C_2(y)$	$C_2(x)$
ϕ_1	$+1$	$+1$	$+1$	0	0	0	0	$+1$
ϕ_2	$+1$	$+1$	$+1$	0	0	0	0	$+1$
Γ	$+2$	$+2$	$+2$	0	0	0	0	$+2$

Now, since only orbitals of the same irreducible representations can combine, the a_{1g} and b_{3u} orbitals of boron and hydrogen must combine, and the b_{1u} and b_{2g} orbitals of boron must be nonbonding. Since there are two nondegenerate bonding orbitals which can accommodate the four electrons, this leads directly to the fact that the bridge structure of diborane is diamagnetic.

Let us now proceed to the problem of determining the molecular orbitals as combination or symmetry orbitals. Table D.4 is constructed by taking each orbital and operating on it by each symmetry operation. To find the correct LCAO that belongs to A_{1g}, we multiply the character appearing in the character table (Table D.1) by the orbital appearing in Table D.4 and sum over all the group operations. Since all of the signs are positive, the only linearly independent combination of boron orbitals belonging to A_{1g} (nondegenerate) is $X_1 + X_2 + X_3 + X_4$ and $\chi_{a_{1g}} = \frac{1}{2}(X_1 + X_2 + X_3 + X_4)$.

The result of the corresponding multiplication for B_{1u} is given in Table D.5. In the first two rows X_1 and X_2 are positive and X_3 and X_4 are negative so that the linearly independent combination belonging to B_{1u} is $X_1 + X_2 - X_3 - X_4$ or $\chi_{b_{1u}} = \frac{1}{2}(X_1 + X_2 - X_3 - X_4)$. The same combination is obtained from rows 3 or 4 by multiplying by -1. Hence only one row is needed to obtain the linearly independent combination of orbitals for a given representation. One can take the first combination of four orbitals from the row with their signs.

The combinations of orbitals belonging to B_{3u} and B_{2g} are found in the same way. They are $B_{3u} \sim (X_1 + X_3 - X_2 - X_4)$ and $B_{2g} \sim (X_1 + X_4 - X_2 - X_3)$.

Repeating the same process for one of the hydrogen orbitals (since they are equivalent) we have the results as given in Table D.6. The hydrogen orbitals belonging to A_{1g} are $\phi_1 + \phi_2$ and those belonging to B_{3u} are $\phi_1 - \phi_2$, so that $\phi_{a_{1g}} = (1/\sqrt{2})(\phi_1 + \phi_2)$ and $\phi_{b_{3u}} = (1/\sqrt{2})(\phi_1 - \phi_2)$.

TABLE D.4.

D_{2h}	E	$\sigma(xy)$	$\sigma(xz)$	$\sigma(yz)$	i	$C_2(z)$	$C_2(y)$	$C_2(x)$
X_1	X_1	X_3	X_1	X_2	X_4	X_2	X_4	X_3
X_2	X_2	X_4	X_2	X_1	X_3	X_1	X_3	X_4
X_3	X_3	X_1	X_3	X_4	X_2	X_4	X_2	X_1
X_4	X_4	X_2	X_4	X_2	X_1	X_3	X_1	X_2
ϕ_1	ϕ_1	ϕ_1	ϕ_1	ϕ_2	ϕ_2	ϕ_2	ϕ_2	ϕ_1
ϕ_2	ϕ_2	ϕ_2	ϕ_2	ϕ_1	ϕ_1	ϕ_1	ϕ_1	ϕ_2

TABLE D.5.

B_{1u}	E	$\sigma(xy)$	$\sigma(xz)$	$\sigma(yz)$	i	$C_2(z)$	$C_2(y)$	$C_2(x)$
X_1	$+X_1$	$-X_3$	$+X_1$	$+X_2$	$-X_4$	$+X_2$	$-X_4$	$-X_3$
X_2	$+X_2$	$-X_4$	$+X_2$	$+X_1$	$-X_3$	$+X_1$	$-X_3$	$-X_4$
X_3	$+X_3$	$-X_1$	$+X_3$	$+X_4$	$-X_2$	$+X_4$	$-X_2$	$-X_1$
X_4	$+X_4$	$-X_2$	$+X_4$	$+X_3$	$-X_1$	$+X_3$	$-X_1$	$-X_2$

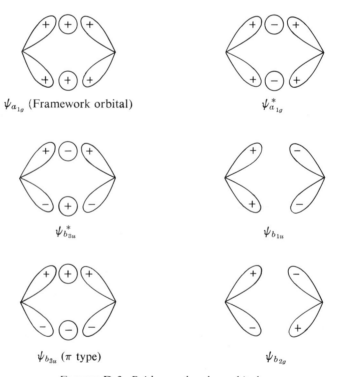

$\psi_{a_{1g}}$ (Framework orbital)

$\psi_{a_{1g}}^{*}$

$\psi_{b_{3u}}^{*}$

$\psi_{b_{1u}}$

$\psi_{b_{3u}}$ (π type)

$\psi_{b_{2g}}$

FIGURE D.3. *Bridge molecular orbitals.*

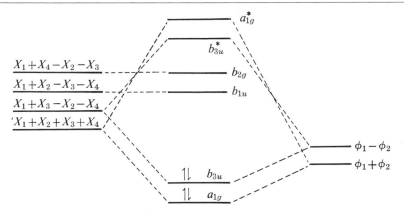

FIGURE D.4. *Correlation diagram.*

TABLE D.6.

A_{1g}	E	$\sigma(xy)$	$\sigma(xz)$	$\sigma(yz)$	i	$C_2(z)$	$C_2(y)$	$C_2(x)$
ϕ_1	$+\phi_1$	$+\phi_1$	$+\phi_1$	$+\phi_2$	$+\phi_2$	$+\phi_2$	$+\phi_2$	$+\phi_1$
B_{3u}								
ϕ_1	$+\phi_1$	$+\phi_1$	$+\phi_1$	$-\phi_2$	$-\phi_2$	$-\phi_2$	$-\phi_2$	$+\phi_1$

The combinations of boron and hydrogen orbitals are:

$$\psi_{a_{1g}} = c\chi_{a_{1g}} + d\phi_{a_{1g}} \qquad \text{bonding}$$
$$\psi^*_{a_{1g}} = c'\chi_{a_{1g}} - d'\phi_{a_{1g}} \qquad \text{antibonding}$$
$$\psi_{b_{3u}} = x\chi_{b_{3u}} + y\phi_{b_{3u}} \qquad \text{bonding}$$
$$\psi^*_{b_{3u}} = x'\chi_{b_{3u}} - y'\phi_{b_{3u}} \qquad \text{antibonding}$$

The orbitals can be represented as shown in Figure D.3. It is relevant to point out that the identical answer could have been obtained by using the point group D_2 and simply adding the g or u subscripts at the end (inversion through the center, like sign, add g, unlike sign, add u).

From this simple treatment, we can guess at the orbital energy levels. The a_{1g} bonding level will be lowest, the b_{3u} bonding level would be next, then the nonbonding levels in the order b_{1u} then b_{2g}, the antibonding b^*_{3u} would be next, and the highest in energy would be the a^*_{1g} antibonding orbital. A qualitative correlation diagram is given in Figure D.4. The four electrons would enter the two bonding orbitals. One must expect that a quantitative treatment might lead to inversions in the order of some of the higher energy orbitals because of differences in the mixing coefficients (c, c', etc.) and the energy separation between boron and hydrogen orbitals.

Standard Half-cell emf Data

Acid Solution (E_A^0)

$$-1.229$$

$$H^- \xrightarrow{2.25} H_2 \xrightarrow{0.00} H^+ \qquad H_2O \xrightarrow{-1.77} H_2O_2 \xrightarrow{-0.69} O_2$$

Group O

$$-1.8$$

$$Xe(g) \xrightarrow{-2.45} Xe^+ \xrightarrow{(-1.67)} XeO_3 \xrightarrow{-3.0} H_4XeO_6$$
$$\xrightarrow{-2.2} XeF_2$$

Group IA		*Group IIA*		*Group III*					
$M \longrightarrow M^+$		$M \longrightarrow M^{2+}$		$M \longrightarrow M^{3+}$		Lanthanides			
Li	3.045	Be	1.85			Ce	2.335	Tb	2.39
Na	2.714	Mg	2.37	Al	1.66	Pr	2.47	Dy	2.35
K	2.925	Ca	2.87	Sc	2.08	Nd	2.246	Ho	2.32
Rb	2.925	Sr	2.89	Y	2.37	Pm	2.42	Er	2.30
Cs	3.08	Ba	2.90	La	2.52	Sm	2.41	Tm	2.28
		Ra	2.92	Ac	*ca.* 2.6	Eu	2.41	Yb	2.27
						Gd	2.40	Lu	2.25

Group III (con't)

$$BH_4^- \xrightarrow{0.36} B_2H_6 \xrightarrow{0.14} B \xrightarrow{0.90} H_3BO_3$$

$M^{3+} \longrightarrow M^{4+}$		$M^{2+} \longrightarrow M^{3+}$	
Ce	−1.70(f)	Eu	0.43
Pr	−2.94	Yb	0.578
		Sm	> 0.9

Actinides

$$Th \xrightarrow{1.90} Th^{4+} \quad Pa \xrightarrow{ca.\ 1.0} PaO_2^+ \quad Np^{3+} \xrightarrow{0.056} Np^{4+} \quad Bk^{3+} \xrightarrow{ca.\ 1.6} Bk^{4+}$$

	$M \longrightarrow M^{3+}$		$\longrightarrow M^{4+}$	$\longrightarrow MO_2^+$	$\longrightarrow MO_2^{2+}$
U	1.80(f)	0.631(f)	−0.58(f)	−0.063(f)	
Np	1.83(f)	−0.155(f)	−0.739(f)	−1.137(f)	
Pu	2.03(f)	−0.9818(f)	−1.1721(f)	−0.9133(f)	
Am	2.32	(−2.6 to −2.9)(f)	−1.04(f)	−1.60(f)	

Group IVA

$$Ti \xrightarrow{(0.83)} Ti^{2+} \xrightarrow{(2)} Ti^{3+} \xrightarrow{(-0.1)} TiO^{2+}$$

$$\xrightarrow{\hspace{2cm} 1.19 \hspace{2cm}} TiF_6^{2-}$$

$$Zr \xrightarrow{1.53} Zr^{4+} \qquad Hf \xrightarrow{1.70} Hf^{4+}$$

$$\xrightarrow{1.43} ZrO_2 \qquad\quad \xrightarrow{1.57} HfO_2$$

Group VA

$$V \xrightarrow{ca.\ 1.2} V^{2+} \xrightarrow{0.255} V^{3+} \xrightarrow{-0.337} VO^{2+} \xrightarrow{-1.00} V(OH)_4^+$$

$$\xrightarrow{\hspace{1.5cm} 0.65 \hspace{1.5cm}}$$

$$Nb \xrightarrow{ca.\ 1.1} Nb^{3+} \xrightarrow{ca.\ 0.1} Nb_2O_5 \qquad Ta \xrightarrow{0.81} Ta_2O_5$$

Group VIA

$$Cr \xrightarrow{0.91} Cr^{2+} \xrightarrow{0.41} Cr^{3+} \xrightarrow{-1.33} Cr_2O_7^{2-}$$

$$Mo \xrightarrow{ca.\ 0.2} Mo^{3+} \xrightarrow{(0.0)} MoO_2^+ \xrightarrow{-0.48} MoO_2^{2+}$$

$$W \xrightarrow{0.11} W^{3+} \xrightarrow{0.15} WO_2 \xrightarrow{0.04} W_2O_5 \xrightarrow{0.03} WO_3$$

Group VIIA

$$\xrightarrow{\hspace{1cm} -1.23 \hspace{1cm}} \qquad\qquad \xrightarrow{\hspace{1.5cm} -1.695 \hspace{1.5cm}}$$

$$Mn \xrightarrow{1.190} Mn^{2+} \xrightarrow{-1.51} Mn^{3+} \xrightarrow{-0.95} MnO_2 \xrightarrow{-2.26} MnO_4^{2-} \xrightarrow{-0.564} MnO_4^-$$

$$\xrightarrow{\hspace{3cm} -1.51 \hspace{3cm}}$$

$$TcH_9^{2-} \xrightarrow{(1)} Tc \xrightarrow{0.5} Tc^{2+} \xrightarrow{-0.281} TcO_2 \xrightarrow{-0.83} TcO_3 \xrightarrow{-0.65} TcO_4^-$$

$$ReH_9^{2-} \xrightarrow{(0.4 \pm 0.2)} Re \xrightarrow{-0.26} ReO_2 \xrightarrow{-0.385} ReO_3 \xrightarrow{-0.768} ReO_4^-$$

Group VIII

$$Fe \xrightarrow{0.409} Fe^{2+} \xrightarrow{-0.771} Fe^{3+} \xrightarrow{-1.9} FeO_4^{2-}$$

$$\xrightarrow{ca.\ 1.5} Fe(CN)_6^{4-} \xrightarrow{-0.36} Fe(CN)_6^{3-}$$

$$\xrightarrow{(-0.4)} RuCl_5^{2-} \xrightarrow{(-1.3)} RuCl_5OH^{2-} \xrightarrow{\hspace{2cm} (-1.5) \hspace{2cm}}$$

$$Ru \xrightarrow{(-0.45)} Ru^{2+} \xrightarrow{\hspace{3cm}} RuO_4^{2-} \xrightarrow{-0.59} RuO_4^- \xrightarrow{-1.00} RuO_4$$

$$\xrightarrow{\hspace{2cm} -0.85 \hspace{2cm}}$$

$$Os \xrightarrow{(-0.85)} Os^{2+} \xrightarrow{(-0.62)} Os(OH)_4 \xrightarrow{\hspace{2cm} -0.964 \hspace{2cm}} OsO_4$$

$$\xrightarrow{(-0.71)} OsCl_6^{3-} \xrightarrow{-0.85} OsCl_6^{2-} \xrightarrow{-1.0}$$

$$Co \xrightarrow{0.277} Co^{2+} \xrightarrow{-1.82} Co^{3+} \xrightarrow{< -1.8} CoO_2$$

$$Rh \xrightarrow{(-0.6)} Rh^+ \xrightarrow{(-0.6)} Rh^{2+} \xrightarrow{(-1.2)} Rh^{3+} \xrightarrow{(-1.4)} RhO^{2+} \xrightarrow{(-1.5)} RhO_4^{2-}$$

$$\xrightarrow{\hspace{3cm} -0.44 \hspace{3cm}} RhCl_6^{3-} \xrightarrow{ca.\ -1.2} RhCl_6^{2-}$$

Group VIII (con't)

$$Ir \xrightarrow{(-1.15)} Ir^{3+} \xrightarrow{(-0.7)} IrO_2 \xrightarrow{-1.3} IrO_4{}^{2-}$$

(with -0.93 bridging Ir to IrO_2)

$$\xrightarrow{-0.77} IrCl_6{}^{3-} \xrightarrow{-1.017} IrCl_6{}^{2-}$$

$$IrBr_6{}^{4-} \xrightarrow{-0.99} IrBr_6{}^{3-}$$

$$Ni \xrightarrow{0.232} Ni^{2+} \xrightarrow{-1.68} NiO_2 \longrightarrow NiO_4{}^{2-} \qquad Pd \xrightarrow{-0.987} Pd^{2+}$$

(with < -1.8 bridging Ni^{2+} to $NiO_4{}^{2-}$)

$$Pt \xrightarrow{ca.\ -1.2} Pt^{2+}$$

$$\xrightarrow{-0.98} Pt(OH)_2 \xrightarrow{ca.\ -1.1} PtO_2$$

Group IB

$$Cu \xrightarrow{-0.521} Cu^+ \xrightarrow{-0.153} Cu^{2+} \xrightarrow{-1.8} CuO^+$$

$$Ag \xrightarrow{-0.7994} Ag^+ \xrightarrow{-1.98} Ag^{2+} \xrightarrow{ca.\ -2.1} AgO^+$$

$$X^- + Ag \longrightarrow AgX \qquad X = Cl, -0.2224 \qquad Br, -0.071 \qquad I, +0.152$$

$$Au \xrightarrow{ca.\ -1.68} Au^+ \xrightarrow{< -1.29} Au^{2+} \xrightarrow{> -1.29} Au^{3+}$$

(with -1.50 bridging Au^+ to Au^{3+})

$$\xrightarrow{-0.959} AuBr_2{}^- \xrightarrow{-0.802} AuBr_4{}^-$$

Group IIB

$$Zn \xrightarrow{0.763} Zn^{2+}$$

$$Cd \xrightarrow{\leq 0.2} Cd_2{}^{2+} \xrightarrow{\geq 0.6} Cd^{2+}$$

(with 0.403 bridging Cd to Cd^{2+})

$$Hg \xrightarrow{-0.792} Hg_2{}^{2+} \xrightarrow{-0.907} Hg^{2+}$$

$$X^- + Hg \longrightarrow Hg_2X_2 \qquad X = Cl, -0.2680 \qquad Br, -0.1392 \qquad I, +0.040$$

Group IIIB

$$Ga \xrightarrow{ca.\ 0.45} Ga_2{}^{4+} \xrightarrow{ca.\ 0.65} Ga^{3+}$$

(with 0.56 bridging Ga to Ga^{3+})

$$In \xrightarrow{0.14} In^+ \xrightarrow{0.40} In_2{}^{4+} \xrightarrow{0.49} In^{3+}$$

(with 0.34 bridging In to In^{3+})

$$Tl \xrightarrow{0.3363} Tl^+ \xrightarrow{-1.28} Tl^{3+}$$

$$\xrightarrow{0.557} TlCl(c) \xrightarrow{-0.89} TlCl_3(aq)$$

Group IVB

$$CH_4 \xrightarrow{-0.13} C \xrightarrow{-0.51} CO \xrightarrow{0.116} CO_2$$

$SiH_4 \xrightarrow{-0.102} Si \xrightarrow{0.86} SiO_2$

$\xrightarrow{\hspace{1cm}1.2\hspace{1cm}} SiF_6^{2-}$

$\xrightarrow{\hspace{1cm}0.15\hspace{1cm}}$

$GeH_4 \xrightarrow{\geq 0.3} Ge \xrightarrow{(0.0)} Ge^{2+} \xrightarrow{(0.3)} GeO_2$

$Sn \xrightarrow{0.136} Sn^{2+} \xrightarrow{-0.15} Sn^{4+}$

$Pb \xrightarrow{0.126} Pb^{2+} \xrightarrow{-1.455} PbO_2$

Group VB

$NH_4^+ \xrightarrow{-0.27} N_2 \xrightarrow{-1.45} HNO_2 \xrightarrow{-0.94} NO_3^-$

$PH_3 \xrightarrow{0.06} P \xrightarrow{0.50} H_3PO_3 \xrightarrow{0.276} H_3PO_4$

$AsH_3 \xrightarrow{0.60} As \xrightarrow{-0.247} HAsO_2 \xrightarrow{-0.56} H_3AsO_4$

$SbH_3 \xrightarrow{0.51} Sb \xrightarrow{-0.212} SbO^+ \xrightarrow{-0.581} Sb_2O_5$

$BiH_3 \xrightarrow{\geq 0.8} Bi \xrightarrow{-0.32} BiO^+ \xrightarrow{ca. -1.6} Bi_2O_5$

Group VIB

$H_2O \xrightarrow{-1.77} H_2O_2 \xrightarrow{-0.69} O_2$

$H_2S \xrightarrow{-0.14} S \xrightarrow{-0.45} H_2SO_3 \xrightarrow{-0.17} SO_4^{2-}$

$H_2Se \xrightarrow{0.40} Se \xrightarrow{-0.74} H_2SeO_3 \xrightarrow{-1.15} SeO_4^{2-}$

$H_2Te \xrightarrow{0.72} Te \xrightarrow{-0.529} TeO_2(c) \xrightarrow{-1.02} H_6TeO_6(c)$

$H_2Po \xrightarrow{\geq 1.0} Po \xrightarrow{(-0.74)} PoO_2 \xrightarrow{-1.5?} PoO_3(?)$

Group VIIB

$F^- \xrightarrow{-2.87} F_2$

$\xrightarrow{-1.27} ClO_2 \xrightarrow{-1.15}$

$Cl^- \xrightarrow{-1.3595} Cl_2 \xrightarrow{-1.63} HClO \xrightarrow{-1.645} HClO_2 \xrightarrow{-1.21} ClO_3^- \xrightarrow{-1.19} ClO_4^-$

$Br^- \xrightarrow{-1.07} Br_2(l) \xrightarrow{-1.59} HBrO \xrightarrow{-1.49} BrO_3^-$

$I^- \xrightarrow{-0.5355} I_2(c) \xrightarrow{-1.45} HIO \xrightarrow{-1.14} IO_3^- \xrightarrow{(-1.7)} H_5IO_6$

$At^- \xrightarrow{-0.3} At \xrightarrow{-1.0} HAtO(?) \xrightarrow{-1.5} AtO_3^- \xrightarrow{-1.6} H_5AtO_6$

Base Solution (E_B^0)

$H_2 + OH^- \xrightarrow{0.828} H_2O$

Group O

$Xe(g) \xrightarrow{-0.9} HXeO_4^- \xrightarrow{-0.9} HXeO_6^{3-}$

Group IIA

$$\mathrm{Be} \xrightarrow{2.62} \mathrm{Be_2O_3^{2-}}(?)$$

$$\mathrm{Mg} \xrightarrow{2.69} \mathrm{Mg(OH)_2}$$

$$\mathrm{Ca} \xrightarrow{3.03} \mathrm{Ca(OH)_2}$$

$$\mathrm{Sr} \xrightarrow{2.99} \mathrm{Sr(OH)_2\cdot 8H_2O}$$

$$\mathrm{Ba} \xrightarrow{2.97} \mathrm{Ba(OH)_2\cdot 8H_2O}$$

Group III

$$\mathrm{Al} \xrightarrow{2.35} \mathrm{H_2AlO_3^-}$$

$$\mathrm{Sc} \xrightarrow{ca.\ 2.6} \mathrm{Sc(OH)_3}$$

$$\mathrm{Y} \xrightarrow{2.8} \mathrm{Y(OH)_3}$$

$$\mathrm{La} \xrightarrow{2.9} \mathrm{La(OH)_3}$$

$$\mathrm{BH_4^-} \xrightarrow{0.78} \mathrm{B_2H_6} \xrightarrow{0.98} \mathrm{B} \xrightarrow{1.82} \mathrm{B(OH)_4^-}$$

Actinides

$$\mathrm{Th} \xrightarrow{2.48} \mathrm{Th(OH)_4}$$

$$\mathrm{U} \xrightarrow{2.17} \mathrm{U(OH)_3} \xrightarrow{2.14} \mathrm{U(OH)_4} \xrightarrow{0.62} \mathrm{UO_2(OH)_2}$$

$$\mathrm{Np} \xrightarrow{2.25} \mathrm{Np(OH)_3} \xrightarrow{1.76} \mathrm{Np(OH)_4} \xrightarrow{-0.39} \mathrm{NpO_2OH} \xrightarrow{-0.48} \mathrm{NpO_2(OH)_2}$$

$$\mathrm{Pu} \xrightarrow{2.42} \mathrm{Pu(OH)_3} \xrightarrow{0.95} \mathrm{Pu(OH)_4} \xrightarrow{-0.76} \mathrm{PuO_2OH} \xrightarrow{-0.26} \mathrm{PuO_2(OH)_2}$$

$$\mathrm{Am} \xrightarrow{2.71} \mathrm{Am(OH)_3} \xrightarrow{0.5} \mathrm{Am(OH)_4} \xrightarrow{(-0.9)} \mathrm{AmO_2OH} \xrightarrow{(-1.1)} \mathrm{AmO_2(OH)_2}$$

Group IVA

$$\mathrm{Ti} \xrightarrow{1.69} \mathrm{TiO_2} \qquad \mathrm{Zr} \xrightarrow{2.36} \mathrm{H_2ZrO_3} \qquad \mathrm{Hf} \xrightarrow{2.50} \mathrm{HfO(OH)_2}$$

Group VA

$$\mathrm{V} \xrightarrow{1.15} \mathrm{HV_6O_{17}^{3-}}$$

Group VIA

$$\mathrm{Cr} \xrightarrow{1.4} \mathrm{Cr(OH)_2} \xrightarrow{1.1} \mathrm{Cr(OH)_3} \xrightarrow{0.13} \mathrm{CrO_4^{2-}}$$

$$\mathrm{Cr} \xrightarrow{1.2} \mathrm{CrO_2^-}$$

$$\mathrm{Mo} \xrightarrow{0.87} \mathrm{MoO_2} \xrightarrow{1.4} \mathrm{MoO_4^{2-}}$$

$$\mathrm{W} \xrightarrow{(1.25)} \mathrm{WO_4^{2-}}$$

Group VIIA

$$\mathrm{Mn} \xrightarrow{1.55} \mathrm{Mn(OH)_2} \xrightarrow{-0.1} \mathrm{Mn(OH)_3} \xrightarrow{0.2} \mathrm{MnO_2} \xrightarrow{-0.60} \mathrm{MnO_4^{2-}} \xrightarrow{-0.564} \mathrm{MnO_4^-}$$

$$\mathrm{ReH_9^{2-}} \longrightarrow \mathrm{Re} \xrightarrow{(0.6)} \mathrm{Re(OH)_3} \xrightarrow{(0.53)} \mathrm{ReO_2} \xrightarrow{(0.5)} \mathrm{ReO_4^{2-}} \xrightarrow{(0.7)} \mathrm{ReO_4^-}$$

$$\mathrm{Re} \xrightarrow{0.576} \mathrm{ReO_2} \qquad \mathrm{ReO_2} \xrightarrow{0.595} \mathrm{ReO_4^-}$$

Group VIII

$$\mathrm{Fe} \xrightarrow{0.887} \mathrm{Fe(OH)_2} \xrightarrow{0.56} \mathrm{Fe(OH)_3} \xrightarrow{< -0.9} \mathrm{FeO_4^{2-}}$$

$$\mathrm{Ru} \xrightarrow{(0.1)} \mathrm{Ru_2O_3} \xrightarrow{(-0.1)} \mathrm{RuO_2} \xrightarrow{(-0.4)} \mathrm{RuO_4^{2-}} \xrightarrow{(-0.6)} \mathrm{RuO_4^-} \xrightarrow{(-0.9)} \mathrm{RuO_4}$$

$$\mathrm{Ru} \xrightarrow{0.04} \mathrm{RuO_2} \qquad \mathrm{RuO_2} \xrightarrow{-0.58} \mathrm{RuO_4}$$

$$Os \xrightarrow{\hspace{1.5cm}} Os_2O_3 \xrightarrow{\hspace{1cm}} OsO_2 \xrightarrow{-0.1} OsO_4{}^{2-} \xrightarrow{-0.3} HOsO_5{}^-$$

with 0.15 bridging from Os to OsO_2

$$Co \xrightarrow{0.72} Co(OH)_2 \xrightarrow{-0.14} Co(OH)_3 \xrightarrow{-0.7?} CoO_2$$

$$Rh \xrightarrow{-0.04} Rh_2O_3 \xrightarrow{> -0.9} RhO_2 \xrightarrow{> -0.9} RhO_4{}^{2-}$$

$$Ir \xrightarrow{-0.1} Ir_2O_3 \xrightarrow{-0.1} IrO_2 \xrightarrow{-0.4} IrO_4{}^{2-}$$

$$Ni \xrightarrow{0.72} Ni(OH)_2 \xrightarrow{-0.49} NiO_2 \xrightarrow{< -0.4} NiO_4{}^{2-}$$

$$Pd \xrightarrow{-0.07} Pd(OH)_2 \xrightarrow{ca.\ -0.73} Pd(OH)_4$$

$$Pt \xrightarrow{-0.15} Pt(OH)_2 \xrightarrow{ca.\ -0.2} Pt(OH)_6{}^{2-} \xrightarrow{< -0.4} PtO_4{}^{2-}$$

Group IB

$$Cu \xrightarrow{0.358} Cu_2O \xrightarrow{0.08} Cu(OH)_2 \qquad Au \xrightarrow{-0.7} H_2AuO_3{}^-$$

$$Ag \xrightarrow{-0.338} Ag_2O \xrightarrow{-0.599} AgO \xrightarrow{-0.74} Ag_2O_3$$

Group IIB

$$Zn \xrightarrow{1.216} ZnO_2{}^{2-} \qquad Cd \xrightarrow{0.809} Cd(OH)_2 \qquad Hg \xrightarrow{-0.098} HgO$$

Group IIIB

$$Ga \xrightarrow{ca.\ 1.22} H_2GaO_3{}^- \qquad In \xrightarrow{1.0} In(OH)_3$$

$$Tl \xrightarrow{0.3445} Tl(OH) \xrightarrow{0.05} Tl(OH)_3$$

Group IVB

$$CH_4 \xrightarrow{0.70} C \xrightarrow{0.52} HCO_2{}^- \xrightarrow{1.01} CO_3{}^{2-}$$

$$SiH_4 \xrightarrow{0.73} Si \xrightarrow{1.73} SiO_3{}^{2-}$$

$$GeH_4 \xrightarrow{> 1.1} Ge \xrightarrow{1.0} HGeO_3{}^-$$

$$Sn \xrightarrow{0.91} HSnO_3{}^- \xrightarrow{0.90} Sn(OH)_6$$

$$Pb \xrightarrow{0.54} PbO \xrightarrow{-0.28} PbO_2$$

Group VB

$$NH_4OH \xrightarrow{0.74} N_2 \xrightarrow{-0.41} NO_2{}^- \xrightarrow{-0.01} NO_3{}^-$$

$$PH_3 \xrightarrow{0.89} P \xrightarrow{2.05} H_2PO_2{}^- \xrightarrow{1.57} HPO_3{}^{2-} \xrightarrow{1.12} PO_4{}^{3-}$$

$$AsH_3 \xrightarrow{1.43} As \xrightarrow{0.68} H_2AsO_3{}^- \xrightarrow{0.67} AsO_4{}^{3-}$$

$$SbH_3 \xrightarrow{(1.34)} Sb \xrightarrow{0.66} H_2SbO_3{}^- \xrightarrow{(0.40)} H_3SbO_6{}^{4-}$$

$$BiH_3 \xrightarrow{> 1.6} Bi \xrightarrow{0.46} Bi_2O_3 \xrightarrow{-0.56} Bi_2O_4$$

Group VIB

$$OH^- \xrightarrow{-0.88} HO_2{}^- \xrightarrow{0.08} O_2 \qquad Po^{2-} \xrightarrow{> 1.4} Po$$

with -0.401 bridging from OH^- to O_2

Group VIB (con't)

$$S^{2-} \xrightarrow{0.48} S \xrightarrow{0.61} SO_3^{2-} \xrightarrow{0.91} SO_4^{2-}$$

$$Se^{2-} \xrightarrow{0.92} Se \xrightarrow{0.366} SeO_3^{2-} \xrightarrow{-0.05} SeO_4^{2-}$$

$$Te^{2-} \xrightarrow{1.14} Te \xrightarrow{0.57} TeO_3^{2-} \xrightarrow{> -0.4} TeO_4^{2-}$$

Group VIIB

$$Cl^{-} \xrightarrow{-1.3595} Cl_2 \xrightarrow{-0.40} ClO^{-} \xrightarrow{-0.66} ClO_2^{-} \xrightarrow{-0.33} ClO_3^{-} \xrightarrow{-0.36} ClO_4^{-}$$

with branch $ClO_2^{-} \xrightarrow{-1.16} ClO_2 \xrightarrow{0.50} ClO_3^{-}$

$$Br^{-} \xrightarrow{-1.07} Br_2 \xrightarrow{-0.45} BrO^{-} \xrightarrow{-0.54} BrO_3^{-}$$

$$I^{-} \xrightarrow{-0.535} I_2 \xrightarrow{-0.45} IO^{-} \xrightarrow{-0.14} IO_3^{-} \xrightarrow{(-0.7)} H_3IO_6^{2-}$$

$$At^{-} \xrightarrow{-0.3} At_2 \xrightarrow{(-0.3)} AtO^{-} \xrightarrow{(-0.6)} AtO_3^{-}$$

(f) denotes a formal emf value for $1M$ perchloric acid (see Chapter IV, p. 143).

REFERENCES

Except as noted below the emf half-cell data were taken from W. M. Latimer, *The Oxidation States of the Elements and Their Potentials in Aqueous Solution* (2nd ed.; New York: Prentice-Hall, Inc., 1952).

Part or all of the data for the elements O, V, Mo, Mn, Ru, Ag, Hg, Ga, and Tl were taken from G. Charlot, *Selected Constants Tables No. 8: Oxydo-Reduction Potentials* (New York: Pergamon Press, 1958).

In addition to these two sources data for individual elements (listed in the order of their appearance in the appendix) were taken from the literature cited below.

Xe   Appleman, E. H., and J. G. Malm, *J. Am. Chem. Soc.*, **86**, 2141, 2297 (1964).

Cs   Friedman, H. L., and M. Kahlweit, *J. Am. Chem. Soc.*, **78**, 4243 (1956).

Ce, Nd   Spedding, F. H., and C. F. Miller, *J. Am. Chem. Soc.*, **74**, 4195 (1952).

Pr   Eyring, L., H. R. Lohr, and B. B. Cunningham, *J. Am. Chem. Soc.*, **74**, 1186 (1952).

B   Sister M. C. Waller, *Inorganic Chemistry of Borohydrides* (Beverly: Metal Hydrides Inc., 1961).

U   Seaborg, G. T., *The Transuranium Elements* (New Haven: Yale University Press, New Haven, Conn. (1958), p. 126.

Np   Cohen, D., and J. C. Hindman, *J. Am. Chem. Soc.*, **74**, 4679, 4682 (1952); G. R. Argue, E. E. Mercer, and J. W. Cobble, *J. Phys. Chem.*, **65**, 2041 (1961).

Pu   Rabideau, S. W., *J. Am. Chem. Soc.*, **78**, 2705 (1956).

Am   Penneman, R. A., J. S. Coleman and T. K. Keeman, *J. Inorg. Nucl. Chem.*, **17**, 138 (1961); L. Eyring, et al., *J. Am. Chem. Soc.*, **74**, 1186 (1952).

Ti   Olver, J. W., and J. W. Ross, Jr., *J. Am. Chem. Soc.*, **85**, 2565 (1963).

Tc   Ginsberg, A. P., *Inorg. Chem.*, **3**, 567 (1964); R. Colton and R. D. Peacock, *Quart. Rev.*, **16**, 299 (1962).

Re   King, J. P., and J. W. Cobble, *J. Am. Chem. Soc.*, **79**, 1559 (1957); J. W. Cobble, *J. Phys. Chem.*, **61**, 727 (1957); Abrahams, S. C., A. P. Ginsberg and K. Knox, *Inorg. Chem.*, **3**, 567 (1964).

Fe	Patrick, W. A., and W. E. Thompson, *J. Am. Chem. Soc.,* **75**, 1184 (1953).
Os	Cartledge, G. H., *J. Phys. Chem.,* **60**, 1468 (1956).
Ni	Carr, D. S., and C. F. Bonilla, *J. Electrochem. Soc.,* **99**, 475 (1952).
Ag	Dirkse, T. P., *J. Electrochem. Soc.,* **109**, 73 (1962).
Au	Evans, D. H., and J. J. Lingane, *J. Electroanal. Chem.,* **6**, 11 (1963).
In	Hepler, L. G., Z. Z. Hugus, Jr., and W. M. Latimer, *J. Am. Chem. Soc.,* **75**, 5652 (1953).
At	Appelman, E. H., *J. Am. Chem. Soc.,* **83**, 805 (1961).

Index

About the Authors

BODIE E. DOUGLAS graduated from Tulane University in 1944. After serving in the U.S. Navy he received an M.S. from Tulane in 1947 for work under Hans Jonassen and a Ph.D. from the University of Illinois in 1949 for work under the direction of John C. Bailar, Jr. He taught at the Pennsylvania State University where he worked with W. Conard Fernelius until 1952, when he joined the faculty of the University of Pittsburgh where he is now Professor of Chemistry. His research interests are concerned with structure, spectra, and bonding in coordination compounds, particularly the stereochemistry, spectra, and circular dichroism of optically active complexes.

DARL H. McDANIEL graduated from Antioch College in 1950. He received a Ph.D. from Purdue University in 1954 for work under the direction of H. C. Brown. He taught at the University of Pittsburgh until 1960 when he joined the faculty of the University of Cincinnati where he is now Professor of Chemistry and Chairman of the Inorganic Chemistry Division. His research interests include acid-base relationships, hydrogen bonds, and metal ion solvation.

THIS BOOK WAS SET IN

TIMES ROMAN AND BULMER TYPES

BY RUTTLE, SHAW & WETHERILL, INC.

IT WAS DESIGNED BY THE STAFF OF

BLAISDELL PUBLISHING COMPANY